BACTERIOLOGY

and

ALLIED SUBJECTS

BY

LOUIS GERSHENFELD, B.Sc., Ph.M., D.Sc.

PROFESSOR OF BACTERIOLOGY AND HYGIENE AND DIRECTOR OF
THE BACTERIOLOGICAL LABORATORIES AT THE PHILADELPHIA
COLLEGE OF PHARMACY AND SCIENCE IN PHILADELPHIA

MACK PUBLISHING COMPANY
EASTON, PENNSYLVANIA
1947

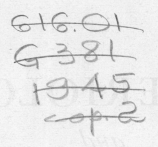

First printing, 1945
Second printing, 1947

Copyright

LOUIS GERSHENFELD

Philadelphia, Pennsylvania

1945

Printed in the United States of America

DEDICATED

to the memory of

MY PARENTS

PREFACE

This volume is an outgrowth of works by the author published under the title of "Bacteriology and Sanitary Science." It was deemed advisable to change to the present title, "Bacteriology and Allied Subjects," as the latter is all-inclusive and more suitable as a title for the contents. Certain data in the previous editions on sanitary science have been deleted to provide space for new material. The various subjects in Bacteriology and in the fields allied to bacteriology considered here concern the bacteriologist and he is expected to have a working knowledge of them. Certainly the physician and pharmacist and occasionally the chemist and biologist are called upon by the laity to answer many questions covering the subjects considered here. Much progress has been made in the development of many subjects directly or indirectly connected with bacteriology in its everyday workings, but no attempt has been made to correlate the available information and to bring it together with the fundamentals of bacteriology into one text. The present volume is the result of the author's own need for a teaching and reference text along these lines.

The developments, fundamentals and techniques in most phases of bacteriology are explained. This volume therefore covers the major portion of the whole subject of bacteriology. Inasmuch as this subject is vast, it is but natural that the entire field could not be adequately detailed. A perfectly balanced consideration of these various subjects is a matter on which disagreement is easy. The author included certain information not found in most textbooks on bacteriology, but which is of value for those for whom this volume is intended. For instance: sterilization, disinfection, fumigation, chemotherapeutic agents, disinfectants and insecticides are generally considered in a superficial manner in most texts on bacteriology. Little or no mention is made in them concerning the production, use, storage, etc., of biological products. The manufacture of ampuls and the marketing of sterile medicaments are rarely included. These are a few among the several subjects considered. Most of these subjects must sooner or later take a place in the curriculum of the respective courses of study.

The author has attempted to deal with the many complexities of the subject presented herein. He hopes that this volume may serve students majoring in bacteriology, biology, chemistry and pharmacy, explaining to them clearly the science of bacteriology in all of its aspects and that it may also serve as an effective and convenient reference for everyone interested in these subjects.

The author wishes to express his thanks to Dr. Ralph Pressman who offered his valued assistance in reading the manuscript and to those who have generously placed their illustrations at his disposal. He is deeply indebted to Miss Eleanor Jaspan for her efforts connected with the proof, which she read with diligence, and to his son, Marvin Aaron, for his never-failing helpfulness.

LOUIS GERSHENFELD

CONTENTS

PART I—BACTERIOLOGY

PART II—THE HIGHER BACTERIA, FUNGI, RICKETTSIAE AND FILTERABLE VIRUSES

PART III—STERILIZATION AND DISINFECTION

XVII.   The Destruction of Bacteria (Sterilization)

PART IV—ANIMAL PARASITOLOGY

XXV. Classification of Animal Parasites—Protozoa

XXVI. Metazoa—Worms

XXVII. Arthropods

PART V—INSECT CONTROL, INSECTICIDES AND FUMIGATION

XXIX. Insect Extermination and Insecticides

PART VI—IMMUNITY, ALLERGY AND BIOLOGICAL PRODUCTS

XXXI. Immunity, Antibodies and Other Defensive Factors

PART VII—APPLIED BACTERIOLOGY

PART I

BACTERIOLOGY

Chapter I

INTRODUCTION

BRIEF HISTORICAL INTRODUCTION AND SCOPE OF BACTERIOLOGY

It is said, "without a historic setting for his work, a man is almost as hopeless as is the man who lacks a sense of humor." One who intends making science his lifework will find it profitable for many reasons to familiarize himself with its history and especially with the history of the branch of science with which he will be associated. For a well-rounded perspective of modern bacteriology and allied branches of science, a knowledge of their historical background is essential. Furthermore, most people today are thrilled and captivated by biography and many are fascinated by stories of colorful careers. The biographies which have been and still are the so-called best sellers frequently fade into dullness in comparison with the unique histories of some of our scientists who as possessors of dynamic characters, remarkable visions and extraordinary courage have left and are leaving indelible impressions upon humanity. You should undertake the task of familiarizing yourself with this history, for obviously it is only possible to present here brief comments. There follows also a list, limited mainly to the discovery of the more important organisms during the period of modern bacteriology, and in addition there are presented the names of a few reference works and volumes which are either biographies or contain data of interest to all.

Science of the ancients and science of today differ in many respects. Studies of a so-called scientific character in ancient times were made primarily for the benefit of man while the true spirit of modern science is to study nature for its own sake, which has and does result in the accomplishment of great wonders for man. The modern scientific attitude of observation and experimentation was not practiced in ancient times. The so-called science of the ancients was to a great extent a theoretical and not a practical contribution. Many of us think too often of the different divisions in science, but science is really one and its many divisions and subdivisions are in reality artificial. Bacteriology illustrates only too well the system of interrelationships among the many branches of science.

The belief that there are living organisms too small to be seen by the unaided human eye, and that such invisible organisms play an important part in various natural phenomena, has found utterance many times since the dawn of history. Several of the philosophers of antiquity were bold enough to surmise that such organisms existed, and some writers even framed their speculations on this subject in phrases that seem like far-seeing anticipations of modern discoveries. Interesting in some degree as these speculations are, they appear to have had no influence whatever even upon the course of scientific investigation. The proof that microorganisms are concerned in various natural processes, many of which were controversial subjects, had to await the discovery of lenses and the development of an optical science. Accordingly all references to the fact that particles too small to be seen were responsible for different conditions and diseases were obviously suppositions and not based on proof. Probably the first record of observing "minute worms" is that of a Jesuit priest, Athanasius Kircher (1602–1680), who in 1659 reported seeing wormlike structures in the blood of plague patients. He later noted the presence of similar bodies in cheese, milk, vinegar and decaying material, and even formulated a theory of the animate nature of contagion (*Science*, 1910, **31,** 264).

Due to the fact that the magnification and refinement of lenses were not great, workers of today doubt that it was possible for Kircher to have seen the true plague bacilli. The first discoveries in bacteriology and protozoölogy are credited to Van Leeuwenhoek (1632–1723), a Dutch linen draper, who in 1675, using a simple microscope with a magnification of 160 diameters, observed microorganisms in water. In his spare time, he ground lenses and utilized them in perfecting the microscope with which, without system but with unremitting industry, he examined almost every available body fluid and many natural substances, describing the peculiar minute bodies, the so-called "animalcules" he observed. Leeuwenhoek's observations remained practically isolated and without fruit for nearly a century. It was not until 1786 that the work of the Danish zoologist, O. F. Müller, added anything of importance to the knowledge of bacteria. Müller recognized clearly the difficulties of studying such minute organisms. Another unequivocal advance was made by Ehrenberg (1795–1876). The chief merit of Ehrenberg's work lay in the system that it introduced into the study of microorganisms. This investigator was able to establish a number of different groups among the organisms now called bacteria, and recognized clearly the fundamental differences between the larger forms, such as the screw-shaped or spirally twisted organisms, and certain of the true protozoa with which they had heretofore been classed. In the two or three decades succeeding Ehrenberg's work, considerable knowledge was amassed concerning the mode of development and physiology of bacteria as well as their position in biologic classification, but the labors of Dujardin, Perty, Cohn, Nageli, and others, although important, are quite overshadowed by the work of Pasteur.

The memorable researches of the great French chemist, Louis Pasteur (1822–1895), upon spontaneous generation and fermentation imparted to the study of bacteria a broad biologic importance that it had not hitherto possessed. Bacteria and kindred microorganisms were shown to be responsible for setting in motion and carrying out many everyday processes, the nature of which had not before been understood or which had been incorrectly assigned to "the oxygen of the air" or to other inorganic agencies. Putrefaction and decay were shown by Pasteur to be, not fields for the "spontaneous generation" of life, but manifestations of chemical disintegration due to the metabolic activities of microorganisms engaged in satisfying their need of food. The profound importance of Pasteur's researches has been universally recognized. If the researches of Pasteur mark the beginning of bacteriology, those of Robert Koch (1843–1910), the German bacteriologist, must be regarded as establishing bacteriology on the basis of an independent biologic science.

The field of microscopy opened many avenues for new investigations. But even here, modern scientific bacteriology as we know it today, had to await the development of the achromatic compound microscope in 1837, the perfection of the high-powered microscope in 1870, the use of dyes for staining in 1875–1878, and in 1876 solid culture media, for a more satisfactory technique of growing, isolating and identifying bacteria.

During the evolutionary period, biologists, botanists, zoologists, chemists, and those serving the healing arts began to utilize these new tools. Many theories, which in former days were highly controversial and divided workers into distinct camps with definite formulated opinions, were again brought to the forefront, but at this time proof and not a theoretical assumption was to hold sway. The theory of spontaneous generation, mentioned above and as postulated by some, held for many centuries that living organisms can be generated spontaneously from nonliving organic substances. That life came only from life (biogenesis) and was not spontaneously generated from nonliving materials (abiogenesis) was later established and was subsequently definitely proved when Pasteur in his brilliant investigations showed that fermentations resulted from physiological activities of living, growing microorganisms. The transition from these investigations to studies on disease in man, animals, plants, etc., and studies on putrefaction was obvious; and soon it was definitely established that different types of fermentation, putrefaction and disease were due to the activities of different kinds of microorganisms. Bacteriology thus came into its own and scientific bacteriology starting in a background of chaos and controversy expanded, as it found itself more and more capable of standing on its own feet.

Scientific Bacteriology during the past half century has developed more as an applied science than a theoretical one, with the result that, unfortunately, the fundamental biological problems of the bacteria themselves have been neglected. Within the past decade, a new impetus has arisen to investigate problems of morphology, structure, development, variation and inheritance, and to uncover many other unsolved problems. This is, indeed, a healthy sign. The introduction of the electron microscope and the aid offered by physics, chemistry and other branches of science may make the task less difficult. The result will undoubtedly aid not only theoretical bacteriology, but practical bacteriology will profit to an even greater extent. It is these facts and principles which are fundamental, and their comprehension is essential for a greater development and progress in the field of bacteriology.

Discovery of Microorganisms Causing Specific Diseases

1837   Bassi saw the protozoa of pabrine in silkworms.
1839   Langenbeck discovered a yeastlike organism causing thrush.
1840   Remak described the first pathogen of plant origin, *Achorion schönleinii*, the cause of favus.
1843   Busk discovered the giant intestinal fluke, *Fasciolopsis buski*.
1843   Dubini described the hookworm.
1846   Leidy discovered *Trichinella spiralis* in pork.
1850   Rayer and Davaine saw the anthrax bacillus.
1851   Bilharz discovered the human blood fluke, *Schistosoma haematobium*, and the small intestinal fluke, *Heterophyes heterophyes*.
1847–1854   Tulasne described certain disease-producing organisms in plants.

1858 Kuhn described certain disease-producing organisms in plants.

1863 Davaine produced anthrax by inoculation.

1865 Pasteur proved a disease of silkworm to be due to a protozoan organism.

1865 Klebs described the organisms of purulent nephritis.

1865 Von Recklinghausen and Waldeyer described the organisms in metastatic abscesses.

1866 Rindfleisch described the organisms of pyemia.

1872 Paulicki reported the similarity between avian tuberculosis and the disease in man and cattle

1872 Hansen found bacilli in lepra cells.

1873 Obermeier described the spirillum of relapsing fever.

1875 Lösch observed the *Entamoeba histolytica* in the intestinal tract in cases of dysentery.

1875 Bollinger presents evidence that blackleg and anthrax are different diseases.

1876 Koch isolated the anthrax bacillus.

1876 Koch introduced gelatin as a means of obtaining a solid medium and later one of his technicians, Frau Hesse, employed agar.

1876 Bancroft recovered the adult filarial worm, *Wuchereria băncrofti*.

1877 Pasteur discovered the bacillus of malignant edema.

1877 Burril discovered the bacillus causing pear blight.

1878 Harz studied and gave the name *actinomyces* to the raylike fungus described by Bollinger in 1877 as the cause of actinomycosis in cattle.

1879 Hansen and Neisser discovered the organism causing leprosy.

1879 Neisser discovered the gonococcus.

1880 Pasteur and Sternberg simultaneously discovered the pneumococcus.

1880 Pasteur discovered the organism of fowl cholera and also staphylococci in pus.

1880 Eberth and Koch independently discovered the typhoid bacillus.

1880 Evans discovered the trypanosome causing surra (trypanosomiasis of the equine species)

1880 Laveran discovered the malarial plasmodium.

1881 Ogston discovered staphylococci in abscesses.

1881–1888 The brilliant work of Pasteur, Chamberland and Roux led to a successful method of immunization against rabies.

1882 Friedländer discovered the Friedländer bacillus.

1882 Koch discovered the tubercle bacillus.

1882 Koch and Ogston discovered the streptococcus.

1882 Several observers reported the glanders bacillus (Babes in 1881) which was isolated in pure culture by Loeffler and Schultz.

1883 Koch discovered the organisms of Asiatic cholera and infectious conjunctivitis.

1883 Fehleisen obtained pure cultures of streptococci in erysipelas.

1883 Klebs saw the diphtheria bacillus.

1883 Malassez and Vignal found *Pasteurella pseudotuberculosis* responsible for an affection of guinea pigs.

1884 Rosenbach demonstrated *Streptococcus pyogenes* in abscesses and in cases of osteomyelitis.

1884 Gaffky obtained pure cultures of the typhoid bacillus.

1884 Nicolaier discovered the tetanus bacillus.

1884 Koch made his full report on tuberculosis.

1884 Marchiafava and Celli described the micrococcus found in meningeal exudates.

1884 Loeffler obtained pure cultures of the diphtheria bacillus.

1884 Chamberland devised a successful unglazed porcelain filter.

1885 Emmerich isolated the colon bacillus.

1885 Bumm obtained pure cultures of the gonococcus.

1885 Kitt discovered *P. boviseptica*, the causative agent of bovine hemorrhagic septicemia.

1885 Golgi described the life history of the parasite of quartan malarial fever.

1885 Salmon and Smith isolated *Salmonella choleraesuis*.

1885 Hauser described several species of the genus *Proteus*.

1885 Loeffler discovered the causative agent of swine erysipelas.

1886 Escherich named the *Bacillus coli*.

1886 Loeffler demonstrated *P. suilla* as the cause of hemorrhagic septicemia of hogs or swine plague.

1887 Bruce described the *Brucella melitensis*, causative agent of Malta fever.
1887 Roux (and Kitasato in 1889) cultivated *Clostridium chauvei*. Arloing, Cornevin and Thomas established its relation to blackleg.
1887 Weichselbaum described and isolated the meningococcus.
1887 Koch observed (in 1883) and Weeks cultured (in 1887) the Koch-Weeks bacillus.
1888 Schütz described *Streptococcus equi* as the causative factor in equine strangles or distemper.
1888 Gaertner identified *Bacillus enteritidis* and *B. paratyphosus*.
1888 Gamaleia discovered *Vibrio metchnikovii*.
1888 Miller described the causative agent of Vincent's angina.
1888 Babes observed but did not recognize species of babesia in the blood of cattle affected with Texas fever.
1888 von Hoffmann-Wellenhof and Loeffler described pseudodiphtheria bacilli.
1889 Kitasato obtained the tetanus bacillus in pure culture.
1889 Roux and Yersin reported that the diphtheria bacillus produces a specific soluble toxin.
1889 Ducrey described the Ducrey bacillus as the causative agent of chancroid.
1889 Klein described the causative agent of fowl typhoid.
1890 Behring demonstrated the protective action of diphtheria antitoxin.
1890 Behring and Kitasato introduced tetanus antitoxin.
1891 Nordtmayer introduced the Berkefeld type of kieselguhr filter.
1891 Kitasato reported that the tetanus bacillus produces an ectotoxin.
1892 Welch and Nuttall described the gas bacillus.
1892 Iwanowski in his investigation of the mosaic disease of tobacco demonstrated the filterable characteristics of disease-producing viruses.
1892 Pfeiffer described the influenza bacillus.
1893 Smith and Kilborne proved the protozoan nature of the organism causing Texas fever.
1894 Kitasato and Yersin simultaneously discovered the plague bacillus.
1894 Bruce described the dreaded tsetse fly disease.
1894 Novy described and isolated *C. novyi* obtained from cases of gas gangrene.
1895 Johne and Frothingham demonstrated acid-fast bacteria in the affected intestinal mucosa in cases of chronic enteritis or dysentery of cattle.
1896 Achard and Bensaude discovered the paratyphoid B bacillus.
1896 Morax (and Axenfeld in 1897) described the *Hemophilus duplex*.
1896 Schenck identified a fungus classed in the genus *Sporothrix* in an ulcerative infection known as sporotrichosis.
1896 Gilchrist described the yeastlike organism causing blastomycosis.
1896 Ermengem isolated the *C. botulinum*.
1897 Bang isolated *Brucella abortus*.
1897 Shiga discovered the dysentery bacillus.
1897 Loeffler and Frosch proved that aphthous fever or foot-and-mouth disease is caused by a filterable virus.
1898 Gwyn described and isolated the paratyphoid A bacillus.
1898 Theobald Smith differentiated between bovine and human tubercle bacilli.
1899 Beyerinck spoke of the causative agent of tobacco mosaic as "a living fluid contagium."
1900 Moro isolated the *Lactobacillus acidophilus* from the feces of infants.
1900 Tissier isolated *Lactobacillus bifidus* from feces of breast-fed infants.
1900 Flexner discovered the Flexner dysentery bacillus.
1902 Lignieres and Spitz described actinobacillosis.
1903 Remlinger showed rabies was caused by a filterable virus.
1903 Negri described certain bodies which are indicative of hydrophobia.
1903 Wright described *Leishmania tropica* in cases of Oriental sore.
1903 Metchnikoff and Roux transmitted syphilis to monkeys and anthropoid apes.
1903 Leishman and Donovan independently described *Leishmania donovani* from cases of kala-azar.
1904 Markus differentiated between Johne's disease and tuberculosis in cattle.
1905 Schaudin and Hoffman described the *Treponema pallidum* of syphilis, which was cultivated by Schereschewsky on artificial media in 1909.

1905 Castellani described the *Treponema pertenue*, causative agent of yaws.

1905 Grigoroff isolated *Lactobacillus bulgaricus* from Bulgarian fermented milk.

1906 Bordet and Gengou discovered *Bacillus pertussis* of whooping cough.

1906 Morgan isolated the Morgan bacillus from cases of summer diarrhea in infants.

1907 Halberstaedter and von Prowazek described the cell inclusion in trachoma.

1908 Rettger and Harvey described *Salmonella pullorum*.

1910 McCoy and Chapin isolated the *P. tularensis*, causative agent of tularemia.

1911 Goldberger and Anderson demonstrate that measles is caused by a virus.

1914 Traum isolated *Brucella suis*.

1914 Kruse (and Foster in 1916) indicated that the common cold is caused by a virus.

1915 Weinberg and Seguin isolated the *C. histolyticum*.

1915 Ashford reports the presence of a species of *monilia* in cases of sprue.

1915 Twort discovered with d'Herelle (in 1917), independently, "bacteriophage."

1916 Inada and Ido isolated the *Leptospira icterohemorrhagiae*, from cases of infectious jaundice.

1917 Smith describes *Actinobacillus actinoides*.

1918 Ido, Ito and Wani isolated the *Lept. hebdomadis* from cases of seven day fever.

1918 Rettger described *Salmonella anatun*.

1918 Weinberg and Seguin described new species of bacteria in war wounds.

1926 Murray, Webb and Swann described *Listerella monocytogenes*.

1930 Western and Simpson demonstrated that psittacosis is caused by a filterable virus

1931 Meyer, Haring and Howitt definitely established that a filterable virus is the cause of equine encephalomyelitis.

1931 Lewis and Shope isolated *Hemophilus suis*, causative agent of swine influenza.

1933 Muckenfuss, Armstrong and McCordock and Webster and Fite report on a specific filterable virus as the cause of St. Louis encephalitis.

1933 Smith, Andrewes and Laidlaw succeeded in establishing influenza in ferrets and proving that the etiological factor is a virus.

1934 Johnson and Goodpasture submitted evidence that mumps is caused by a filterable virus.

1935 Stanley demonstrated that tobacco mosaic virus was a nucleoprotein, obtainable in a crystalline form.

Some Suggested Popular Reading and Reference Works

Bayne-Jones—*Man and Microbes*, Williams and Wilkins, Baltimore, 1932.

Birkeland—*Microbiology and the Man*, F. S. Crofts and Co., New York, 1942.

Bulloch—*The History of Bacteriology*, Oxford University Press, New York, 1938.

——"History of Bacteriology," *System of Bacteriology*, London Med. Res. Council, 1930, Vol. I, p. 15.

Castiglioni—*History of Medicine*, translated and edited by Krumbhaar, Alfred A. Knopf, New York, 1941.

Clark—"Alice in Virusland," *J. Bact.*, 1938, **36**, 223 (also Williams and Wilkins, Baltimore).

Conn—*History of Staining*, Commission on Standardization of Biological Stains, Geneva, N. Y., 1933.

de Kruif—*Microbe Hunters*, 1926; *Hunger Fighters*, 1928; Harcourt, Brace and Co., New York.

Dobell—*Van Leeuwenhoek, Antony and His Little Animals*, Harcourt, Brace and Co., New York, 1932.

Duclaux—*Pasteur—The History of a Mind*, translated by Smith and Hedges, W. B. Saunders Co., Philadelphia, 1920.

Eberson—*The Microbe's Challenge*, Jacques Cattell Press, Lancaster, Pa., 1942.

Flexner—*Life of William Henry Welch*, Viking Press, New York, 1941.

Garri:on—*History of Medicine*, W. B. Saunders, Co., Philadelphia, 4th Ed., 1928.

Haagensen and Lloyd—*One Hundred Years of Medicine*, Sheridan House, New York, 1943.

Haggard—*Devils, Drugs and Doctors*, Blue Ribbon Books, Inc., New York, 1929.

Hill—*Germs and the Man*, Putman's Sons, New York, 1940.

Kopeloff—*Man versus Microbes*, Alfred A. Knopf, New York, 1931.

McClung—*Early American Publicat.*, etc., *Bact. Revs.*, 1944, **8**, 119.

Metchnikoff—*The Life of Elie Metchnikoff*, Constable & Co., London, 1921.

Parran—*Shadow on the Land—Syphilis*, Reynal and Hitchcock, New York, 1937.

Parsons—*Trail to Light*, Bobbs-Merrill, New York, 1943.
Sorsby—*Medicine and Mankind*, Faber and Faber, London, 1942.
Taylor—*Conquest of Bacteria*, Philosophical Library, New York, 1942.
Throne—*The Microscopic World*, Messner, Inc., New York, 1940.
Vallery-Radot—*Life of Pasteur*, Doubleday, Page & Co., Garden City, N. Y., 1923.
Wilson—*Ambassadors in White*, Holt and Co., New York, 1942.
Zinsser—*Rats, Lice and History*, Little, Brown & Co., Boston, 1935.
—— *As I Remember Him*, Little, Brown & Co., Boston, 1940.

Scope of Bacteriology.—Bacteria are closely associated with life and intimately related to human existence. They not only disintegrate and destroy dead bodies, human, animal and plant life and attack and kill living organisms, but some forms are also constructive to a high degree, and transport important chemical elements, like nitrogen and carbon, from unavailable combinations into substances that can be utilized by higher forms of plant life.

Bacteriology and the allied branches of science bear a direct relation to medicine, public health, sanitation, sanitary engineering, to various industries and technological pursuits and even to household administration. These studies present certain aspects which tend to widen the outlook upon a variety of human interests.

As in other growing sciences, so in bacteriology a noticeable differentiation has occurred. The relation of bacteria to disease early took a conspicuous place among the subjects included within the scope of the new science, and it is highly probable that this side of bacteriology bearing upon the science of pathology and the art of medicine will always remain, what it is today, its most broadly important aspect. There is at present a tendency for the workers in this field to specialize either along strictly pathologic or along sanitary and hygienic lines. In pathologic bacteriology consideration is given chiefly to the effects produced upon the animal body by the presence of bacteria and their products, to the distribution of bacteria within the body, and to the reactions, defensive and otherwise, evoked by bacterial invasion. Thus there is a close association between Bacteriology and Immunology. Hygienic or Sanitary Bacteriology deals more particularly with the channels by which bacteria leave the human body and pass into the outer world, with the mode and duration of the life of disease-producing microbes in water, soil and air, and with the avenues by which these disease organisms are able again to approach and infect healthy individuals. No sharp line can be drawn between pathologic and sanitary bacteriology.

Aseptic Surgery, based on bacteriological knowledge, has not only reduced pain and postponed death, but has also been the means for making discoveries in physiology. Bacteriology has provided medicine and biology with a storehouse of interesting and useful substances, together with investigative methods of great power.

We, of course, are apt to think of medical bacteriology in its restricted usage, which limits it to the study of bacteria that attack man. However Veterinary Bacteriology is a wide field of its own. Man is frequently afflicted with diseases which occur primarily among the lower animals and an intimate relationship will be found between Veterinary Bacteriology and Medical Bacteriology. Plant Bacteriology is in its embryonic state and as soon as we know more about plant diseases, much will have been accomplished for the benefit of mankind.

Although, from a practical point of view, the part played by bacteria in the causation of disease must be admitted to be of surpassing importance, it must not be forgotten that bacteria exert a marked influence upon the welfare of mankind in many other directions. It has been discovered, for example, that certain kinds of bacteria profoundly modify the composition of the soil and the character of crops, and hence are of importance to the agriculturist. Agricultural Bacteriology, with its divisions of Soil Bacteriology and Dairy Bacteriology, is playing more and more an important role in our everyday life. Bacteria play both a destructive and a constructive part in industrial operations. In Industrial Bacteriology, we find the fermentative industries depend in large part upon bacteria for their existence. There are those organisms, which produce such valuable chemicals as ethyl alcohol, acetone, butyl alcohol, isopropyl alcohol, lactic acid and butyric acid. Certain species of bacteria impart the characteristic flavors and aromas to wine and alcoholic beverages, to butter, cheese and other dairy products, and others determine the success or failure of various industrial processes, such as the retting of flax, the tanning of hides and, perhaps, the curing of tobacco.

Food Bacteriology considers the contamination of foods by bacteria pathogenic to man and by organisms which will cause its decomposition and spoilage. More recently, the use of bacteria in nutrition has received and is receiving considerable attention. Bacteria as therapeutic agents are known, and yeast and acidophilus cultures are in use. In biochemical and microbiological studies bacteria are of value. Various assays used today for some of the vitamins depend upon the employment of techniques requiring particular species of bacteria. The applications of bacteriology to various industries, to manufacturing processes, to agriculture, in investigations of food and nutrition and in microbiological studies are likely to become more numerous in the near future.

The scope of bacteriology is a wide one. Few of its many fields have been studied fully; some of them have been neglected and are practically untouched; and most of them have been only partially explored. Much remains to be done. The student in this field, if he will apply himself, has before him many opportunities. The interest is great and the resulting possibilities in promise of benefit to mankind are numerous.

Chapter II

GENERAL CHARACTERISTICS, ACTIVITIES AND CLASSIFICATION OF BACTERIA

The POPULAR terms germ and microbe, used indiscriminately when speaking of microorganisms, are not exact enough for scientific use. Either term may be taken to mean any microscopic organism, animal or vegetable. · In the animal kingdom the lowest forms of life are called protozoa.

The bacteria classed as the lowest forms of life in the vegetable kingdom have been described as consisting of a single cell (unicellular). The typical bacterial cell is not well differentiated. Unfortunately, various designations by workers are employed to represent the probable structures of bacteria. We must remember that on account of the small size of bacteria and the limitations imposed by optical resolution, it may be difficult to determine the exact nature of bacterial structures. Furthermore, bacteriology developed more as an applied science than as a theoretical one and the important fundamental problems of the bacteria have been neglected until recently. Perhaps, with more intensive research with the use of the electron microscope, the existing confusion will be cleared and our knowledge will be more exact. The bacterial cell appears to be composed of a mass of protoplasm contained within a thin delicate nonprotoplasmic cell wall (so-called envelope), the latter being firm, rigid and somewhat elastic. The surface of the protoplasm is a differentiated semipermeable (cytoplasmic) membrane composed of surface-active substances (lipoids and lipoproteins), which form a rather firm surface structure enclosing the cytoplasm. The physical and chemical changes necessary to the life of the cell are carried on within the homogeneous protoplasmic cell contents, designated by some as the nucleoplasm. It is both convenient and desirable to refer to the nucleated mass of cytoplasm as the *protoplast*, and accordingly speak of the bacterial cell as consisting of a protoplast, surrounded by a cell wall and containing on its surface a semipermeable cytoplasmic membrane. Additional structures are present in some cells. Arbitrary designations, as *endoplasm* and *ectoplasm*, have no definite meaning and should be discontinued. The term endoplasm is employed by some workers to designate the cell contents or inner portion of the cell, and ectoplasm is used to denote the outer portion of the cell, including the cell membrane and capsule and flagella when present. Among the bacteria, as in the lower fungi generally, cellulose is absent. The bacteria resemble in many respects the lower animals in their chemical composition.

Nuclear Material.—The presence or absence of a bacterial nucleus has been the subject of much controversy, some observers regarding this as a nucleus in a divided state (*i. e.*, micronucleus). Claims for the absence of a nucleus, a naked nucleus, a polymorphic nucleus, a true vesicular nucleus, a central body and a chromidial system have been presented but rejected by most workers as based on faulty evidence. In the present state of our knowledge, no definite conclusion concerning the nature of the nucleus in bacteria is possible. Though a nucleus proper has not been demonstrated by any of the commonly used techniques, special methods of staining may reveal the presence of nuclear material (chromatin and plastin) in some bacteria. Due to the behavior of bacteria in general both in their method of multiplication as well as their behavior toward aniline dyes, the opinion on a whole prevails that bacteria contain nuclear matter which in most cases is diffused, or the nuclear material is in a so finely divided state as to make its detection exceedingly difficult or even impossible.

Polar-staining Bodies.—Certain species of bacteria show the presence of various sized refractile granules. In some instances these granules, being perhaps a reserve food substance, are pushed to either end or to one side, leaving a vacuole in the center of the cell. This gives rise to the commonly known "polar-staining bodies," "Babes-Ernst granules," "metachromatic granules," or "volutin grains." These granules will frequently show a greater affinity for a certain dye than the remainder of the organism, so that it becomes practical to treat such bacteria with suitable staining solutions, showing the granules as deeply stained areas in contrast with the rest of the organism, which is colorless or may be stained with a different colored dye. This characteristic is of differential value especially in the case of the diphtheria bacillus. The true nature of these bodies is by no means certain, though many regard them as reserve food substances. They are not permanent organs of the bacterial cell and are observed more frequently in mature rather than in very young actively growing cells. Their presence depends not only upon the age of the cell, but also upon the species of microorganism and the condition of the environment which are important factors. They occur in all species of *Azobacter* and *Spirillum*, and in some species of *Aerobacillus, Bacillus, Corynebacterium, Lactobacillus, Mycobacterium* (?) and *Pseudomonas*. They are widely distributed among *actinomycetes*, yeasts, molds and higher fungi. These granules disappear quickly from cells when placed in boiling water and within five minutes in water at 80° C.

Other Cell Inclusions.—Inclusion bodies other than volutin grains, all nonprotoplasmic bodies, may be found deposited in the protoplast. *Fat bodies, glycogen, iogen, starch, sulfur, aleurone* and *mineral crystals* have been found. The occurrence of inclusion bodies in bacteria has been the cause of some erroneous interpretations of cell structure and cell behavior. Various microchemical tests and staining procedures are used as aids in identifying these bodies. The biological significance of these inclusion bodies appears to be, in most instances, that of serving as reserve food. In few instances, as in the case of fat bodies, the presence of the latter may indicate a fatty degeneration of the cells.

Capsule.—In some bacteria the cell proper becomes conspicuously surrounded by a broad colorless zone, of variable thickness, appearing like a halo about the cell, which does not stain by the common methods used in staining bacteria, but requires a special staining technique to bring it out more clearly. This zone probably originating from the cell membrane by swelling, and sometimes called an expanded cell wall, is known as a *capsule*. Recently it has been revealed that the capsular substance is a complex polysaccharide and that the carbohydrate varies in composition in the various capsules possessed by different bacteria, and is concerned with the specificity of the respective microorganisms in immunological reactions. Well-marked capsule formation is met with in only few bacteria. Notwithstanding this fact, many investigators believe that capsule formation is a property common to all types of bacteria, and that this substance is more highly developed in some forms than in others. It may, however, be advisable to attribute the possession of this capsular substance to only those organisms that actually show such material present microscopically or when stained by special methods. The demonstration of the capsule frequently aids in the differentiations of closely related bacteria. Capsules are best demonstrated in material taken direct from the body of man or animals. Organisms possessing capsules, when cultivated artificially, may not reveal the presence of these capsules unless the media employed for growth contain milk, blood or other natural albuminous material. Even with the presence of the latter, frequent transplantation will cause the capsule to disappear, but passage of the organism into laboratory animals and their examination from the body fluids of the latter afford an excellent technique to again demonstrate definitely and easily that the organism under examination does possess a capsule. Bacteria possessing marked capsular formation are more resistant to external agents (heat, chemicals, etc.), and are not readily agglutinated or phagocytized. The presence and abundance of this substance among disease-producing bacteria appear to bear a relationship to the virulence or invasive power of the particular microorganism.

Flagella and Locomotion.—Bacteria, when examined in their living conditions will generally exhibit forms of motility. These movements may be real or apparent. The independent bacterial motion is a real active movement coming from within the cell and observed (under the conditions in which motility of bacteria are usually studied) by the organism actually traveling from one place to another (*i. e.*, locomotion). This in turn is distinguished from the apparent motility, which is a swaying or quivering movement exhibited by all minute particles suspended in the air or in a fluid. The latter movement, an impulse coming from without the cell, is a physical phenomenon due to a molecular vibration or bombardment, and known as *Brownian movement* or *pedesis*. The latter movement is manifested by dead as well as living cells. To be assured that such motion is real or apparent, it would be necessary to resort to the following simple experiment: Inoculate tubes of bouillon culture medium. After eighteen to twenty-four hours' growth at the most suitable temperature, examine the culture in question microscopically on a hanging-drop slide, after applying vaseline along the edges of the cover slip. Then heat the culture in a water bath at 60° C. for one hour, or mix 1 drop of the liquid culture with 1 drop of 5 per cent phenol solution. Such treatment will kill the organism and in turn stop real motility. Examine the heated or chemically treated culture. If the bacteria in the latter exhibit a less rapid motion than the living organism and one which is sluggish, then the movement of the original organism is real. If the motion after heating or after treatment with a disinfectant is the same as before, it is clear that this is not active motility but a physical condition.

The oxygen in the air and other chemicals, electricity, light and heat may influence movements by bacteria. When the latter are affected by these forces, the phenomenon is spoken of as *taxis* or *tropism*. We differentiate between *positive taxis*, when forces attract, and *negative taxis*, when forces repel.

Only a small percentage of the bacteria exhibit real locomotion. It may be that all bacteria possess the power of locomotion, and that this can only be observed in the case of many of the bacteria under unusual conditions, not as yet discovered by scientists. Except in the case of certain forms of spirochetes, which are motile by means of a type of undulating membrane, motility of bacteria is carried on by means of the organs of locomotion, known as *flagella*. The latter are long, thin, delicate, hairlike appendages, protruding from the sides of the cell and are supposed to originate either from the cell membrane or in the cytoplasm proper and grow out through openings in the cell wall. The precise manner of origin is difficult to ascertain. The motion exhibited by bacteria appears to be directly dependent upon the number and arrangement of the flagella. Special methods of staining must be applied so as to reveal the presence of these organs of locomotion, as they cannot be detected by the ordinary methods employed in staining bacteria. Flagella are best demonstrated in young cultures grown in a liquid culture medium at the most suitable temperature. According to the number and arrangement of the flagella, bacteria are referred to as:

1. Gymnobacteria or atricha organisms: bacteria possessing no flagella.
2. Trichobacteria: bacteria with flagella.
    (*a*) Monotricha—single flagellum at one end (Vibrio of Asiatic cholera).
    (*b*) Lophotricha—several or a tuft of flagella at one end (or pole) (*Spirillum undula*).
    (*c*) Amphitricha—flagella at both ends (poles) (many of the spirilla).
    (*d*) Peritricha—flagella surrounding the entire organism (typhoid bacillus).

Recent studies by Pijper (*J. Path. Bact.*, 1938, **47**, 1) and by Pietschmann (*Arch. Mikrobiol.*, 1939, **10**, 133) question the actual occurrence of peritrichous flagellation.

Conn and Wolfe (*J. Bact.*, 1938, **36**, 517) recommend flagella staining as a routine test for bacteria. The technique as given by them (see page 47) yields results which are more clear cut and supplies data (as kind of flagellation) not observed in the conventional hanging-drop technique to detect true motility. Tittsler and Sandholzer (*J. Bact.*, 1936, **31**, 575) recognizing the inaccuracy of the hanging-drop technique recommend as a check on the latter method the use of stabs in a semisolid agar medium (containing 0.3 per cent meat extract, peptone 0.5 per cent and agar 0.5 per cent). The inoculated culture is incubated at the optimum temperature and examined at the end of eight, twenty-four, forty-eight and every twenty-four hours thereafter for at least six days, unless positive results are obtained sooner. Motile organisms produce a diffuse zone of growth spreading from the line of inoculation; nonmotile organisms do not. A "Dehydrated Motility Test Medium" which is a modification of the above medium is marketed for use in the testing of bacteria for motility.

Fission.—Growth and reproduction are a characteristic of living organisms. The multiplication or actual increase in number of bacteria results by a process known as simple cell division or fission. Under conditions favorable for bacterial growth (which will be discussed later) the cell, after reaching the fully developed adult stage, divides or splits into two, giving rise to two new cells. These young cells, leading a separate existence, grow, develop, attain their full size and then reproduce by the same process. The actual division appears to be by cytoplasmic retraction and the subsequent formation of two transverse cell walls, the latter being separate from the beginning. For further details, see Knaysi (*J. Bact.*, 1941, **41**, 141). Under favorable conditions the commonly observed bacteria begin to divide within thirty minutes after their existence. Owing to such rapid multiplication, one can realize what an enormous number may develop in a short space of time, assuming the continuance of favorable conditions. See also page 103.

Stages of Growth—Growth Curves.—Even under the most favorable conditions, it has been observed that absolute equal multiplication among all bacteria occurs for only very limited periods of time. Practically bacterial multiplication presents a situation in which the rate of growth, though continuous, may be divided arbitrarily or for convenience into several phases. During the (*a*) first or *lag phase*, growth does not occur or proceeds very slowly. Why this occurs is not definitely known, but it is thought that the initial adjustment of the bacterium to the new environment is the cause for this initial stationary phase. The *phase of logarithmic increase* is the (*b*) stage of maximum growth and most rapid multiplication. The rate of increase is constant and maximum growth tends to occur almost by geometric progression. Then follows a *stationary or a resting phase* (*c*), a short period during which time there is no increase in the rate of growth. Finally there is (*d*) the *phase of decline* progressing to a point where death results and few or no living cells are found. Numerous factors, (many are self-apparent) influence the different phases and the form of growth curves which may occur among not only the different species of bacteria, but among the same species found under varying conditions. It therefore is not possible to present a definite and typical growth curve for bacteria.

As in higher forms of life, the occurrences in the various phases of growth among bacteria reveal differences not only in activity but also in morphology and structure of the bacterium, which appear to be constant and characteristic for the various periods or phases. This succession of forms or cell changes occurring continually through all stages has been termed *cytomorphosis.* It is possible that these different forms also display differences in activity definitely correlated with the specific phases of growth. For further details, see Henrici (*Morphologic Variation and the Rate of Growth,* Charles C Thomas, Springfield, Illinois, 1928).

Bacterial Spores.—Bacteria, while growing and multiplying, are said to be vegetating. The forms represented during such period are known as the *vegetative forms.* Microorganisms when in the actively growing stage are relatively weak organisms. So as to resist destruction from outside forces (especially the presence of an accumulation of deleterious metabolic products, dryness, unsuitable temperature famine, etc.), a small percentage of the numerous species of bacteria assume another form or stage known as a spore-bearing phase, and produce what is commonly known as a *bacterial spore* or *endospore.* A single cell forms only one spore. These spores, really condensed cell contents surrounded by a very dense envelope, are round or oval bodies appearing in the center (*central* or *equatorial*) or at either end (*terminal* or *head spore* or *plectridium*) or midway between the center and the end (*subterminal* or *eccentric*) as a bulge in the wall of the original cell or as a bright refractive body within the bacterium. If unfavorable conditions persist, the vegetative form soon dies, the cell wall softens and disappears, and the spore is set free. Under the latter condition the spores appear as round or oval bodies, surrounded by a dense impenetrable wall, which does not stain readily with aniline dyes. Special methods of staining are used to stain it. (See page 46.) Available evidence seems to indicate that the spore content is a dehydrated protoplasm with a high lipoidal concentration. In laboratory cultures, spores if present are best observed in cultures which have been grown for several days at a suitable temperature in an atmosphere plentifully supplied with oxygen or in the case of anaerobes in the complete absence of oxygen.   The spore phase considered as a resistant form is in reality the resting or perpetuating stage of those species of bacteria.   As a rule, only one spore can be formed from an individual cell.   The vegetative form usually disintegrates and disappears after a spore forms. The vegetative cell can reproduce and multiply but the spore cannot.   It is, therefore, apparent that spore formation is not a process of reproduction or multiplication. Definite spore formation has only been observed among some of the bacillary forms. Only few spore-forming bacteria of known pathogenicity are encountered in daily routine as the aerobic anthrax bacillus and certain anaerobic bacilli (tetanus bacillus [*Clostridium tetani*], *C. botulinum*, *C. welchii*).   The pathogenic obligate anaerobic bacilli are generally spore producers.   Spores are characterized by their extreme resistance to destruction by external agencies.   A boiling-water or a steam bath will kill instantly the vegetative forms of bacteria, but it requires anywhere from five minutes to several hours to destroy spores.   The spores of different species possess different degrees of resistance, but as a class they are more highly resistant to all outside forces than the respective vegetative forms.   It is because disease producing spore bearers may be present, that in practice rigid sterilization methods are employed to be assured of the destruction of spores.   When conditions again become favorable for development and growth, the spores *germinate* and redevelop into the bacterial forms similar to those forms whence they came.   The now fully developed cells will begin to reproduce again by fission and continue thus through their cycle of life.   •

Spore formation is sometimes mistaken for what is known as *arthrospore* or *false spore formation*.   The cell walls of some individual species of bacteria thicken, harden and become impenetrable, but the cell itself germinates and multiples.   Such condition gives rise to what is known as an *arthrospore* or *false spore formation*.

The term *spore* as used in bacteriology is employed in a sense entirely different than as used in botany proper.

Classification.—A great many attempts have been made to classify bacteria.

For a historical survey of classifications, rules of nomenclature and fundamental characteristics of satisfactory biological classification, see Abridged Fifth Edition, *Bergey's Manual for Determinative Bacteriology*, Biotech Publications, Geneva, N. Y., 1939.

The line of demarcation between the lowest forms of vegetable and animal life is not as clear cut as one might expect.   As a matter of fact, most scientists are agreed upon the fact that all living organisms are fundamentally alike and perhaps originated from a common state.   It is largely a consideration of convenience and an established habit, which has resulted in the grouping of bacteria among the plants, and, possessing no chlorophyll, they are regarded as fungi.   But it is within the group of bacteria that classification is desirable for practical purposes.   This is especially needed when one realizes that bacteria in comparison with higher plants and animals are more variable and unstable and that conformity to type, as found in Holstein cows, white rats and specific vegetables, etc., is not apparent nor to be expected.

Jensen's physiological (1909), Lehman and Neumann's (1896), Migula's morphological (1897), Fischer's, Chester's (1901), Buchanan's (1925), Castellani and Chalmer's (1919), Janke's (1929), Pribram's (1933) and Kluyver and van Niel's (1936) classifications are frequently cited.   Various modifications and other systems of classification of bacteria have been published.   In all, some sixty odd classifications have appeared to date, including the classification introduced in 1920 by a Committee of well-known American bacteriologists, headed by Professor Bergey. Various peculiarities and characteristics have been utilized in these classifications, but most of them extend only to the habitat, physiology and especially the morphology of the organisms. They are all valuable to the well-trained bacteriologist, but confusing to the beginner in this science. Students as they advance in the study of bacteriology should familiarize themselves with many of the previously mentioned systems of classification, especially the Bergey classification (see page 91) as it appears that the Bergey classification, after some revision, will be internationally recognized as an authoritative manual on bacterial taxonomy. For practical purposes the following broad, simple grouping (based upon the morphological characteristics of bacteria) will be useful for the beginner, who, however, should refer to the other classifications as greater familiarity is attained with the subject.

THALLOPHYTA OR THALLOPHYTES (Thallos—a young branch; phyton—plant).— This is the lowest of the four great divisions (phyllum) in the plant kingdom, so named because their bodies (each of which is called a thallus) do not show differentiation into stems, leaves or roots. The other three large divisions (sing.—phyllum) are the *Bryophyta* (mosses); *Pteridophyta* (ferns); and *Spermatophyta* (seed-bearing plants). To the division (phyllum) *Thallophyta* belong the subdivisions (subthyllum) *algae* and *fungi* (thallophytes containing no chlorophyll). To the latter subdivision belong the bacteria. It is a common practice in bacteriology, when grouping such of the fungi as are of interest (and unfortunately the generic term bacteria frequently is used instead of the terms fungi or thallophytes), to consider three principal groups:

1. *Lower Bacteria.*—Bacteria (specific term) or *schizomycetes* (so called because they reproduce by fission).
2. *Higher Bacteria.*—*Leptotrichia, proactinomyces, actinomyces* and *erysipelothrix.*
3. *True Fungi* (*Eumycetes* or *Hyphomycetes*).—Molds (appearing as cotton or threadlike growths and known as *thread fungi* or *hyphomycetes*); *yeasts* or *blastomycetes* (so-called because they multiply by a process known as budding).

The bacteria or schizomycetes are the most important of the three groups.

A broad classification within this group itself, is, therefore, further advisable. These are:

(*a*) *Coccus or Micrococcus* (plural, Cocci or Micrococci).—Organisms, spherical in shape. They may be flattened on one side, concave or elliptical. Those commonly observed are generally nonmotile and nonspore-forming.
   1. Single-file formation—streptococci.
   2. Double-file formation—diplococci: (*a*) Encapsulated—pneumooccus; (*b*) nonencapsulated with side flattened—gonococcus, meningococcus and *Micrococcus* (*Neisseria*) *catarrhalis.*
   3. Tetrad formation—tetrads: *Micrococcus tetragenus; Sarcinae* (packets of 8 or multiples of 8).
   4. Multiple and irregular formation (like grapes).—*Staphylococci.*
(*b*) *Bacillus* (plural, Bacilli).—Organisms, pencil- or rod-shaped. They may be long or short, slender or stout, square or round ended, curved, in chains or rows. A number of the bacilli are motile and some possess endospores. They are the most numerous of all types of bacteria.

(c) *Spirillum* (generic term) (plural, Spirilla).—Spirilla are the least numerous of
the three types. Many of them are motile and most of them are nonspore-
forming.
1. Vibrio—shaped like a comma or a bacillus with both ends distinctly curved.
2. Spirochete—long, slender, flexible spirals, shaped with pronounced den-
tations.
3. Spirillum (specific term)—a true "S" or rigid spiral-shaped organism,
which can be revolved about a cone.

The various types are not interchangeable. It is impossible for a coccus to become
a bacillus or a spirillum, or *vice versa*.

Size of Bacteria.—Bacteria have been spoken of as being infinitely small. Their
size is usually expressed in terms of *microns*, designated by the Greek letter μ. The
average size of the individual coccus is about 1 μ. Bacilli vary greatly in size, from
the smallest, 0.2 μ in width (*i. e.*, thickness) by 0.5 μ in length (*e. g.*, influenza bacillus),
to others as long as 25 μ. The same is true of the spirilla. The sizes or dimensions
of bacteria vary greatly in the different species as well as among strains of the same
species.

The term *micron* (μ) denotes one-millionth of a meter (10^{-6} M.) or one-thousandth
of a millimeter (10^{-3} mm.), which is approximately $1/_{25,000}$ of an inch. The limit of
resolution of the compound microscope using ordinary means of illumination is about
0.2 μ. Below this range, particles are termed *ultramicrons*, and their size is usually
expressed in terms of the *millimicron* (*milli-mu*) (mμ), which is 10^{-9} M. (*i. e.*, one-
thousandth of a micron). Still smaller particles, *e. g.*, those in the range of ordinary
molecules, are measured in terms of *micromicrons* ($\mu\mu$)*, which is 10^{-12} M. (or one-
millionth of a micron). Particles below the limit of resolution of a compound microscope and which are detectable with an ultramicroscope or by using a dark-field condenser are termed *submicrons*, and these are found in the range covered approximately
by 1 to 200 mμ. Those not detectable by this means are classified as amicrons. It
should be clearly understood, however, that factors other than size alone will make a
particle *amicroscopic* (*e. g.*, a refractive index comparable to that of the medium in
which the particle is suspended). The range 1 to 200 mμ is also about the same as that
usually given for colloid dispersions, although some authorities give a higher upper
limit. The ultramicroscope has been employed to measure bacteriophage corpuscles
(calculated at about 20–30 mμ) and the infective agents or particles in diseases caused
by the *filterable viruses* (suggested average diameter of virus units—25 mμ).

Measurements by direct microscopy are made by the use of a special micrometer
eyepiece, containing graduations. The dimension between these graduations is
gauged by comparison with a standard graduation micrometer (stage) slide. Measurements beyond the limit of resolution of direct microscopy are made by means of filtration through graded collodion membranes, which allow the passage of particles of
known size. As more information becomes available in the use of the ultramicroscope
and electron microscope, it is possible that other more exacting measuring procedures may be introduced. An approximation of the size of bacteria may be made
by comparison with that of human red blood cells, which average 7.7 μ in diameter.

---

* Considerable confusion has arisen in the misinterpretation of this unit. Since the prefix micro
signifies one-millionth, this term is one-millionth of a micron and not one-thousandth as frequently
stated.

The following gives the relative sizes of some representative bacteria, viruses, protozoa, bacteriophages, red blood cells, and protein molecules in terms of *milli-mu* (mμ), one-thousandth of a micron.

Name	Diameter or length mμ
Endamoeba histolytical	25,000 (average)
Red-blood cells	7,700
Staphylococcus	800
Serratia mercescens (B. prodigiosus)	750
Rickettsial	300
Psittacosis (virus)	275
Vaccinia (virus)	175
Rabies (virus)	125
Influenza (virus)	120
Bacteriophage (different varieties)	25 to 60
Yellow fever (virus)	22
Poliomyelitis (virus)	10
Foot-and-mouth disease (virus)	10
Serum globulin (molecule)	6.5
Serum albumin (molecule)	5
Oxyhemoglobin (molecule)	5
Egg albumin (molecule)	4

Life Requirements of Bacteria.—The distribution of bacteria in Nature is practically universal. It must not, however, be supposed that they are capable of growing wherever they lodge or may be found. The following conditions are essential for the active growth and propagation of bacteria, commonly referred to as "life requirements."

1. Proper nourishment.
2. Moisture.
3. Air or oxygen or the absence of a direct supply of air or oxygen.
4. Proper temperature.
5. Absence of direct sunlight, retarding chemicals, and antagonistic organisms.

Nourishment for Bacteria.—Like all plants, bacteria require food. A proper source of carbon, hydrogen, nitrogen, oxygen and inorganic salts form their food. Bacteria differ from the higher plants in one marked respect, that is, they do not contain chlorophyll. It is by the aid of the latter constituent that the higher plants synthesize the carbon dioxide of the air by means of sunlight and in the presence of water (in moisture). The carbon is retained by the plant, while the oxygen is returned to the outside atmosphere. It is, therefore, apparent that the simple inorganic compound carbon dioxide found in the air acts as the source for the carbon present in organic combination in the higher plants. Bacteria, however, cannot utilize this source of carbon owing to the absence of chlorophyll (for the exceptions, see page 218). The exceptions, which include a number of soil bacteria, are distinguished by the fact that they are capable of utilizing carbon dioxide, ammonia or nitrites as sources of carbon and nitrogen. Such bacteria growing in the absence of organic matter and building up their own food supply from simple inorganic substances are known as *autotrophic bacteria*. In order to build themselves up, the vast majority of known species of bacteria must obtain their carbon from the complex organic compounds, the proteins, fats and carbohydrates. Bacteria requiring complex organic substances for their sustenance are known as *heterotrophic bacteria*. In this respect they closely resemble animal life. Such elaborate compounds are mainly found in animal and vegetable matter. Bacteria are, therefore, dependent upon the latter for their nourishment. Bacteria are, however, provided with suitable enzymes or ferments to digest this complex pabulum. Among the latter are to be found: saccharolytic enzymes to digest starches and sugars; proteolytic enzymes to digest proteins; and lipolytic enzymes to digest fats (see also pages 26 and 221).

Bacteria are sometimes classed as saprophytic, saprozoic or parasitic. The *saprophytic* bacteria (noun, saprophytes) are bacteria that thrive and develop on vegetable matter and the *saprozoic* bacteria thrive on animal matter, which in both instances are usually dead or lifeless. Bacteria that grow and thrive in the living body or host or on living animal or vegetable matter are called *parasitic bacteria*. In the latter case it may be the waste products of the dead cells as well as the living cells in the living body that may furnish the required food supply. Many of the parasitic bacteria may produce injury to the host by forming metabolic products of a deleterious nature. Organisms producing disease are known as *pathogenic bacteria*. There are other parasitic bacteria, as those constantly found in the mouth or other body fluids, that are nonpathogenic and harmless to those harboring them, due probably to the attenuation of the organism or the great resistance of the host. The vast majority of bacteria belong to the saprophytic or saprozoic groups and do not produce disease, hence termed *nonpathogenic*.

Many of these saprophytic organisms are of considerable value to mankind. (See page 218.) Yeast commonly found in the form of compressed yeast is the living cells of *Saccharomyces cerevisiae* combined with a starchy or absorbent base. It is of value in the fermentation industries in the production of alcohol from sugars, used in baking, used extensively in medicine today as a therapeutic agent, and pharmaceutically and commercially in the preparation of koumyss, a fermented milk. The pharmacist has a sale for cultures of *Lactobacillus acidophilus*, which are sold under a variety of trademarked names. The bacilli of the *lactobacillus* genus are all of a saprophytic nature and either alone or in association with another saprophyte, *Streptococcus lactis*, are sold in suitable liquid culture media, or the latter are mixed with starch, sugar or sugar of milk, dried and compressed into tablets or, better still, in blocks which are chocolate covered. They are employed as therapeutic agents in arresting putrefaction. (See page 224.) Then there are the aceti microorganisms (produce acetic acid), the lactic acid bacilli and a host of organisms of value in the ripening of cheese and in other industries. Other bacteria primarily considered as saprophytes may at times become accidental parasites, lead a temporary parasitic existence (then known as *facultative parasites*) and cause disease. An example illustrating such a condition takes place when one becomes infected with the tetanus bacillus from a rusty implement and tetanus or lockjaw sets in.

In conjunction with pathogenic the term *virulent* is used frequently, as speaking of virulent bacteria. Microorganisms that possess a high or marked disease-inciting power are called *virulent bacteria*.

Bacteria obtain the nitrogen necessary for their development from organic nitrogenous compounds, the proteins being the main source of such supply. Native proteins, however, are not utilized in most instances. Amino acids and, in some cases, nitrates give up the nitrogen to the bacteria. In rare cases some bacteria are capable of assimilating the free nitrogen in the air. The nodules found upon the roots of leguminous plants are mainly masses of bacteria which possess the latter remarkable property (see page 219). Among some of the bacteria, especially many of the pathogenic ones, only particular kinds of animal albumin may be utilized by them, so that for their artificial development it becomes necessary to employ a medium composed of or containing these special proteins. Bacteria that do not require any particular protein generally obtain their nitrogen (under laboratory conditions) from *peptone*, the most common nitrogenous ingredient of culture media, which provides a readily available source of nitrogen. ZoBell and Grant (*Science*, 1942, **96**, 189) recently reported that concentrations of utilizable organic matter smaller than 0.1 mg./L. will provide for bacterial multiplication.

The hydrogen is supplied by the complex organic compounds or in combination as water. The quantity of inorganic salts required for nutrition is exceedingly small. They include mainly the sulfates, phosphates or chlorides of sodium, potassium or magnesium with traces of calcium and iron. Moisture is indispensable to the growth of bacteria, and the amount required by the individual organisms varies considerably. This is taken up by the cell from the moisture in the surrounding medium, and is mainly used to dissolve the food material upon which bacteria thrive.

Recent studies have revealed that minute quantities of different substances are required and serve as *accessory growth factors* for bacteria. Some of these *growth factors* enter into the structure of enzymes or coenzymes concerned with cell oxidations and respiration. In many instances, identification of these substances has been unsuccessful, though in other cases known chemical compounds are now recognized as serving as growth-promoting agents. Among the latter are to be found thiamine, riboflavin, nicotinic acid (niacin), nicotinamide, hemin, pyridine nucleotide phosphate, *i*-inositol and biotin. For further details see Koser and Saunders (*Bact. Reviews*, 1938, **2**, 99). Numerous investigations are now in progress regarding the nutritive requirements of bacteria and these developments will make available a better understanding of the many factors concerned with the normal growth of bacteria. Furthermore, it is of interest to note that these studies in bacterial nutrition have advanced the whole field of animal nutrition and biochemistry.

Oxygen Requirements.—All bacteria require oxygen in some form in order to thrive and multiply. An examination of the life processes of many bacteria will show that some are dependent upon the presence of free oxygen or air. Those organisms which require the direct or free oxygen for their development are known as *aerobes* or *aerobic bacteria*. Some bacteria, however, will not grow at all where free oxygen is present. The latter are known as *anaerobes*, or *anaerobic bacteria*. Though they do not require direct oxygen for propagation, it is not to be supposed that the anaerobes are not dependent upon this element for proper development. They obtain the necessary oxygen indirectly by splitting up the various decomposable organic compounds in the environment where they grow. Proteins and carbohydrates in particular are utilized for this purpose, and for this reason it is customary to add some carbohydrate, usually glucose, to culture media, when anaerobes are to be cultivated An examination of the many anaerobes will reveal the fact that some of them are dependent upon the total absence of oxygen or air. Any free oxygen present will promptly check their growth. Such bacteria are termed *strict* or *obligate anaerobes*. *Obligate* or *strict aerobes*, on the other hand, are bacteria that require the presence of total free air or oxygen and stop growing when the supply of the latter is diminished. Between these two extremes are found bacteria that will more or less readily adapt themselves to either of the two conditions. This has given rise to the following groups:

Aerobic and Facultative (or Optional) Anaerobic Microorganisms.—Bacteria which thrive best in the presence of air or oxygen, but develop less abundantly or to a diminished extent in the nonpresence of free oxygen.

Anaerobic and Facultative (or Optional) Aerobic Microorganisms.—Bacteria which thrive best in the absence of free air or oxygen but grow to a certain extent in the presence of oxygen.

Micro-aerophiles are bacteria which grow best in an atmosphere from which the oxygen is partially but not entirely removed. During culturing this may be accomplished by making a stab culture in a tube of semisolid medium. *Capnophile* is a term recently suggested for designating those bacteria requiring carbon dioxide in the atmosphere during incubation (see page 81). Recent studies tend to indicate that carbon dioxide plays an important but little understood role in bacterial physiological processes (*Ann. fermentations*, 1938, **4**, 547).

Temperature Requirements.—In addition to the previously mentioned requirements, a suitable temperature is essential for the proper development of bacteria. Each species has a minimum (below which growth ceases), maximum (above which growth ceases and death may occur) and an optimum or most suitable and best temperature at which it will develop and produce luxuriant growth. The optimum for the various species should be sought when cultivating bacteria. There is a slight variance between the most suitable temperature for the different types of microorganisms, but, as a general rule, it may be said that in the case of parasitic bacteria (microorganisms developing on living matter), multiplication is limited to a narrow temperature range and the temperature of the living host may be considered as best adapted for their growth. Such temperature (where the human being is the host) is usually 37.5° C. Saprophytic bacteria, on the other hand, grow on matter at a temperature ranging between 20° to 30° C. (a broader latitude), with 25° C. being considered as the average. The maximum temperature for the development of the commonly observed bacteria is 40° C. A temperature considerably over this will attentuate or weaken the ordinary forms of bacteria. *Attenuated bacteria* is a term used to describe those microorganisms in which physiological alterations have occurred, so that their virulency is partially or wholly lost. There are, however, some isolated species of bacteria that will thrive exceptionally well at a temperature from 60° to 75° C. They are usually nonpathogenic and are known as *thermophilous* or *thermophilic bacteria* or *thermophiles*. As the temperature is increased, a point is reached at which the bacteria under investigation are killed. This temperature varying for the different species of bacteria is known as the *thermal death point*. It is important to note that the latter is not constant, as the particular temperature is influenced by such factors as moisture and general content, age, numbers present, time of exposure, *p*H, etc. The following classification according to the temperatures at which bacteria develop is at times given:

Psychrophilic Bacteria: minimum at 0° C.; optimum at 15° to 20° C.; maximum at 30° C. (yeasts and molds).

Mesophilic Bacteria: minimum, 5° to 25° C.; optimum, 37.5° C.; maximum, 43° C. (all pathogens).

Thermophilic Bacteria: minimum, 25° to 45° C.; optimum, 50° to 55° C.; maximum, 60° to 70° C. (many spore bearers in soil and feces).

It is, of course, frequently possible by artificial methods to create conditions so that certain bacteria may adapt themselves to grow luxuriantly at temperatures which may not be their normal optimum. But usually various characteristics may be lost in doing this. Some pathogens have their virulency destroyed by such procedure. Other organisms may lose their power of producing pigmentation by such treatment, etc. The minimum temperature for bacteria (commonly observed) is 10° C. Cold, therefore, prevents the growth of bacteria. Freezing destroys many bacterial species, though some microorganisms and most spores seem to resist almost all low temperatures for long periods of time.

Bacteria develop best in the dark or in diffused daylight. The direct rays of the sun first weaken or attenuate the bacteria and finally in most cases kill them. .

Variations and Transformations of Bacterial Forms.—There is no evidence to indicate that bacteria can become permanently transformed under normal conditions from their basic structure or type. The transmutation or change of bacilli to cocci or from cocci to spirilla is unknown. It is, however, known that the sizes and even shapes of certain species of organisms may vary, depending upon the medium on which they are grown or if unfavorable conditions exist. *Degenerative* or so-called *involution* forms are seen with certain organisms after prolonged growth upon artificial culture media without transplantation or in media of unsatisfactory reaction, or if grown under unfavorable atmospheric conditions. This is especially true of the causative agent of diphtheria. *Pleomorphism* is the term used when bacteria show variations in forms even as young cultures, growing under the most favorable conditions. The causative agent of glanders, *Bacillus mallei*, displays this tendency. See also page 100.

Antagonism, Symbiosis and Commensalism.—When the simultaneous presence of two different bacteria in the same culture or in the same body or lesion favors the development of both (mutual benefit), the condition is spoken of as *symbosis, association* or *mutualism*. It has been shown that disease is produced where an organism is present symbiotically with another bacterium, which condition is not produced by the presence of either organism alone. It also has been shown that growth is produced in artificial culture media in symbiosis with another organism under conditions which would not result in growth if the primary organism alone is present. *Synergism* is a term used frequently to designate the living together of two organisms, with the production of a change which neither alone could bring about. Some microorganisms exert an influence upon each other, resulting in the inhibition of growth of one or more of the less vigorous types. This behavior is known as *antagonism* or *antibiosis* and is due to the fact that the metabolic products produced by the predominant species, or the change in reaction of the culture medium, are detrimental to the existence of the less vigorous varieties. An organism which exists on the by-products or profits by the activities of another organism (the latter is unaffected) and does not in turn extend any benefits is known as a *commensal*. *Commensalism* or *metabiosis* is frequently observed.

Filterability of Bacteria.—The problem of bacterial filterability has more recently taken on added significance especially due to the work of Kendall, Mellon, Hadley and others. These researches and studies on bacterial variations revealed that the characteristics of the cells of each individual species are vastly more complex than was heretofore supposed. Mention is made in a later chapter concerning the so-called *filterable viruses.* Diseases caused by the latter are, in their clinical course, and their method of dissemination and of inducing immunity, akin to bacterial diseases in which the causative agents are presumably known and can be cultivated in suitable media. As yet the incitants of the *filterable virus* group have not for the most part been cultivated upon laboratory media; and until more definite data are available it may be best not to regard these incitants as bacteria existing in the infected body in the filterable state. What is of significance is that workers have reported known etiological agents which can be cultured on appropriate media and, in particular, the typhoid, dysentery, diphtheria, colon, and tubercle bacilli and other organisms, have been shown to be capable of a dual existence, both in a nonfilterable and a filterable state. Kendall found that by serial and prolonged cultivation of the organism in the so-called "K" medium, a protein-rich medium prepared from the dried hog intestine and containing Tyrode solution, there results an acclimatization of the organism in its filterable state to the protein medium, with a concomitant loss of accommodation to the simpler (peptone, meat extractives) medium. It has, in other words, become *proteophilic* instead of *peptophilic.* It is surmised that the principal function of filtration through Berkefeld "N" and "W" filters (which he used) is to strain out, and hold back the nonfilterable forms of the organism, passing those forms which not only are indeed filterable but also which have become more and more acclimatized to the protein environment. The peptophilic or nonfilterable form can be recovered from the protein "K" medium where the filterable form prevails after cultivation for several transfers.

There are some workers who attribute the presence of these filterable forms to flaws or leaks in the filtration equipment and even to contamination. There is available, however, sufficient evidence to regard the possible existence of these forms among some species of bacteria. Furthermore, they appear to have no relation to the majority of the filterable viruses. We have thus a new concept of the properties of bacteria commonly observed. There is no doubt that these observations will have important bearing upon microbic infection and the communicability of disease. The practical possibilities of these researches are apparent.

Chemical Composition of Bacteria.—Bacteria are composed of water varying from 75 to 85 per cent. The remaining contents are solids, being essentially proteins (23 to 72 per cent of total solids), carbohydrates (12 to 28 per cent), fats (0.17 to 40 per cent) and inorganic salts. Among the elements present are carbon, hydrogen, oxygen, nitrogen, phosphorus, sulfur, chlorine, iron, calcium, sodium, potassium, magnesium and silicon. Bacteria possess the capacity of accommodating their chemical compositions to the existing environmental conditions wherein they may find themselves. The percentage of the different basic elements varies, therefore, over a wide range not only with different species of bacteria, but also with the same species under varying environmental conditions and even under the same environmental conditions, depending upon such factors as age, etc. True cellulose has not been found in bacteria, but a substance similar to hemicellulose was found. Not only the simple proteins but nucleoproteins are present in considerable quantities. The carbohydrates include the simple sugars, starch, glycogen, gums and complex polysaccharides. Some of the latter are of special significance, as the "*soluble specific substance*" (*S. S. S.*) found in the capsular substance of the pneumococcus (see page 115.) The lipoids present are simple fats, waxes and phospholipids. Specific organisms may contain pigment, higher alcohols and other compounds, characteristic of the particular species.

Activities of Bacteria.—The numerous species of bacteria produce and elaborate different chemical compounds. Even heat and light may be generated by bacterial growth.

Heat.—In the breaking down of complex organic bodies brought about by bacterial activity the evolution of heat is to be expected. The increase of temperature in organic substances, when stored in large quantities in a moist condition or allowed to undergo fermentation, is due, partly at least, to the action of bacteria. This is observed when storing moist potatoes, turnips, etc., in the fermentation of tobacco to obtain a special flavor or aroma, in the preparation of snuff, sauerkraut and fermented hay. Such heat production rarely attracts attention in laboratory cultures, due to the fact that on a small scale the temperature rise is slight, and there is no sensation of warmth apparent when fermenting liquid cultures with abundance of bacteria are touched by the hand.

Light.—An interesting vital phenomenon is the property of emitting light (phosphorescence or photogenesis) common to certain microorganisms, known as *photogens*. The latter are primarily inhabitants of salt water. They grow best and emit light only under free access of oxygen. It is said that a living substance, photogen, which is closely bound to the cell protoplasm, is responsible for the light production.

Toxin.—Most all pathogenic microorganisms produce a toxic or poisonous substance, called *toxin*. The majority of the bacteria hold this toxin within the cell, the latter being liberated only when the cell wall is destroyed or after the death of the organism. Such toxin is known as *intracellular toxin* or *endotoxin*. It seems that the latter is not a definite preformed constituent of the bacterial cell. In all probability it is the poisonous product of broken down bacterial protein. Other bacteria produce a toxin which is thrown forth from the cell into the surrounding environment. The latter is called *extracellular toxin, exo* or *ectotoxin*. Most all commonly observed bacteria produce intracellular toxins, while only few microorganisms elaborate extracellular toxins. The diphtheria and the tetanus bacilli are organisms that produce the latter type of toxins. Extracellular toxins are detected by injecting sterile filtrates (obtained by passing inoculated broth cultures through Mandler or Berkefeld filters) into guinea pigs or other suitable animals and observing the highly pathogenic properties of such injected material. Some bacteria, as the diphtheria bacillus, produce their specific toxin in the animal body; others as the *C. botulinum* have been found producing their toxin in organic substances outside of the body (preformed toxin). An interesting and not fully understood feature of the action of toxins is that a definite period of incubation must elapse before symptoms appear after the ectotoxin is injected into the animal body.

Other Characteristics of Bacteria.—Various bacteria seem to possess different properties characteristic of the individual species. Numerous terms have been employed in this connection designating the peculiar characteristic. Bacteria that have the power of decomposing organic substances with the liberation of gaseous products are known as *aerogenic bacteria*. *Chromogenic bacteria* or *chromobacteria* are microorganisms which produce pigments. The loss of this property is easily influenced by slight changes, as change of temperature, lack or presence of too much air, and other environmental factors. The various pigments are usually divided into groups, depending upon the solubility of the pigment in water, and their behavior with volatile solvents. Pigment production by bacteria, other than its practical importance in identifying the latter, is receiving special emphasis especially on their probable role in metabolism, pathogenicity and to discover their true function. Sobin and Stahly (*J. Bact.*, 1942, **44**, 265) recently presented an interesting study on the isolation of bacterial carotenoid pigments. *Photogenic bacteria* are so named due to the fact that they possess the property of emitting light (*i. e.*, phosphorescence). *Saprogenic bacteria* possess the power of decomposing proteins or albuminous substances with the production of disagreeable smelling end products, the change being commonly known as *putrefaction*. Some workers restrict the use of the latter term to protein decomposition under anaerobic conditions. Proteolysis under aerobic conditions is more complete, the end products are less offensive and the process is termed *decay*. Both decompositions, *putrefaction* and *decay*, usually occur side by side, the latter following the former. *Suppurative* or *pyogenic bacteria* are pus-producing microorganisms.

Zymogenic bacteria are microorganisms that possess the property of breaking down organic bodies (usually carbohydrates) into relatively simpler compounds, which are usually useful. Such a change is designated as the process of *fermentation*.

Bacteriophage.—Twort (*Lancet*, 1915, **2**, 1241) and later d'Herelle (*Compt. rend.*, 1917, **165**, 373) observed that when Berkefeld filtrates of cultures of certain bacteria are added to the cultures of these and even other bacteria, the microorganisms disappear or go into solution. The substance which produces this apparent autolysis has been termed a *bacteriophage*, and briefly *phage*.

Much discussion has centered around the nature of the bacteriophage of Twort-d'Herelle. The exact nature of this bacteriolytic agent is unknown. The two leading views are: (1) that it is an ultramicroscopic filterable organism, which is widely distributed and grows only in contact with and at the expense of living bacteria; (2) that the bacteriophage is an enzyme or enzyme-like substance produced by the bacteria analogous perhaps to lysozyme, but autocatalytic. The claim by d'Herelle, that the bacteriophage is an ultramicroscopic organism, a sort of parasite living on bacteria, although greatly upheld by him and his supporters, has not been universally accepted. Only few workers accept a third theory advanced by Hadley that phage is a genelike substance, representing a phase in the life history of the susceptible bacterium. Bacteriophages were first regarded as specific, that is, each bacterial species required its respective bacteriophage to dissolve it. This was, however, disproved by later observations.

Evidence presented by many workers indicates that this product possessing lytic properties of its own is a self-perpetuating substance exhibiting a stimulating effect on homologous or closely related bacterial species. Whether it is a living parasitic organism, a product of bacterial metabolism, an enzyme, etc., will require further investigation. d'Herelle's claim that the bacteriophage is a living bacterial species is based mainly on its capacity of unlimited self-multiplication. But recently Bordet has advanced a theory which accounts for the singular phenomenon of self-multiplication without postulating a truly "living" nature for the bacteriophage. Hadley agrees with Bordet that the bacteriophage is of bacterial origin. Having had some contacts with this subject and due to various personal observations in experimental work with bacteriophage, it becomes, however, difficult to accept Hadley's view that bacteriophage is a result of bacterial dissociation, connected as it were with a definite stage in the life-cycle of the bacterial species. It is just as difficult to accept d'Herelle's more recent assumption that dissociation is necessarily and always a result of bacteriophagy.

In the preparation of bacteriophage the author has found (as have other workers) marked differences in the yield by different strains of the same species. In like manner cultures of bacteria reveal marked variation in resistance to the action of bacteriophage. Experimentally a greater yield of phage is obtained from young actively growing liquid cultures (six to eight hours old and immediately filtered), repeating the process of inoculating for eight hours and immediate filtration until a rather potent bacteriophage is the result. The hydrogen-ion content, salt content, presence of buffer salts, etc., effect the lytic principle. Acclimating the organisms to a rich protein environment before the broth cultures are started is advisable. Bacteriophagy is inhibited by the presence of many different substances. In some instances it may be due to the phospholipids (see Williams and Associates, *J. Bact.*, 1940, **40,** 517). Evidence available to evaluate the specificity of bacteriophage is such as to disagree with d'Herelle who believes that "there is but a single bacteriophage, common to both man and animals, capable by adaptation of acquiring an incidence toward all bacterial species." Most investigators cannot do otherwise than feel convinced of the diversity of the lytic principle. A considerable degree of specificity prevails among bacteriophages originating from different bacterial species. Rakieten and associates (*J. Bact.*, 1940, **40,** 529) recently described bacteriophages acting on mucoid strains of bacteria, which were type-specific when acting on members of the *Klebsiella* genus, strain-specific for mucoid varieties of *Escherichia*, and either strain- or group-specific for members of the genus *Aerobacter*. They even suggest the possibility of these specific phages as being useful in classifying *Klebsiella* strains into their respective types.

Bacteriophage is very active in weak dilutions. It is produced only in contact with living bacteria (active cultures) and not in environments containing dead organisms. It is inactivated when heated at 72° to 75° C. for thirty minutes and by various chemicals. It passes through the compact clay and infusorial earth filters which retain bacteria, and from ultrafiltration experiments, the size of phage has been estimated as from 20 to 75 mμ. If to bacterial colonies on a medium in a Petri dish there is added some phage, clearing of the culture where the phage is present will be noted. These cleared areas are known as *plaques* and though variable in size are constant for a given strain of phage. In Nature, phage can be obtained from feces or sewage. When injected into animals, a specific antibody is produced which inhibits the lytic action of the bacteriophage, a process closely paralleling the neutralization of soluble toxin by its specific antitoxin. See also page 342.

Acid, Alkali, Hydrogen Sulfide, Gases and Other Products.—It is difficult to classify with clearness or exactness the many chemical changes caused by bacteria. In their metabolism the different organisms are continually producing various products which depend in character upon the specific bacterium and its particular en-viroment.   (See also page 69.)

Acid and Alkali Production—Enzymes.—The production of acid and alkali by bac-teria is most frequently a manifestation of enzyme action.   An *enzyme* may be de-fined as a colloidal substance produced by a living cell, which acts as a *catalyst, i. e.,* bringing about or hastening a chemical reaction without entering into the reaction itself.   They are usually only recognized by their activities.   A single organism may secrete many of the different enzymes.   The latter frequently result due to the in-fluence of various environmental factors.   There are many enzymes in addition to the following soluble ferments which bacteria produce primarily as necessary to them-selves for the absorption of certain foods.   They are usually named by noting the substance acted upon and attaching the suffix "ase," as: proteases (proteolytic en-zymes); lipase (fat-splitting enzyme); carbohydrases (carbohydrate-splitting en-zymes); coagulase (rennin-like or "lab" enzyme); and amylase (diastatic or amylolytic enzyme).

Oxidizing enzymes are divided into the *oxidases* which catalyze oxidations in which oxygen plays a part and the *dehydrogenases,* which catalyze anaerobic oxidations in which the oxidations result by the removal of hydrogen from the molecule.

Enzymes appear to be of protein composition, possess properties generally asso-ciated with living matter, are relatively thermolabile (inactivated at 56° to 60° C. for one-half hour), are resistant to freezing, often destroyed by strong alkalies and acids, inhibited in their action by various chemicals, exert their activity best at an optimum pH and optimum temperature, and exhibit a high degree of specificity.

Fermentation.—The production of either acid or gas or both in the bacterial fer-mentations is frequently employed in the laboratory as a means of special differentia-tion between many closely related organisms that possess almost identical morpholog-ical and staining characteristics.   This ability to ferment certain sugars is one of the more constant physiological characteristics of bacteria.   The production of some of these acids for commercial use is made possible by these same bacterial processes. Among the acids produced are acetic, butyric, formic, lactic and propionic acids. Acetone, aldehyde, butyl alcohol, isopropyl alcohol and ethyl alcohol may also be formed by bacterial fermentations.   The gases are generally carbon dioxide mixed with some hydrogen.   Marsh gas is formed by specific bacteria that are capable of decomposing cellulose.

Putrefaction.—In many of the putrefaction changes one or more of the following substances are produced: various amino acids, indol, skatol, the mercaptans and hydrogen sulfide, substances most of which possess offensive odors.   Indol production as a means of bacterial differentiation will be considered in another chapter.

When present, alkali production by bacteria usually occurs with the formation of ammonia in environments that are rich in proteins and low in or free from sugars.

Vitamin Production.—The ability of specific microorganisms to produce vitamins has recently been receiving attention.   It has been shown that the synthesis of vitamin B_1 by different groups of bacteria is possible.   Strains of organisms of different genera have been found capable of producing the growth-promoting vitamin for white rats.

Mention may be made that different *microbiological methods for vitamins* and other accessory growth factors are available in which specific bacteria are used in such assays.   It appears that these microbiological assays will be employed as the methods of choice in some cases, not only due to the accuracy resulting, but also due to the comparative reduced cost as compared with other techniques.

Osmosis.—The delicate cell membrane of a bacterium is semipermeable for different substances. Water usually passes through, but individual differences are exhibited in its permeability by salts in solution. This phenomenon of diffusion or permeability by the solvent (but not the solute) through the cell membrane is known as *osmosis.* This, a constant and important phenomenon of life, is due also to a difference in pressure between the medium and the bacterium. When the pressure within the cell is equal to that of the surrounding medium, *isotonicity* prevails. An isotonic environment is most suitable for normal development. Bacteria, however, are resistant to changes in osmotic pressure, unless the latter becomes marked. If a bacterium is placed in a solution (*hypertonic solution*) which possesses a higher osmotic pressure than the cell constituents and if the cell membrane is impermeable to the solution, water is abstracted from the cell, the contents shrink, and the bacterium loses its normal fullness and shape. This is called *plasmolysis.* When the bacterium is placed in a medium having a lower osmotic pressure than that within the cell (as is present in a *hypotonic solution*), the bacterial cell swells and finally bursts. This phenomenon is known as *plasmoptysis.*

Surface Tension.—The surfaces of all liquids (and solids) are in a state of stress or tension due to the play of intermolecular forces. The degree of tension depends upon the nature of the fluid and the matter present in solution or suspension in this fluid. Surface tension is the force per centimeter in the plane of surface required to overcome the tendency of a liquid to maintain a minimum surface area. The unit of measurement is the *dyne.* The surface tension of the commonly employed culture media varies from 57 to 63 dynes per centimeter, as compared with water, which is 73. Bacterial growth may raise the surface tension of a medium. By removing various substances present in the medium, the surface tension may be raised. Such removal may be accomplished by treatment with charcoal or other agents. Osmosis and diffusion are accelerated by lowering the surface tension. Alcohol with a surface tension of 22 dynes will lower the surface tension of a liquid in proportion to the amount added, although it is not adsorbed onto the surface of the liquid. Other organic substances, however, even in small amounts remain concentrated at the interfacial surfaces and produce a marked lowering of the surface tension. Sodium and potassium soaps of the unsaturated fatty acids and the saponins are effective surface-tension depressants, thus lowering the surface tension. Surface-tension depressants have a marked effect upon bacterial growth, and considerable experimental information has been compiled, which has proved of practical value especially in sterilization and disinfection procedures.

Electrophoresis.—Investigators have found that colloids (and bacteria fall in this class) when suspended in water are electrically charged. When placed in an electric field they are found to be negatively charged, that is, they migrate toward the anode. The phenomenon of the movement of small particles in an electric field is known as *electrophoresis.* Such a relative charge carried by bacteria can be measured. Differences in P. D. (electrical potential difference between a particle and its menstruum or immediate surroundings) appear to parallel differences in virulence. It is believed that a high P. D. indicates high virulence and a low P. D. low virulence. Electrophoresis measurements by the use of comparatively simple and easily carried-out techniques are being employed experimentally to detect toxigenicity of bacteria, especially where other methods fail or at least require considerable time. This may be found to be of practical value in routine procedure for differentiating diphtheria from nonpathogenic diphtheroid bacilli, as pointed out by Falk and associates (*Proc. Soc. Exptl. Biol. Med.*, 1928, **25**, 248). A relationship has also been suggested between electrophoresis, agglutinability and virulence of organisms by other workers. It is possible that the electrical charge possessed by bacteria, which is represented by electrophoretic migration velocities, varies, depending upon the behavior and characteristics of the specific organism. It may be that, as this work progresses, practical application will be found convenient so that this procedure may be used to determine these characteristics more readily than is possible by other methods now in use.

Animal Inoculation.—Certain pathogenic bacteria which often occur in body fluids and other substances mixed with different microorganisms are at times more readily isolated by inoculating a suitable animal with the material containing the mixture of organisms. After allowing time for the bacteria to develop, the animal is killed and the organism in a pure state is obtained from the blood, other tissue, or a characteristic lesion. Suitable media can then be inoculated. This procedure is frequently practiced for the isolation and detection of tubercle bacilli in sputum, urine and other material; for the isolation and detection of the causative agents of botulism, gas gangrene, tetanus, glanders, anthrax, tularemia and other organisms in various discharges and material; for the isolation, and, in particular, to procure a rapid growth of pneumococci so as to determine the specific type and thus be enabled to employ a more specific serum in the treatment of pneumonia, etc.

It might be mentioned at this time that suitable animals are also indispensable for other laboratory procedures as: for testing the virulency of different organisms, and especially in the case of diphtheria bacilli, to differentiate the latter from nonvirulent diphtheroid bacilli; for the preparation and later testing the potency or antibody strength of antitoxins, antimicrobic and other immune sera, modified smallpox and rabies virus, the toxoids and the diagnostic toxins; for the preparation of sera to be employed as diagnostic agents and aids in the identification of different organisms and disease conditions; for testing the toxicity and activity of various chemicals and other therapeutic agents, etc.; for the maintenance for stock purposes of causative agents of disease such as the filtrable viruses which cannot be cultivated on lifeless media; passage through animals to increase the virulency of an organism; etc.

Small animals are most frequently employed in the laboratory. They are rabbits, guinea pigs, white rats, white mice, and less frequently fowls (ferrets, canaries, pigeons, chickens, etc.), monkeys, cats and dogs. On a large scale, horses, calves and sheep are also used.

Chapter III

APPARATUS AND METHODS OF STUDYING BACTERIA

THE UBIQUITY of bacteria was observed as soon as the microscope was discovered. Bacteriology is really an outgrowth of microscopy. In view of the fact that most students in the different professional courses begin the study of bacteriology with a previous experience in the use of a compound microscope, it will not be necessary to explain here in detail the construction and principle of the microscope. It is, however, desirable to describe briefly the important parts again, laying special emphasis upon the adjustments which are mainly employed in bacteriological procedures, and to mention briefly the technique used in preparing material for examination.

The Microscope.—The compound microscope, the common usage of the term referring to an instrument used directly by the eye, consists of a simple microscope, known as an ocular or eyepiece and a combination of lenses. The eyepieces commonly used are capable of fitting any standard tube in a microscope. The main function of eyepieces is to magnify the image produced by the lens or objective to such an extent that the observer's eye can readily perceive the details of that image. They are usually engraved with their respective magnification value and magnify 5 ×, 10 ×, etc. The three objectives used in a bacteriological laboratory are also known as the low-power dry lens, the high-power dry lens and the oil-immersion lens, which when used with a high-power ocular (10 ×) magnify approximately 100 ×, 500 × and 1000 ×, respectively.

The binocular microscope of the new single objective type is preferred by many workers. A binocular tube attachment is available for use with the ordinary microscope, so that any monocular microscope can be transformed into a bincocular microscope. In the use of binocular microscopes, the distance between the eyes is adjustable, so that the worker can keep both eyes open with less strain. Sharper images and clearer fields are apparent.

Any of the microscopes of standard make will be found satisfactory. A good microscope means good objectives. Consequently, it is desirable to pay special attention to the quality of the objectives. As mentioned, three are required, 16 mm. or $^2/_3$ inch (low power), 4 mm. or $^1/_6$ inch (high power) and 1.9 mm. or $^1/_{12}$ inch (oil-immersion lens). The oil-immersion objective is so named due to the fact that a small quantity of a specially prepared cedar oil is placed on the slide before examination, and the objective is immersed directly into this oil and then the object is focused. If air bubbles are present in the oil, remove the latter and apply a fresh quantity. The presence of air bubbles or dust in the oil will affect or even destroy the definition of any objective. Immersion oil, as the specially prepared cedar oil is known, has the same index of refraction as is possessed by crown glass; therefore, a ray of light entering the cover glass is not refracted but passes in a straight line directly into the objective. A mechanical stage, not necessarily essential, is nevertheless convenient and a time-saving adjunct.   An Abbé condenser is an important accessory and should be found on all microscopes intended for bacteriological work.   A low-power objective, having the greater portion of the lens visible, will permit a large amount of illumination providing the proper light will be thrown on the object.   With the higher powers which have but a small portion of their lenses visible it is evident that the rays of light must be condensed so that more light should pass through than would enter ordinarily.   The purpose of the Abbé condenser is to control the rays of light so that an object placed in focus will receive all the light that enters the condenser.   The plane mirror (rarely employed when a condenser is not present) is always used with the condenser, inasmuch as the concave mirror gives off converging rays, which would not bring the object into a clear focus.   The condenser is accompanied by an iris dia-

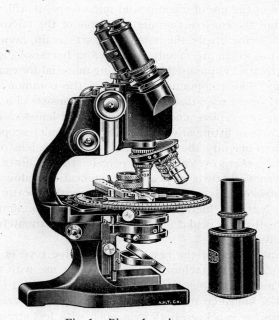

Fig. 1.   Binocular microscope.

phragm, which is used to enable workers to regulate the amount of light.   Stained specimens, being visible because of the color, are unaffected by the light, while unstained material is not rendered visible unless the amount of light is reduced to a minimum.

Use of the Microscope.—Other than the usual directions to be followed, the following measures should also be observed.   Before attempting to focus the light adjust the tube length, which is determined for each microscope by the manufacturer.   This is the distance between the object below and the ocular above (generally 160 mm.).   Direct the rays of light with the mirror or reflector.   Direct sunlight is to be avoided.   White cloud or blue sky light is satisfactory.   A northern exposure is desirable for microscopic work.   Artificial light is most frequently used, because it is always at hand and uniform.   The low-power lens should be used to obtain an even, central and not too bright illumination. It is best to work with the microscope in its vertical position.

When examining stained specimens the diaphragm should be opened wide; and to see the colored objects best use central illumination with strong light. When examining unstained specimens, as in a hanging drop, the diaphragm should be partly closed or light otherwise restricted.

The general rules for the care of the microscope which are usually taught to all in the laboratories where microscopes are used are important. The same care should be observed with microscopes used for bacteriological work, with the following additions:

Be sure that the low- and high-power lenses are always dry. They should never be touched with immersion oil. If by accident the latter finds its way on these lenses, wet a piece of lens paper with xylol, benzin (petroleum ether) or chloroform, nothing else, and quickly wipe off the oil. As soon as one is finished using the oil-immersion lens the oil should be removed by wiping it off with a piece of lens paper moistened with xylol, benzin (petroleum ether) or chloroform. Do not use any cloth or paper other than a soft tissue or fine silk lens paper to clean the objectives, as otherwise they may be scratched or their surfaces may be etched.

Other Types of Microscopes.—The microscopes with which most students and workers are familiar are also known as *light* or *bright-field microscopes*. The entire field of view is always lighted and the objects under examination appear as shadows or colored. Light microscopes are applicable almost universally and are employed in most of the microscopic study commonly carried on.

Dark-Field Microscopy, on the other hand, is of great value though it has a limited applicability. Here, the entire field is dark and the objects to be studied appear self-luminous in this dark field. In practice, dark-field illumination is generally obtained by the use of a special condenser, which is inserted after removing the Abbé condenser. A brilliant source of illumination is essential. A small arc or high-power incandescent lamp is generally employed. The condenser must be centered accurately. A series of concentric circles is generally ruled on top of the condenser to facilitate centering. Using the low-power lens, these circles are brought to the center of the field by means of centering screws provided on the condenser. Slides and cover glasses must be scrupulously clean and free from scratches, and their thickness must be selective and of the proper dimensions to correspond to that required by the special condenser. For preparing mounts of fluid preparations, a thin layer of the latter is placed in the center of a suitable clean slide. A suitable ground cover glass is placed over it and pressed down moderately. Any liquid pressed out is wiped away. The edges of the cover glass are sealed with some thick oil or shellac. A drop of immersion oil, free of air bubbles, is placed on top of the condenser. The slide to be examined is put on top of the condenser, so that the oil forms a contact with the under-surface of the slide. Another drop of immersion oil free of air bubbles is placed on top of the cover slip and the oil-immersion lens is focused in the usual way. Any fresh preparation and especially any of the body fluids, secretions and excretions are objects suitable for studying unstained bacteria therein by dark-field microscopy. For diagnostic purposes, the material most frequently examined by this procedure is fresh chancre exudate for detecting the presence of *Treponema pallidum*, the causative agent of syphilis. Hematologists are also employing this method in the study of fresh blood films.

The Polarizing Microscope used to note the optical characteristics of objects has been used more extensively by chemists and physicists rather than by biologists. Information made available by the use of the *polarizing* and *ultraviolet microscopes* and by employing other optical devices as the microspectroscope with the compound microscope will supply data concerning the detailed internal structure of biological material. Our efforts should be extended to conduct investigations with the polarizing and ultraviolet microscopes on plant and animal life and fresh tissues, so that definite observations will be noted and later sought for as persistently as we proceed to determine definite staining and other microchemical reactions.

The polarizing microscope combines the compound microscope with a micropolariscope. The latter consists of a Nicol prism placed under the stage of the microscope, that is, between the source of light and the object. As the polarizer, it polarizes the light before it reaches the object. Another Nicol prism is placed over the ocular. This, the analyzer, is turned so that it excludes the light from the polarizer and thereby reveals whether the object under examination has produced any change in the polarized light. To determine more fully the optical characteristics of the objects under examination, it is advisable to have cross hairs in the oculars, a stage which is centered and revolving, and a graduated analyzer so as to be able to determine accurately the amount of rotation.

In the Ultraviolet Microscope objects are submitted to the action of ultraviolet radiation and the resulting observations are noted. A quartz prism is used as the ultraviolet reflector and acts as the mirror. The substage and other condensers used must be made of quartz to insure the transmission of ultraviolet radiation and the upper element of the condenser is to be for dark-field illumination. A high-pressure mercury arc lamp with quartz tube is the best source of ultraviolet light for microscopic study. This lamp is enclosed by an opaque lamp house having a window directly opposite the quartz condenser. Ultraviolet screens or filters are used for covering the window. Special mounting slips and a high-grade liquid petrolatum as the immersion fluid are required. A study of objects using the polarizing microscope and the ultraviolet microscope and comparing these observations with those noted in examining such objects, stained and unstained, in the routine manner will reveal in many instances many differences and show how complex the internal structures are. For complete details concerning the microscope and microscopical methods, see S. H. Gage, *The Microscope*, The Comstock Publishing Company, Inc., Ithaca, N. Y., 1942; and Munoz and Charipper, *The Microscope and Its Use*, Chemical Publishing Co., Brooklyn, N. Y., 1943.

Electron Microscope.—Before presenting a description of this new tool in the field of microscopy and especially in bacteriology, a brief consideration of certain fundamental data is necessary. The term *visibility* refers to the observation of or seeing the presence of an object, while the term *resolution* refers to the observation of details of the particular object. The purpose of any microscope is not only to make small objects visible, but also to reveal the minute details in such objects and to discriminate between different minute objects in close proximity to each other. Each microscope has a limiting distance beyond which it is not capable of distinguishing or discriminating between two objects that lie close together. This is known as the *resolving power*. The measure for the resolving power is the N. A. (*numerical aperture*). The higher the N. A. the greater the resolving power of the objective and the finer the detail it can reveal. Resolving power depends upon the wave length of the light used, and the refractive index of the object space and the angle of the cone of light emanating from the objects and used by the objective to form the image. To increase the resolving power of the microscope, ultraviolet light can be used instead of visible light to reduce the wave length of the light. Immersion fluids will increase the refraction index. Improving the lens system will alter the angle of the cone of light. But even with all of these methods under the best of conditions, there is a limit to the resolving power of the microscope, a limitation well known to bacteriologists, who have been unable to study in detail many of the minute bacteria and viruses, because of this impasse. The limit of magnification of the average light microscope is about 2000 diameters and many objects are too small to be seen even by this magnification.

Light in the visible spectrum has a definite wave length. When the size of an object under microscopic examination approximates or is less than this wave length, it cannot be resolved into an image. By the use of the recently introduced *electron microscope*, the visibility of small particles is possible. Electrons possess a wave length far shorter than that of waves of visible light. Within the last decade, a new branch of physics, "electron optics" or "geometric electron optics," was introduced. The latter finds application in radio tubes and especially in television tubes.

Electron optics has made possible the introduction of the electron microscope, making available an instrument with incomparably better resolving powers, as the fast-moving electrons possess a wave length considerably shorter than that of the waves of visible light. Concentrated efforts have been and are being directed toward the construction and improvement of the electron microscope. This instrument has undoubtedly not been perfected to the high degree it will be in the near future, but the practical form made available by the RCA Manufacturing Company gives a magnification 50 times that of the best light microscope, or a magnification of 100,000. The high-power electron microscope presents an appearance differing markedly from that of the light microscope and the difference in the cost between the two instruments is very great. Electrons instead of light are used as the source of illumination, so as to form a magnified image of the object being studied. As electrons do not readily traverse matter, the electron microscope must be freed of air (carefully evacuated). Thus the electron source in the electron microscope is comparable to the light source in the light microscope. Instead of lenses, the latter elements are suitably shaped fields. The manipulation of an electron microscope differs from that of a light microscope. The electron rays cannot be focused as is done by lenses nor can they be seen by the human eye or pass through a glass slide, as the latter is opaque to electrons. However, the actual operation of the electron microscope is simple, and a few days' experience on the part of a competent worker familiar with microscopy is the only training required.

In the light microscope, there is a fixed optical system which is moved up and down, and focusing is accomplished by changing the position of the specimen with respect to the lenses. In the electron microscope, the distances are constant and the lens power is varied. This is possible as the lenses are created, in the case of electron optics, by a current flowing through a coil. With the electron microscope, the magnification is continuously variable instead of the step-by-step variation of the light microscope.

In the available instruments, the electron source is operated at voltages between 30,000 and 60,000, and is enclosed in a lead-encased upper hood to provide ample protection of the operator from the high voltage and x-rays. The electron beam coming from this source is concentrated on the specimen by the field produced in a condenser lens coil. The specimen under examination is therefore mounted on a very thin film of collodion (two-millionth inch in thickness), supported on a fine mesh metal screen; the latter is clamped in the tip of a cartridge very close to the second field lens produced in the objective coil. A plate which supports the specimen cartridge constitutes the movable stage. The specimen motion is transmitted to this plate from the exterior of the evacuated system by means of fine screws and metal flexible bellows. The electrons, after passing through the specimen, are focused by the object lens coil into an intermediate image. The projection lens coil then produces a further magnified image on the large fluorescent screen in the final viewing chamber. Six observation windows, which are placed to allow binocular vision for careful observation, enable a number of spectators to view the image simultaneously. After a selected field of view is focused, and the magnification adjusted to the desired value, a photographic record may be made by merely removing the fluorescent screen and allowing the electron image to strike a photographic plate, which is carried in a holder in the vacuum, immediately below the screen. Specimens and photographic plates are easily and quickly interchangeable by the use of special technique and devices without breaking the vacuum of the main body of the instrument. This is accomplished by the use of the "air-lock" principle.

The preparation of the specimen and specimen support is very important in the technique of bacteriological study with the electron microscope and research is now under way to develop the most suitable techniques. It is apparent that the usefulness of the electron microscope is for the time being in the field of research and investigative study. Already significant developments have been presented in biologic research. New internal structures and greater details of surface observations have been made visible among different species of bacteria by the use of electron micrographs. It may take years before the exact significance and value of these new findings will be known. Even more striking have been the observations made in the study of the viruses with the electron microscope. The reaction of viruses and antibodies, stains and bacteria, and the action of antiseptics in contact with microorganisms are other studies recently presented.

The author has considered the details of the electron microscope in greater length than one would expect in a textbook on bacteriology. This was deemed advisable inasmuch as students will undoubtedly hear more and more of the remarkable discoveries made available by this new instrument, which will not be accessible to most of them. This brief consideration may serve to answer many questions and make possible a better appreciation of the many valuable researches which will undoubtedly appear in the literature in the immediate present. For further information, the student can refer to several recent volumes on the electron microscope and to "A Survey of Research Accomplishments with the RCA Electron Microscope," G. A. Morton, *RCA Review*, 1941, **6**, 131, *J. Bact.*, 1941, **41**, 397–415 and *J. A. M. A.*, 1944, **126**, 632.

Slides and Cover Glasses.—Slides (3 by 1 inches; $1^{1}/_{2}$ mm. thick) and square cover slips ($^{7}/_{8}$ inch), No. 1 or No. 2, are most frequently used. Number 1 cover slips are more satisfactory but usually more fragile than No. 2. Best results are obtained by employing slides of the same thickness (1.5 mm.), so as to obtain at all times the proper focusing of the illuminator on the object. They are seldom, if ever, clean enough for use as purchased. The usual procedure is to clean a large quantity at once by immersing them in an acid alcohol and wiping with a clean linen cloth until dry. Some workers keep a quantity of each in acid alcohol constantly and dry them when needed. The acid alcohol may be 1 or 3 per cent hydrochloric acid or 2 per cent glacial acetic acid in alcohol. It frequently happens that on some slides and slips a thin layer of fatty matter will be found, which cannot be removed by any process of washing or cleansing. The fat film prevents an even spread of material when placed on the surface of the slide and afterward dried. The easiest thing to do under such conditions is to pass the cover glass or slide rapidly several times through the Bunsen burner, care being taken not to warp the cover slip. To have a supply on hand, the slides and cover slips after washing and wiping are placed in Petri dishes or suitable receptacles and heated in a hot-air oven at 200° to 250° C. for one hour. The slides and slips which are to be scrupulously clean should always be handled with a pair of forceps. The Stewart cover glass forceps are best adapted for cover slips.

Slides are grasped by a slide forceps or immersed in jars containing the staining fluid. The Jefferson or Coplin jars are most frequently used for this purpose (so named because they were introduced by the late Dr. Coplin, of Jefferson Medical College).

Plastics and other substances have been recommended to replace cover slips due to the high cost of the latter (during wartime). As yet none of these materials have proved of sufficient practical value for such replacement. Penny (*Can. J. Med. Tech.*, 1940, March) tried various mounting media as substitutes for cover glasses, and found clear Duco as fairly satisfactory and a new quick-drying clear lacquer as most suitable.

Platinum Loops.—The transfer of bacteria and material for examination or for purposes of cultivation is usually accomplished by means of platinum wire. One end of a 3- or 4-inch piece of wire (platinum or platinum-iridium) is fused into the end of a glass rod. Aluminum, wood or other handles are also used and are to be preferred. A No. 26 wire seems to be the best. A lighter wire does not possess a sufficient amount of rigidity, while a heavier one requires a longer time for cooling after

Fig. 2. Cover glass forceps.

it has been sterilized in the flame. A straight wire has only a limited use, but is especially useful in picking up colony growths from solid media, and making "stab" cultures. It is customary to make a small loop at the end of the wire, so that material may be more readily handled and picked up. In some instances (as in performing a phenol coefficient test), standardized loops, which carry and deliver a definite quantity of fluid, are required.

Due to the high cost of platinum, chromal or nichrome wire has been used extensively by some workers and found satisfactory. This wire requires a longer time for cooling than ordinarily required by platinum.

Hanging-Drop Preparation.—When bacteria are to be examined unstained or other special characteristics are to be noted, as motility, etc., the simplest method of examining them is to make what is known as a *hanging-drop* preparation. A concave hollow-ground, or so-called hanging-drop slide is used. The latter is a thick glass slide having a concave depression or a circular pit (ground into the glass on one side) in the center. The examination is made as follows: A small drop of water, or preferably saline solution, is placed on a clean cover slip. The growth or material containing the bacteria (the latter if in a liquid medium can be used direct, water is not necessary) is then touched to the liquid by means of a loop (previously passed through a Bunsen burner, so as to be sterilized). By means of a match or a camel's-hair brush a ring of immersion oil or vaseline is placed around the edge of the concave depression. This prevents the cover slip from sliding and the liquid from evaporating. The cover glass is now inverted and placed over the cavity of the slide, so that the drop of fluid is suspended directly in the center of the depression, being sure that the liquid is not touching the bottom. The slip is gently pressed to spread the vaseline or oil so as to make a perfect seal. This can then be examined under the microscope. It will be necessary to arrange the iris diaphragm, so as to shut out some of the light. If there is no diaphragm attached, use oblique and not a bright illumination. Care must be taken when focusing not to break the cover glass.

Preparing Material for Microscopic Examination.—Bacteria are most frequently examined after being stained. Before the latter procedure they must be fixed to a slide or cover slip so that subsequent washing or strong wind currents will not carry away the bacteria. If the material to be examined is a fluid (as pus, sputum, bouillon or liquid cultures, urine or other sediments) the technique is as follows: Place a small drop of the material obtained by means of a sterile (cool) platinum loop on a perfectly clean cover slip. With the sterile loop, spread this in a thin even film. If the material to be examined is viscid or too concentrated, dilute with sterile water. If a bacterial growth is to be examined (as from solid culture media) a drop of sterile water is placed on the slide or cover slip; the bacterial growth is picked up with a sterile platinum loop and transferred to the slide by touching the water until a slight cloudiness appears. The loop is again sterilized by being passed through a Bunsen burner, and when cool a thin even film is made. The mistake of taking up too much bacterial growth should be avoided. Liquid cultures generally do not need dilution.

After the fluid is spread into a thin even film the water is allowed to evaporate. This is done either by drying at room temperature or hastened by passing over a gentle flame, holding the slide or slip by a forceps. Such process, at the end of which there is left an even distributed thin residue, is known as *fixation*. The material is fixed to the slide, and nothing but scratching or a strong force will remove a film once fixed. The material is then stained by immersing (for a few minutes) the slide or slip in a jar containing the dilute staining solution or by dropping the latter directly on the film and allowing it to act for a few minutes. The use of microburners or hot plates to warm the staining solution so as to hasten the staining procedure is also practiced. The slide is then washed in tap water, the excess of water drained off (aided by a piece of blotting paper) and then passed over a gentle flame to be dried. It is now ready for microscopic examination. It is good practice always to keep the smeared side of the slide or slip up so that one will always know which is the film side, thus avoiding errors when staining, mounting, etc. Whether smears should be made on slides or cover slips is a matter determined by convenience. Slides are less fragile than cover slips in making the smear, but slips are easier to handle during staining. It is also unadvisable to use slides alone without cover slips, if it is desired to keep the smears for a permanent collection. Cover slips must be mounted in Canada balsam, and for a permanent collection they keep well and make a neat preparation.

Glassware for Sterilization.—Material for bacteriological examination must be collected in sterile containers. Bacterial cultivation likewise is carried out in sterile glassware of varied shape. It is, however, apparent that all glassware must be prepared for sterilization (process of ridding material free of bacteria). Test tubes, flasks, pipettes, Petri dishes, etc., should be made of thick, good quality alkali-free glass capable of withstanding repeated sterilization. Containers for storing liquids should be made of glass which is insoluble in water.

Preparation of Glassware.—All glassware, even when new, should be first thoroughly cleansed. The easiest and quickest procedure is by boiling in soapsuds for fifteen minutes to a half hour, then rinsing well and drying. Some immerse the glassware in a 1 per cent solution of nitric or hydrochloric acid, and then transfer it to a 1 per cent solution of NaOH for a few hours. Following this it is washed in running hot water. Others have recommended soaking for at least one hour in the chromic acid cleaning mixture:

Potassium dichromate	60 parts
Water	300 parts
Concentrated sulfuric acid	460 parts

This is then followed by thoroughly washing in running water and drying. In the case of glassware containing old cultures or other material harboring pathogenic organisms, the containers are usually autoclaved for a half hour or boiled for one hour in a covered container in which is present a 3 to 5 per cent compound cresol solution. The containers are then cleansed as directed in the preceding paragraph. In some laboratories, especially where dangerous pathogenic organisms are frequently present, a routine procedure is to sterilize all glassware (new or old) before cleaning.

These clean containers must be stoppered, as otherwise, even though sterilized, material placed therein would quickly become contaminated from the bacteria in the air. Cork and other stoppers commonly employed have been found unsatisfactory, due to many reasons:

1. They are more expensive.
2. The heat commonly employed in sterilization would affect the ordinary cork or rubber stopper.
3. Last but not least, such stoppers do not allow a constant inflow of air, which is required in culturing bacteria, as most of them are aerobic.

Flasks and all tubes (plain and centrifuge tubes) are, therefore, stoppered with cotton. *Nonabsorbent* and not absorbent cotton should be employed. The latter, when used, frequently absorbs water if steam sterilization is employed, and thus the material in the container would be diluted. The technique of plugging or stoppering with cotton is very important. The plugs should fit snugly, should be evenly firm throughout, not too tight (as they are then hard to remove), and not too loose (as sterility is not safeguarded, due to the fact that bacteria from the unfiltered air may gain entrance through the channels formed along the surface of the glass). The plugging itself is performed by obtaining a small piece of cotton about 2 by 2 inches and folding over the ends. By means of a glass rod or by grasping the folded portion between the fingers it is then gently pushed into the mouth of the tube, half of the plug being extruded. After plugging, the containers are sterilized, as later described. Some workers wrap the cotton plug in cheesecloth and this is inserted into the flask. These sterilized plugs have been found to act as an efficient seal against the bacteria of the air. They seem to act as a filter, the bacteria being caught in the meshes of the fibers, and the filtered pure air passes on through. Test tubes are usually packed in various types of wire baskets found on the market. Flasks are kept individually and are usually capped in addition to being plugged. The cap is a piece of heavy paper, muslin or gauze tied with string, or in some instances metallic foil is used. Caps are employed, due to the fact that all flasks usually have a slight flared top or a lip upon which dust containing bacteria will find its way unless protected. The bacteria if present will in turn quickly contaminate any material in the container when the plug is removed. It is for this reason that flasks, test tubes and other plugged glassware have their openings passed through a naked flame (of a Bunsen burner) as soon as the plug is removed, so as to completely prevent or reduce to a minimum outside contamination when introducing material into the containers. Clean *glass-stoppered* containers usually employed for the collection of water, milk and foodstuffs are also capped before sterilization, but in addition a piece of cotton, paper or gauze is usually inserted between the stopper and the opening. This is to prevent the annealing of the glass stopper to the container during the high heat developed in the process of sterilization.

Pipettes, graduated or ungraduated, are either wrapped in paper or placed in a so-called pipette box. This is a narrow, oblong, rectangular or cylindrical copper box, fitted to hold at least a dozen pipettes of any size. Petri dishes, about 10 cm. in diameter, are placed in a wire basket or other holding device and then sterilized. If they are to be kept on hand for some time before use, or if they are to be transported, it is advisable to place them in suitable cylindrical copper containers (12 by 25 cm., holding at least 10 dishes), or they may be wrapped in paper in packages of 3 or 4 and then sterilized.

Fermentation Tubes.—There are many types of fermentation tubes. They are all constructed with a closed arm which retains the gases produced during bacterial decomposition. In preparing any of the several types they are plugged, hung over the edge of a wire basket if a base or other supporting devices are not present and they are then sterilized.

Swabs.—Sterile swabs can be used for many purposes in the laboratory. A piece of copper or aluminum wire of any desired length (usually from 7 to 9 inches) is flattened at one end with a stroke of a hammer. A pledget of plain absorbent cotton is twisted around the flattened end or around one end of a (wooden) applicator. These are then placed in plugged test tubes, wrapped in paper or placed in waxen envelopes or in any other suitable container and sterilized. Swabs are employed for obtaining material from the throat, nose, vaginal tract or elsewhere and are used for inoculating suitable culture media, so as to detect the presence of any microorganisms which may be present. The material obtained with such a swab can also be distributed over slides, cover slips, etc.

Chapter IV

STAINS AND STAINING

IT IS DIFFICULT to determine accurately the exact shape and size of bacteria, even though they may be highly magnified. Most organisms are colorless and, therefore, invisible. Details unnoticeable in the unstained bacteria are apparent in the stained preparation. It is, therefore, advisable to stain bacteria so that they may become distinctly visible.

Dyes.—For staining purposes, dyes are used. The latter are generally classed in two groups, the natural and the artificial. The natural dyes are few in number; and though preparations of cochineal, logwood (hematoxylin) and carmine are used as biological stains, they and other natural dyes are not employed for staining bacteria routinely. The first artificial dyes were prepared from aniline, and the aniline dyes are most frequently employed at present for the staining of bacteria. Since a number of these dyes are not derived from nor chemically related to aniline, and since all of them are derivatives of benzene, it might be best, as has been suggested, to call them benzene *coal-tar dyes*. Benzene compounds may contain certain groups of elements (radicals) which impart to the latter the property of color. Such colored compounds are known as chromogens and the attached radicals as chromophoric groups. Chromogens, though colored, do not necessarily serve as dyes. To serve as a dye, chromogens or any other substance must contain a group of elements which, by imparting to the compound the property of electrolytic dissociation, confers upon it an affinity for fibers or tissues and thereby the property of dyeing or coloring other substances. Such auxiliary groups are known as auxochromes or auxochromic groups. The latter may be either acidic or basic, and depending upon the auxochromic group, aniline dyes are usually classified as acid or basic dyes. This does not mean that the dyes or stains are actually acids or bases, as chemically they are mainly salts. The acid dye is a salt of a color acid. The basic dye usually is a salt of a color base, unless occasionally a free base is possible, whence the suffix "base" is present. *Basic Fuchsin* refers to the salt of fuchsin (with some colorless acid), and *Fuchsin Base* refers to the color base itself not combined with any acid. The acid dyes stain bacteria feebly and seem to possess no special affinity for any particular cell structure. The basic dyes (or nuclear stains) are more generally employed inasmuch as they stain the nuclei of cells and the bacteria equally well. The basic aniline stains most commonly employed for staining bacteria are:

Blue stains—methylene blue (tetramethyl thionin)
Violet stains—crystal violet and methyl violet (both of these are pararosanilines) (the name gentian violet is being discontinued as being meaningless).
Red stains—basic fuchsin (pararosaniline or a mixture of the latter with rosaniline) and safranin.

Brown stain—Bismarck brown.

Pink stain—eosin.

Bismarck brown and eosin are both weak stains, but may be used as counterstains.

These stains are powders (more or less crystalline) which may be either definite
chemical compounds or mixtures. Unfortunately, some confusion exists in the
nomenclature of biological stains. It is important for workers to recognize this and to
familiarize themselves with the preferred designation so as to receive the desired dyes
when ordering the latter. The above comment concerning gentian violet requires
further elucidation. What has been sold under this name has been a poorly defined
mixture of violet rosanilines with or without dextrin. For bacteriological work, users
should order and employ crystal violet in all formulas in which gentian violet is called
for. The Biological Stain Commission has given notice that in the near future cer-
tification will be refused any dye bearing the name gentian violet. The various dyes
should be obtained only from reliable firms, whose brands have been found to produce
satisfactory staining solutions. Only stains of known dye content should be employed. A proper adjustment for the particular formula is possible by increasing or
decreasing the quantity of dry stain. Dyes certi-
fied by the Biological Stain Commission (designated in this volume as C. C. (Commission Certified)) are to be preferred wherever possible.

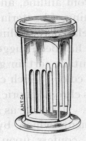

Fig. 3.   Coplin staining jars.

Preparation of Staining Solutions.—The bacteriologist, pharmacist, chemist, nurse, technician,
etc., should be in a position to prepare the most
important staining solutions which may be required by the physician in their daily routine.
The stains and staining solutions which are considered here will suffice for all ordinary bacteriological examinations, and it is therefore advisable
that one shall familiarize himself with these products and their preparation.

Staining solutions should be kept in suitable dropping bottles and neatly labeled.
Only sufficient stain for covering the smear should be used. It may be spread with
the tip of a dropping bottle or dropper. For staining large numbers of slides, various
dishes or jars holding four or more slides are used. The latter may be stained at one
time and the same staining solution used many times. The use of this procedure is
not advocated when staining for tubercle bacilli, as it is claimed by some workers that
these solutions may retain tubercle bacilli washed off from former specimens. For
further details on the use of dyes and formulas for staining solutions employed in the
biological laboratory, see National Formulary VII and Conn, *Biological Stains*,
Biotech. Publication, Geneva, N. Y., 1940.

Stock Solutions.—Aqueous solutions of aniline dyes are most frequently employed
for staining bacteria, as pure alcoholic solutions do not stain well. These watery
solutions, for convenience, are frequently prepared from concentrated alcoholic
preparations called *stock solutions*. The latter when used are saturated solutions of
the basic dyes in 95 per cent alcohol. They should be kept in amber-colored bottles
in a dark, cool place. When such saturated alcoholic solutions are used, a permanent

sediment should always be found in the container to insure saturation and the solution should be filtered before use.

Due to the variance in the *actual dye* content of saturated alcoholic solutions, the latter should be discontinued as stock solutions. *Staining solutions should be prepared by using a weighed amount of the dry stain of known dye content*, if it is desired to have the finished preparation of uniform composition at all times. If it is deemed advisable to employ a concentrated alcoholic solution as a stock solution, it will be found more satisfactory to prepare (instead of a saturated solution) a solution containing a known weighed amount of the dry stain of known dye content so adjusted (grams of stain per cubic centimeter of alcohol) to give a concentration readily measured for subsequent dilution when preparing the diluted staining solution. In formulas for staining solutions, unless otherwise designated, alcohol refers to ethyl alcohol; water refers to distilled water; chemicals are to be c. p. or reagent grade; and dry stains are to be *Commission Certified* or the equivalent.

Action of Stains.—The staining of bacteria by dyes is partially physical, wherein there is a mechanical saturation of the cell body with the stain (one or two or more of the following: adsorption, absorption, diffusion or precipitation may occur). In other instances a chemical salt may be produced by the combination of the dye and the protoplasm of the cell. It also is possible that definite cell structures may display specific chemical affinities with the dyes used. In all probability, both chemical and physical phenomena are displayed in staining processes. The staining power of the dye solutions may be increased by heat, by prolonging the staining process (ordinarily the time limit is not more than five minutes), or by adding to the aqueous staining solution certain substances known as *mordants*. The latter act as fixatives and seem to possess the property of preparing the bacterial cell so as to take up the staining solution more readily, thus intensifying the color. Phenol, aniline and small quantities of an alkali (as NaOH or KOH) are most frequently used as mordants.

Differential Staining Characteristics.—Certain liquids possess the property of removing the color from the bacterial cell after the latter has been stained. This constitutes a very important method for the identification of and differentiation between bacteria. Diluted alcohol and weak acid solutions are the substances most frequently employed for removing the stain already embedded in a given bacterial cell.

Bacteria that do not lose their color after being stained and subsequently washed with alcohol are said to be or known as *alcohol-fast* or *alcohol-proof bacteria*. Those that lose their color and cannot resist the decolorizing process are known as *non-alcohol-fast bacteria*. Bacteria that do not lose their color after being stained and subsequently washed with an acid are known as *acid-fast* or *acidproof bacteria*. Those that lose their color are called *nonacid-fast bacteria*. Acid-fast bacteria have been isolated from butter, grass, hay, etc. Bacteria that resist the decolorizing process with both acids and alcohol are known as *alcohol- and acid-fast bacteria*. There are only two organisms commonly observed that seem to possess this property. They are the various types of the tubercle bacillus and the bacillus of leprosy.

Gram's Method of Staining.—Many microorganisms possess about the same morphological characteristics as to make it impossible for one to distinguish microscopically between different species if they are stained by the technique mentioned on page 40. It was, however, soon observed that some bacteria are colored by certain stains, while others will not retain the original stain after special treatment. This difference constitutes a very important method commonly employed for the correct identification of many bacteria, and especially as a method of differentiation for those organisms that possess identical microscopic characteristics. One of the most important of the special methods is called *Gram's method*, being named after the discoverer. This method consists of four important steps and utilizes a *primary stain*, *Gram's iodine solution, a decolorizer*, and the *counterstain*.

Solutions Used in Gram's Method of Staining
(For original formula, see: *Fortschr. d. Med.*, 1884, **2**, 185)

1. *Aniline Gentian Violet* (Ehrlich).

   (*a*) Aniline water.. 100 cc.

A saturated aqueous solution of aniline in distilled water:

Aniline.. 2 cc.
Distilled water..98 cc.

Agitate well. Filter several times until *perfectly clear*. Prepare freshly when needed.

   (*b*) Filtered alcoholic stock solution of 10 per cent crystal violet (85 per cent dye content).. 12 cc.

or

   Crystal violet (85 per cent dye content) . . . 1.2 Gm., dissolved in 12 cc. of alcohol

Mix *a* and *b* and store away from the light. The solution should possess a thick, creamy violet appearance with no suspended particles. Some workers add filtered stock solution of crystal violet in quantities other than given in this formula (10 to 16 cc.). However, unless requested otherwise, the above proportions are to be used.

Different gentian violet or crystal violet solutions other than the above are also recommended as the primary stain. The following are used frequently.

Gentian Violet Solution (Hucker)

Crystal violet (85 per cent dye content)...................................	2	Gm.
Ammonium oxalate..	0.8	Gm.
Alcohol..	20	cc.
Distilled water...	80	cc.

Dissolve the dye in the alcohol and the oxalate in the water. Mix both solutions and filter. A proportionate quantity of a 10 per cent stock alcoholic solution of the dye can be used.

Carbol-Gentian Violet (Nicollé)

Crystal violet (85 per cent dye content)...................................	1	Gm.
Phenol...	1	Gm.
Alcohol..	10	cc.
Distilled water...	100	cc.

Dissolve the dye in the alcohol and the phenol in the water. Mix both solutions and filter. Stock solutions of 1 per cent aqueous phenol and 10 per cent alcoholic crystal violet can be kept on hand and mixed in proper proportions to prepare this solution.

2. *Gram's Solution.*

Iodine...	1	Gm.
Potassium iodide...	2	Gm.
Distilled water...	300	cc.

Do not keep too large a quantity on hand for stock purposes. Store in an amber-colored bottle in the dark. It is easily made and can be prepared frequently. To overcome the tendency to acid production, 3 Gm. of sodium bicarbonate are added by some workers to the iodine solution in the above formula.

Technique in Gram's Method.—(*a*)   Apply aniline gentian-violet or other crystal-violet solution for two to five minutes (this stains everything blue or violet).

(*b*)   Wash with water (to wash off excess of stain).

(*c*)   Apply Gram's iodine solution for exactly two minutes.

(*d*)   Wash specimen with 95 per cent alcohol or other decolorizer, drop by drop until no more color comes away.

Do not decolorize too much.   Stop adding alcohol or other decolorizer, as soon as no more color comes away.   Acetone, and mixtures of acetone and alcohol (1:1 and 1:3) are used by some workers as the decolorizer.   Other decolorizers (aniline, xylol, or equal parts of each, etc.) are employed but infrequently.

(The Gram's solution seems to possess the property of fixing the crystal-violet color more permanently in some bacteria than in others, so that after washing with alcohol or other decolorizer the latter will remove the color from those organisms that have not been fixed more permanently with coloring by the iodine solution.)

The exact action of the iodine is not definitely established.   It has been suggested that the results of Gram's method may be due to the formation of an iodine-pararosaniline-protein compound in the Gram-positive bacteria.   It has also been suggested that it may be that the iodine renders the cell membrane in Gram-positive bacteria impermeable to alcohol or other decolorizer.   Those bacteria that retain the gentian-violet color after this treatment are known as *Gram-positive bacteria*.   Those microorganisms that lose their color are called *Gram-negative bacteria*.

The Gram-negative bacteria are colorless and their morphological characteristics are thus not discernible.   It is advisable to counterstain them, *i. e.*, to again stain those organisms which are now decolorized.

(*e*)   Therefore, after washing with alcohol or other decolorizer, wash with water (to wash off the latter).

(*f*)   Apply a counterstain for one-half minute.   A color which will be a contrast to blue or violet is employed, either red or brown.

The simple red staining solutions employed are any one of the following:

3.   *Counterstains* (can also be used for simple staining).

Eosin Solution

Eosin Y (85 per cent dye content)	0.1 to 1 Gm.
Distilled water	100 cc.

Dilute Fuchsin Solution

Basic fuchsin (90 per cent dye content)	60 mg.
Distilled water	100 cc.

Safranin Solution

Safranin O (90 per cent dye content)	0.25 Gm.
Distilled water	100 cc.
Alcohol	10 cc.

Dissolve the safranin O in the alcohol and add the distilled water.

The brown coloring solution frequently employed as a counterstain or as a simple staining solution is the following:

Bismarck Brown Solution

Bismarck brown Y (55 per cent dye content)	0.2 Gm.
Boiling distilled water	100 cc.
Mix and filter.	

Bacteria that (when in young cultures or freshly obtained from body fluids) show a tendency to stain both positive and negative in the same smear when this technique is employed are known as *Gram amphophiles*.   Gram-amphophilic organsims are also spoken of as Gram-variable or unstable Gram-positive bacteria.   When an organism is found to display this variability, it is necessary that it should be stained by two or more Gram techniques and cultures of different ages are to be examined.   Gram variability is observed most frequently among the spore-bearing anaerobes and higher forms of bacteria. The characteristic of retaining the crystal-violet color when stained by Gram's method seems to be a property almost entirely confined to bacteria and yeasts from among the group of living cells.

This is the most frequently used and widely applied differential method of staining in bacteriological technique and it is important for beginners to become familiar with this procedure or modifications of it (if employed) and keep in mind the following points.

Material for examination should be spread evenly and thinly on a slide or cover slip, air dried, and fixed with gentle heat. Staining observations in this and in all other techniques can be controlled, if desired, by employing known controls. In this technique, place a known Gram-positive and a known Gram-negative organism on either side of the unknown smear to be stained. Cultures of bacteria when used should be young (twenty-four to forty-eight hours old), as in old cultures known Gram-positive bacteria may be found to appear as Gram-negative. Laboratory cultures (which have been subcultured frequently) kept around for many years may be found to have bacteria which have lost their original Gram-staining characteristics.

Of the commonly observed bacteria, most cocci are Gram-positive, except the meningococcus, gonococcus and *Micrococcus catarrhalis* types (all species of *Neisseira*). Most bacilli are Gram-negative except the diphtheria and diphtheroid bacilli (*Corynebacteria*), the tubercle bacillus and acid-fast bacteria (*Mycobacteria*) and most spore bearers. All spirilla and spirochetes are Gram-negative. Yeasts and molds, though frequently Gram-positive, are variable and may appear Gram-amphophilic.

Modifications of Gram's Method.—Since Gram published his technique in 1884 many modifications have been advocated. Some of these modifications employ a primary or initial stain which differs in composition from the aniline gentian violet, due to the fact that the latter decomposes quickly, especially if kept exposed to the air and light. An alcoholic aniline sulfate gentian-violet solution in Atkin's Modification and a 5 per cent solution of methyl violet in Jensen's Modification (*J. Bact.*, 1920, **5**, 331) are employed as the primary stains. More satisfactory decolorizing reagents have also been advocated. Substitutes for ethyl alcohol which have been tried are methyl alcohol, acid alcohol, aniline, xylol, ether, chloroform, acetone and mixtures of acetone and alcohol. Results have shown that next to strong ethyl alcohol (absolute is even better than 95 per cent), acetone is most satisfactory, especially since a shorter length of time is required for decolorization. In the author's hands Atkin's and Burke's (*J. Bact.*, 1922, **7**, 159) Modifications worked most satisfactorily. Burke's technique which employs acetone as the decolorizing agent gives more consistent and satisfactory results than Lyon's Modification (*J. A. M. A.*, 1920, **75**, 1017) which is used by many workers.

For further details on methods of Gram's staining, see Hucker and Conn (*N. Y. Expt. Sta. Tech. Bull.* **128** (1927)) and Kopeloff and Cohen (*Stain Tech.*, 1928, **3**, 64).

Gabbett's Method.—Gabbett's method is a procedure employed *for staining acid-fast bacteria:*

1. Apply carbol fuchsin for ten minutes in the cold or steam for two minutes.
2. Wash with water.
3. Apply Gabbett's solution for ten minutes.
4. Wash with water. Dry and mount. (Acid-fast bacteria will be colored red; nonacid-fast bacteria will be colored blue.)

Carbol Fuchsin

Basic fuchsin (90 per cent dye content)	0.3	Gm.
Alcohol	10	cc.
Liquefied phenol	5	cc.
Distilled water	95	cc.

Dissolve the basic fuchsin in the alcohol and the liquefied phenol in the water. Mix the solutions. This solution also can be prepared by mixing 10 cc. of a 3 per cent stock alcoholic basic fuchsin (90 per cent dye) solution with 100 cc. of a 5 per cent aqueous solution of phenol.

Gabbett's Solution

Methylene blue (90 per cent dye content)	2	Gm
Twenty-five per cent aqueous solution of sulfuric acid (sp. gr., 1.018)	100	cc.
Mix.		

Method of Staining Acid- and Alcohol-fast Bacteria.—This is most frequently known as the *method of staining for the tubercle bacillus*, inasmuch as the latter organism is the most important of the two commonly known acid- and alcohol-fast bacteria and the methods are mainly employed to detect this bacterium.

For many reasons it is difficult to detect the tubercle bacillus in different specimens. Usually when present only few tubercle bacilli can be found in comparison to the exceedingly large numbers of other microorganisms present, some of which would be mistaken for the tubercle bacillus; therefore, staining the material with a simple dye solution or even by Gram's method will not assist one in any attempt to find this organism. But by taking into consideration the fact that the tubercle bacilli are acid- and alcohol-fast, special methods of staining have been devised which make it very easy to detect the latter. In the following methods (which are most frequently employed) the acid- and alcohol-fast bacteria appear red, while all other microorganisms and cellular elements appear blue. Spores, if present will also retain the red stain.

Slides used for making smears of material to be later stained and examined for the presence or absence of tubercle bacilli should be free of scratches and should be scrupulously clean. The former as well as crystals, fibers and other foreign particles may retain the fuchsin stain, resist decolorization and thus may be mistaken for acid-fast bacilli by the inexperienced worker.

1. ZIEHL-NEELSEN METHOD.—(*a*) Apply carbol fuchsin, fifteen minutes in the cold or steam for three to five minutes (do not boil). If steaming is used, preferably allow to cool until sediment appears (about two minutes).

(*b*) Decolorize with acid until subsequent washing with water will give only a faint pink color to the preparation. (The acid most frequently used is either strong or 30 per cent nitric acid, 5 per cent nitric acid, 5 to 15 per cent sulfuric or 1 to 3 per cent HCl.)

(*c*) Wash with water.

(*d*) Wash with 95 per cent alcohol until no further color is removed.

(*e*) Wash with water. Most workers combine steps *b*, *c* and *d*, and use an acid alcohol, consisting of 3 per cent HCl c. p. in 95 per cent alcohol (by volume).

(*f*) Apply Loeffler's methylene blue for one-half to two minutes.

(*g*) Wash with water, dry and mount.

Loeffler's Methylene Blue

Methylene blue (90 per cent dye content)................................. 0.3 Gm.
Alcohol... 30 cc.
Potassium hydroxide, 1:10,000 aqueous solution....................... 100 cc.
Dissolve the dye in the alcohol and add the potassium hydroxide solution.
Mix.

The dye solution can be kept on hand as a 1 per cent stock solution. One cubic centimeter of a 1 per cent or 0.1 cc. of a 10 per cent aqueous solution of potassium hydroxide (kept on hand for stock purposes) in 100 cc. of distilled water gives a 1:10,000 solution.

This solution is most widely used for the simple staining of bacteria.

The tubercle bacilli appear red; other bacteria and cellular elements appear blue.

Counterstaining may also be conducted with either a saturated alcoholic solution of picric acid, or a brilliant green solution, when the acid- and alcohol-fast bacteria will appear pink or red in a soft yellow or green background.

2. PAPPENHEIM'S METHOD.—This method is one in which the decolorization and counterstaining are accomplished by one solution. It has been found suited for the purpose of differentiating between the tubercle bacillus and certain acid-fast bacteria, which are closely related and at times may cause confusion (especially the smegma bacillus found in urine and feces and rarely in sputum).

(*a*) Stain with carbol fuchsin for ten minutes in the cold or preferably steam for three minutes.

(b) Pour off dye. Do not wash.

(c) Apply Pappenheim's solution for ten minutes, and preferably longer. Some workers flood the slide with the Pappenheim solution four or five times, allowing the latter to drain off slowly following each application.

(d) Wash with water, dry and mount.

Pappenheim's Solution.—Add 1 Gm. powdered corallin (also known as rosolic acid) to 100 cc. of absolute alcohol. Stir until dissolved. Add 1.3 Gm. methylene blue (90 per cent dye content) and then add 20 cc. of glycerin as a preservative. Mix well and filter.

The combination of rosolic acid and alcohol decolorize the nonalcohol- and nonacid-fast bacteria, and the latter are counterstained by the methylene blue.

Neisser's Stain for Diphtheria Bacilli (*Ztschr. f. Hyg.*, 1897, **24**, 443).—Prepare the smear in the usual way and place thereon for two or three seconds Neisser's Acid Methylene Blue (methylene blue (90 per cent dye content), 0.1 Gm.; alcohol, 2 cc.; glacial acetic acid, 5 cc.; distilled water, to make 100 cc.). Wash in water and apply Bismarck brown solution for three to five seconds. Wash, dry and mount. True diphtheria bacilli reveal blue dots (granules) and the remainder of the body or cell is brown. Pseudotypes stain brown with but very few, if any, blue bodies.

In the hands of the author, Albert's method (*Am. J. Pub. Health*, 1920, **10**, 334) seems best as a differential staining procedure and gives better results than Kinyoun's Modification of Ponder's stain (*Am. J. Pub. Health*, 1915, **5**, 246) or Neisser's method for staining diphtheria bacilli.

Staining Capsules, Flagella, Spores.—The special methods for staining capsules, flagella and spores are infrequently employed routinely, being used on occasions for class demonstration and mainly in experimental observations. The solutions used are simple chemical combinations.

The important methods of demonstrating the capsule are: Hiss's copper sulfate method (*J. Exp. Med.*, 1905, **6**, 317), Huntoon's method (*J. A. M. A.*, 1914, **62**, 1397), Anthony's technique, Muir's and Welch's glacial acetic acid techniques (*Bull. Johns Hopkins Hosp.*, 1892, **3**, 84), and Churchman's method (*J. Exp. Med.*, 1933, **57**, 485). It may be noted that a hanging-drop preparation reveals most satisfactorily the presence of capsules, especially if the greater part of the light is shut off by the diaphragm. The simple method of mixing and fixing with India ink and even Gram's method bring out capsules very clearly. Methods used to reveal the presence of flagella can be employed to demonstrate the presence of capsules. Anthony's method • (*Science*, 1931, **73**, 319) and Liefson's technique (*J. Bact.*, 1930, **20**, 203) are simple and dependable procedures.

Welch's Method for Staining Capsules.—Cover film with glacial acetic acid; drain and treat film several times with aniline-gentian-violet solution (pouring stain on and off three or four times and then finally leaving it on for three minutes). Wash in a 2 per cent NaCl solution and mount in same. *Avoid the Use of Water at Any Stage.* The capsule appears as a pale violet halo around the deeply stained organism.

A simple and yet satisfactory method of demonstrating spores is by fixing and staining bacterial preparations by the acid-fast methods previously mentioned as employed for staining tubercle bacilli. Best results are obtained by decolorizing lightly. Abbott's, Huntoon's and Möller's methods are other techniques which may be employed. Burke (*J. Infect. Dis.*, 1923, **32**, 433) employs direct steaming with carbol fuchsin staining solution. Viable spores are unstained; dead spores are stained. See also Snyder's modification of Dorner's method (*Stain Techn.*, 1934, **9**, 71) and Schaeffer and Fulton's modification of Wirtz's technique (*Science*, 1933, **77**, 194).

Möller's Method for Staining Spores.—Prepare films in the usual way. Place in chloroform for two minutes; then wash with water. Cover with a 5 per cent solution of chromic acid for two minutes, and then wash with water. Apply carbol fuchsin and steam for three to five minutes. Decolorize with 5 per cent H_2SO_4 for five to ten seconds. Wash thoroughly in water. Stain with methylene-blue solution for thirty seconds. Wash, dry and mount. The body of the cell appears blue; the spores will be stained red.

Dorner's Spore-Staining Method.—To a heavy suspension of the organism, add an equal quantity of a freshy filtered Carbol Fuchsin Staining Solution and place the mixture in a boiling water bath for ten to twelve minutes. To a loopful of this mixture on a slide or cover slip add a loopful of a 5–10 per cent aqueous solution of nigrosin C. C. Make thin even spreads and dry. The spores are stained red, while the vegetative forms are colorless against a darkened background.

The author has found that the addition of *wetting agents* in the concentration of 0.1 per cent in the primary spore-staining solution increased the intensity of the color in the spores. *Tergitol 08* proved more efficient in this respect than other wetting agents.

Flagella Staining Techniques.—The staining of bacterial flagella is one of the most difficult of bacteriological procedures. For good results all flagella-staining methods are most satisfactory if used after making films from young (fourteen to twenty-four hours old) agar cultures emulsified in sterile salt solution and the latter dried *quickly* on particularly *clean* cover slips or slides. All manipulations are to be performed quickly and with care, to avoid breaking the flagella. Craige's, Van Ermengem's, Loeffler's (and Kulp's Modification (*Stain Tech.*, 1926, **1**, 60)), Zettnow's and Muir's Modification of Pittfield's Method, Weiss Method (*J. Infect. Dis.*, 1928, **43**, 228), and Casares-Gil Method (*Pure Culture Study of Bacteriology*, 1932, **1**, 12) are techniques commonly employed for staining flagella.

Gray's Flagella Stain (*J. Bact.*, 1926, **12**, 273) and *the Conn and Wolfe Modification* (*J. Bact.*, 1938, **36**, 5) have been found more satisfactory by the author than other techniques.

Technique.—Use warm slides and make a thin even film. Air dry, apply mordant for ten minutes (Gray's) or (Conn and Wolfe's) for five minutes. Wash in tap water. Apply carbol fuchsin for five to ten minutes. Do not steam. Wash with water, air dry and examine.

GRAY'S FLAGELLA STAINING REAGENTS

Mordant

Solution A

Potash alum (sat. aq. sol.)	5 cc.
Tannic acid (20 per cent aq. sol.)	2 cc.
Mercuric chloride (sat. aq. sol.)	2 cc.

Solution B

Basic fuchsin (sat. alc. sol.)	0.4 cc.

Keep solutions separately and mix before use or within twenty-four hours before using.

See also Hofer and Wilson (*Stain Tech.*, 1938, **13**, 75) on Gray's Flagella Stain, and Fisher and Conn (*Stain Tech.*, 1942, **17**, 117), who recently presented a flagella staining technique, a further improvement on the Conn and Wolfe Method, which they found to be satisfactory for a wide variety of organisms and suggest its routine use to reveal flagella in any motile species. Their original paper is to be consulted.

Dyes for Other Purposes.

It is important to point out that dyes, even those certified, are used for purposes other than for staining. Certified stains for the latter purpose only are tested for (1) identification (qualitative examination); (2) quantitative analysis; and (3) biological tests, this being actual staining procedures for materials as the stain is to be used in practice. The biological tests are in the final analysis, the more valuable techniques for determining the suitability of dyes for use as stains in bacteriological procedures. Toxicological tests are not conducted and stains for laboratory use, certified or noncertified, are not to be used internally as medicinal agents for humans unless tests for toxicity have been conducted. Stains for laboratory use, however, are employed and certified for use as bacteriostatic agents in the preparation of differential culture media (as in Endo's medium, eosin-methylene-blue agar, etc.).

Chapter V

CULTURE MEDIA

CULTURE MEDIA are sterile liquids and semisolids used for the cultivation of bacteria By means of these products, information may be obtained as to the life histories or biology of microorganisms. Large enough quantities of the different species and types of bacteria can be obtained to enable workers to study and classify them. Mixtures of organisms can be more readily studied and the different bacteria present can be separated or isolated from one another. The presence, number and kind of bacteria can be detected in water, milk, foodstuffs, body fluids, etc. Organisms having similar morphological characteristics are frequently identified, due to their peculiarity of growth as observed in semisolid media or due to the varied chemical changes that are made apparent in some of the culture media. On a commercial scale it is necessary to grow large quantities of bacteria for the manufacture of the many varied biological products. One must also remember that *Koch's postulates* were based on the ability to obtain pure cultures of the organism. Before any microorganism may be accepted as the causative agent of a disease (etiological factor), the following four requirements (as formulated by Koch) should be fulfilled:

1. The specific organism should be constantly present and associated with that disease.

2. Pure cultures should be isolated from the pathological material.

3. These pure cultures inoculated into suitable healthy animals should produce the same pathological conditions (disease).

4. The organism should be recovered in pure culture from the experimental animal to which the disease was given. For further details concerning the practical application of *Koch's postulates*, see Leaflet VII of the *Manual of Methods* prepared by the Society of American Bacteriologists.

It is apparent that, for the preparation of a suitable culture medium for bacterial growth, the nutritive requirements of the bacterium under investigation should be known, if the optimum conditions for artificial cultivation are to be made available. However, it has been only within the last decade that bacterial nutrition has received the attention it deserves. As the subject of active investigation from many different viewpoints, these studies are bound to elucidate worth-while facts; and perhaps we will discontinue the present empirical practice in the compounding of culture media formulas and arrive at some agreement upon more uniform methods for the preparation of media in common use. Various groups have attempted from time to time to standardize ingredients in and to undertake the supervision of recommending approved formulas for culture media, but without much success. The recently formed National Formulary Special Committee on Ingredients of Bacteriological Media (of which the author is a member) appears to be working along the proper lines and will present data which should prove of value.

There is a great variety of culture media, but only a few are used in routine work. The others must be available, inasmuch as certain organisms will not grow on the commonly employed media. At times it becomes necessary to add or introduce proper kinds and quantities of essential food material so as to create an environment which simulates the natural one, peculiar for the particular variety of bacteria under examination. However, the general basis of bacteriological culture media is a suitable source of carbon, nitrogen and inorganic salts. Meat infusions have been and still are in certain instances supplying these basic constituents. Inasmuch as the native proteins are not readily metabolized by bacteria, *peptone* is employed to supply an available form of nitrogen. As a time saver, *beef extract* is used wherever possible to replace infusions of meat. It is important to use only suitable marketable products. It is understandable that, in a treatise such as this, a detailed consideration of the various ingredients used in culture media cannot be given. Nor is it possible to include formulas other than those which have proved of value and are in current use. For reference to a large variety of formulas, see Levine and Schoenlein (*Compilation of Culture Media*, Williams and Wilkins, Baltimore, 1930). However, a word of caution should be directed in the use of peptone. The latter is a mixture of the products of protein hydrolysis (resulting from the digestion of proteins) from which water is removed to produce a dry powder. Bacteriological peptones can be and are made not only from meat (beef and pork), but also from casein, egg albumen, blood fibrin, etc. It is necessary to test the culture medium prepared from the peptone used, to be sure it will serve its most useful purpose in the bacteriological procedure being carried out. Most bacteriological peptones on the market will be suitable for routine work. For indol testing, the presence of tryptophane in the peptone is essential. For use in Endo's medium, fermentable carbohydrate must be absent. In like manner, special peptones are more suitable when noting hemolysis, for the production of certain toxins and bacteriophage, and in the testing of antiseptics by bacteriological methods. Distilled water should be used as well as c. p. chemicals in the preparation of culture media, unless otherwise specified. Dyes as ingredients should be of C. C. (Commission Certified) grade, specially certified for culture media.

Any of the liquid or solid artificial media may be fortified or enriched with natural fluids as egg, bile, blood, blood serum, ascitic and hydrocele fluids, with the production of blood agar, blood-smeared agar, Loeffler's blood serum media, serum bouillon, serum agar, ascitic agar, etc. So-called growth factors, growth activators, accessory food substances, vitamins and allied substances are being used to assist in the growth of certain species of bacteria. It is generally agreed that a medium is to be regarded as nonsynthetic if it contains plant or animal extracts, infusions, digests or tissues. Usually the chemical composition of such media is complex and unknown other than in a general way. "Synthetic media," on the other hand, are compounded with ingredients of known composition and can be duplicated readily from batch to batch.

The following divisions of culture media (used in practice) may be made:

NATURAL MEDIA

Liquid	*Semisolid*
Egg	Blood serum
Milk	Egg
Whey	Potato

ARTIFICIAL MEDIA

Liquid	*Semisolid*
Bouillon	Agar
Sugar bouillon	Sugar agar
(with or without litmus)	(with or without litmus)
Glycerin bouillon	Egg media
Dunham's solution	Glycerin agar
Riva's media	Gelatin media
	Endo's agar
	Russell's agar

Solid media are frequently designated as reversible or irreversible. Reversible solid media are fluid while hot and solid when cold. Irreversible media are prepared by adding a heat-coagulable albumin (egg, serum and other natural fluids) coagulated by heating and when thus solidified cannot be liquefied by physical methods as commonly used. Loeffler's blood serum medium is typical of the irreversible media.

The basis for the preparation of most of the media is plain broth or bouillon, an infusion or aqueous extract of meat. The latter, itself an efficient culture medium, is designated as the "basic liquid medium" or "basal medium" and possesses an isotonicity approaching that of the bacterial cell. It contains the proper quantity of inorganic salts, water, nitrogen, etc., which is obtained by the combination of the soluble constituents of meat, peptone, salt and water.

It is a sound practice and one highly recommended to check all media. Especially is this to be practiced when using special formulas and the various differential media. Inoculate the latter with known positive and known negative controls (from stock cultures). Incubate these controls and treat in an identical manner (with reagents, etc.) as is practiced with the unknown being examined.

PREPARATION OF CULTURE MEDIA

Meat (Beef) Infusion (or Nutrient) Broth or Bouillon.

Minced lean meat (beef or veal)... 500 Gm.
Water... 1000 cc.

Mix well and place in a shallow dish in an ice chest to soak overnight or preferably for about twenty-four hours. Skim off fat (a piece of absorbent cotton can be used), filter through cheesecloth, and express juice contained in the meat. Boil for one-half to one hour or until the fluid is clear; strain through cheesecloth and then filter. Add and dissolve:

Peptone (Bacto-peptone or its equivalent).................................. 10 Gm.
Sodium chloride, c. p.. 5 Gm.

and then boil for fifteen minutes. Bring to original volume with water. Adjust reaction, so that it will be faintly alkaline to litmus (if to be used for routine work; otherwise adjustment is to a designated reaction) and filter. The pH of broth for routine laboratory work may range from 6.8 to 7.4, with the average being 7.2. Sterilize in the autoclave at 15 pounds' pressure (121.5° C.) for twenty minutes.

Meat infusion broth is used by itself or for the preparation of other liquid media or agar and other semisolid media, which are to be used for the cultivation of the more fastidious bacteria.

For the cultivation of the vast majority of bacteria a more easily prepared and a more economical product is employed, as it is just as satisfactory for many of the organisms observed in daily routine. This is:

Meat (Beef) Extract (or Nutrient) Bouillon

Beef extract (Liebig type or its equivalent)...............................	3 Gm.
Peptone (Bacto-peptone or its equivalent).................................	10 Gm.
Sodium chloride, c. p..	5 Gm.
Distilled water...*q. s.* 1000 cc.	

Make a paste of the peptone and salt and dissolve this in the water. Add the beef extract. Bring to a boil and boil slowly for fifteen minutes, stirring frequently. Make up for evaporation by the addition of water and adjust the reaction. Filter and sterilize in the autoclave at 15 pounds' pressure (121.5° C.) for twenty minutes. (During heat sterilization, a change in reaction may occur in some culture media. Nutrient broth with an initial pH of 7.0 or less changes very little, but if higher, it may become about 0.2 more acid after heat sterilization. It therefore is advisable to make suitable corrections for this possible change in this and other media.)

Nutrient Bouillon (Meat Infusion or Meat Extract Broth) without sodium chloride is preferred for some purposes and in other instances the quantity of beef extract and peptone may be increased or decreased. In *Standard Methods of Water Analysis* the basic medium, *Nutrient Broth for Water Analysis* is prepared as above, and contains 3 Gm. of beef extract and 5 Gm. of peptone to each 1000 cc. of water. Sodium chloride is not added. The reaction is adjusted so that the pH reading after sterilization is between 6.4 and 7.0.

Nutrient Agar (Standard A. P. H. A.) (Tryptone–Glucose–Meat Extract–Milk Agar) (for the Examination of Dairy Products).—This medium consists of beef extract, 0.3 per cent; tryptone, 1.5 per cent; agar, 1.5 per cent in distilled water. All ingredients are placed in a flask or other suitable container, and the mixture exposed in an autoclave or steam sterilizer to the action of flowing steam. One per cent of skim milk is to be added just before final sterilization in all cases where dilutions greater than 1:10 of the samples under examination are to be made. The reaction is adjusted so that the pH of the finished medium is between 6.6 and 7.0, preferably pH 7.0. Sterilization is carried out by autoclaving at 15 pounds' pressure for twenty minutes. The skim milk is to be of good quality and may be kept in stock by storing in a sterile condition in suitable containers. A reconstituted skim milk may be used and is prepared by dissolving 10 Gm. of a spray process skim milk powder in 100 cc. of water.

CLARIFICATION OF MEDIA

If the medium is cloudy it may be necessary to pass the liquid through the filtering paper several times. Should this not clarify the medium it may be necessary to add a clarifying agent.

(*a*) The whites of two eggs (or a whole egg mixed with an equal amount of water or 1 to 2 Gm. of egg albumen dissolved in 20 cc. of water) to each 1000 cc. are added, the mixture brought slowly to a boil and boiled briskly for five minutes and filtered. This procedure not only adds an additional expense but there is the possibility of there being added sulfur and fermentable substances which tend to interfere with the growth of some bacteria.

(*b*) Add shredded filtering paper and filter.

(*c*) Best of all is to add a few teaspoonfuls of kieselguhr or purified talc, preferably the former, and filter.

(*d*) In the preparation of "hormone broth" and "vitamin media," the minimum degree of filtration is advocated, so as not to remove growth-stimulating substances. Accordingly, sedimentation and decantation of the supernatant fluid culture medium without disturbing the sediment is practiced. On a large scale, centrifugalization is at times practiced for certain media. The Sharples supercentrifuge, which works on the principle of the milk separator, gives excellent results. The reaction, unless otherwise stated, should be one that is faintly alkaline to litmus. If the medium is acid, drop by drop of a 10 per cent solution of NaOH should be added until the reaction is faintly alkaline.

Agar.—Agar is the dried mucilaginous substance derived from plants which grow along the coasts of Japan. These plants are the several species of Gelidium and closely related algae. The extractive substance is washed and carefully cleaned, dried and marketed as agar. Chemically, agar is a carbohydrate (consisting of about 80 per cent of hexosan, a polysaccharide), resistant to the action of most bacteria, though some higher forms will hydrolyze agar; see also marine agar—decomposing bacteria (*J. Bact.*, 1941, **42**, 527). It is insoluble in cold water but slowly soluble in hot water. Aqueous solutions (containing 1 per cent or more of agar) remain liquid or fluid when hot but solidify at a temperature below 40° C. Inasmuch as the ordinary market agar is a product variable in its pectin content, it is advisable either to test each lot purchased for its pectin content (upon which its solidifying property depends) or to purchase each time the same fine quality agar for bacteriological use. Due to the scarcity of agar during war conditions and inasmuch as substitutes have not been found to replace it, reclamation of agar from culture media containing it is practiced by some. For different techniques, see *Canad. Pub. Health J.*, 1942, **33,** 461 and *Science*, 1943, **97, 75.** Among the substitutes, chondrus and fibrous sodium pectate (*Science*, 1943, **97,** 428) have been recommended.

Nutrient Agar Medium

Nutrient Broth (Meat Infusion or Meat Extract)............................ 100   cc.

Agar.. 1.5 Gm.

    (Powdered or shredded and cut into small pieces)   (or from 1 to 3 per cent)

Boil slowly and stir frequently until the agar is dissolved. The agar may be put in with the meat infusion or meat extract, peptone and salt (and other ingredients) or it may be added to the finished broth or bouillon and brought into solution by heat (and preferably by placing the entire mixture in a flask and the latter in an autoclave). Add water to make up for the loss by evaporation. Adjust the reaction and bring to a boil. Filter while hot and liquid through a filtering paper, placing the entire outfit in an Arnold steam sterilizer, or it can be, if necessary, filtered by passing through a moderately thick layer of absorbent cotton contained in a funnel which is adjusted to a vacuum flask and to the latter there is attached a vacuum pump. It is advisable to pass hot water through the cotton first, so as to warm the funnel and flask. This is then sterilized in the autoclave at 15 pounds' pressure (121.5° C.) for twenty minutes.

Agar medium when warm (therefore in a fluid state) can be filled into sterile test tubes and sterilized in the latter containers. Upon removal from the sterilizer, the tubes are placed in a slanting position. The medium upon solidifying is designated as an *Agar Slant*. After solidifying and cooling, water will frequently appear over the agar medium. This, "water of syneresis," erroneously named "water of condensation," is water squeezed out by the "agar sponge" which is under pressure. "Water of syneresis" is found in other solid media.

Gelatin.—This substance is made from collagen, a constituent of white fibrous tissue. It was first used by Koch to prepare a solid gelatin culture medium. Not all market gelatin is suitable for bacteriological use. A porkskin gelatin with a Bloom rating of 250 or higher should be used for preparing Nutrient Gelatin (see author's paper, *J. Bact.*, 1941, **41,** 645). Though having the advantage over other solid media in allowing the development of a larger number of colonies, it has the decided disadvantage of being utilized as a food by bacteria resulting frequently in a liquefaction of the solid medium. Gelatin culture medium is, therefore, but infrequently employed as a solid medium for the cultivation of material in routine work.

Liquefaction of Gelatin.—Gelatin is used as a differentiating medium to detect and differentiate bacteria that possess the property of liquefaction. When incubated, a temperature varying from 20° and 25° C. (room temperature) is employed. The usual method of studying to observe the presence of gelatinases (enzymes liquefying gelatin) is to make shake—or stab—or even plate cultures and incubate the latter at the previously mentioned temperature for from one to six weeks. The rapidity of liquefaction and the extent or shape of the liquefied zone in stab or plate cultures may be of considerable aid in the identification of the organism. A more rapid but somewhat less reliable method to observe this proteolytic activity of bacteria is to incubate the prepared gelatin cultures at 37° C. for from one to seven days. Place a sterile, uninoculated tube of gelatin medium as the negative control and one inoculated with a known gelatin liquefier as the positive control in at the same time. All cultures will liquefy at this temperature. After incubation, place the cultures in an ice chest or in ice water. The sterile negative control will solidify and the positive control will remain liquid. If liquefying enzymes have been produced in the inoculated culture being tested, the gelatin medium will remain semisolid or liquid.

Gelatin Medium

Nutrient Broth (Meat Infusion or Meat Extract)...................... 100 cc.
Gelatin (for bacteriological use)....................................... 10 to 30 Gm.
(usually 15 per cent)

Allow the gelatin to soak in the bouillon for five minutes (or use suitable powdered gelatin), then heat, preferably in a water-jacketed container, and stir frequently until the gelatin is dissolved. Adjust the reaction and make up for evaporation. Filter while hot and liquid as directed under agar. Sterilize in the Arnold steam sterilizer for fifteen minutes each day for three consecutive days or autoclave (some of the market gelatins cannot withstand the autoclave temperature).

Carbohydrate Media.—Any desired carbohydrate or sugar (usually glucose or lactose) may be added to enrich bouillon, agar, gelatin or any of the other culture media. Unless otherwise stated, 0.5 to 1 per cent of the particular sugar is used. This is dissolved in the warm liquid or liquefied medium, and after the finished preparation is placed in sterile containers, these sugar media are sterilized in the Arnold steam sterilizer for fifteen minutes each day for three consecutive days. Some workers sterilize sugar media by autoclaving, as investigation tends to reveal this method as less harmful than the fractional procedure. The best technique for sterilizing carbohydrate media containing sugars especially sensitive to heat is to prepare 10 per cent or 20 per cent aqueous solutions of the respective carbohydrates, which are sterilzed by bacteriological filtration. Where facilities for the latter technique are not available, these concentrated solutions are sterilized separately by autoclaving, using as low a heat for as short a period of time as is practicable. For the preparation of the carbohydrate medium, the basic medium is prepared and sterilized as usual. The sterile solution of the desired carbohydrate is added to the fluid sterile basic medium under aseptic conditions, using such proportions as will give the desired sugar content in the finished preparation (10 cc. of a 10 per cent sugar solution added to 90 cc. of basic medium will give a finished preparation containing 1 per cent sugar). All final media prepared by aseptic manipulation should always be incubated at 37° C. and also at 20° C. to insure their sterility.

Many of the sugar media are most frequently used to observe whether bacteria possess the property of decomposing the particular sugar with the production of acid, or gas or both. So as to readily detect any acid, various indicators are added to the original medium or it is colored with litmus, by adding a sufficient quantity of a saturated aqueous solution of litmus to give a faint blue tint. The blue dye present in litmus, known as *azolitmin*, is to be preferred as it is more satisfactory than the litmus itself. This can be prepared conveniently in the laboratory or purchased in powder form. When azolitmin is used, a neutral 5 per cent aqueous solution is made and 1 cc. of the latter is added to each 100 cc. of media. Culture media containing sugars and indicator are best sterilized as above. (See also Litmus Milk.)

Brom cresol purple, brom thymol blue, phenol red and Andrade's indicator (acid fuchsin decolorized with alkali) may be used instead of litmus (see under Litmus Milk). For use in indicator media, the first three dyes are added each separately in the proportion of 1 cc. (of 1.6 per cent alcoholic solution) to 1000 cc. of medium. Media commonly used for demonstrating acid or gas formation are: glucose, lactose, saccharose or other sugar broths in fermentation tubes; litmus milk; Hiss's serum water media containing carbohydrates; Russell's double sugar medium; etc.

Simple carbohydrate broths or carbohydrate agar media are named by including in the title the name of the carbohydrate and frequently the name of the indicator, such as: Litmus Lactose Agar, Litmus Dextrose Broth, Brom Cresol Lactose Broth, etc.

Hydrolysis of Starch.—Starch is broken down by many bacteria which possess the enzyme diastase or amylase. The hydrolysis is somewhat complicated and occurs in two stages, first to the disaccharide maltose and in the second stage, hydrolysis to glucose. The ability to hydrolyze starch is receiving attention as a differential aid in the identification of bacteria. The hydrolysis of starch may be demonstrated by culturing on nutrient agar medium containing from 0.2 per cent to 0.5 per cent of either raw starch or preferable "soluble starch." The semisolid medium is inoculated by streaking on its surface. Examine growths that are two, four, six and eight days old, by flooding the surface with Lugol's solution (or any other iodine solution). The presence of starch is revealed by a blue color. If the color is reddish, partial hydrolysis occurred; if clear, the hydrolysis is complete. To note acid production or an increase in H-ion concentration, make another set of plates but containing brom cresol purple media, and note the change of color of the latter. For a more detailed procedure, see Eckford (*Am. J. Hyg.*, 1927, **7**, 208).

Media Containing Insoluble Carbonates.—The addition of insoluble carbonates, especially calcium carbonate powder or crushed marble, to fluid media (usually 1 per cent) aids in neutralizing acid produced during growth by bacteria which would be unable to develop further due to the excess of acid. *Calcium Carbonate Broth* is especially useful for streptococci and pneumococci in massive liquid cultures.

Sugar-free Broth.—In routine practice, the minute quantities of sugar in Nutrient Broth and in other media are disregarded when adding specific sugars to note later acid or gas production by bacteria. For critical work, however, a sugar-free medium is used. Dunham's peptone solution or a synthetic medium can be employed where Nutrient Broth is needed; the latter can be prepared sugar-free. The meat infusion is prepared in the usual manner. To each 1000 cc. of the meat juice add 10 cc. of a twenty-four hour old broth culture of *E. coli* and incubate at 37° C. for twenty-four hours. Heat in the Arnold steam sterilizer for one hour, replace the evaporated water and filter. Continue from here by adding the other ingredients as given under Meat Infusion Broth on page 50, and autoclave.

Glycerin Media.—From 2 to 6 (most frequently 5) per cent of glycerin is added to bouillon or melted agar and the resultant product is sterilized in the autoclave. Peppler (*J. Bact.*, 1942, **44**, 233) found synthetic glycerin as useful in bacteriological culture media as glycerin obtained from fats and oils and, in view of its high degree of purity, suggested its use in synthetic media.

CULTURE MEDIA FORTIFIED OR ENRICHED WITH NATURAL FLUIDS

Blood.—Blood is obtained from horses, cattle, sheep, rabbits, humans or from other sources. This is usually collected under sterile conditions, defibrinated, citrated or laked, and employed to fortify agar bouillon or other semisolid media. If the fluid blood when collected and defibrinated is not added immediately to the medium it may be stored in a refrigerator after one of the following treatments: *Defibrinating* is accomplished by shaking the sterile blood in a sterilized container in which are present sterile glass beads. The shaking is performed vigorously until all the fibrin which is formed is disintegrated. *Citrated blood* is prepared by adding to each 9 parts of sterile blood, 1 part of sterile isotonic salt solution containing 10 per cent sodium citrate. *Laking* blood consists in hemolyzing the sterile blood by the addition of sterile distilled water, or gradual additions of the smallest amount of ether (needed for complete hemolysis) have been used by some workers. The ether eventually volatilizes or is lost when added to the warm artificial culture medium employed as a base. In practice, human blood is obtained under sterile precautions from patients from whom blood is taken for a blood chemistry, Wassermann test or other diagnostic test, and from 10 to 15 cc. more than is required for the tests mentioned are immediately placed in a sterile container in which there is present the proportionate amount of sterile citrate solution.

Blood Serum.—The blood collected under sterile conditions is placed in a refrigerator in a sterile container. After the blood coagulates, the sterile serum is collected and used for fortifying bouillon, agar, etc. If the serum is contaminated it may be sterilized preferably by bacteriological filtration or by heating at 58° C. for one hour each day for six consecutive days.

Ascitic Fluid.—Due to obstructive lesions in the liver, etc., dropsy of the peritoneum sets in. The fluid that forms in these peritoneal effusions is known as ascites or ascitic fluid, which if collected under sterile conditions will be found as an efficient nitrogenous natural medium for the fortification of artificial culture media.

Hydrocele Fluid.—This is obtained from the scrotum in pathological conditions, and is collected under sterile precautions. If hydrocele or ascitic fluids are contaminated they can be sterilized as directed under Blood Serum.

Some workers preserve their serum, ascitic and hydrocele fluids with 0.5 per cent chloroform. The latter is volatilized before using the fluids by immersing the containers in a water bath at 55° C. A more satisfactory method of preserving these and other natural fluids is by distributing the latter in suitable containers and employing the lyophile or similar process, wherein a dehydrated powder of the respective albuminous fluids is obtained. Such products can be stored in convenient amounts for long periods of time (five years) and used as desired by merely adding sterile water to restore to the fluid condition and in the identical original volume. Though whole blood can be lyophilized, the restored fluid cannot be employed as an indicator of hemolysis, but can be used as an enrichment for culture media.

Preparation of Culture Media Containing Natural Fluids

In preparing serum, ascitic or hydrocele bouillon and serum, ascitic, hydrocele and blood agar, unless otherwise stated, 1 part of the sterile natural albuminous fluid or tissue extract is added to the sterile artificial culture medium in a sterile container in the proportion of 5 to 15 per cent (usually 10 per cent). In the case of agar this should be first melted and cooled to 45° C. The albuminous natural exudate should preferably be warmed to this temperature and then added to the liquefied sterile agar. Mix thoroughly (but carefully and not too vigorously, so as to avoid getting air bubbles into the media). The prepared media can be placed in sterile tubes and slanted, in Petri dishes or in any other sterile container. It is advisable to incubate the latter at 37° C. for twenty-four hours or more so as to be assured of the sterility of the medium. Some workers add these natural fluids in amounts of only 5 to 15 per cent, and when using Nutrient Agar as the basic medium may employ 2 per cent of agar in the latter, inasmuch as such solid medium will possess more stiffness and a surface not easily broken. When making slants, allow to set thoroughly and firmly (preferably overnight); otherwise slipping will occur upon raising the tubes.

Blood-smeared or Blood-drop Agar.—If blood agar is not available blood-smeared agar will frequently be found satisfactory. The simplest way to prepare this is to smear several drops of blood (obtained by puncturing a finger which had been sterilized) over the surface of an agar slant. This should be incubated for twenty-four hours, to make sure of sterility.

Chocolate (Cooked) Blood Agar.—This is prepared as given under Blood Agar but by adding the blood to the agar medium at 95° C. This medium is used especially for growing the influenza bacillus.

Loeffler's Blood Serum Media.

Blood serum (horse, beef or sheep)... 3 parts
Dextrose bouillon.. 1 part

Place in tubes and slant in the steam sterilizer. Allow the temperature to rise slowly to between 80° and 90° C. Allow to remain in this slanted position until coagulated. Then heat at 80° C. for one hour or at 100° C. for twenty minutes each day for three consecutive days; or, after slanting in inspissator or steam sterilizer, they are coagulated and then sterilized in the autoclave at 7 pounds' pressure for thirty minutes or 10 pounds' for twenty minutes. Other methods of autoclave sterilization may be used (*J. Bact.*, 1923, 8, 315; 1924, 9, 179). The medium should be incubated at body temperature to test its sterility. This medium was originally introduced and is employed chiefly for cultivating the diphtheria bacillus. It has been found a satisfactory general culture medium to be used when a natural medium is desired.

Liquefaction of Coagulated Serum.—The production of proteolytic enzymes by certain bacteria will produce liquefaction of coagulated blood serum, and this is used as an aid in differentiation and identification. To detect this proteolytic activity, inoculate Loeffler's blood serum medium and incubate at the optimum temperature. The first evidence of digestion is indicated frequently by the appearance of a small depression around the area of growth.

Egg Medium.—This has been found a satisfactory substitute for blood serum media.

White and yolk of eggs.. 9 cc.
Dextrose bouillon.. 1 cc.

Fresh perfect eggs should be used. These should be preferably wiped with a weak bichloride solution, 5 per cent phenol or other disinfectant, then with several portions of sterile water. After partial drying, the contents from the egg are deposited in a sterile flask or mortar, and a smooth mixture of the white and yolk should be made. Holes can be made in each end of the egg with a sterile implement and the contents thus deposited into the sterile container. To this is added water (10 per cent by volume of the weight of the eggs). The product is then tubed and sterilized in a slanted position in a sterilizer by heating at 70° C. for two hours each day for three consecutive days or proceed as given under Loeffler's Blood Serum Media. To prevent the medium from drying, sterile water or bouillon may be added to cover the slants. The finished preparation should be incubated to test its sterility.

If this medium is to be used for culturing the tubercle bacillus, add 1 cc. of glycerin broth to each tube before final sterilization. This medium will serve conveniently to replace *Dorsett's Egg Medium* (*Am. Med.*, 1902, **3**, 555) and other egg media.

Potato Medium.—Smooth, sound, large white potatoes are selected and scrubbed thoroughly with a stiff brush in warm water. They are then pared and again washed, and the eyes cut out and other defects removed. Cylindrical pieces (about 1 to 1½ inches long and of a diameter smaller than the tubes in which they are to be placed) are cut with an apple corer or best by means of a cork borer. After the ends of the cylinders are trimmed and straightened they are split diagonally into two wedges through the long axis to obtain two good slants. Only pieces with good butts should be used, and kept under water at all times to prevent discoloration. The pieces after several washings in a 0.1 per cent solution of sodium carbonate or, better still, washing in running water overnight to remove all traces of acid, are then inserted into plain sterile test tubes or into the large variety of the so-called *potato tubes*, usually containing a small wad of absorbent cotton. Sufficient distilled water is added to cover the butt and never more than about one-fifth the slant. They are sterilized in the autoclave at 15 pounds' pressure (121.5° C.) for twenty to thirty minutes or in the Arnold steam sterilizer one-half hour each day for three consecutive days.

Glycerin potato, occasionally used for the cultivation of tubercle bacilli, is prepared as above. In addition, before tubing the pieces of potatoes are soaked for one hour in 6 per cent glycerin and the slants are covered with the glycerin solution instead of water.

Potato medium is of value in observing whether bacteria have the property of producing chromogenesis or reactivating the latter, which may have been lost by an organism, due to prolonged transplanting over artificial culture media. It also finds some use in determining the presence of diastatic action as produced by some microorganisms.

Potato Dextrose Agar (*Standard Methods for the Examination of Dairy Products*, 1941, p. 112) is the official medium employed for the determination of yeasts and molds. It contains 2 per cent dextrose, 1.5 per cent agar in each 1000 cc. of an infusion (from 200 Gm.) of potato, and sterilized by autoclaving. At the time of pouring (for plating), the reaction is adjusted with a 10 per cent solution of tartaric acid to pH 3.5. This acidity will inhibit bacterial growth but is most suitable for the development of yeasts and molds.

Corper's Crystal Violet Potato Medium (*J. A. M. A.*, 1928, **91**, 371) is prepared by treating potato cylinders in a 1 per cent sodium carbonate solution containing crystal violet (1:75,000) and after wiping, introducing the plugs into tubes containing 1.5 cc. of 5 per cent glycerin broth and autoclaving It is used in a special technique of treating material and subsequent culturing for detecting the presence of tubercle bacilli.

Bordet-Gengou Medium is recommended for use in the "cough plate" method for the detection and isolation of *H. pertussis* in the diagnosis of whooping cough. A potato extract is prepared using 500 Gm. sliced potato to each 1000 cc. of 8 per cent aqueous glycerin. To each 500 cc. of extract add 1500 cc. of salt solution (0.6 per cent) and 3 per cent agar. Dissolve in autoclave, filter if necessary, and sterilize in Arnold steam sterilizer or by autoclaving. This stock medium is mixed with an equal quantity of defibrinated blood, when used. Various modifications are being employed (*Am. J. Pub. Health*, 1936, **26**, 506; *J. Path. Bact.*, 1937, **45**, 472).

Potato infusion preparations are advocated for the isolation of different bacteria as in the case of *Brucella abortus*, as luxuriant growths are produced.

Milk Media.—*Plain Milk.*—This is made from fresh milk (raw, not pasteurized). Steam in the Arnold steam sterilizer for one-half hour and keep in a refrigerator overnight. Remove the milk from below the fat and tube this skimmed milk. (For routine laboratory work, 125 Gm. of dehydrated skim milk powder may be rubbed with water in a mortar to make a smooth paste and enough water added to make 1000 cc.)   Sterilize either product in the Arnold steam sterilizer one-half hour each day for three consecutive days.

Litmus Milk.—Sufficient aqueous solution of litmus or preferably azolitmin (see Azolitmin Solution and Litmus Test Solution in the National Formulary VII) is added to freshly skimmed milk obtained as mentioned above to give a violet-blue or lilac color.   This is tubed and sterilized as directed under Milk. Litmus milk is of value for the detection and identification of bacteria that possess the property of acidifying or coagulating this medium.   The indicator shows not only the production of acid but also decolorization of the litmus by organisms that are able to reduce it.

With other indicators—brom cresol purple has been recommended as of more value in detecting acid than litmus, this being especially true when the indicator is used for coloring all sugar media and even milk in some instances.   This is prepared by dissolving 0.4 Gm. of dibromo ortho-cresolsulfonphthalein in a small quantity of alcohol and diluting with water to 1000 cc.   To each liter of the medium 40 cc. of the latter are added.   Some workers employ 6 cc. of a 0.25 per cent (or 1 cc. of a 1.6%) alcoholic solution per liter of medium.   This indicator gives a blue or purple color which fades with the slightest production of acid, disappearing completely when the acid reaches 0.00001 normal or greater (below the curdling point of milk).   The pH range of this chemical is 5.2 to 6.8.

Andrade's indicator, another stable indicator, may be used.   Five-tenths per cent solution of acid fuchsin (70% dye content) in distilled water is decolorized to a yellow tint by adding N NaOH. The color changes to pink, brownish red and finally to yellow and about 16 cc. of alkali solution are generally needed for each 100 cc. of the solution of coloring.   Ten cubic centimeters of this indicator are employed for each 1000 cc. of media.   Sterilization is effected by autoclaving.   The indicator solution is colored pink at 100° C. but is colorless at temperatures below 40° C.   The presence of acid is revealed by the indicator turning magenta-red.

Plain milk, whey and modifications of these are used for the cultivation of bacteria, especially the *Lactobacillus bulgaricus, Lactobacillus acidophilus* and organisms closely related.   Milk is a useful medium for determining the production of acid as the result of lactose fermentation.   In a high acid environment, coagulation results due to the precipitation of casein.   A rennin-like enzyme present in some bacteria is capable of coagulating the milk independent of the acids.

Whey.—Fresh (unpasteurized) milk is allowed to stand in an ice box several hours or overnight until the cream separates; siphon off the milk.   Heat, stirring continuously until ready to boil To each 1000 cc. of milk add 2 cc. glacial acetic acid to coagulate the casein.   Strain through cheesecloth.   Add 2 per cent peptone and 0.5 per cent sodium chloride.   Adjust the reaction.   Clarify if necessary.   Filter and sterilize in the autoclave at 15 pounds' pressure (121.5° C.) for one-half hour.

Bile Medium.—Fresh ox or pig bile is obtained in the slaughter house. To this are added 1 per cent lactose and 1 per cent peptone, and the resultant product is tubed and sterilized in the Arnold steam sterilizer for twenty minutes each day for three consecutive days. Bile medium is used frequently for the differentiation of pneumococci and streptococci and in blood cultures for growing the typhoid bacillus.   It has also found an extensive use for the isolation of the latter organism from contaminated water, feces, etc.

Bile Salt Agar (MacConkey) is one of the well-known earlier plating media used for the isolation of organisms of the colon-typhoid group.   As prepared today it is a nutrient agar, containing 2 per cent lactose, 0.5 per cent sodium taurocholate and 69 mg. of brom cresol purple to each 1000 cc.   *Brilliant Green Lactose Bile Agar Medium* is recommended for differential plate counts in *Standard Methods of Water Analysis* (1936, 263, which see).   *Brilliant Green Lactose Bile Medium* (*ibid.,* p. 203) contains in each 1000 cc.:   peptone 10 Gm.; lactose 10 Gm.; 200 cc. of fresh bile or 20 Gm. of dehydrated oxbile and 13.3 cc. of 0.1 per cent aqueous solution of brilliant green (85–90 per cent dye content). Adjust reaction to between pH 7.1 and 7.4 after sterilization.

Endo's Medium.

Nutrient Agar (3 per cent) (pH 7.4).. 1000 cc.
Lactose, c. p.. 10 Gm.
Filtered 3% alcoholic solution of basic fuchsin (90% dye content)............ 10 cc.
Sodium sulfite solution (freshly prepared) (5 per cent)........................25 cc.

Dissolve the lactose in the liquefied agar.   Add the basic fuchsin and sulfite solution in the order named, agitating after the addition of each substance.   Tube and sterilize in the Arnold steam sterilizer twenty minutes each day for three consecutive days. Store in a cool, dark place. It is advisable to make this in quantities which can be used within a short space of time, not more than about two weeks. The finished, cool preparation should be colorless or possess only a faint salmon color at room temperature and light pink when hot.

Some workers keep the sterile lactose agar on hand. The fuchsin and sulfite solutions are added in the designated quantities to the latter each time before the medium is to be used. This medium is of especial value in isolating E. coli from other closely related bacteria. The colonies of E. coli appear red while those of E. typhosa and most other organisms are grayish. The typical reaction is not due to acid production but is caused by acetaldehyde, an intermediate product, which is fixed by the sodium sulfite (see Margolena and Hansen, Stain Tech., 1933, 8, 131). Efforts have been made from time to time to modify Endo's original formula so as to correct some of the defects which lead to a lack of uniformity of results. So we have many varied formulas as in Robinson and Rettger's formula, and modifications by Kendall, Levine and others. Color diffusion is still causing considerable annoyance in securing a satisfactory Endo's medium. Levine's Modification appears to be the most satisfactory formula of the latter (for formula, see National Formulary VII, p. 530, and also Harris (Military Surgeon, 1925, 57, 280)).

Presence of Other Dyes.—In addition to basic fuchsin, as used in Endo's medium, other basic aniline dyes are employed in various culture media, for their differential restraining action on the growth of some bacteria. Many special media are employed in which these dyes are present. Dyes are also employed in other formulas; their purpose is to serve as indicators of metabolic activity. Examples of some of the most frequently used culture media in these classes are:

Brilliant Green Agar (Krumwiede or Other Formulas).—The brilliant green, in appropriate dilutions, inhibits the growth of all Gram-positive and many Gram-negative bacteria, but exhibits differential action on the colon-typhoid group. This medium is used for the isolation of Eberthella typhosa and the paratyphoid bacilli. The crystal violet is omitted if the medium is used for Shigella dysenteriae. For complete formula, see National Formulary VII, p. 529 and Krumwiede, et al. (J. Infect. Dis., 1918, 23, 275).

Conradi-Drigalski Medium.—This is a litmus-lactose agar preparation containing crystal violet in a 1 to 100,000 concentration, and is used for colon-typhoid differentiation. Escherichia coli colonies appear large and red. Colonies of Eberthella typhosa are small and blue. For complete formula, see National Formulary VII, p. 530 and Ztschr. f. Hyg., 1902, 39, 283.

Gentian Violet-Egg (Petroff's) Medium.—This is a very satisfactory and valuable medium for isolating tubercle bacilli directly from fresh sputum or pus. For complete formula, see National Formulary VII, p. 535 and J. Exp. Med., 1915, 21, 38.

Methylene Blue-Eosin Agar (Teague Medium).—On this medium the colon colonies are deep black and opaque, while other allied organisms are colorless and transparent. This is Nutrient Agar (pH 7.4) containing 0.5 per cent lactose, 0.5 per cent saccharose, 0.04 per cent yellowish eosin and 0.01 per cent methylene blue. Saccharose is omitted when isolating Shigella dysenteriae. The Shiga bacillus may fail to grow. For complete formula, see J. Infect. Dis., 1916, 18, 596.

Russell's Double Sugar Medium.—This is a litmus-tinted agar medium containing 0.1 per cent glucose and 1 per cent lactose. Tube, sterilize in the Arnold steam sterilizer, slant, leaving a generous butt. Modifications of this formula are also recommended. Krumwiede (J. Infect. Dis., 1913, 12, 199) substitutes 1 per cent of the Andrade indicator and adds also 1 per cent saccharose. In inoculating this medium, a stab culture of the suspected growth is made deeply into the butt. Color changes and presence or absence of gas along the slant and butt aid in differentiating the colon-typhoid group of bacteria. The typhoid bacillus reveals a brilliant red color in the lower part and a uniform color in the upper part of the tube. Paratyphoid bacilli produce no change in the upper part of the medium and a small amount of gas in the lower half of the tube. Escherichia coli shows abundant gas and acid formation while Alcaligenes faecalis reveals no changes throughout the medium. With the Andrade indicator, sharper color changes are produced; and with saccharose, fermentation of the latter excludes paratyphoid-like "intermediates."

Eosin Methylene-Blue Agar (E. M. B. Medium).—The formula as given by Levine (Iowa State College of Agr. and Mech. Arts, Bull. 62, 117 (1921)) is the formula to be used for water analysis and is given in Standard Methods, 1936, p. 202 and in National Formulary VII, p. 531. It is recommended for the confirmation of presumptive tests of bacteria of the coliform group in the examination of water and milk. It is valuable especially for the differentiation of E. coli and A. aerogenes, the former producing colonies having a greenish metallic sheen with a dark center. Colonies of *A. aerogenes* are usually larger, not as dark as *E. coli* and the centers are usually colored brown.

Bismuth Sulfite Agar (*Wilson and Blair Medium*) (*J. Hyg.*, 1938, **38**, 507) and a formula as modified by Hajna and Perry (*J. Lab. Clin. Med.*, 1938, **23**, 1185) are used especially for the isolation of *E. typhosa*. The growth of Gram-positive bacteria and of *E. coli* is inhibited. *Eberthella typhosa* grows luxuriantly and the colonies are dry and flat and appear black with a metallic sheen due to the reduction of the sulfite to sulfide by this organism in the presence of glucose. This medium is also satisfactory for the isolation of species of the *Salmonella* genus.

Other media for differentiating the intestinal bacteria are:

Desoxycholate Agar (Leifson) and *Desoxycholate-citrate Agar* (Leilson) (*J. Path. and Bact.*, 1935, **40**, 581) (*Pub. Health Rep.*, 1939, **54**, 287). Most all Gram-negative rods grow well on desoxycholate agar but cocci and Gram-positive bacilli are inhibited. The citrate agar inhibits the latter bacteria and also most strains of *E. coli*, *Alcaligenes*, and some species of *Salmonella* and *Shigella*. The growth of the normal intestinal flora are mostly inhibited by the latter medium.

Phenol-red Tartrate Medium (Jordan and Harmon) (*J. Infect. Dis.*, 1928, **42**, 238) is an agar medium containing 1 per cent sodium potassium tartrate (tartar emetic) and 0.0024 per cent phenol red. It is useful in the differentiation and identification of species of the *Salmonella* and especially the paratyphoid species. The latter produce an alkaline reaction. Other species of *Salmonella* and *Escherichia coli* and *Eberthella typhosa* produce an alkaline reaction.

Violet-red Bile Agar is a medium containing 1 per cent peptone, 1 per cent lactose, 0.5 per cent yeast extract, 0.1 per cent bile salts, 1.5 per cent agar, 0.005 per cent neutral red and 0.0004 per cent crystal violet. It is recommended in *Standard Methods* for the direct plate count of coliform bacteria in dairy and in food products.

Crystal Violet Lactose Broth is suggested in *Standard Method* for primary and parallel planting with lactose broth for detecting the presence of members of the *coli-aerogenes* group. For its value see Salle (*J. Bact.*, 1930, **20**, 381) and Ruchhoft (*J. Am. Water Works Assoc.*, 1935, **27**, 1732).

Fuchsin Lactose Broth is suggested in *Standard Methods* for parallel planting for the detection of members of the *coli-aerogenes* group. McCrady has recommended its use rather as a confirmatory medium (*Am. J. Pub. Health*, 1937, **27**, 1243).

Formate Ricinoleate Broth is recommended in *Standard Methods* both for the examination of water and dairy products for members of the coliform group. The sodium formate accelerates growth and gas formation of the latter and the sodium ricinoleate inhibits the development of Gram-positive bacteria and most of the other organisms which give positive presumptive but negative confirmatory tests. For further details see Stark and England (*J. Bact.*, 1935, **29**, 26) and Noble and White (*J. Bact.*, Abst. G 28, 1935, **29**, 23).

Tetrathionate Broth is employed in the isolation of *E. typhosa* and members of the *Salmonella* genus from feces, urine, water, foodstuffs, sewage and other substances.

Eijkman Lactose Medium (for Modified Eijkman Test).—This medium is employed in the confirmation of *E. coli* from other coliform bacteria.

Hiss's Serum Water Medium.

Blood serum (clear beef or human)..................................... 1 part
Water.. 2 or 3 parts

Mix and heat in a steam sterilizer for fifteen minutes. Add litmus or azolitmin to give a violet-blue color or 1 per cent Andrade indicator. Finally add inulin, 1 per cent, or any desired sugar, 1 per cent. Tube and sterilize in the Arnold steam sterilizer at 100° C., twenty minutes for three consecutive days. This medium is used for the determination of the fermentative powers of various microorganisms for purposes of differentiation, by the observation of the decomposition of the different sugars and the coagulation of the serum proteids. The inulin medium (which is prepared by dissolving the inulin in water, sterilizing in the autocalve [to destroy spores], cooling and then proceeding as in the directions) is useful in distinguishing between the pneumococcus and the streptococcus.

Dunham's Solution.—Dunham's peptone solution has been largely used as a culture medium favorable to indol production, but Riva's trypsinized peptone medium has been found superior.

Salt	5 Gm.
Peptone	10 Gm.
Water	1000 cc.

Dissolve by boiling for fifteen minutes. Make up for evaporation, adjust to pH 7.6 to 7.8, filter, tube and sterilize in the autoclave at 15 pounds' pressure (121.5° C.) for twenty minutes.

Riva's Trypsinized Peptone Water.—1. Dissolve 10 Gm. of peptone in 250 cc. of water.

2. Dissolve 0.5 Gm. of trypsin in 20 cc. of water (heated to 38° C.).

3. Mix 1 and 2 and digest for three hours at 38° C., stirring occasionally.

4. Neutralize, dilute to 1000 cc., bring to a boil, filter, tube and sterilize in the autoclave at 15 pounds' pressure for twenty minutes.

Special Media.—During recent years many formulas for special culture media have been introduced as best suited for the growth of certain groups of organisms, individual species, or when products from their growth are desired.

Sterile fresh tissues added to media not only add nutrient material, but, as noted above, aid in the production of anaerobic conditions. Rabbit's kidney or heart tissue is used in some special media for culturing anaerobes and organisms that ordinarily grow but feebly. Water extracts of tissues, liver, brain, placenta, etc., are used also to fortify or enrich artificial media. The finished preparations have been found more satisfactory for the growing of bacteria that do not develop luxuriantly or with difficulty on the commonly observed media.

Selective media for *V. comma* and closely allied organisms are available. Their value rests on the ability of these organisms to grow in a reaction so extremely alkaline as to inhibit the growth of most other fecal bacteria (bacteria found in stools). The important ones are Aronson's, Dieudonné's, Esch's, Goldberger's and Krumwiede's media.

"Hormone" or "Vitamin" Media.—It has been demonstrated that the filtration of bouillon, agar and media in general, through cloth, cotton or paper, removes from them certain substances, spoken of as vitamins and originally referred to as hormones. The presence of the latter is frequently desirable as they enhance the nutritive value of media. So as to conserve these hormones or vitamins, media are clarified by sedimentation or, better still, by centrifugalization, employing the Sharples centrifuge. The basis for hormone or vitamin media is usually beef heart instead of beef or veal. The method of preparation as recommended by Huntoon or a modification of this technique is most commonly employed. Hormone media are generally recommended to be used for the growth of those bacteria that develop but feebly on ordinary media. Some workers use hormone media almost exclusively even in routine work.

Like the hormones of higher plants, certain plant juices and internal secretions derived from rootlets have been found to cause a luxuriant growth of pathogenic and nonpathogenic bacteria when added to routine agar plates, control plates of the latter not yielding demonstrable growth.

Hormone Agar (Huntoon)

Ground lean beef heart	500 Gm.
Peptone	10 Gm.
Sodium chloride	5 Gm.
Agar	18 Gm.
Water	1000 cc.

Add one whole egg well beaten. Mix well and heat slowly to 68° C., stirring constantly. Hold at this temperature for ten minutes, or until the color changes brown, adjust until slightly alkaline to litmus (or pH 7.4). Place in Arnold steam sterilizer. Allow to boil for one hour or until the coagulum settles, leaving a clear supernatant liquid. Place in ice chest overnight and then strain through a wire sieve. Allow to stand one hour and then siphon off the clear broth. Sterilize in Arnold steam sterilizer for twenty to thirty minutes on three consecutive days.

Synthetic Media.—The ideal culture medium is one which could be prepared with substances of known composition and which could be obtained in such definite composition at all times and the finished preparation be suitable for the cultivation of the bacteria under investigation. With bacterial nutrition receiving much attention within recent years, it is possible that synthetic media will be more and more a reality and different formulas will be presented and used. There are different synthetic media now in use in soil and industrial bacteriology and those interested are referred to volumes on the latter subjects. *Long and Seibert's Medium* for the production of tuberculin (*Am. Rev. of Tuberc.*, 1926, **13**, 393) and *Sauton's Medium* for cultivating B. C. G. vaccine (*Ann. inst. Pasteur*, 1927, **41**, 358) are two synthetic media used in medical bacteriology.

Synthetic Nitrate Medium (*Pure Culture Study of Bacteria*, 1942, **10**, 15) is used in detecting nitrate reduction for those bacteria incapable of producing nitrite in a peptone nitrate medium. *Synthetic Carbohydrate Media* (*Pure Culture Study of Bacteria*, 1942, **10**, 15) are used when peptone-free media are needed as in the detection of an increase in hydrogen-ion concentration when only small amounts of acid are produced. They are prepared by dissolving 1 Gm. of $NH_4H_2PO_4$, 0.2 Gm. of KCl, 0.2 Gm. of $MgSO_4.7H_2O$, 1 per cent of the respective sugar and 1000 cc. distilled water. Adjust to pH 7.

Media for Pathogenic Yeasts and Molds.—Most of the pathogenic yeasts and molds can be cultivated on any of the commonly observed culture media. Growth is improved if a slightly acid reaction prevails and adding one or more of the several sugars, either glucose, maltose or saccharose.

Sabouraud's medium is most frequently employed in dermatological work for culturing pathogenic molds, especially those affecting the skin. The formula is:

Peptone.	1.0 Gm.
Agar.	1.8 Gm.
Maltose (crude).	4.0 Gm.
Water.	100 cc.

Reaction $+2$. Sterilize at 100° C. for thirty minutes on three consecutive days. Glucose may replace maltose and some add 0.5 per cent glycerin. For further details see Weidman and Spring (*Arch. Dermat. & Syph.*, 1928, **18**, 829). Ch'in (*Proc. Soc. Exptl. Biol. Med.*, 1938, **38**, 700) suggests the addition of 0.05 per cent copper sulfate and 0.015 per cent potassium tellurite to Sabouraud's dextrose agar when isolating fungi from scales and crusts.

Culture Media for Isolating the Tubercle Bacillus.—In addition to *Petroff's Medium* and *Corper's Medium*, previously mentioned, other media advocated for isolating tubercle bacilli are: *Petragnani's Medium* (*J. Trop. Med.*, 1932, **35**, 157), *Loewenstein's Medium* (*Ann. inst. Pasteur*, 1933, **50**, 161), and *Loewenstein's Medium with Silica* (*Tubercle*, 1933, **14**, 502).

Tellurite Medium for the Isolation of C. diphtheriae.—This is prepared by adding to each 10 cc. of cool liquefied sterile dextrose agar, 1 cc. of sterile defibrinated rabbit blood and 1 cc. of a sterile 2 per cent solution of potassium tellurite. Allison and Ayling (*J. Path. and Bact.*, 1929, **32**, 299) suggest the use of a *trypsinized serum tellurite copper sulfate agar*. See also Gilbert and Humphreys on the use of potassium tellurite (*J. Bact.*, 1926, **11**, 141). Surface colonies of *C. diphtheriae* on tellurite agar are black in color, have entire or irregular margins and are slightly raised. Most other bacteria fail to grow.

Digested Meat and Milk Media.—Meat and milk digested by various ferments or enzymes contain degradation products of the proteins, the nitrogen of which is more readily assimilated by the bacteria than in the native proteins of the original substance. Such *digest media* are favored by some workers. Among the latter are to be found: *Hottinger's Broth* and *Hottinger's Agar* (*Centralbl. f. Bakt.*, Abt. 1 1912, **67**, 178) in which the meat is digested by pancreatin; and *Douglas' Tryptic Digest Broth* (*Brit. J. Exp. Path.*, 1922, **3**, 263) in which lean beef or horse muscle is digested by pancreatin. Stickel and Meyer (*J. Infect. Dis.*, 1918, **23**, 78) present a formula for *Peptic Digest Broth of Liver, Beef or Human Placenta*.

Peptonized Milk is used either alone or as an ingredient in other media for the isolation and cultivation of members of the genus *Lactobacillus* and for other bacteria in the examination of dairy products *Trypsin Digest Agar* is used either alone or more frequently as an ingredient in other media for the cultivation and counting of *L. acidophilus.*

Chapter VI

REACTION AND STORAGE OF CULTURE MEDIA.
CULTURE TECHNIQUE

REACTION OF CULTURE MEDIA

THE REACTION of a culture medium exerts a marked influence upon the bacteria that will develop and upon the luxuriancy of the particular growths. At times the morphology, and frequently toxin production or the formation of other products may vary due to a difference in the reaction of media. In routine work it has usually been found sufficient to test for the reaction with litmus paper, as many organisms grow within a rather wide range of reaction. The most favorable reaction is one which gives but a faint alkalinity to litmus. There are some organisms in which the range of reaction is a rather narrow one, so that the reaction of the medium used for their growth is as much to be considered as other factors. When a greater accuracy is demanded more accurate methods are preferable. This is desired especially when the observations of different workers are to be compared. A culture medium, uniform in reaction, will greatly assist in lowering the percentage of error. This is important when the bacterial content is to be determined when culturing water, milk, sewage, foodstuffs, etc.

Titratable or Titrable Acidity.—By the reaction of a fluid, we generally refer to the fact that the latter is acid, basic (alkaline) or neutral. Acidity is due to the presence of hydrion (H^+) in excess of the hydroxyl ion (OH^-). The latter in excess produces an alkaline environment. An acid, such as HCl, is practically completely dissociated in aqueous solution and is known as a strong acid, while those, like acetic and boric acids, are present in aqueous solutions almost entirely in the form of undissociated molecules and are known as weak acids. A similar distinction is noted between strong and weak bases. The amount of alkali or base necessary to neutralize a definite volume of acid and spoken of as the *titratable acidity* is dependent entirely upon the concentration of the acid and is independent of its degree of dissociation. The titratable or titrable acidity (or alkalinity) is expressed in terms of normal or tenth-normal acid (or base). Occasionally the minus and plus signs are used to designate reaction. The American Public Health Association at one time recommended the following procedure for determining the reaction:

In a medium that is acid the reaction is designated by a plus sign (+). In a medium that is alkaline the reaction is designated by a minus sign (−). A medium that is so acid as to require 1.5 cc. of normal sodium hydroxide (40 Gm. of absolute NaOH dissolved in 1 liter of water) to neutralize 100 cc. of the end product has its reaction designated by +1.5. This (also expressed by "1.5 per cent acid") was regarded as a medium possessing the standard reaction. In determining the titratable acidity, the following technique is used: Place 5 cc. of the culture medium in a porcelain dish, add 45 cc. of distilled water, steam for a few moments to drive off carbon dioxide. Add 1 cc. of phenolphthalein indicator (0.5 per cent alcoholic solution), and from a burette run in decinormal sodium hydroxide solution until the neutral point is reached, indicated by the appearance of a permanent pink color. Should the contents of the dish turn red when the indicator is added it is alkaline, and titration should be performed with decinormal hydrochloric acid.

Having neutralized a measured sample of culture medium with a definite quantity of alkali or acid, it is easy to compute the degree of acidity or alkalinity as compared with +1, which is an acidity requiring 1 cc. of normal sodium hydroxide to neutralize each 100 cc. of media, or −1, which is an alkalinity requiring 1 cc. of normal hydrochloric acid to neutralize each 100 cc. of media.

Example: If 5 cc. of medium were used in the titration, twenty times the amount of NaOH $N/10$ required to neutralize the latter will give the amount of the NaOH $N/10$ required to neutralize 100 cc of the culture medium. The amount of NaOH N can be obtained by dividing this figure by 10.

HYDROGEN-ION CONCENTRATION

This method is based upon the ionic theory of electric dissociation, which claims most chemicals in aqueous solution are dissociated into ions (atoms or groups of atoms that are electrically charged). The acidity of a given medium, for instance, is based upon the concentration (number) of free and dissociated hydrogen ions. It has also been proved that, though a number of acids were accurately titrated and an accurate (chemically) normal solution prepared, the amount of hydrogen ions that were free and dissociated in the different normal acid solutions showed wide variations. It has also been pointed out that, by titrating a medium to determine its acidity, inaccurate results were frequent, due to the fact that certain organic substances, which find their way into the solutions (as in culture media through the material used in its preparation), act as buffers (*i. e.*, combine with the alkali during the titration, and the acid which was intended to react with the alkali is not neutralized until the buffers are taken care of first). Due to its affinity for either acid or alkali, buffers tend to inhibit any change and thus preserve the original or desired hydrogen-ion concentration of any solution, so that the content of the latter is but rarely affected. The actual acidity of a medium depends upon the hydrogen-ion concentration. The total (titratable) acidity includes all acid whether dissociated or undissociated. The actual acidity (hydrogen-ion concentration) is of more value when an accurate method of adjusting the reaction of any medium is desired.

The actual acid strength, or, best expressed, the hydrogen-ion content, of not only acid but even neutral and alkaline solutions is measurable. The amounts of the latter encountered in physiological and bacteriological solutions are so small, as compared with concentrations ordinarily observed in the commonly used chemical solutions, as to necessitate the use of unwieldy figures. The chemist has so framed his thoughts on analytical solutions as to express quantities in terms of *normal solutions*. The standard concentration of hydrogen ions is also regarded as the normal solution, and may be defined as a solution containing the equivalent of 1 Gm. of hydrogen ions in each liter of end product. Based upon this, the hydrogen-ion concentration of solutions will run up to the millionth, billionth and even trillionth normal; for instance, the hydrogen-ion concentration of pure water is 0.0000001 N, because pure water under normal conditions ionizes itself, producing 1 Gm. of ionized H in 10,000,000 liters. This, regarded as true neutrality, was abbreviated to the following convenient figure, 1 x 10^{-7} N. The hydrogen-ion concentration of NaOH $N/10$ is about 0.00000000000009 N and written 9 x 10^{-14} N. Any solution with a hydrogen-ion concentration expressed in a figure or power greater than 1 x 10^{-7} N is alkaline. Any solution with a hydrogen-ion concentration expressed in a figure or power less than 1 x 10^{-7} N is acid. So that the average laboratory worker who is not acquainted with higher mathematics and advanced chemistry shall not be confused with these unwieldy figures, those interested in the subject have adapted themselves to the use of the following symbols as suggested by Sorensen: The symbol pH is used to express hydrogen-ion concentration. The hydrogen-ion concentration of pure water, which is taken as neutrality is 0.0000001 N and written in the pH scale pH 7.0. Ionization varies with the temperature. The pH 7.0 represents the pH of water at a definite temperature, namely, 22° C. The pH increases as the temperature is lowered and decreases as the temperature is raised. At 20° C., the pH is 7.03; at 28° C., 6.90; at 37° C. (body temperature), the pH is 6.75. In practice, this slight difference is generally disregarded.

HYDROGEN-ION CONCENTRATION EXPRESSED IN "pH" AND COMPARED WITH "NORMAL SOLUTIONS"

Acidity	pH	Normal Hydrogen-ion Concentration
HCl N	0.0	1.0
HCl N/10	1.0	0.1
	2.0	0.01
	3.0	0.001
	4.0	0.0001
	5.0	0.00001
	6.0	0.000001
Neutrality	7.0	0.0000001
Alkalinity	8.0	0.00000001
	9.0	0.000000001
	10.0	0.0000000001
	11.0	0.00000000001
	12.0	0.000000000001
NaOH N/10	13.0	0.0000000000001
NaOH N	14.0	0.00000000000001

(The method adopted is to take the logarithm of 1/10000000, which is -7. In practice the minus sign is omitted.) A pH lower than 7 indicates acidity; a pH higher than 7 indicates alkalinity. The lower the pH of a particular solution, the greater the acidity or the higher is its hydrogen-ion concentration. The higher the pH, the lower the acidity or the hydrogen-ion concentration. In order to have some idea of the degree of acidity or alkalinity corresponding to pH values, the chart above is given. It will be observed that a solution that has a pH value of 5 is ten times as acid a one with a pH 6, and a pH value of 4 is ten times as acid as one of pH 5 or one hundred times as acid as one of pH 6. A similar relationship exists on the alkaline side of the scale. A solution having a pH 9 is ten times as alkaline as one of pH 8 and only one-tenth as alkaline as a solution possessing a pH value of 10.

The hydrogen-ion concentration may be determined by (1) the electrometric or (2) colorimetric methods. The former method is more accurate, but it involves the use of special electrical apparatus and some skill. Electrometric determinations must be made with reliable equipment. The *potentiometer* and various electrode assemblies are available on the market and the manufacturers and literature supplied by them should be consulted concerning the details of their respective equipment and their use. (Apparatus as supplied by Leeds and Northrup Co., Philadelphia, have been widely used.) In the bacteriological laboratory, the electrometric method, when used, is employed for special problems, in research investigations, and for standardizing the buffer solutions used in the colorimetric method. For routine purposes, the colorimetric method is employed. This is inexpensive; the technique is simple to perform and, though not as accurate as the electrometric method, the error is but slight. Though many pathogenic bacteria will grow within a wide range of reaction and some organisms, as the influenza and typhoid bacilli, require a narrow range, the optimum reaction for most commonly found bacteria is a pH between 6.4 and 7.4.

The principle of making pH measurements colorimetrically is based on the fact that different indicators display distinct color changes (within short pH ranges), when they are acted upon by solutions of different acidities or alkalinities. It is, therefore, to be noted that a worker must be familiar with the seven or eight indicators used in hydrogen-ion concentration determinations, and their pH range and color changes; otherwise he will have difficulty in arriving at a decision. Just as it is necessary to be familiar with the color changes due to litmus, so must one be familiar with the color changes produced by various indicators that may be employed in hydrogen-ion concentration determinations. Brom thymol blue and phenol red, with pH ranges of 6 to 7.6 and 6.8 to 8.4, respectively, will usually suffice to make it possible to ascertain the approximate pH of most media commonly employed in bacteriological routine. At times, brom cresol purple (pH range, 5 2 to 6.8) is required. Other indicators and their respective pH values are given in laboratory manuals.

In making use of indicator dyes in the colorimetric method for determinations of hydrogen-ion concentration, the first step is to choose a suitable indicator, one whose effective range includes the pH of the medium or solution being tested, and which produces a very gradual distinct color change through that range. If the pH range of the medium is known, the problem of choosing the indicator dye is simplified; otherwise a few tests will usually make available the necessary information. To several measured portions (10 cc.) of the medium are added separately 0.5 cc. of each of the different indicators (the pH range and color changes of which are known). Test papers (prepared from these indicators) may be substituted and supply a convenient and rapid as well as an inexpensive procedure. So-called *universal indicators* have been suggested in place of the several indicator solutions or papers. They consist of combinations of two or more indicator dyes and produce distinct gradual color changes over a wider pH range than is displayed by only one of the indicators alone.

In practice, the determination of hydrogen-ion concentration or pH is achieved by adding an indicator dye to the medium or solution and comparing the resulting colored solution with a set of standards representing known pH values. The standard solutions used in the colorimetric method generally consist of mixtures of some acid and its alkali salt, so-called buffer substances. Mixtures of solutions of these buffers in suitable proportions will possess definite H-ion concentrations. The addition of a suitable indicator dye will make available a series of graded standard colors. Standards thus prepared and at known pH values, if properly kept, will remain unchanged and stable for at least one year. They serve as standards with which to compare unknown solutions to which the same indicator is added. These standards must be accurately prepared and tested by the electrometric method. The standards of Clark and Lubs (*J. Bact.*, 1917, **2**, 1) are used most frequently. As it is not always convenient to prepare accurately standard sets representing various known pH values, they are best purchased from reliable manufacturers; and under such conditions, it is advisable to follow in detail the instructions supplied with the purchased set.

There are several simple methods in use for determining and adjusting the pH of culture media by aid of color standards.

A *comparator block* in which are grooved several holes is conveniently used. A test tube containing 10 cc. of medium to which has been added 0.5 cc. of the same indicator dye present in the color standards is placed in the left hole (or center, if there are three holes); and immediately behind it place a test tube containing 10 cc. of distilled water. In the right front hole of the comparator block place the color standard, which closely matches the color in the unknown; and immediately behind this standard, place 10 cc. of the medium to which no indicator is added. Hold the comparator block toward the daylight or a suitable artificial light-source, and note whether the colors match. If not, change the color standards until one is found which matches the color of the unknown. In the use of comparators with three or more holes, it is suitable to place the unknown in the center; and to the left and right of the latter, two different color standards (one lower and one higher in pH reading) are placed in the block (with a tube containing the medium without indicator in the back of each). By changing one or both of the pair of color standards, a suitable match is obtained more readily.

If the medium is within the desired pH range, adjustment is not necessary.   Where this is required the following procedure is used.   To 5 or 10 cc. of the medium add 0.5 cc. of the indicator dye and titrate with tenth-normal (or weaker) alkali or acid (as necessary) until the colored medium matches the color in the standard tube, possessing the desired H-ion concentration.   Note the volume required for this adjustment, compute the approximate amount of normal alkali or acid required to adjust the entire batch of medium, and after the final addition of the required amount, recheck the pH. Inasmuch as heat sterilization, especially autoclaving, tends to render culture media more acid, thus lowering the pH, it is desirable in practice to make suitable correction for this.   Usually, if the initial pH of the medium is 7.0 or less, very little change occurs; but if the initial pH is over 7.0, the final reaction generally is 0.2 pH less (*i. e.*, it becomes 0.2 more acid).   Where accurate pH readings of media are to be known, always determine this after sterilization.

Instead of employing hydrogen-ion concentration determinations, the titration method with the use of the more accurate pH indicators (in adjusting reactions of culture media) is employed occasionally as a convenient and yet accurate method of adjusting reactions in culture media.

Mention should be made that the colorimetric method has been found to have various sources of error.   These occur due to the presence of color, turbidity, certain acids, salts, colloids and proteins, oxidation-reduction factors, and temperature changes.   In certain cases where experience has been gained, allowance is made for any marked change in pH readings caused by one of the latter, by adjusting the reaction with acid or alkali.   In routine bacteriological work, other than previously mentioned (as due to effects of sterilization), adjustments for the above factors are made but infrequently.   In fact, if such adjustment is required, it is best to use the electrometic method for more accurate observations.   For further details on pH and titrable acidity, see *Pure Culture Study of Bacteria*, 1941, **9**, 3–19.

DEHYDRATED CULTURE MEDIA

These products are media in a dried powdered form ready to be prepared into the various liquid or solid media by merely restoring the moisture with distilled water and sterilizing the end product.   The value of these products lies in the fact that it is possible to obtain anywhere at any time any quantity of a medium of a constant adjusted reaction or hydrogen-ion concentration which will be identical in composition and reaction with all other lots of the same medium prepared at a previous occasion. The dehydrated media have also made possible the more extensive use of many of the media of special formulas or media fortified with natural fluids.   Furthermore, large amounts of any formula can be prepared at one time by a uniform or even standardized procedure, and such product is then available over a long period of time to yield an end product of identical composition during the life of the dehydrated material.   In the case of small laboratories, these dehydrated products can be highly recommended both as far as a reduction in production costs and for the conservation of time.   As a dry powder, they are kept in containers, which if tight will preserve the contents indefinitely.   For best results with the use of dehydrated products, the directions as given by the manufacturers of the latter should be followed in detail.   Users of dehydrated culture media may find much useful information in the literature and publications usually supplied by the manufacturers, as in the case of such concerns as the Difco Laboratories (Detroit) and the Baltimore Biological Laboratory (Baltimore).

Other Factors.—In addition to such important factors as the kind and quantity of different constituents in culture media, reaction and methods of sterilization, considerable attention has been directed to other factors, which may affect the growth and activities of bacteria. Studies along the lines of such factors, as vitamin content and other accessory growth substances, general nutritive requirements, oxygen tension, temperature, osmotic pressures and the relation of surface tension to bacterial development have and are receiving attention in the present program which embraces a study of those environmental factors which affect bacterial development.

CONTAINERS FOR CULTURE MEDIA

Media kept in bulk are distributed in sterile, clean (and free of foreign chemicals) flasks or bottles of from 100 to 1000 cc. capacity. The finished product may be placed also in smaller amounts into sterile test tubes. This is done by means of a funnel or percolator fitted with rubber tubing to which is attached a glass tip and a pinchcock. In order to avoid the sticking of the cotton stopper care should be taken not to smear the inside of the mouth of the tube with any of the medium. Tubes are generally filled to a depth of 1 to $1^1/_2$ inches or with a definite volume of the medium. After tubing or placing the media in sterile containers, the latter are sterilized as described (even though the media were previously sterilized). The only exception to this is when preparing some of the so-called artificial media enriched with natural fluids. All solid media (except gelatin) in tubes are usually cooled in a slanting position, so as to secure a large surface for inoculation. Slants of blood agar (in test tubes) are usually not disturbed for at least sixteen to eighteen hours, as frequently the slant is not firm and slips down. If the media are to be used for stab culturing, slants are not made.

The use of the ordinary prescription bottle (6 ounces, 8 ounces and 1 pint) with screw-cap seal, and with one side nearly flat can be used in the laboratory for a variety of purposes. It serves well for the storage of media, for sterile water and sterile isotonic salt solution even as a Petri dish for isolation purposes, and for the growth of mass cultures of bacteria for the preparation of vaccines and antigens. By placing the cap on loosely during the incubation period, there is sufficient diffusion of oxygen to support the growth of aerobes and at the same time to keep out contamination, especially molds. Cotton plugs may be used but the screw caps have been found most satisfactory.

All containers should be properly labeled for storage. The use of colored beads for carbohydrate media (red for dextrose, blue for maltose, and even combinations of these) in the containers is practiced by some workers as a means for identification. Others use colored nonabsorbent cotton for plugging as a means for identification. Wherever possible, it is desirable to incubate all batches of media for at least twenty-four to forty-eight hours so as to be assured of their sterility before storing them.

STORAGE OF CULTURE MEDIA

Culture media keep best when placed in a cool, moist atmosphere, preferably in a clean refrigerator. Sterile distilled water is frequently added to the slants of certain media, as blood serum and egg media, so as to prevent drying. The water is poured off before the medium is used. Evaporation and contamination due to the penetration by molds which tend to take place may be prevented by capping with paper or linen before sterilization. Covering the tops of the containers with tin foil, rubber caps or rubber tissue after sterilization is also useful. The top of the tube and plug may be dipped in melted paraffin as an aid to avoid drying. Placing media in small tubes and sealing them as is practiced in the case of ampuls will aid in the keeping qualities of the preparations. Sterile cotton plugs are placed in the same or in separate. smaller sealed containers.

Fig. 4. Culture tube caps.

Prolonged storage of sterile media is not recommended. Media kept for any length of time should be reheated, wherever possible, just before use. Liquid media can be placed in the steam sterilizer for a few minutes (to remove dissolved gases) and immediately cooled prior to inoculation. Solid media can be remelted and allowed to solidify so as to secure a moist surface. Repeated heatings, however, may change the reaction of media and also may reduce the solidifying properties of agar, gelatin, etc. In other instances other changes may occur, as sedimentation, color changes, etc.

CULTURE TECHNIQUE

The transfer of bacteria from material or from medium to medium for the purpose of cultivation is accomplished by means of sterile glass pipettes, sterile platinum wire or sterile loops of platinum or platinum-iridium or nichrome wire. When culturing is done it is desirable to have the air in the room as still and as free from dust as possible. Windows and doors should be closed. The best results are obtained by working within a small, closed compartment, the top of which is entirely or partly glass. Small rooms supplied with filtered sterile air under positive pressure and irradiated with suitable ultraviolet light are also in use. Whenever possible, the air in testing and culturing rooms should be filtered or sprayed with water, ethylene glycol or other aerosols. The room itself should be washed with a disinfectant solution each time transfers are to be made, or at least once daily when in use, the room being allowed to remain closed for fifteen minutes thereafter. To prevent contamination, all bacteriological testing or culturing is to be carried out under the most rigid aseptic conditions. To minimize the danger of infection to the worker, laboratory coats or gowns are to be worn; and when handling highly infectious material, use sterile gowns, caps and a face mask to cover the nose and mouth. In so far as is practicable, work with an assistant. When large amounts or definite volumes of fluid material are to be transferred, use a sterile pipette (in which a cotton plug has been inserted within the opening where the mouth is placed). If the material is infectious, use a pipette fitted with a rubber bulb or attach a piece of sterile rubber tubing with sterile mouthpiece to the pipette.

Cotton plugs are removed from flasks or tubes containing culture media by grasping and holding the plugs between the third and fourth fingers of the right hand, care being taken that it must not come in contact with anything and become contaminated. The tube or container should be passed through a Bunsen flame before and after the removal of the plug, so as to destroy any microorganisms that may have settled on the lip, and which may otherwise contaminate the media. If the plugs adhere to the glass they should be first loosened by a slight twisting motion. Pipettes and loops when passed into and removed from culture media containers are not allowed to touch the sides of the glass. If a fluid medium is to be inoculated the wire should be submerged only into the upper part of the liquid and the bacteria gently rubbed into an emulsion. If the material is to be inoculated on the surface of solid media (either slants or in Petri dishes) a slight stroking motion along the surface will deposit the bacteria upon the medium. Care should be observed to avoid breaking the smooth surface. Tubes to be inoculated are held almost parallel with the table top to avoid air contamination. Loops are flamed immediately and pipettes are placed in suitable containers to be disinfected or sterilized as soon as the cultures are made or in which a disinfectant solution is present.

It is sound practice when using the different culture media formulas to note various reactions and characteristic observations when inoculating an unknown, also to inoculate at the same time a known positive and a known negative organism (*i. e.*, a

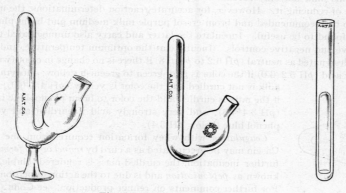

Fig. 5. Fermentation tubes.

bacterium producing definite positive and one producing negative findings), as a check on the media, reagents and technique.

Stab Cultures.—Stab cultures in solid media (unslanted agar or gelatin) are made by thrusting a sterile straight (not looped) platinum wire (coated with the material to be inoculated) directly downward to the bottom, as nearly as possible along the axis of the medium.

Shake Cultures.—Shake cultures, made so as to determine the character of growth beneath the surface, to observe gas formation and other phenomena, are made in solid media, usually gelatin. A tube of the media is liquefied (by placing in a boiling water bath), then cooled to 45° C., the bacteria introduced, shaken and quickly cooled in cold water.

Shake cultures make possible a satisfactory method of determining the oxygen requirements of an organism. A tube half full with a solid medium (suitable for the growth of the bacterium under examination; dextrose-agar medium is frequently found satisfactory) is liquefied and cooled to 45° C. It is inoculated heavily with the organism and shaken well to insure thorough mixing and cooled. Incubate at the optimum temperature. Obligate aerobes will grow profusely on the surface and less luxuriantly in the upper layers only. Obligate anaerobes will grow only at the bottom in the lowest layers. Microaerophiles will develop luxuriantly a few millimeters below the surface, and facultative anaerobes will grow throughout the medium.

Gas, Alkali and Acid Formation.—Gas and acid or alkali formation by bacteria is best observed by culturing in liquid media (containing carbohydrates or other fermentable substances) placed in Smith *fermentation tubes*. The latter are so constructed as to make easily discernible the gas in the closed arm which displaces the fluid, the latter being forced out into the bulb. The *Durham tube* consists of a samll test tube (10 × 75 mm.) inverted in a larger tube (18 × 150 mm.) and gas formation is noted in the small tube where the liquid is displaced.   Frost's *gasometer card* is a convenient chart for measuring in fermentation tests the amount of gas in terms of percentage of the length of the closed arm.   In the case of solid media, gas is recorded as being present or absent if cracks or bubbles become apparent as growth progresses.   Tests for gas production are less useful if the gas is carbon dioxide, as none or very little will accumulate due to its rapid diffusion into the air and its marked solubility. Indicators are added to the culture media to note acid or alkali production or, if desired, the indicator need not be incorporated with the media but added subsequently when the reaction is being determined.   The method of choice is the use of indicator media, as the procedure is more practical and more rapid.

If it is desired to note whether a specific fermentable substance is attacked by a specific bacterium, all culturing in fermentation tubes is done in duplicate, using a basal medium (suitable for the organism under examination) in one instance with and in the other instance without the fermentable substance.   Acid and gas production is noted in both instances and if this occurs only in the presence of the fermentable substance it may be concluded that cleavage of the latter occurred.

Acid Production, Coagulation and Peptonization of Milk.—Inoculate milk medium containing an indicator.   Litmus milk not only reveals acid production but also decolorization of the litmus by bacteria capable of reducing it.   However, for accurate reaction determinations, the more useful pH indicators are to be recommended and brom cresol purple milk medium and brom phenol blue milk medium will be found to be useful.   Inoculate the latter and carry also uninoculated tubes of media as well as positive and negative controls.   Incubate at the optimum temperature, and note findings. The reaction is designated as neutral (pH 6.2 to pH 6.8) if there is no change in color (with brom cresol purple); weakly acid (pH 5.2–6.0) if the color is gray-green to greenish yellow; moderately acid if the

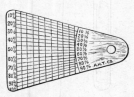

milk is not curdled and the color is yellow (pH 4.7–6.0); strongly acid, if the milk is curdled and the color to brom phenol blue is blue or green (pH 3.4–4.6); and very strongly acid if curdled and yellow to brom phenol blue (below pH 3.4).

Coagulation with whey formation requires from one to seven days. Casein may be precipitated as a curd by *rennet* or *lab ferments*.   If, upon further incubation, the curdled mass is rendered soluble, the process is known as *peptonization* and is due to the action of peptonizing enzymes. For further comments on rennet production, see Conn (*J. Bact.*, 1922, **7**, 447) and Gorini (*J. Path and Bact.*, 1932, **35**, 637).

Fig. 6.   Gasometer scale, used for estimating percentage of gas in a fermentation tube.

Needles and other implements should be immediately sterilized in the flame or by other suitable means after they have been in contact with bacteria.

Pigment Production.—Some species of bacteria may give rise to colored substances in the course of their growth, a characteristic which makes it easy to identify them.   Great variation in the amount and even character of the pigment produced by different strains of the same species may occur at times.   Chromogenesis or pigment production is best observed on solid media and in most cases only when grown under aerobic conditions.   Media containing starch or carbohydrates, as potato medium, are especially suited to reveal chromogenesis and such media are generally employed to reacquire a lost chromogenic power.   Antiseptics, light and high temperatures may check or even inhibit pigment production.   To demonstrate chromogenesis, the surface of various solid media including potato medium are inoculated and incubated under the following conditions; at 20° C. and at 37° C. aerobically, and exposed to and in the absence of light.

The pigments themselves are of diverse nature, as to their solubility in water or in the volatile solvents, their chemical composition, their exact relation to the individual cell, etc.   In most cases, these pigments are mere by-products and appear to possess no particular value to the organisms producing them.   Perhaps in some few instances, the pigment may serve as an oxygen conveyor as does the red pigment of the red blood cells, hemoglobin.   The chromogenic organisms commonly observed in diseased conditions are: *Staphylococcus aureus* (orange);   *Staphylococcus citreus* (lemon-yellow); *Pseudomonas aeruginosa* or *Bacillus pyocyaneus* (blue and green).   Species in the genus *Sarcina*, *Rhodococcus* and *Serratia*, the *Bacillus fluorescens* found in water, and the *Corynebacterium hoagii* found in the air are commonly found chromogenic saprophytes.

The color and shade of the pigment produced should be recorded.   Note: the observations in different liquid and solid media;   the optimum temperature for its production;   differences, if any, when exposed to air and in the absence of air, and in the presence or absence of light; whether pigmentation is diffused through the medium or limited to the area of growth (in solid media especially); its solubility in different solvents (ether, chloroform, alcohol, benzene, etc.), these frequently revealing the presence of two or more pigments. The pH and range of different colors may be of interest as the pigment may either reveal different colors at different levels of H-ion concentration or itself actually acts as a pH indicator. If there is any difficulty in deciding whether growth on solid media reveals pigment, a spread of the growth on a piece of white glazed paper or a porcelain slab is apt to make pigmentation evident more readily. Such spreads can also be used for measuring or approximating the amount of pigment produced by comparing them with standard color scales.

Reducing Power by Bacteria.—Some bacteria are capable of reducing various substances. This reducing power may be measured by the loss of color as is practiced in the so-called *reductase test* or the *methylene-blue reduction method* or it may be the reduction of nitrates to nitrites.

Reductase Tests.—To a broth culture of the organism, add 0.1 cc. of a 1 per cent aqueous solution of methylene blue. Incubate at the optimum temperature and note color change. Complete decolorization is a strong positive; green coloration is weak positive; and no color change is positive.

This test, when used in practice, is employed in raw milk samples. The reduction is due to the metabolic products (possibly enzymes) of the bacteria present and provides an approximation of the quality of the milk. There exists a direct relation between the number of bacteria present and the time required for the reduction of the added methylene blue. The test is useful in dairies where trained workers or laboratory facilities are not available or where speedy findings are needed. Although milk cannot be graded with any degree of accuracy by this method, it is generally recognized that milk decolorizing under the standard conditions (see *A. P. H. A. Standard Methods of Dairy Products*) in less than two hours is poor in quality and that which does not decolorize within five and one-half hours is of good quality.

Nitrate Reduction.—Incubate the organism for four days in broth containing 0.1 per cent potassium nitrate (nitrite free). To 4 cc. of the culture add 1 cc. each of the following reagents: (1) 0.5 Gm. α-naphthylamine is dissolved in 100 cc. of 5 N acetic acid or in 100 cc. of dilute sulfuric acid (1 part of concentrated acid to 125 parts of water); (2) 0.8 Gm. sulfanilic acid is dissolved in 100 cc. of 5 N acetic acid (1 part glacial acetic acid to 2.5 parts of water) or in 100 cc. of dilute sulfuric acid (1 part concentrated acid to 20 parts water). The mixture is placed in warm water for fifteen or twenty minutes. The development of a rose or pink color indicates the presence of nitrites. A tube of the sterile medium should be treated and tested as a control. If a fermentation tube containing the nitrate broth is inoculated, the evolution of gas indicates a further reduction to free nitrogen. For reagent No. I, some workers have recommended a solution prepared by dissolving 0.6 cc. dimethyl-α-naphthylamine in 100 cc. of 5 N acetic acid, as it yields a permanent red color in the presence of high concentrations of nitrite. For routine diagnostic tests, this technique is sufficient to indicate that nitrates are not reduced.

Cholera-red (nitroso-indol) Reaction.—This test is to note both nitrate reduction and indol production and is revealed by the production of a red color upon the addition only of concentrated sulfuric acid to a twenty-four hour old (or preferably older) Dunham's or Riva's peptone culture. Nitrite is produced from nitrate present in the peptone. The presence of fermentable carbohydrate interferes with the test.

Indol (C_8H_7N).—Some bacteria, particularly those belonging to the colon and proteus groups, when cultured on appropriate media break down the higher complex nitrogenous compounds (containing the tryptophane radical) with the production of a simpler compound known as indol, which remains in the culture medium. This fact is taken advantage of in the identification and differentiation of certain microorganisms. The important consideration concerning the medium used is that the peptone in the latter must contain tryptophane. Instead of a lean-meat digest as is commonly used in the manufacture of peptones, a casein digest is to be preferred. *Tryptone* and *tryptophane* broth, available on the market, are casein digests. To be assured of the effectiveness of the peptone, each lot used should be tested for indol with a known *Vibrio comma*.

Tests for Indol.—The organism to be tested for indol production is planted in several tubes containing Dunham's or Riva's media and incubated at 37° C. or at the optimum temperature for the organism under examination.   If the latter will not grow in the medium, add such ingredients (natural fluids, etc.) as will make growth possible.   The presence of carbohydrate, however, may inhibit indol production.   Controls, employing tubes of sterile media and one inoculated with a strain of *E. coli* known to produce indol are also tested.   At the end of twenty-four, forty-eight, seventy-two and one hundred and twenty hours and every two days for a period of two weeks an inoculated tube is tested for the presence of indol.   With rapid-growing bacteria, the reaction may be positive in a twenty-four hour old suitable liquid culture and negative in older cultures.   In other instances, a positive reaction is only obtained in old cultures.   It is therefore best to make several cultures and incubate as mentioned above and then test for indol by any one of the following methods:

Kovac's Test.—To about 10 cc. of fluid culture, add 5 cc. of reagent (para-dimethyl-amino-benzaldehyde, 5 Gm.; amyl or butyl alcohol, 75 cc.; conc. HCl, 25 cc.) and shake.   A red color is indicative of a positive indol test.

Ehrlich-Böhme Test.—To 10 cc. of the culture medium, add 5 cc. of *Solution No. 1* (containing 1 Gm. of para-dimethyl-amino-benzaldehyde in 95 cc. alcohol and 20 cc. concentrated hydrochloric acid).   Then add 5 cc. of *Solution No. 2* (a saturated aqueous solution of potassium persulfate $(K_2S_2O_8)$ and shake.   A red color indicates the presence of indol.   In *Standard Methods of Water Analysis* the test reagent is a 5 per cent solution of para-dimethyl-amino-benzaldehyde in a mixture of 75 cc. of any alcohol and 25 cc. of concentrated HCl.   To 5-cc. portions of medium, 0.2 to 0.3 cc. of the reagent is added.   A dark red color in the alcohol surface layer will develop in about one minute if indol is present.   In a negative test the original color of the reagent will prevail.

Several modifications of this test are used.   In one of them, the culture medium is shaken well with a few cubic centimeters of ether.   Then add carefully *Solution No. 1*, dropping the latter down the sides of the test tube to form a layer between the ether and culture medium.   The red color will appear without adding the other reagent.   Positive tests obtained when adding reagents directly to the medium reveal the presence of indol and alpha-methyl-indol.   Inasmuch as the latter is nonvolatile, where a more specific test for indol alone is desired, the *Goré-Modification* or the *Gnezda test* is used.

In the *Goré-Modification*, the white absorbent cotton plug from the culture tube is removed, moistened with 0.5 cc. of *Solution No. 2* and then with 0.5 cc. of *Solution No. 1*.   The plug is replaced, pushed down within one inch of the surface of the fluid culture, placed upright in a boiling water bath and kept there for fifteen minutes, avoiding contact of fluid culture and plug.   A positive indol reaction will be revealed by the appearance of a red color on the plug.

In the *Gnezda oxalic acid test*, strips of sterile filter paper are impregnated with a saturated aqueous solution of oxalic acid.   After drying thoroughly, they are inserted into the culture tubes (under aseptic conditions) at such an angle that it presses against the side of the tube and remains near the mouth.   The culture tubes are incubated.   The presence of indol will be revealed by a pink coloration of the oxalic acid crystals which cover the filter paper strips.

Vanillin Test.—Five drops of 5 per cent vanillin in 95 per cent alcohol and 2 cc. concentrated acid (HCl or H_2SO_4) are added.   Indol is indicated by the production of a clear orange color.   This test yields a high percentage of positive reactions, not confirmed by other techniques and therefore is not regarded as reliable.

Voges-Proskauer (V. P.) Reaction.—Prepare a sterile *buffered dextrose-peptone solution* of Difco or Witte peptone (0.5 per cent), K_2HPO_4 (0.5%) and dextrose 0.5 per cent in distilled water.   Sterilize preferably at 100° C. on three days or by autoclaving.   This is at times known as *M. R.-V.P. Reaction Medium* or *Clark-Lubs Medium*.   Inoculate tubes containing 10 cc. of this medium with the organism to be tested and incubate for at least four days at the optimum temperature.   Add 2 cc. of a 50 per cent (or 10 cc. of 10 per cent) KOH solution and leave the tubes at room temperature exposed to the air overnight or for twenty-four hours.   To hasten the reaction, incubate at 37° C. or 45° C. and examine periodically for six hours.   Frequent shaking or blowing into the tube hastens a positive reaction by promoting oxidation.   The development of a pink (weak eosinlike) color, usually at the top of the tube, resulting from the presence of acetyl-methyl-carbinol, is a positive reaction, while a yellow color (in the control) is produced when the reaction is negative.   The addition of 0.1 per cent copper sulfate or a cupric-ammonium sulfate reagent ($CuSO_4 \cdot 5H_2O$, 0.1 Gm.; conc. NH_4OH (sp. gr. 0.90), 4. cc.; 10% KOH solution, 96 cc.) to the caustic alkali increases the rate of reaction so that a bright red coloration appears in from ten to twenty minutes   Werkman (*J. Bact.*, 1930, **20**,

121) adds 2 drops of ferric chloride (2 per cent aqueous) solution to each 5 cc. of culture followed by 5 cc. of 40 per cent NaOH solution. After shaking well, a stable copper color is given by a positive test. In the alpha-naphthol test (*J. Path. and Bact.*, 1936, **42**, 441), to each 1 cc. of culture there is added 0.6 cc. of a 5 per cent solution of alpha-naphthol in absolute alcohol followed by 0.2 cc. of 40 per cent KOH solution. This test is used to differentiate between *E. coli* (and members of the genus *escherichia*, which give a negative reaction) and closely related bacteria (especially members of the genus *aerobacter*), which give a positive reaction. Positive and negative controls carried out at the same time are advocated.

It is important to see that for this test and the methyl red test, a proteose peptone is used when preparing the media (Witte or Difco products are satisfactory), as with other peptones false negative findings may result. The dry K_2HPO_4 should produce a distinct pink color to phenolphthalein. For testing aerobic spore formers, better results are obtained by using a medium in which the phosphate is replaced by the same quantity of sodium chloride. Acetyl-methyl-carbinol is not produced by *A. aerogenes* during the first few days of culturing, so that a four-day or, better still, an older culture must be used. In the reaction, acetyl-methyl-carbinol is oxidized to diacetyl upon standing in the presence of the alkali which is added. The diacetyl reacts with the peptone (an unknown constituent present therein) to form the colored (pink) substance, indicative of a positive test.

Methyl Red (M. R.) Test.—Inoculate tubes of *M. R.- V. P. Reaction Medium* and incubate at 37° C. (or the optimum temperature) for at least four days. Add methyl red indicator (a 0.02 per cent solution in 60 per cent alcohol), 5 drops to each 5 cc. of liquid medium. An orange-red color reveals a positive reaction, while a yellow color is indicative of a negative reaction. This test is of value in differentiating *Escherichia coli* and *Aerobacter aerogenes*. The latter gives a negative and the former a positive methyl red reaction. The test is merely the determination of the pH by methyl red as the indicator (pH range 4.4–6.0). *E. coli* produces and maintains a high acidity.

Citrate Utilization.—As an aid in differentiation between closely related bacteria, advantage is taken of the ability possessed by some to utilize sodium citrate as a sole source of carbon in a synthetic medium. Use a loop and inoculate Petri dishes or slants containing citrate agar (see below) to which brom thymol blue indicator has been added. Incubate at the optimum temperature and examine growth for color change. *A. aerogenes* grows in this medium (said to be citrate-positive) and changes the color from green to blue. *E. coli* (said to be citrate-negative) grows only slightly, if at all, and does not change the color of the medium.

Koser's Citrate Medium, included in Appendix 1 of *Standard Methods of Water Analysis*, can be used. This is prepared by dissolving 1.5 Gm. sodium ammonium phosphate (microcosmic salt), 1 Gm. potassium dihydrogen phosphate (anhydrous), 0.2 Gm. magnesium sulfate and 3 Gm. sodium citrate (crystals) in 1000 cc. distilled water. Sterilize by autoclaving at 15 pounds' pressure (121.5° C.) for twenty minutes. A loopful (do not introduce excessive amounts of organic nutrient material from other cultures as this may invalidate the results) of the material is transferred into this medium. Incubate at 37° C. for three to four days and observe growth. The latter, revealed macroscopically by marked turbidity, is given by *Aerobacter aerogenes*. *E. coli* fails to grow. The *citrate agar slants* mentioned above are prepared by adding to Koser's Citrate Medium 2 per cent agar and 20 cc. of brom thymol blue indicator (0.4 per cent solution) to each liter. Sterilize by autoclaving. *Simmons Citrate Agar* (*J. Infect. Dis.*, 1926, **39**, 209) differs but little from the above citrate agar formula.

Uric Acid Test.—Prepare a medium by dissolving 0.5 Gm. sodium chloride, 0.2 Gm. magnesium sulfate, 0.1 Gm. calcium chloride, 1 Gm. dipotassium hydrogen phosphate, 1000 cc. distilled water. Sterilize by autoclaving. The procedure for noting uric acid utilization is carried out in the same manner as for noting citrate utilization. For further details see Koser (*J. Infect. Dis.*, 1918, **23**, 377).

Production of Hydrogen Sulfide.—Inoculate Dunham's Peptone Solution and incubate at the optimum temperature for at least four days. To 10 cc. of culture add 0.1 cc. of 1 per cent aqueous lead acetate or ferric tartrate. A black precipitate indicates H_2S production. Lead acetate test papers (prepared by soaking strips of white filter paper, 2 inches by $1/4$ inch, in a saturated solution of lead acetate and drying in an oven at 110° C.) may be used. One strip is placed in the mouth of each culture tube before incubation so that one-half of the strip is below the bottom of the cotton plug. The tubes are examined daily to note blackening of the test paper. Known positive and known negative controls should be inoculated in other tubes of the medium and incubated at the same time. The medium used must contain utilizable sulfur compounds. Sodium thiosulfate may be added as a source of sulfur.

Different formulas of culture media containing lead compounds have been advocated for the detection of hydrogen sulfide producing bacteria. The growth of some bacteria, however, is inhibited by lead salts. Bismuth sulfite media (*J. Bact.*, 1938, **35**, 185) have been advocated, as have media containing nickel or cobalt salts (*J. Bact.*, 1940, **40**, 449) instead of lead compounds. A satisfactory procedure is the use of lead acetate test paper, placed above the medium, as this technique is not only more sensitive but metallic salts are not introduced into the medium, thus eliminating the possibility of inhibiting bacterial growth if the concentration of metallic salt in the medium may become too great.

The test paper technique is more sensitive than the use of media containing lead or iron compounds. The latter, due to their probable toxicity, introduce the possibility of inhibiting bacterial growth due to a too great concentration of such compounds. *Kligler's Lead Acetate Agar* (*Am. J. Pub. Health*, 1917, **7**, 1042), *Baily and Lacy's Modification* (*J. Bact.*, 1927, **13**, 183), *Wilson's Iron Medium* (*J. Hyg.*, 1923, **21**, 392) and *Levine's Iron Agar* (*Am. J. Pub. Health*, 1934, **24**, 505) may, however, be used for plating, especially when it is desired to note the approximate number of strong hydrogen sulfide producing colonies. The latter colonies are black. For a formula for *Lead Acetate Agar Medium*, see National Formulary VII, page 531. This and still better *Kliger's Iron Agar* (*J. Expt. Med.*, 1918, **28**, 319; *J. Bact.*, 1927, **13**, 183) are also used in the differentiation of Gram-negative intestinal bacteria.

Semisolid Media—Media for Anaerobes

For bacteria which grow best or only in the absence of atmospheric oxygen, various methods are employed to produce the latter conditions (see page 79). Reducing substances present in culture media may themselves create the desired conditions, or media containing them may be used in combination with special methods.

Dextrose (0.5 to 1%) furnishes a readily available source of energy for bacteria and also favors anaerobiosis. It, therefore, is frequently present in media used for culturing anaerobes. Sodium formate (0.5 to 1%), cystine (0.02 to 0.5%) and sodium thioglycollate (0.1%) are reducing substances used in culture media. Fragments of sterile tissue, such as brain, kidney, liver and chopped meat, are added at times and, by reducing oxygen tension, serve to increase the value of the medium. Occasionally glass wool or cotton may be added, these serving to hold back reducing substances during transplantation.

Semisolid Media.—Many different kinds of so-called *semisolid* or *semifluid* media are available. These terms though convenient are not satisfactory. Actually the finished preparation is slightly viscid. Small quantities of agar (0.1 to 0.3%) in media produce a *Semisolid Agar Medium*. The small amount of agar in the liquid medium makes possible different degrees of oxygen tension throughout the latter (*J. Bact.*, 1939, **37**, 121). This aids not only in the growth of anaerobes and microaerophiles, but also in the development of many fastidious aerobes. Semisolid media may be enriched with different substances to meet the requirements of specific problems.

Ground or Chopped Meat Medium (for Anaerobes).—Place meat infusion nutrient broth containing 0.1% dextrose in test tubes and add sufficient ground or chopped lean beef or veal to reach half the column of the liquid. Sterilize in the autoclave. The final *p*H is to be 7.2 to 7.5. Some workers prefer to mix the meat with two parts of tap water and heat in the Arnold sterilizer for from one to one and one-half hours. After filtering, the cooked meat is distributed as above and with either nutrient broth or the liquid infusion after filtering, and the finished product is known as *Cooked Meat Medium*. Each tube can be covered with a layer of petrolatum before sterilization or the latter, in a sterile condition, is added subsequently.

Liver, Heart and Brain Media.—In the use of the anaerobic culture dish described by Spray, a *liver veal agar medium* is employed (*J. Bact.*, 1931, **21**, 23; 1936, **32**, 135). Formulas for the latter and for a *Brain-Broth* and a *Brain-Heart Infusion Broth* are given by Spray (see above) and in the National Formulary VII, pages 524 and 527.

Oxidation-Reduction Potentials.—The investigations of Gillespie and Rettger (*J. Bact.*, 1936, **31**, 14) and Kligler and Guggenheim (*J. Bact.*, 1938, **35**, 141) reveal that anaerobic growth is controlled by the oxidation-reduction potential and that growth in the presence of atmospheric air is possible if the latter is sufficiently low. Brewer (*J. Bact.* 1940, **39**, 10), making use of this fact and of other established principles, developed a clear liquid medium, in which anaerobes grow, using the usual aerobic techniques. Seals and special equipment are not necessary. He has introduced a *sodium thioglycollate broth* and *thioglycollate agar medium*. The *fluid thioglycollate medium* is the culture medium approved at present by the National Institute of Health for making the sterility test on biological products and a modification of this is being considered by the Sterile Advisory Board of the U. S. Pharmacopoeia (of which the author is a member) for use in sterility tests for U. S. P. products.

Fluid Thioglycollate Medium

Fluid Thioglycollate Medium.—The Memorandum issued by the National Institute of Health on December 30, 1941, gives the method of preparation by either of two formulas:

Method A—Fluid Thioglycollate Medium (Brewer):

Ground fresh beef (freed of fat)	500 Gm.
Sodium chloride	5 Gm.
Dipotassium phosphate (K_2HPO_4)	2 Gm.
Peptone	10 Gm.
Distilled water	1000 cc.

Place the ground meat into the distilled water, mix thoroughly and allow to stand at 5° C. for twenty-four hours. Collect the liquid by straining through cloth, then heat for one hour in streaming steam followed by thirty minutes at 15 pounds' pressure (121° C.) in the autoclave. Filter while hot through moistened filter paper and make up to the original volume. Add the remaining ingredients and stir until solution is completed. Adjust the reaction with sodium hydroxide to such a point as experience shows will result in a pH of 7.5, ± 0.1, in the completed broth. Heat in streaming steam for thirty minutes, clear by filtration, fill into suitable containers and sterilize in the autoclave at 15 to 17 pounds' pressure (121° to 123° C.) for twenty minutes.

To 1000 cc. of this stock broth add the following ingredients:

Dextrose (anhydrous)	10.0	Gm.
Sodium thioglycollate	1.0	Gm.
Agar (less than 15 per cent moisture by weight)	0.5	Gm.
Methylene blue (use 1 cc. of a 1:500 solution)	0.002	Gm.

Add the agar to the cold broth, mix well and heat gradually to the boiling point. Cool to approximately 80° C. and add the remaining ingredients. Stir until solution is completed and the ingredients are uniformly distributed. Adjust the reaction with sodium hydroxide to such a point as experience shows will result in a pH of 7.5, ± 0.1, in the completed and sterile medium. Distribute in final containers of the desired size and sterilize in the autoclave for eighteen to twenty minutes at 15 to 17 pounds' pressure (121° to 123° C.).

Method B—Fluid Thioglycollate Medium (Linden):

Peptone	20.0 Gm.
Dextrose (anhydrous)	5.0 Gm.
Yeast extract	2.0 Gm.
Sodium thioglycollate	1.0 Gm.
Sodium chloride	5.0 Gm.
Agar (less than 15 per cent moisture by weight)	0.5 Gm.
Dipotassium phosphate (K_2HPO_4)	2.5 Gm.
Distilled water	1000.0 cc.
0.2 per cent solution of methylene blue (cert.)	1.0 cc.

Dissolve the agar in half the volume of distilled water by boiling or heating in the Arnold sterilizer Dissolve the remaining ingredients, except the methylene blue, in the remaining water with the aid of heat. Now mix the two portions, adjust the reaction with sodium hydroxide to such a point as experience shows will result in a pH of 7.5, ± 0.1, in the completed and sterilized medium. Filter clear while hot and add the methylene-blue solution. Distribute into final containers of the desired size and sterilize in the autoclave for eighteen to twenty minutes at 15 to 17 pounds' pressure (121° to 123° C.). A more recent formula employs only 0.5 Gm. sodium thioglycollate.

This medium permits the growth of both aerobic and anaerobic organisms in open containers. It is particularly effective in neutralizing the growth-inhibiting action of mercurials, and is especially useful for testing preparations to be used parenterally containing mercury compounds as bacteriostatic agents. In each instance the inoculum should be mixed thoroughly into the medium. When smears are to be made from cultures in this medium it is recommended that they be fixed with methyl alcohol instead of heat since this gives a clearer background.

The author has used *fluid thioglycollate medium*. Other than the fact that the medium after preparation is satisfactory for only one month, it is superior to most other available formulas and especially when the fact is considered that it is not necessary to employ special methods to obtain anaerobiosis. In our laboratories we have grown in this medium most of the commonly found aerobes and anaerobes including all pathogenic *clostridia* and have found that the microscopical, biochemical and other biological characteristics of these bacteria are not changed.

Recently Brewer (*J. Bact.*, 1942, **43**, 36) described a *sodium formaldehyde sulfoxylate* medium as being superior to the thioglycollate product, easier to prepare and less costly. The tentative formula suggested by him (*Am. J. Med. Tech.*, 1942, **8**, 174) consists of infusion agar or blood agar base (containing 1.5 to 2 per cent agar), 1000 cc.; dextrose, 10 Gm.; aqueous solution methylene blue (1:500), *p*H 7.5, 1 cc.; sodium thioglycollate, 2 Gm. or, still better, a mixture of 2 Gm. of the latter and 1 Gm. of sodium formaldehyde sulfoxylate.

HEMOLYSIS OF RED BLOOD CELLS

Blood-plate Hemolysis.—In routine procedure to detect hemolytic bacteria, blood-agar plates are streaked with the material under examination and incubated under the optimum conditions. Hemolysis is apparent by the appearance of zones of varying degree of clarity and discoloration (from pink to no color) in contrast to the bright cherry-red opacity of the medium. It is advisable, wherever possible, to test the efficiency and inoculate each lot of blood-agar medium with strains of organisms of known hemolytic activity and to use only those batches producing distinct hemolysis with positive controls and no hemolysis with negative controls, if the medium is to be employed especially to detect hemolytic activity.

Filterable Hemolysins.—These hemolysins are demonstrable by adding 0.5 cc. of a (whole) culture of the organism or of a filtrate of the latter (free of bacteria) to 0.5 cc. of a 2 per cent suspension of washed (red blood cells washed three times with isotonic salt solution) erythrocytes in isotonic salt solution. The mixture is incubated at 37° C. for two hours and then placed in an ice box overnight. Avoid agitating the tubes. Note the appearance of the contents after the first and second hours and after the ice-box incubation. Compare this wherever possible with a known negative and a known positive control. A clear, colorless supernatant liquid above the cells which settle to the bottom is a negative test, while positive findings reveal a clear ruby-red color in the supernatant liquid above a few cells at the bottom (or all cells may have been hemolyzed).

Due to its inhibitory effect on hemolytic activity, dextrose should not be added to media used for detecting hemolysis. Hemolysins may display differences in their activity on the erythrocytes of various species of animals. A given hemolysin may hemolyze human and sheep red blood cells but not rabbit cells, or its hemolytic activity may extend to the erythrocytes of either only one or to many species of animals. It is therefore important to use red blood cells in the media or in the test which are known to be sensitive to the hemolysins being sought or under examination. In general, the red blood cells of the species of animal from which a bacterium is isolated or for which it is pathogenic are more sensitive to its hemolysins than are the red cells of other species. Certain strains of the same species of bacteria may produce more than one hemolysin, each having different characteristics (as in the case of streptococci (see Todd, *J. Path. and Bact.*, 1934, **39**, 299)). Furthermore, different temperature conditions may be required for hemolysins of other species (as in some strains of staphylococci (see Glenny and Stevens, *J. Path. and Bact.*, 1935, **40**, 201)).

The relation between blood-plate hemolysis and filterable hemolysis is obscure. Bacteria displaying hemolysis on blood plates may at times fail to reveal filterable hemolysis by known techniques in use at present. Since filterable hemolysins are difficult to demonstrate, it is claimed by some workers that failure to detect them is not significant. It appears that the actual mechanism involved in both reactions is different; and it is possible that as soon as these processes are more definitely understood, the relationship between blood-plate hemolysis and filterable hemolysis will become clearer.

COAGULASE

Some bacteria produce a substance known as coagulase which increases the coagulability of blood, so that the formation of blood clots is accelerated. Various staphylococci, in particular, are especially characterized by their ability to produce coagulase. This activity is demonstrated *in vitro* by the addition of bacteria to oxalated or citrated blood plasma. The latter is prepared by adding one of the two anticoagulants (20 mg. of neutral potassium oxalate or 200 mg. of sodium citrate for each 10 cc. of blood) to blood (usually rabbit). The mixtures of bacteria and blood plasma (containing anticoagulant) are allowed to stand (preferably one at 37° C. and one at room temperature) for at least three hours, within the period whence the formation of a gel will occur. If possible, carry along positive and negative controls. Filtrates of bacteria do not reveal the presence of coagulase. The latter is relatively thermostable and is probably a substance of protein character. The exact relationship between coagulase and the virulency of the bacteria producing the latter is not definitely known.

FIBRINOLYTIC ACTIVITY

Some bacteria possess the capacity to transform the solid clot of normal blood into a liquid state (*i. e.*, liquefy blood clots). This is due to the presence of fibrinolysin—an extracellular enzymic substance produced by the living bacteria. Fibrinolytic activity has special characteristics of bacteriological and immunological interest, and it appears to be associated with virulency and the ability to invade body tissues. In the case especially of the streptococci, the positive finding of fibrinolysis is a useful procedure to aid in detecting human pathogenic strains from nonpathogenic ones. Negative findings, however, do not always exclude pathogenicity. For further details, see Tillett (*Bact. Rev.*, 1938, **2**, 161).

The *in vitro* conditions under which the presence of fibrinolysin is best demonstrated consist in mixing a suitable culture (0.5 cc.) of the organisms under examination (one of abundant growth at maximum growth period) with blood plasma (0.2 cc. of a 1:5 dilution) or fibrinogen before inducing clot formation. This mixture is allowed to clot by the addition of calcium chloride and incubating the mixture at 37° C. Some workers advise a higher temperature. The time required to dissolve the fibrin clot is noted. It may vary from a few minutes with some strains to only a partial effect within twenty-four hours. In weakly positive cases, visual estimation of lysis is made and the shape and size of the fibrin clot remaining as compared with negative and positive controls are noted. In the great majority of normal individuals, lysis of the fibrin clot of their blood will occur within an hour, if the fibrinolysin is present.

As in the case of the hemolysins, fibrinolysins appear to exhibit a degree of specificity between their source and the kind of fibrin used. Bacteria isolated from man and producing fibrinolysin will yield positive findings with human fibrin and negative or inconclusive findings with animal fibrins. Negative or inconclusive findings are obtained most frequently when bacteria isolated from animal sources and producing fibrinolysin are tested against human fibrin. The plasma, therefore, used in routine tests is obtained from the blood of normal humans against which positive and negative controls are also employed.

Fibrinolysin when produced appears to be freely excreted by viable growing bacteria and is present in filtrates (free of cells). It is relatively heat-stable, is of protein origin, and is antigenic. Though many strains of bacteria producing fibrinolysin possess also proteolytic, hemolytic and toxicogenic properties, the fibrinolysin characteristic is distinct from the latter.

Plating.—The cultivation of bacteria in a broad, shallow, circular, glass-covered dish (called Petri dish) is referred to as plating. There are many advantages of plating instead of mere culturing on slants. A bacterial cell wherever deposited will grow and multiply if conditions are suitable. In liquid media, growth is apparent when the latter which is clear becomes clouded, but on solid nutritive material growth becomes visible to the naked eye as a pinhead or elevated mass. This, a pure culture of the organism, derived from a single cell in the original material, is known as a *colony*. These colonies (masses of the same type of cells) possess salient peculiarities which are highly characteristic of the species causing their production. Their shape, size, appearance, outline, adherence to medium, color, elevations, topography, consistency and margin characteristics, etc., are frequently of service in differential diagnosis. There is a greater facility of observing and studying the appearance of colonies as they develop on any medium in a Petri dish. Inasmuch as the different colonies that develop from the individual bacteria do not crowd together immediately (*i. e.*, confluence, as on slants), it is possible to procure discrete colonies and even count the number of such colonies that are present. Plating, therefore, affords the best means of determining the number of bacteria per cubic centimeter

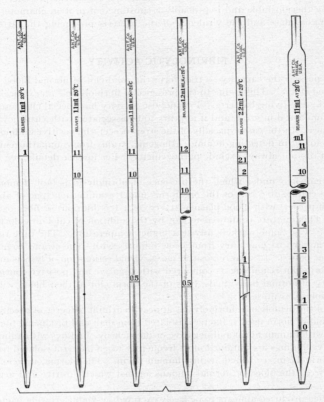

Fig. 7. Bacteriological pipettes.

or in a definite quantity of a substance. Also, when several species of microorganisms are present, and it is desired to procure one or more of them, plating is usually resorted to for such isolation. More recently the characteristics or colony form have assumed important significance, especially as it concerns bacterial dissociation (which see).

In all instances when plating is employed the technique most frequently used consists in liquefying the solid medium (gelatin or agar by placing in a boiling water bath) and cooling to 45° C. The latter is then inoculated with the material contained on a sterile loop or with a definite amount of the substance measured from a sterile pipette. The bacteria are then thoroughly distributed throughout the cool liquefied media by agitating with a slight rotary motion. This thoroughly distributes the organisms without allowing the formation of air bubbles. From this tube, 2 loopfuls are transferred to a second liquefied, cool tube of sterile agar medium. After mixing thoroughly, 2 loopfuls from the second tube are carried to a third tube of liquefied, cool, sterile agar. The contents of the several tubes are then poured into sterile Petri dishes, care being observed that the lip of the tube is first flamed and that the cover of the dish is raised only along one side, simply far enough as to permit the insertion of the end of the tube. The cool, liquefied, sterile, solid medium is poured into the Petri dish, care being taken not to touch the bottom or sides of the dish, and to avoid getting any culture medium on the cover. The latter is then replaced, the dish tilted cautiously back and forth or rotated to evenly distribute the medium which is then allowed to harden. The dishes are finally covered with the porous earthenware lids that are at times provided, or the glass tops, wrapped in paper and turned upside down in an incubator or at any temperature desired. Such procedure is advisable so as to prevent the water of syneresis (so-called water of condensation), forced out of the medium during hardening, from collecting on the surface of the latter and as a droplet forming a nucleus for the spread of bacteria.

For quantitative work plates are also made by placing in a sterile Petri dish the desired amount of material to be cultured. The suitable liquefied, cooled, solid medium, an amount sufficient to cover the bottom of the dish, is then added and the contents are gently agitated. The procedure from here on is the same as given in the previous paragraph. Smeared or surface streaked plates are also used for the cultivation and isolation of bacteria. In this method a sterile loop or spatula or a sterile

Fig. 8. Petri (culture) dish.

bent rod is used for conveying the material. This is streaked lightly over the surface of the suitable sterile, solid, culture medium present in sterile Petri dishes. Two or more plates are inoculated in succession without further sterilization of the loop or rod. This dilutes the material so that isolated colonies are formed.

Aerobic Methods.—Aerobic bacteria, those requiring atmospheric air or oxygen to develop, will grow well in flasks or tubes (containing the medium) and stoppered with cotton plugs, or in Petri dishes. Sufficient oxygen passes through the cotton plugs or percolates through the sides of the Petri dishes, when the containers are placed in an incubator, closet or room, where the atmosphere is pure enough to contain sufficient quantities of air.

Anaerobic Methods.—Anaerobic bacteria will only develop in an environment from which free air or oxygen has been excluded.

For anaerobic growth, it is advisable to have dextrose present in the media. The latter immediately before use should preferably be heated in a boiling water bath for fifteen to twenty minutes to expel absorbed oxygen and other gases. Cool to 45° C. before inoculating and immediately thereafter place in cold water to solidify if agar or gelatin media are used. Almost every laboratory has its preferred method of producing anaerobiosis.

Different methods are practiced for the exclusion of air or oxygen during incubation: (a) exclusion by physical methods or mechanical devices; (b) displacing the oxygen by an inert gas (hydrogen); (c) absorbing the oxygen by chemicals.

(a) On a large scale the exclusion method can be practiced by placing the inoculated tubes or Petri dishes in specially devised jars fitted with taps and stopcocks. The air is pumped out by exhaust pumps, leaving a vacuum. Any type of pump, however, may be employed. The pumps for attachments to faucets where water under pressure is available are convenient. Any kind of jar of appropriate size, fitted with a tight cover and a stopcock opening, can be used.

The physical methods are widely employed on a small as well as on a large scale. This consists in making stab cultures in solid media and sealing the tubes or quickly pouring on the top a layer of cool, liquefied sterile agar or sterile petrolatum and, better still, sterile liquid petrolatum. Shake cultures can also be conveniently made, the latter quickly cooled in cold water, and then covered with a layer of the cool, liquefied medium or sterile liquid petrolatum.

(b) The principle of air displacement by hydrogen also can be applied to the cultivation of anaerobes. The inoculated tubes or Petri dishes are placed in a tight-fitting jar (as the Novy (*J. Exp. Med.*, 1922, **35**, 467) or Smellie (*J. Exp. Med.*, 1917, **26**, 59) or preferably a McIntosh-Fildes jar) and the hydrogen (generated from zinc and sulfuric acid in a generator and washed to remove impurities [a Kipp hydrogen generator is satisfactory]) is introduced into the jar through a tap, while the air or oxygen passes out as the hydrogen enters. Within ten minutes the stopcocks are closed. In the method of McIntosh and Fildes (*Brit. J. Exp. Path.*, 1921, **2**, 153) platinized or preferably palladinized asbestos wool or a small resistance coil (electrically heated) is used to oxidize the hydrogen and thus remove any residual oxygen. The Brewer modification of the Brown jar (*J Lab. & Clin. Med.*, 1939, **24**, 1190) and the Plasticine-sealed jar (Brewer and Brown, *J. Lab. & Clin. Med.*, 1938, **23**, 870) make possible the use of illuminating gas.

The Rosenthal (*J. Bact.*, 1937, **34**, 317) chromium sulfuric-acid method for culturing anaerobes is used by some workers. In this procedure, both hydrogen and CO_2 are evolved. Mueller and Miller (*J. Bact.*, 1941, **41**, 301) have slightly modified Rosenthal's method and also present an inexpensive suitable jar for practical use.

(c) Absorption of oxygen does not require any special apparatus; any jar that can be made airtight (preferably with a ground-glass stopper) will do. The tubes or plates are placed in the jar on a support that elevates them 1 or 2 inches above the alkaline solution of pyrogallate, which is added to absorb the oxygen in the jar. In the chemical reaction ensuing in the formation of the pyrogallate considerable heat is evolved which would kill any microorganism on the medium if the latter were placed in the warm solution. After the tubes are supported on a stand or any support extending so that the test tube will not touch the liquid to be poured in, about $1/2$-inch layer of pyrogallic acid is placed in the bottom of the jar. A 5 to 10 per cent solution of sodium or potassium hydrate is poured in and the jar quickly sealed after the ground surface of the jar has been anointed with petrolatum. Ten grams of dry pyrogallic acid and 30 cc. of a 5 per cent solution of sodium hydroxide per liter of air space are more exacting proportions to use.

Fig. 9. Anaerobic culture apparatus with culture dish holder.

A tube of alkaline dextrose broth containing just enough methylene blue to give a light blue color (approximately 0.005 per cent methylene blue) (or mix equal parts of a 6 per cent dextrose solution, $N/160$ NaOH, and 0.015 per cent aqueous solution methylene blue and boil until reduced) will serve as an indicator for anaerobiosis. If the latter prevails, there will be complete decolorization after overnight exposure and the indicator remains colorless if anaerobic conditions are maintained.

Another simple and even more satisfactory method is the use of a small crystallizing dish which has as a cover one of the parts of a Petri dish. The bottom of the former is fitted with a partition, thus making two compartments. Into one there is placed dry pyrogallic acid and into the other a 5 per cent solution of caustic soda. Into the cover or smaller Petri dish top, there is placed the inoculated solid medium or the material is spread on the surface after the medium is hardened. This Petri dish top is then inverted into the larger dish, serving as a covering for the latter. Modeling clay is employed as a seal. After sealing, the crystallizing dish is tilted so as to allow the interaction of pyrogallic acid and alkali. This can then be placed in an incubator or at any desired temperature. The Spray anaerobic culture dish is similar to the above arrangement. This and a new anaerobic culture dish recently announced by Brewer are available for use by simply inoculating the surface of the suitable medium. The thioglycollate medium (see page 75) is recommended for use in the Brewer culture dish.

(d) The presence of small amounts of certain chemicals, as succinic acid, cysteine and glutathione, permits the growth of anaerobes under aerobic conditions. Agar or broth media containing 0.3 per cent of cysteine hydrochloride, with a reaction of pH 7.4, have been successfully used for growing anaerobes without the necessity of special apparatus. The cysteine gives up hydrogen, becomes cystine, and the hydrogen absorbing oxygen produces the desired "reduction potential," the latter being the necessary reducing power required in the media. See page 74 for media for anaerobes.

Attention is directed to the fact that most aerobes will also grow under anaerobic conditions and under reduced oxygen tension. It is therefore incorrect to report the presence *only* of anaerobes under these conditions, unless growth was not obtained under aerobic conditions of culturing.

Oxygen Tension.—Methods of cultivating obligate aerobes and obligate anaerobes are comparatively simple, but the cultivation of the so-called *facultative organisms* has been a matter which has only recently received a degree of attention. Some microorganisms do not grow luxuriantly when cultivated by the ordinary methods as commonly practiced. It has been shown, however, that if the oxygen present is modified to suit the particular requirements of the different facultatives, as found by experimentation, the growth is profuse and more satisfactory than that obtained when such procedure is not adopted.

The use of thioglycollate media (page 75) and the Brewer culture dish (*Science*, 1942, **95**, 587) are very satisfactory for growing bacteria requiring reduced oxygen tension or complete absence of air. The introduction of carbon dioxide in the environment or atmosphere where bacteria are being incubated has been found most useful for the isolation and growing not only of some of the fastidious organisms but also of many of the commonly observed pathogens. This *partial oxygen tension* or *carbon dioxide culturing method* is being widely used, employing especially an incubation environment where the atmosphere contains from 3 to 10 per cent carbon dioxide. A simple procedure is merely to place the inoculated media in tubes or jars or other suitable containers in a nonventilated carbon dioxide incubator as suggested by Rose (*J. Bact.*, 1942, **43**, 142). He further proposed that carbon dioxide incubation be designated *capneic* (Greek for CO_2) and that the bacteria requiring such incubation be known as *capnophiles*. Cultures to be studied can be placed in a Novy jar, or a museum jar or any suitable jar with a tight-fitting lid. Calculate the inside volume. Replace about 10 per cent of the air in the container with carbon dioxide from a tank of liquid carbon dioxide or place the following mixture in a beaker or glass: 0.5 Gm. sodium bicarbonate followed by 10 cc. of 10 per cent sulfuric acid for each 2500 cc. capacity. Place airtight cover over jar, and incubate. For further details, see Thompson (*Am. J. Clin. Path.*, 1935, **5**, 313) and Shaughnessy (*J. Bact.*, 1939, **37**, 153).

Isolation of Single Cells.—For the isolation of single cells of bacteria, the Barber pipette method (*Philippine J. Sci.*, Aug., 1914, Sec. B, **9**: No. 4) and Chamber's modification (*J. Bact.*, 1923, **8**, 1) or the method of direct observation on agar medium as suggested by different workers are used (*J. Bact.*, 1922, **7**, 537; *J. Exp. Med.*, 1925, **41**, 587). These original articles should be consulted for a description of the apparatus and techniques used.

Incubation of Cultures.—Bacteria in cultures must be exposed to a temperature favorable to their development. The saprophytes grow best at a temperature of 20° C. In some well-equipped laboratories there are rooms that are maintained constantly at this temperature. But in most cases the ordinary room temperature is sufficiently near the optimum and can be used in place of special apparatus for maintaining this temperature. In cultivating pathogenic bacteria it is advisable, however, to grow these whenever possible at the temperature of the human body, 37.5° C., so that they may be supplied with one of the conditions most suitable for their proper development. The apparatus employed for obtaining a uniform temperature is known as an incubator or thermostat.

Incubators.—Incubators, though made of all kinds of material and in all sizes and shapes, are constructed upon the same principle. They consist of a double-walled box, copper or other chambers which are fitted with a double door or lid, the outer being preferably covered with asbestos or felt, the inner door made of glass. The space between the two walls is filled with water, which is heated by a gas flame, placed under the surface of the chamber. The size of the flame is automatically regulated by a thermoregulator, which communicates with the water compartment or jacket, through an opening provided at the top of the chamber. Both walls are perforated by an opening which communicates with the interior of the incubator and which receives a thermometer. The constant temperature is maintained by the thermoregulator and it is, therefore, advisable to be assured that this instrument which regulates the supply of gas should be efficient. There are a number of different types of thermoregulators on the market, all constructed somewhat on the same principle of the unequal expansion of two different substances when heated. Alcohol, ether or mercury is usually placed in the bulb of the instrument. The latter is immersed in the water between the walls of the incubator and also connected by rubber tubing to the gas supply and

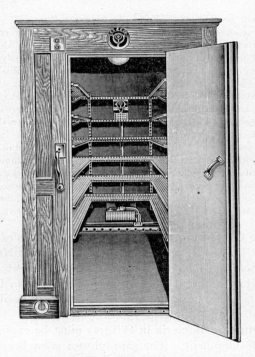

Fig. 10. Incubating room.

to the Bunsen burner beneath the chamber. A small opening in the delivery tube permits the passage of an amount of gas sufficient to constantly maintain a small light. By an adjustment present on the regulator or by raising or lowering the tube, the temperature can be adjusted to remain permanently at any arbitrary degree. Once this is established, it will be observed that should the temperature of the water rise, the liquid (alcohol, ether or mercury) will expand and restrict the opening, thus shutting off the supply of gas. This will lower the flame of the Bunsen burner, which in turn will cause the temperature of the water to fall.

For detailed accounts of the description and construction of incubators and in fact all equipment and apparatus used in the bacteriological laboratory, reference should be made to the catalogues and circulars of manufacturers and distributors.

Other Incubators.—Incubators heated by electricity are used by some workers. Electric carbon lamps are employed as the heating medium in 37.5° C. incubators. They heat and cool quickly. Electric incubators are well ventilated, so that the temperature may be kept uniform in all the working parts of the apparatus. Cold air is allowed to enter through holes at the bottom. This rises as it becomes warmer, and escapes through holes at the top. An electrothermostat is used for automatically controlling the temperature.

In emergencies chicken incubators can be used or a vacuum thermos bottle may be suitable for the incubation of inoculated tubes or small containers. Three-quarters

Fig. 11. Incubator.

of the bottle is filled with water at 38° C. The cultures are tied with string, lowered into the water and attached to pins in the cork of the bottle. The temperature will not vary more than 1 or 2 degrees during the twenty-four hours.

The use of an incubator for growing microaerophiles, as suggested by Rose, has been mentioned (see page 81). He employs carbon dioxide and obtains and maintains the desired carbon dioxide content in a nonventilated incubator by burning a "candle jar." Casman (*J. Bact.*, 1942, **43**, 33) reports on the superiority of this "candle jar" incubation procedure over the aerobic incubation method used routinely. It may be of interest to determine whether the increase of moisture which occurs plays a role as important as or more so than the CO_2 present.

Storage of Cultures.—The maintenance of viability of bacteria for observation and used at subsequent periods are frequently an important consideration even in routine work. Collections of cultures are also needed for teaching purposes, as standards in various diagnostic procedures, for the manufacture of vaccines, sera and other biological products, etc. For the majority of organisms capable of growing on agar medium, cultures are kept on slants or preferably on a semisolid stock agar culture medium, as described by Ayers and Johnson (*J. Bact.*, 1924, **9**, 111). These stock cultures are kept at room temperature and transplanted once a month; or by placing sterile light liquid petrolatum over the slant after growth has started, viability can be maintained by transplanting once every four to six months. For some fastidious organisms, it may be necessary to employ special media, body temperature incubation and more frequent subculturing.

Storage in the dry state is also practiced, and where dehydrating procedures are available such methods are highly recommended. Brown (*J. Bact.*, 1940, **39**, 10) suggests the use of rapid drying and storage in a high vacuum. Roe (*J. Bact.*, 1940, **39**, 11) uses a desiccation method, employing strips of paper on which have been impregnated cultures of the organisms. The method of Swift (*J. Bact.*, 1937, **35**, 411) and modifications of this procedure are employed by many workers. Preservations of cultures by the lyophile process (page 459) is also practiced and favorable results have been reported by its use.

Viruses are preserved by passage through animals, by dehydration methods (especially the lyophile technique) and by refrigeration procedures. Horsfall (*J. Bact.*, 1940, **40**, 559) recently described a low-temperature storage cabinet for the preservation of viruses.

Identification of Bacteria

In an attempt to identify an organism, even a complete microscopical study and staining reaction (where such observations as morphology, motility, presence or absence of spores, flagella, Babes-Ernst granules or other structures and behavior toward different stains are observed) may not be sufficient, it may be necessary to note its cultural characteristics (food, oxygen and temperature requirements), carry out various biochemical tests, observe the reaction of the organism in various immunological and serological tests, and to note the effects when the organism is injected into laboratory animals. In most instances, however, microscopical characteristics and staining reactions, aided by biochemical tests and especially by observations of cultural characteristics, supply the necessary data for purposes of identification.

In studying bacterial cultures, care must be observed to avoid contamination as impure cultures will necessarily lead to errors in identification. The possibility of variability of bacterial species must be understood and kept in mind. Frobisher (*J. Bact.*, 1933, **25**, 1917) discusses in more detail some of these pitfalls to be avoided in studying bacterial cultures. Furthermore, the method or technique to be followed in any study must be adequate. The *descriptive chart* and the *Manual on Methods* prepared by Committees of the Society of American Bacteriologists (see *Pure Cultures Study of Bacteria*, 8th Edit., Leaflet IV, 1943) are most useful guides and should be consulted and followed. Most of the terms used in the Descriptive Chart are either self-explanatory or have been described in this volume. The following terms used here and elsewhere by workers under cultural characteristics are briefly defined:

Acid curd, coagulation of milk due to acid production.

Arborescent, branched, treelike growth.

Ascogonium, female organ in fungi which develops into an ascus after fertilization.

Ascopore, one of a set of spores contained in a special sac, called an ascus.

Beaded (in stab or stroke culture), separate or semiconfluent colonies along the line of inoculation.

Bleb, blister-like swelling or vesicle.

Brittle, dry growth, friable under (platinum or nichrome) needle.

Butyrous, growth is of butter-like consistency.

Clavate, club-shaped.

Columella, in molds, the central axis of the spore case, around which the spores are arranged.

Compact, refers to sediment in the form of single fairly tenacious mass *concentrically ringed*—marked with rings, one inside the other.

Contoured, an irregular, smoothly undulating surface, like that of a relief map.

Crateriform, a saucer-shaped liquefaction of the medium.

Cuneate, wedge-shaped.

Curled, composed of parallel chains in wavy strands, as in anthrax colonies.

Echinulate, a growth along line of inoculation with toothed or pointed margins.

Effuse, growth thin, veily, unusually spreading.

Endospores, thick-walled spores formed within the bacteria; *i. e.,* typical bacterial spores like those of *B. anthracis* or *B. subtilis.*

Endotoxin, a toxic substance produced within a microorganism and not excreted.

Entire, with an even margin.

Erose, irregularly notched.

Excentric, slightly to one side of the center, between the positions denoted central and subterminal.

Exogenous, originating outside the organism.

Exotoxin, a toxic substance excreted by a microorganism and found outside the cell.

Filamentous, growth composed of long, irregularly placed or interwoven threads.

Filaments, applied to morphology of bacteria, refers to threadlike forms, generally unsegmented; if segmented, the organisms are enclosed in a sheath.

Filiform, in stroke or stab cultures, a uniform growth along line of inoculation.

Fimbriate, fringed.

Flaky, refers to sediment in the form of numerous separate flakes.

Flocculent, containing small adherent masses of various shapes floating in the fluid.

Fluorescent, having one color by transmitted light and another by reflected light.

Gonidia, asexual spores.

Gonidial, referring specifically to a bacterial phase producing gonidia-like bodies.

Granular, composed of small granules.

Infundibuliform, in form of a funnel or inverted cone.

Iridescent, exhibiting changing rainbow colors in reflected light.

Lobate, having lobes, or rounded projections.

Membranous, growth thin, coherent, like a membrane.

Metabolite, a substance produced by metabolism.

Metatrophic, using organic matter for food.

Mucoid, mucus-like, referring specifically to a bacterial phase producing slimy growth.

Mycelioid, colonies having the radiately filamentous appearance of mold colonies.

Napiform, liquefaction in form of a turnip.

Opalescent, milky white with tints of color as in an opal.

Opaque, not allowing light to pass through.

Papillate, growth beset with small nipple-like processes.

Pellicle, bacterial growth forming either a continuous or an interrupted sheet over the culture fluid.

Peptonization, rendering curdled milk soluble by the action of peptonizing enzymes.

Phase variation, separation of a species into strains, having somewhat different characters.

Photogenic, glowing in the dark, phosphorescent.

Pulvinate, cushion-shaped.

Punctiform, very small, but visible to naked eye; under 1 mm. in diameter.

Radiate, showing ray structure.

Raised, growth thick, with abrupt or terraced edges.

Rapid, growth produced within twelve to twenty-four hours.

Reduction, removing oxygen or its equivalent from a chemical compound; or addition of hydrogen or its equivalent. Refers to the conversion of nitrate to nitrite, ammonia or free nitrogen; also to the decolorization of litmus.

Rennet curd, coagulation of milk due to rennet or rennet-like enzymes, distinguished from acid curd by the absence of acid.

Rhizoid, growth of an irregular branched or rootlike character, as *B. mycoides*.

Ring, growth at the upper margin of a liquid culture, adhering to the glass.

Rugose, wrinkled.

Saccate, liquefaction in form of an elongated sac, tubular, cylindrical.

Sheath, an envelope similar to a capsule, but surrounding a filamentous organism.

Spindled, larger at the middle than at the ends. Applied to sporangia, refers to the forms frequently called clostridia.

Sporangium (*pl.*-ia), cells containing endospores.

Spreading, growth extending much beyond the point of inoculation, *i. e.*, several millimeters or more.

Stratiform, liquefying to the walls of the tube at the top and then proceeding downward horizontally.

Transient, lasting a few days.

Translucent, allowing light to pass through without allowing complete visibility of objects seen through the substance in question.

Truncate, ends abrupt, square.

Turbid, cloudy with flocculent particles; *i. e.*, cloudy plus flocculence.

Umbonate, having a button-like raised center.

Undulate, wavy.

Villous, having short, thick, hairlike processes on the surface, intermediate in meaning between papillate and filamentous.

Viscid, growth follows the needle when touched and withdrawn; sediment on shaking rises as a coherent swirl.

Centrifugalization and Centrifuges

Solid matter suspended in a liquid will settle by gravity (a vertical force) to the bottom of the container. The rate of settling or the time required for sedimentation will depend upon many factors such as the nature of the liquid, the size of the particles and the attraction of gravity upon them. In bacteriological, biological and most clinical laboratory procedures, too much time would be consumed waiting for the segregation or sedimentation of bacteria and other cellular elements present in suspensions. It is, of course, impractical to speed up the settling process by either changing the nature of the liquid or the size of the suspended particles. Gravity itself cannot be altered. So as not to change in any way the material being treated, the use of centrifugal force can be and is introduced. The increased force will tend to separate the particles from the liquid. This centripetal force pulls the body toward the center of rotation and is applied by having the material as it moves in a circle change its direction continuously at a constant rate. Centrifugal force applied through the use of centrifuges is the commonly practiced method of separating bacteria and other cellular elements from suspension. The centrifuge and centrifugalization save time and money in bringing about quickly a settling of particles (bacteria, etc.) from liquids.

Types of Centrifuges.—There are available on the market various types of strong and substantial centrifuges assuring vibrationless operation and designed to meet any and all demands. There are hand-driven, electric and turbine drive centrifuges. Models with various head combinations are marketed, the different heads having been developed to be used interchangeably on all standard types of centrifuges. Accessories are available to suit any particular work. Speeds varying from several hundred to many thousands of revolutions per minute (r. p. m.) are supplied.

A centrifuge is part of universal laboratory equipment and is used for a large variety of purposes. The electric centrifuges furnished with an enclosing case and a speed control rheostat offer the best possible solution to the many centrifugalization problems normally met with in the bacteriological laboratory. One which is mounted on a heavy base casting, provided with holes for bolting to foundation or portable stand, is to be preferred. An indicating tachometer can be attached if it is desired to gauge

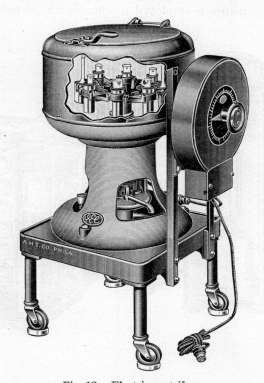

Fig. 12.   Electric centrifuge.

the speed of the centrifuge and to be able to duplicate the same speed and obtain uniform results at all times.

Angle Centrifuges are preferred by some workers. Centrifuges using the angle principle revolve or are whirled at an angle less than 50°, usually a fixed angle of 35°. When suspensions are whirled at an angle less than 50°, sedimentation occurs more rapidly than when the containers swing about at the full 90° angle. In the latter instance, suspended particles must travel through the entire depth of the solution and are subject to interparticle friction. In an angle centrifuge, the particles move very quickly to the sides and fall to the bottom of the container.

Supercentrifuges are not used, as yet, to any great extent in the general bacteriological laboratory. Their application and efficiency are, however, not fully under-stood and appreciated. With the supercentrifuge, a much greater speed than is possible with the ordinary laboratory centrifuge, is attained and the action can be made continuous. These supercentrifuges can be used for clarifying agar, gelatin and other culture media, in the preparation of antitoxins, serums and other biological products and in research investigations.

Ultracentrifuges are different and unique when compared to the centrifuges com-monly used. They generate a stupendous centrifugal force and operate with an almost complete absence of temperature differential in the sample, thus avoiding the intense convection currents which this increased centrifugal force would normally produce. The ultracentrifuge is employed specifically for particle size analysis and

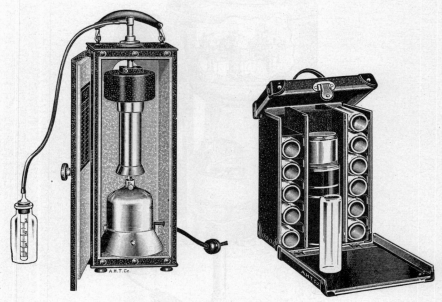

Fig. 13.   Wells air centrifuge.

molecular-weight determination by studying sedimentation velocity. In bacteriologi-cal studies, it is employed to note the size of the unit present in filterable viruses and in bacteriophages. Their use is entirely different from that of the ordinary centri-fuge. In operating an ultracentrifuge, the solution is placed in a small sector-shaped cell having glass or quartz windows and this is inserted in the rotor. The chamber which encloses the latter has corresponding transparent windows with electromagnetic shutters. When the speed of the machine reaches 10,000 r. p. m., the chamber is evacutated to approximately 0.2 μ pressure. The speed is then increased to 80,000 r. p. m. A beam of light is directed through the windows in the rotating cell and photographs are taken at various time intervals. At the termination of the pro-cedure, the photographs are checked with a microphotometer for density as compared to a blank, the amount of settling in each is determined and the rates of settling are calculated. For further details, see Svedeburg (*Chem. Revs.*, 1937, **20**, 81) and Bauer and Pickels (*J. Exp. Med.*, 1936, October).

Well's Air Centrifuge is an electrically driven centrifuge used especially for studying the bacterial content of the air. This centrifuge creates the air flow, measures the amount of air drawn through it and collects the bacteria, pollen and gases. In the cases of bacteria, they are collected on suitable culture media in sterile bottles. The latter containing the bacteria are incubated and the colonies counted and studied without the need of transfer to Petri dishes or other procedures of treatment.

Chapter VII

BERGEY CLASSIFICATION

FROM THE TABLES in this and data in other chapters, one may observe that a morphological classification of bacteria is perhaps somewhat confusing. A system based solely on an organism's morphology has many shortcomings. It is advisable to inform students who have familiarized themselves with the nomenclature and grouping of such system of classification (and it is perhaps best for beginners to learn this broad grouping, for it is simple and easier to comprehend), that as they advance in the study of bacteriology, they should refer to the literature for further information in regard to attempts at a more systematic classification. Under the system of classification compiled by a committee headed by Professor Bergey, before an organism is classified under this (frequently termed Bergey's) classification, its morphological, cultural and pathogenic properties must be determined. The presence or absence of flagella, capsule, spore, staining characteristics, pigment production, biological activities (as immunological and biochemical reactions) is also considered, so that the name of an organism and its place in this system at once indicate many of these characteristics, and do not merely suggest its morphology (shape and size). Wherever possible the International Rules of Botanical Nomenclature are observed in so far as they can be made to apply to bacteriology. Bergey's compilation has some shortcomings, but it possesses many advantages. Here we have a sincere and bold attempt to systematize the imperfect data of the past and to develop a workable outline. It is as yet inadequate, but if the idealists and realists work together, a worth-while classification can result. If advanced students and bacteriologists will unite in employing this as a working classification, present constructive and useful criticism, we may after making some changes have available a stable systematic classification, which will not only be understandable to all workers, but the rightful relationships of microorganisms may be made available.

The following table lists the important orders, families, tribes, genera and type species as given in the Bergey classification and which are of interest in medical bacteriology. (See also pages 14 and 99 for explanatory remarks.)

91

SCHIZOMYCETES

Order	Family	Tribe	Genus	Type species (number of species listed)
I. Eubacteriales	I. Nitrobacteriaceae (usually rod shaped, occasionally coccoid; nonspore forming; nonparasitic, usually found in water and soil; utilizes hydrogen, methane, ammonia, carbon monoxide, nitrite, sulfur or thiosulfates)	I. Nitrobacterieae (oxidize ammonia or nitrites)	I. Nitrobacter (oxidize nitrites to nitrates)	Nitrobacter winogradskyi (6 species)
			II. Nitrosomonas (oxidize ammonia to nitrites)	Nitrosomonas europaea (4 species)
			III. Nitrosococcus (oxidize ammonia to nitrites)	Nitrosococcus nitrosus (1 species)
		II. Protobacterieae (oxidize simple inorganic compounds of carbon or hydrogen)	IV. Hydrogenomonas (oxidize H to H_2O)	Hydrogenomonas pantotropha (3 species)
			V. Methanomonas (oxidize methane to CO_2 and H_2O)	Methanomonas methanica (1 species)
			VI. Carboxydomonas (oxidize CO to CO_2)	Carboxydomonas oligocarbophila (1 species)
		III. Thiobacilleae	VII. Thiobacillus (oxidize S and sulfur compounds)	Thiobacillus thioparus (8 species)
	II. Rhizobiaceae (rod shaped; utilize dextrose or occasionally other sugars without producing organic acids in appreciable quantity)		I. Rhizobium (fix free N when growing symbiotically on Leguminosae)	Rhizobium leguminosarum (6 species)
			II. Chromobacterium (soil and water bacteria producing violet chromogenesis)	Chromobacterium violaceum (3 species) (also 13 inadequately described)
			III. Alcaligenes	Alcaligenes faecalis (10 species)
	III. Pseudomonadaceae (rod to spiral shaped; Gram-negative; nonspore forming; found usually in water and soil; some species are animal and plant parasites)	I. Spirilleae (spiral shaped)	I. Vibrio (short curved rods, found singly or united in S or spiral forms)	Vibrio comma (21 species) (also 33 inadequately described)
			II. Cellvibrio (long, curved, round ended rods; oxidize cellulose)	Cellvibrio ochraceus (4 species)

Family	Genus	Type species
	III. *Cellfalcicula* (short, curved rods with pointed ends; oxidize cellulose)	*Cellfalcicula viridans* (3 species)
II. Pseudomonadeae (rod shaped)	IV. *Spirillum* (long, curved spirals)	*Spirillum undula* (4 species) (also 20 inadequately described)
	V. *Pseudomonas* (chromogens, found in water and soil; bluish or yellowish-green pigment diffuses through media)	*Pseudomonas aeruginosa* (31 species) (also 6 inadequately described)
	VI. *Phytomonas* (chromogenic plant pathogens; yellow, white, green or blue pigment)	*Phytomonas compestris* (137 species) (also 33 inadequately described)
	VII. *Protaminobacter* (attack protamines; found in water and soil)	*Protaminobacter alboflavum* (5 species)
	VIII. *Mycoplana* (soil bacteria, capable of utilizing phenol and other aromatic compounds)	*Mycoplana dimorpha* (2 species)
IV. Acetobacteriaceae	I. *Acetobacter* (rods, showing branching; oxidize alcohol to acetic acid)	*Acetobacter aceti* (15 species) (also 7 species to be classified)
V. Azotobacteriaceae	I. *Azotobacter* (large, oval-shaped rods; utilize free N)	*Azotobacter chroococcum* (2 species)
VI. Micrococcaceae (spherical or almost so; generally Gram-positive; endospores absent)	I. *Micrococcus* (occur in irregular packets or groups, never in chains; pigment when present is yellow, orange or red)	*Micrococcus luteus* (46 species)
	II. *Staphylococcus* (usually parasitic and Gram-positive; singly, pairs or irregular groups)	*Staphylococcus aureus* (9 species)
	III. *Gaffkya* (appear as tetrads in animal body and in special media)	*Gaffkya tetragena* (4 species)

SCHIZOMYCETES (Continued)

Order	Family	Tribe	Genus	Type species (number of species listed)
I. Eubacteriales—(Continued)	VI. Micrococcaceae—(Continued)		IV. Sarcina (regular packets; pigment usually yellow or orange)	Sarcina ventriculi (14 species listed)
	VII. Neisseriaceae (strict parasites; require special media for growth; Gram-negative)		I. Neisseria (coffee-bean-shaped diplococci)	Neisseria gonorrhoeae (11 species)
			II. Veillonella (occurring in masses; anaerobic)	Veillonella parvula (2 species)
	VIII. Parvobacteriaceae (Gram-negative rods; parasitic on warm-blooded animals; do not liquefy gelatin)	I. Pasteurelleae (show bipolar staining)	I. Pasteurella (milk not coagulated)	Pasteurella avicida (8 species) (also 20 species inadequately described)
			II. Malleomyces (milk coagulated slowly)	Malleomyces mallei (2 species)
		II. Brucelleae (do not ferment carbohydrates)	III. Brucella	Brucella melitensis (4 species)
		III. Hemophileae (parasitic; require special factors contained in whole blood or plant tissues for growth)	IV. Hemophilus (nonmotile)	Hemophilus influenzae (8 species) (also 17 species to be classified)
			V. Noguchia (motile; encapsulated)	Noguchia granulosis (3 species)
			VI. Dialister (non-motile anaerobes)	Dialister pneumosintes (2 species)
	IX. Lactobacteriaceae (Gram-positive cocci or rods; ferment carbohydrates; usually nonmotile, do not liquefy gelatin and require natural fluid media for growth)	I. Streptococceae (cocci in pairs or short or long chains, never packets)	I. Diplococcus (lanceolate, encapsulated diplococcus, parasitic, bile soluble)	Diplococcus pneumoniae (7 species)
			II. Streptococcus (short or long chains; not soluble in bile)	Streptococcus pyogenes (21 species) (also 9 species to be classified)
			III. Leuconostoc (saprophytes; chains of cocci to short rods)	Leuconostoc mesenteroides (3 species)

Tribe / Family	Genus	Subgenera	Species
II. Lactobacilleae	IV. Lactobacillus (long, slender, nonmotile rods; Gram-positive; ferment carbohydrates)	SUBGENERA *Theobacterium* *Streptobacterium* *Betabacterium*	*Lactobacillus caucasicus* (15 species) (also 7 species to be classified)
	V. Propionibacterium (catalase-positive; ferment carbohydrates, producing acetic, lactic and propionic acids)		*Propionibacterium freuden-reichii* (11 species)
X. Enterobacteriaceae (Gram-negative rods; grow well on artificial media; attack carbohydrates; do not form spores)			
I. Eschericheae (do not liquefy gelatin; ferment dextrose and lactose)	I. Escherichia (Voges-Proskauer test negative; methyl red test positive)		*Escherichia coli* (2 species) (also 10 species inadequately described)
	II. Aerobacter (Voges-Proskauer positive; methyl red test negative; citric acid used as source of carbon)		*Aerobacter aerogenes* (2 species)
	III. Klebsiella (usually encapsulated; V.-P., M.-R. and citric acid usually as under *Aerobacter*)		*Klebsiella pneumoniae* (6 species) (also 3 species inadequately described)
II. Erwineae (plant parasites; attack dextrose and lactose; attack pectin)	IV. Erwinia (motile plant pathogens)		*Erwinia amylovora* (13 species) (also 21 species inadequately described)
III. Serrateae (produce red pigment; liquefy gelatin; ferment lactose and dextrose)	V. Serratia (small aerobic rods)		*Serratia marcescens* (6 species)
IV. Proteae (liquefy gelatin; ferment dextrose but not lactose)	VI. Proteus		*Proteus vulgaris* (8 species) (also 6 species inadequately described)
V. Salmonelleae (do not liquefy gelatin; attack dextrose and only infrequently lactose)	VII. Salmonella (produce acid and usually gas in dextrose)		*Salmonella choleraesuis* (37 species) (also 28 species inadequately described)

SCHIZOMYCETES (*Continued*)

Order		Family	Tribe	Genus	Type species (number of species listed)
I. Eubacteriales— (*Continued*)		X. Enterobacteriaceae— (*Continued*)	V. Salmonelleae— (*Continued*)	VIII. *Eberthella* (produce acid but no gas in dextrose)	*Eberthella typhosa* (14 species)
				IX. *Shigella* (nonmotile)	*Shigella dysenteriae* (15 species) (also 11 species inadequately described)
		XI. Bacteriaceae (nonspore-forming rods)		I. *Listerella* (Gram-positive; motile; acid from sugars)	*Listerella monocytogenes* (1 species)
				II. *Microbacterium* (Gram-positive; nonmotile; acid from sugars)	*Microbacterium lacticum* (3 species)
				III. *Kurthia* (Gram-positive; motile; no acid from sugars)	*Kurthia zopfii* (2 species)
				IV. *Cellulomonas* (Gram-negative cellulose digesters)	*Cellulomonas biazotea* (26 species)
				V. *Achromobacter* (nonchromogenic)	*Achromobacter liquefaciens* (42 species)
				VI. *Flavobacterium* (yellow chromogens)	*Flavobacterium aquatile* (58 species)
				VII. *Actinobacillus* (nonmotile)	*Actinobacillus lignieresi* (3 species)
				VIII. *Bacteroides* (anaerobes)	*Bacteroides fragilis* (23 species) (also 52 inadequately or to be classified)
				IX. *Fusobacterium* (anaerobic; spindle shaped)	*Fusobacterium plauti-vincenti* (4 species) (also 3 species inadequately described)
				X. *Bacterium*	*Bacterium triloculare* (16 species) (also 230 species inadequately described or to be classified)

II. Actinomycetales (cells usually elongated, frequently filamentous; Gram-positive; nonmotile; aerobic; grow slowly on culture media)	XII. Bacillaceae (spore formers; usually Gram-positive; decompose protein actively)	I. *Bacillus* (aerobic saprophytes)	*Bacillus subtilis* (146 species) (also 28 species inadeq. described)	
		II. *Clostridium* (anaerobes, frequently parasitic)	*Clostridium butyricum* (51 species) (also 101 species inadeq. described)	
	I. Mycobacteriaceae (rods or filaments with only slight branching)	I. *Corynebacterium* (rods, frequently club shaped; non-acid-fast)	*Corynebacterium diphtheriae* (21 species) (also 41 species inadequately described)	
		II. *Mycobacterium*	*Mycobacterium tuberculosis* (13 species)	
	II. Actinomycetaceae (filamentous forms, branched, and may form mycelia; conidia may be present)	I. *Leptotrichia* (unbranched, frequently clubbed rods or filaments; mouth parasites)	*Leptotrichia buccalis* (2 species)	
		II. *Erysipelothrix* (thickened filaments, occasionally branched; skin parasites of hog)	*Erysipelothrix rhusiopathiae* (3 species)	
		III. *Proactinomyces* (soil forms)	*Proactinomyces agrestis* (9 species) (also 6 species inadequately described)	
		IV. *Actinomyces* (branched filaments, usually forming mycelia)	*Actinomyces bovis* (62 species) (also 108 species inadequately described)	

III. Chlamydobacteriales. This order contains one family, which is subdivided into 4 genera (*sphaerotilus, clonothrix, leptothrix* and *crenothrix*) and 13 species. The individual species are filamentous bacteria, alga-like, and are generally found in swamps, stagnant water or water containing iron. Many of them possess sheaths which are frequently impregnated with iron. (See under Useful Bacteria.) They are rarely encountered by the bacteriologist.

IV. Caulobacteriales. This order contains four families, which are subdivided into 5 genera and 9 species. The various species are stalked bacteria, typically aquatic in habitat, and multiplication of the cells is usually by transverse binary fission.

V. Thiobacteriales. This order contains three families, which are subdivided into 2 subfamilies, 5 tribes, 32 genera and 62 species. Some are filamentous and others are not. The cells are plantlike and not protozoan-like. The several species vary in size and shape. Granules of free sulfur or a red pigment known as bacteriopurpurin or both are present in the cell contents of these species. These organisms are usually found in water (mainly sea water), swamps, ocean beds, thermal springs and in sulfur water. (See under Useful Bacteria.)

SCHIZOMYCETES (*Continued*)

Order	Family	Tribe	Genus	Type species (number of species listed)
VI. Myxobacteriales. Motile rodlike organisms reproducing by fission. After a peculiar vegetative period they come together and produce more or less encysted masses of spores. There are four families which are divided into 11 genera. In the latter are to be found 45 species, which are mainly found in manure or on dung of various animals. They are of little interest to the bacteriologist.				
VII. Spirochaetales (slender, flexous spirals, protozoon-like in many ways.	Spirochaetaceae (cells altered but not disintegrated by 10 per cent bile salts)		I. *Spirochaeta* (saprophytes, possessing a flexible undulating body, commonly found in foul water and sewage)	*S. plicatilis* (5 species)
			II. *Saprospira* (saprophytes of no interest to the bacteriologist; found in oysters)	*S. grandis* (3 species)
			III. *Cristispira* (undulating body possessing a crest or ridge, known as a crista; parasitic in shell-fish)	*C. balbianii* (8 species)
			IV. *Borrelia* (long, flexible spiral filaments varying in the number of turns; parasitic in warm-blooded animals and man)	*B. gallinarum* (15 species)
			V. *Treponema* (usually parasitic)	*T. pallidum* (8 species)
			VI. *Leptospira* (sharply twisted cylinders with tapering ends, one extremity frequently curved into a "hook"; usually parasitic)	*L. icterohaemorrhagiae* (4 species)

See *Bergey's Manual of Determinative Bacteriology*, by a large group of well-known bacteriologists, under the leadership (until his death) of Prof. David H. Bergey, 5th ed., 1939. Baltimore, The Williams & Wilkins Company. See also *Abridged Fifth Edition, Bergey's Manual of Determinative Bacteriology*, 1939. Geneva, N. Y., Biotech Publications.

The Bergey system (fifth edition, 1939) begins by placing all forms of bacteria under the general designation of class "Schizomycetes." Seven orders (ending in "ales") are recognized under this class:

1. *Simple and Undifferentiated Forms.*—These are the true bacteria.
   Order I: Eubacteriales. This is the largest order.
2. *Specialized or Differentiated Forms.*
   a. Moldlike.
      Order II: Actinomycetales.
      Order I and Order II contain most of the organisms encountered in bacteriology.
   aa. Alga-like. Filamentous, aquatic forms without true branching.
      b. Sheathed; sheath usually contains iron.
         Order III: Chlamydobacteriales.
      bb. Not sheathed.
         c. Stalked.
            Order IV: Caulobacteriales.
         cc. Not stalked; sulfur bacteria.
            Order V: Thiobacteriales.
   aaa. Slime moldlike organisms.
      Order VI: Myxobacteriales.
   aaaa. Protozoan-like.
      Order VII: Spirochaetales.

Each order is next divided into one or more "families" (ending in "aceae"). In one order (the thiobacteriales) one of the families is divided into "subfamilies." The name of the subfamily is the same as the name of the genus or one of the genera in the group and ends in "oideae." The subfamilies and families (which are not divided into subfamilies) are then divided into "tribes." The name of the tribe is the same as the name of the genus or one of the genera in the group and ends in "eae." The tribes are then divided into genera (although the families spirillaceae and bacillaceae of the first order [eubacteriales], all families in Order II, III, VI and VII are divided directly into genera without intervening subfamilies or tribes). The various genera are then divided into species. To summarize and mention any organism, we will find that the latter due to several characteristics is first placed in the class "schizomycetes"; then under a particular order; next in a family under this order; in some instances, it is placed in a subfamily and tribe or tribe only under the family; next in a genus (or it may be placed directly in a particular genus under the family because the latter is not divided into subfamilies or tribes); and finally the organism is classified as a species of the genus.

The various species of the many genera or even a given genus are differentiated, generally due to variances in morphology; the absence or presence of chromogenesis; the kind of pigment produced; the oxygen requirements for growth; cultural characteristics (especially behavior in sugar media, gelatin liquefaction, effects when grown in milk, hemolysis of blood or other coloration when grown on blood agar, indol production, reduction of nitrates to nitrites and other biochemical reactions, whether ordinary or special media are needed, solubility in bile [pneumococcus or streptococcus]): staining characteristics; presence of capsules, spores, flagella, polar-staining bodies, etc.; whether parasitic in man or lower animals; whether saprophytic; anti-body production (serological or immunological reactions) when injected into animals, and the specific characteristics of these antibodies (agglutinins, precipitins, bacterioly-sins [amboceptor and complement], etc.). For a critique of Bergey's system and other suggested outline of bacterial classification, see Stainer and Van Niel (*J. Bact.*, 1941, **42**, 437).

Races or Strains.—Bacteria of the *same species* may at different occasions show characteristics, which are not precisely similar to those which are ordinarily observed by the parent form. These variations of the individual species are known as *races* or *strains*. The variations in the races or strains of an individual species may be merely one of difference in virulency or pathogenicity, difference in resistance, or it may be the loss of some property possessed at a previous occasion and usually present in most in-dividuals of the same species. Powers of producing pigment, of liquefying gelatin, of fermenting a specific sugar, etc., are some of the definite qualities, which may vary in different individuals of the same species. These powers, when lost, may be regained at times if the proper treatment is applied. Adaptation to different temperatures and the selection or preference of certain strains of an individual species for particular body tissues are examples of variancy or perhaps examples of specialization. The latter characteristic has been observed among several of the strains of streptococci.

BACTERIAL VARIABILITY

The term *variation* may be used in a general sense to describe all changes displayed by bacteria, those that are transient or temporary and those which are more lasting or stable (hereditary). We must always remember that bacteria are living organisms and therefore are flexible and changeable to some degree during life. These variations include changes in morphology and physiology, alteration in biochemical properties, antigenic differences, modifications in pathogenicity, differences in cultural charac-teristics, etc. Variation may arise from intra- or extracellular causes. Differences in osmotic pressure, pH, surface tension and temperature, the absence of some essential nutritive constituent or the presence of different added chemicals or some metabolic substance or bacteriophage and other agents may be the cause for the variation pro-duced. It is a common characteristic among bacteria displaying variation to find as mentioned a strain of the same species losing its power to produce pigment or to fer-ment sugars or to liquefy gelatin or there is a disappearance of the power of lo-comotion and even the loss of virulence. These differences may be very slight and there is no reason for laying too much stress on their significance as of great classifica-tory value. On the other hand, differences in virulency, and in some instances other characteristics, as in the case of inagglutinable strains of dysentery bacilli, may give rise to serious practical difficulties. This so-called "fluctuation" type of variation, once lost, may under certain conditions be regained. It is known that chromogenic power present at 20° C. may in some instances disappear at 37° C. Pigmentation, once lost, can be reacquired in many cases if transplants are made on potato or starch media. Virulency of many organisms can be attenuated by exposure to unfavorable environmental conditions. This may be regained by attenuated pathogenic races or enhanced by weakly pathogenic species by passage through suitable animal hosts. Adaptation by colonies of varieties of bacteria and which is interpreted as mutation by some workers is known. Bacteria may become adapted to grow under the most adverse conditions, resulting frequently in an alteration of various properties of the original organism. In the latter instances changes take place by gradual progressive steps rather than suddenly, and for the most part they are closely and directly related to environmental conditions. In general most of these variations are those grouped by workers as variations of the ordinary "fluctuating" types. This merely serves as a convenient grouping.

The variations, which at present are of greatest interest are the "dissociative variation," recognized by colony form or type and certain allied attributes. It has been demonstrated that *rough* (R) and *smooth* (S) colonies can develop in a number of bacterial groups from an individual apparently pure culture and regarded as the "normal." Transplants from the R and S colony forms or phases, respectively, breed true under ordinary conditions, but inter-transformations occur. The transformation from smooth (S) to rough (R) is usually accomplished with greater ease than R to S transition, the latter requiring persistency of effort. In addition to these extreme colony types, varying intermediate types (SR and RS) are obtainable. Another culture phase is the *mucoid* (M) type in which cells of the smooth phase are not definitely capsulated. Some species develop a *gonidial* (G) phase, in which the colonies are small, and appear to be made up of small cells of varying morphology. Reversion of the G type to the parent form can take place, but usually very gradually. The G forms appear to be associated with the filterable stages of bacteria. The *diphtheroidal* (D) phase is present in few species. The S, R and the G phases are at present of greatest biological significance.

Rough and smooth types differ in colony formation and they also may be associated with other important differences and characteristics affecting the physiological and biochemical properties. Weil and Felix also presented the O type of colony to distinguish them from the ordinary spreading H type of colony. (H, Hauch, film; O, Ohne Hauch, without film). The H type is motile and the O type is nonmotile. Serologically they noted differences between these two types. In certain lines of practical bacteriological work and immunological procedure it may become necessary to know whether one is working with the R or S type or with the H or O type. See page 102 for the important differences between the three phases of greatest interest at present.

The universality of the phenomenon of bacterial dissociation has been demonstrated beyond question. Hadley's magnificent memoranda on this subject are, indeed, convincing. Bacteria of very widely separated groups, themselves in pure cultures and at times even cultivated from a single cell, may be found to break up into two or more different types possessing characteristics that are in themselves definite and which clearly differentiate them from each other. These characteristics may manifest themselves in the types of colonies as previously mentioned, or in cell morphology, pigmentation and even capsule formation, in virulency or in biochemical differences. Transformations from one phase to the other may occur in Nature, in the body, in laboratory experiments and they may be hastened by modifying the environment of the growing organisms. The variants thus produced may breed true for generations, yet on the other hand, as is observed in many instances, they tend in whole on in part to revert to the parent type or even to change from one type to another under suitable environmental stimuli. This process is not one of random variation or of mutation in the ordinary biological sense. A true mutation is not reversible (that is, a coccus becoming a bacillus and the latter reverting back to the coccus stage); on the other hand, this phenomenon of dissociation or the production of variants is reversible. The dissociation of a score or more pure bacterial strains into two or more cultural or morphological variants is now confirmed. Much of our present knowledge concerning dissociative variation is based on *in vitro* observations. The problem of dissociative variation *in vivo*, especially from the practical viewpoint of chemoserotherapy is of

DIFFERENCES BETWEEN IMPORTANT PHASES OF BACTERIAL DISSOCIATIVE VARIATION

S Type	R Type	G Type
Normal colony for most bacterial species	Normal only for few and abnormal for most species	Found only infrequently
Colonies are small, round, translucent with smooth, shiny surface and even margin	Colonies are large, flattened, opaque, with slightly raised center, coarsely granular surface and irregular thin edged margin	Colonies are minute, round, translucent, with a smooth shiny surface and even margin
Individual organisms are of normal shape and size	Individual organisms are of variable size and shape and filamentous, branching or abnormal forms may be present	Individual organisms are very small and coccoid or rod-shaped
Motile bacteria show flagella	Flagella are absent	Flagella are absent
Encapulated bacteria reveal the presence of the capsule	Capsule is absent	Capsule is absent
Display Gram-positive or Gram-negative characteristics	Display Gram-positive or Gram-negative characteristics	Are Gram-positive
Broth cultures are uniformly turbid	Sedimental granular deposit in broth cultures, supernatant fluid clear, surface film may be present	Broth cultures homogenous
Agar growth is soft	Agar growth is tenacious and friable	No growth visible macroscopically on agar
Suspensions in isotonic salt solution are stable and remain clouded	Suspensions in isotonic salt solution clump spontaneously and settle out	
Biochemically active	Biochemical activity reduced	Biochemically inert or activity reduced
Pathogenic species are virulent	Virulence reduced or absent	Virulence reduced
Effective antigen	Poor antigen	
Somatic and flagellar or type-specific antigens are present; flocculent agglutination	Only somatic antigens present, type-specificity is lost; granular agglutination	
Resistant to phagocytosis	Susceptible to phagocytosis	
Found in acute cases of disease	Found in chronic cases of disease	
Readily changed to R type	Transition to S type only after persistency of effort	Very slow gradual change to S type

importance. Only further investigative studies will reveal the significance of dissociative variation *in vivo*.

Within the past two decades, other evidence has been presented which tends to change the previously held concept of the simplicity of the bacterial life-cycle. It has been shown that in few instances some bacteria pass through a spore stage as part of their life-cycle. The formation of gonidial bodies as part of a definite reproductive stage in the life of the colon-typhoid group of organisms and of other bacteria has been described by different workers. On the basis of our present knowledge, it is impossible to state definitely that gonidia are found in some species of true bacteria. Other workers even suggest a whole life-cycle involving complexities, as are observed in some of the higher fungi. Conclusive evidence, however, has not been presented to prove that sexual reproduction occurs in bacteria. More recently, bacteria of widely separated and different groups have been found capable under certain conditions of passing through a *filterable stage*, the latter being able to reproduce later the original type cell from which it was derived. This type of variation is differentiated from the dissociative type of variation and is called by some cyclogenic variation, implying a relationship with the life-cycle. Accordingly such terms as *life-cycles*, *hibernating phases*, *free gonidial units*, *primordial revisions* and *conjugations* are appearing in bacteriological literature.

Chapter VIII

COMMONLY OBSERVED PATHOGENIC AND NONPATHOGENIC BACTERIA

COCCI

THE FAMILY *micrococcaceae* consists of cocci found in the following genera: *micrococcus* (46 species), *staphylococcus* (9 species), *gaffkya* (4 species) and *sarcina* (14 species).

STAPHYLOCOCCI

Staphylococcus Aureus (*Orange or Golden Staphylococcus; Staphylococcus or Micrococcus Pyogenes Aureus*).—Cocci occurring in irregular masses or groups resembling clusters of grapes are known as staphylococci (singular, staphylococcus). They are important members of the pyogenic, suppurative or pus-producing cocci. Found widely distributed in Nature, they are commonly found on the skin and mucous membranes of man and all animals. They are accordingly frequent contaminants of cultures, including blood cultures. Pathogenic strains are found in connection with various inflammatory and suppurative processes and septicemia. Several varieties of staphylococci have been differentiated primarily because of differences in pigment production. Classification based on such criteria as pathogenicity, hemolysin production, specificity in agglutinin and other antibody production and biochemical reactions has proved less satisfactory.

Staphylococcus aureus producing a golden-yellow pigment is the type most frequently observed, and is one of the most commonly found parasitic organisms. It generally occurs as spheres, singly, in pairs and usually in irregular groups or grapelike clusters, varying in size from 0.7 to 1 μ; like all cocci which will be mentioned in this chapter, this organism is nonmotile and does not produce endospores. *Staphylococcus aureus* is not encapsulated, is Gram-positive, aerobic and facultative anaerobic, and will grow on all common laboratory media, preferably slightly alkaline, and at 8° to 43° C., best at 28° to 38° C. This species can be grown in synthetic media with an ammonium salt as the sole source of nitrogen. Nicotinic acid, thiamine and an organic source of sulfur are required, and uracil must be supplied for anaerobic growth. The presence of biotin yields more luxuriant growth (*Bact. Revs.*, 1938, **2**, 106). Growth on gelatin medium is characteristic and with most strains is soon followed by liquefaction. Milk is usually coagulated. Acid, but no gas, is produced in media containing carbohydrates. Chapman (*J. Bact.*, 1942, **43**, 105) recommends the use of a brom thymol blue lactose agar and a phenol red mannitol agar for the isolation of probable pathogenic staphylococci. Of all non-spore-forming bacteria frequently encountered, staphylococci are more resistant to freezing, heat, sunlight, desiccation and bactericidal agents. The thermal death point is not constant. Though many strains are killed at 60° C. for ten minutes, some require thirty minutes' exposure, and others will succumb only after an exposure to 80° C. for thirty minutes. Evidence seems to point to the fact that man is more susceptible to staphylococcic infections than the lower animals. Though most frequently found in circumscribed processes, such as boils or furuncles, acne pustules, carbuncles, etc., it may, however, cause acute focal inflammations which may be severe or mild, depending upon the tissues involved and the virulency of the organisms. Infections of the bone tissue, giving rise to osteomyelitis or periostitis, is most frequently caused by this organism. Staphylococci may cause abscesses or pus in almost any part of the body, and even septicemia. Sinus, ear and mastoid affections, lymph gland swellings, otitis media, pleurisy, pneumonia, bronchopneumonia, endocarditis, meningitis, cystitis, pyelitis, nonspecific urethritis and vaginitis, skin affections and other maladies may be caused by this organism. Staphylococci are frequently associated as secondary invaders in many infections. A lowering of resistance and the presence of a cachectic condition or a constitutional disease, as diabetes mellitus, appear to render individuals especially susceptible to infection by the staphylococcus. Certain strains of *Staphylococcus aureus* have been found to produce a substance which hemolyzes red blood cells (disintegration of the red blood cells causing the liberation of the hemoglobin, which goes into solution). This substance is known as a hemolysin and specifically as *staphylolysin*, and the organisms producing this are known as hemolytic staphylococci. In like manner some strains of *Staphylococcus aureus* produce *leukocidin*, which is capable of destroying leukocytes or white blood cells. Staphylolysin and leukocidin are in all probability true soluble toxins. The filtrates of cultures of staphylococci have been found to display other effects, distinct from that producing hemolysis or destroying leukocytes. These may be: a necrotic action upon intradermal injection into animals (caused by a *necrotizing* or *dermonecrotic toxin*); almost immediate death upon injection intravenously into rabbits (*lethal toxin*); and a gastro-enterotoxic action, effective only upon ingestion, and of considerable significance in food intoxications and poisonings (*gastro-enteric toxin*). *Staphylocoagulase*, a plasma coagulating agent, is also elaborated. Whether these effects are due to separate distinct toxins or are manifestations of the activity of only one toxic substance is uncertain. In general, toxin production is a property of pathogenic staphylococci, especially strains of the *aureus* species. *Albus* strains produce toxin only infrequently, while *citreus* strains never produce the latter. The ability of staphylococci to coagulate citrated plasma and display other previously mentioned characteristics can be demonstrated by appropriate techniques.

Attempts have been made to differentiate staphylococci by serologic reactions and to establish some relationship between pathogenicity and the groups thus established. A satisfactory distinction by means of agglutination tests appears impossible at present and only a broad division appears possible on the basis of precipitin reactions. Considerable discussion has arisen in an attempt to detect pathogenic staphylococci in other *in vitro* tests. From the data presented in the large number of researches, the following conclusions may be drawn. Coagulase-positive strains of staphylococci are pathogenic, but a negative coagulase test does not exclude pathogenicity. Pigment production, hemolysis and positive mannitol fermentation are strong evidence of pathogenicity, but nonpigment formers may also be pathogenic, and nonpathogenic strains may ferment mannitol and even produce at times hemolysis. Davey and associates (*Can. J. Pub. Health*, 1942, **33**, 82) detail findings in the fourth large outbreak of staphylococcic food poisoning in Hamilton, Canada, and Tixton and Smiley (*U. S. Naval Med. Bull.*, 1943, **41,** 565) report a ham-borne staphylococcal food poisoning affecting 225 persons. See also Blair ("Pathogenic Staphylococci," *Bact. Rev.*, 1939, **3,** 97).

Bacterins, toxoids and bacteriophage are used and have proved of some value in the treatment of infections caused by staphylococci. The use of staphylococcic antiserum and of a staphylococcic antitoxin, both marketable products, is not widespread, as they possess only limited value. The sulfonamide compounds, especially sulfathiazole, and penicillin appear to be very effective in the treatment of many of the staphylococcic infections.

Staphylococcus Albus (*White Staphylococcus; Staphylococcus Pyogenes Albus*).— *Staphylococcus albus* is similar to *Staphylococcus aureus* in its morphological, staining, cultural and biological characteristics and in its resistance. It produces a white pigment, is found at least one-half as frequently as the *Staphylococcus aureus*, is less virulent than the latter and seldom produces grave infections.

Staphylococcus Citreus (*Lemon Staphylococcus; Staphylococcus Pyogenes Citreus*).—*Staphylococcus citreus* is distinguished from the other types only by the formation of a lemon-yellow pigment. It is not found as frequently nor is it as virulent as *Staphylococcus aureus* or *Staphylococcus albus.*

Staphylococcus Epidermidis (*Staphylococcus Epidermidis Albus; Staphylococcus of Stitch Abscess*).—*Staphylococcus epidermidis* is said to be a variety of *Staphylococcus albus,* differing from it in that it is less virulent, liquefies gelatin more slowly and does not coagulate milk as quickly, if at all. It may give rise to suppuration along the drainage tube and is regarded as the common cause of "stitch abscess."

Organisms Resembling Staphylococci.—There are many organisms resembling staphylococci in appearance and in other characteristics. These are mainly saprophytes grouped under the genus *micrococcus.* The latter includes 46 species, which appear in plates or irregular masses (never in long chains or packets). They are facultative parasites or saprophytes; some do not form pigment but others produce yellow and infrequently orange or red pigment; gelatin is liquefied but not rapidly; and indol is usually not produced. A few species in this genus are anaerobes. Some are Gram-variable and few are known to possess flagella. They are nonpathogenic and are generally found in air, water, milk, dust, manure and soil, so that they are encountered as contaminants.

TETRADS

Gaffkya Tetragena (*Micrococcus Tetragenus*).—*Gaffkya tetragena* appears as tetrads or groups of cocci, about 0.6 to 1 μ in diameter, arranged in fours and surrounded by a broad pseudocapsule, when found in body fluids. It is an aerobe, Gram-positive, and grows on ordinary laboratory media slowly. In cultures the organism when examined may show the absence of the capsular-like substance, and the tabular arrangement may not be characteristic. Gelatin is not liquefied. Indol is not produced; nitrates are not reduced to nitrites; hydrogen sulfide is not formed; milk is only slightly acidified; acid is produced only in dextrose and lactose; starch is not hydrolyzed; and ammonium salts are not utilized for the nitrogen required. *G. tetragena* is pathogenic for mice and guinea pigs; rabbits are less susceptible. This organism has been found repeatedly in the mucous membranes of the respiratory tract, in the saliva of healthy individuals and in the sputum of tubercular patients. It is probably nonpathogenic, or at most possesses a low-grade virulency, but as a secondary invader, it may on occasions cause purulent inflammations. It is claimed by some workers that as secondary invaders in tuberculosis and purulent infections greater and more extensive tissue destruction appears than when this organism is not present. Recently, Tobin (*J. A. M. A.*, 1943, **121,** 41) reported a case of bronchopneumonia complicated by bacteremia and urologic infection due to *M. tetragenus*. He cites three other cases in the literature in which this organism was found as the primary cause of pneumonia.

Gaffkya anaerobia, an obligate anaerobe, has been isolated from the female genital tract and is widely distributed in the natural cavities of man and animals. It is nonpathogenic for man and laboratory animals.

Sarcina Forms

Sarcina Aurantiaca; Sarcina Flava; Sarcina Lutea; Sarcina Lactea; Sarcina Subflava; Sarcina Ventriculi; Sarcinae ureae; Sarcinae Citrea.—Sarcina forms are Gram-positive aerobic spheres, from 0.8 to 2.5 μ in diameter, and occurring in regular cuboidal packets. They grow on all ordinary media, usually with the formation of yellow or orange pigment. The morphology is best demonstrated from liquid media. Spores and capsules are absent. The commonly found species are nonmotile and aerobic. Motile forms and anaerobic species are present among the 14 species classified in the genus *Sarcina*. They are saprophytes and nonpathogenic. Different species have been isolated from the air, water, soil, sewage, dust, occasionally fresh milk, in intestinal and stomach contents, urine, skin and conjunctiva of man and animals. Sarcina forms may therefore be found frequently as contaminants of media, etc.

STREPTOCOCCI

The tribe *streptococceae* contains 3 genera: *streptococcus*, consisting of 21 species of short or long chained cocci; *diplococcus*, consisting of 7 species of lanceolate, encapsulated cocci occurring usually in pairs; and *leuconostoc*, consisting of 3 species of saprophytes, which form chains of cocci to short rods and are found in acid fruit and vegetable juices.

All cocci, commonly found, which tend to arrange themselves in chains are usually described as streptococci. These chains may be short or long, or the cocci may appear occasionally in pairs but never in packets. The individual cocci vary from 0.5 to 1 μ in diameter; and they are nonmotile, nonspore-bearing, aerobic and facultative anaerobic, usually Gram-positive and are insoluble in bile. Many carbohydrates are fermented only with acid formation, but inulin is rarely attacked. They generally fail to liquefy gelatin or reduce nitrates. Indol is not produced. Streptococci are rather widely distributed in Nature. The pathogenic streptococci outweigh in importance all other disease-producing bacteria. But it must be borne in mind that the finding of a streptococcus does not necessarily mean that the latter is pathogenic, as there are many saprophytic species that are nonpathogenic. Also there are species which are anaerobic, and some species which are Gram-negative. From the practical standpoint, it is especially necessary to differentiate pathogenic forms from nonpathogenic forms, and to even ascertain the degree of virulency and other characteristics between the various varieties pathogenic for humans. The problem of differentiating and classifying streptococci has been not only difficult, but one of the most perplexing problems. A classification based solely on morphology, as short- and long-chained streptococci, *Streptococcus brevis* or *Streptococcus longus*, was used but is not tenable nor satisfactory. At first, it was thought by some workers, and recently evidence has accumulated to show at least in some instances this is so, that the various pathogenic streptococci are specific for the particular lesion or disease in which they were found, so that we hear of the *Streptococcus erysipelatis*, *Streptococcus scarlatinae*, *Streptococcus mastitidis*, etc. When it was shown that the streptococcus from some lesion might produce different lesions or diseases, another method of classification was attempted. Here a broad grouping of the pathogenic forms was made, taking into consideration morphology and behavior in plates containing blood-agar culture media. Three types were designated: (1) *Streptococcus pyogenes*, which shows hemolysis on blood-agar plates; (2) *Streptococcus viridans* or *mitior*, which produces a green halo about the colonies on blood agar; (3) *Streptococcus mucosus* which produces a mucoid growth and a dark green zone. The latter is now placed with the pneumococci under the common name *Pneumococcus mucosus*.

Another broad but more commonly used classification based on observations when grown on blood agar is that of Smith and Brown. They recognize three types: (*a*) green-producing streptococci (*α*-hemolytic or *Streptococcus viridans*), which form colonies surrounded by a greenish discolored zone, at one time said to be due to the production of methemoglobin and probably hydrogen peroxide, but now regarded as a derivative of hemoglobin formed by reduction; (*b*) hemolytic streptococci (beta, *β*-hemolytic, type), which produce a definite, clear-cut zone of hemolysis around the colonies on blood agar; (*c*) nonhemolytic or indifferent streptococci (gamma type or *Streptococcus anhemolyticus*), which do not produce hemolysis or a green discoloration of the blood agar. These groups are broad and heterogenous and therefore are not applied as a name to a single species, but are made up rather of different species. Attempts to classify streptococci as to their action in decomposing various carbohydrates have been unsuccessful when applied to streptococci as a whole. On the other hand, fermentation tests (acid production) play a useful role in the differentiation of closely related species if the streptococci are first subdivided by some other procedure or methods either based on serological observations or their behavior on blood-agar medium. With this in mind, observations of acid production may be noted in media containing lactose, sucrose, raffinose, inulin, mannitol, maltose, arabinose, trehalose, sorbitol, salicin, esculin and glycerin, and hydrolysis of starch and of sodium hippurate are also of value as aids in the differentiation of specific species. Classification of various strains, and especially of hemolytic streptococci, according to specific serological reactions (due to the production of specific antibodies by the different species of streptococci) are advocated. Distinct immunological groups have thus been presented.

On the basis of agglutination tests, Griffith (*J. Hyg.*, 1935, **35**, 23) has divided the pathogenic streptococci into 27 different types. Lancefield (*J. Exp. Med.*, 1933, **57**, 571) used the precipitin test and on this basis described five groups among the hemolytic streptococci. Group A, pathogenic for man, and conveniently designated as *Streptococcus pyogenes;* Group B, derived for the most part from cases of mastitis and known as *Streptococcus mastitidis* or *Streptococcus agalactiae;* Group C, found in various pathologic processes of lower animals and only occasionally in man; Group D, isolated from cheese; and Group E, found in milk. To these five original groups, others have been added recently: Group F, "minute hemolytic streptococci," occurring as a harmless human parasite and may probably be the cause of human disease; Group G, found widely distributed as secondary invaders among lower animals and humans and are regarded as of little importance as pathogenic organisms; Group H, isolated from human feces and discharges of the nose and throat, but rarely causing serious human infections; and Group K, suggested only provisionally as some doubt whether these species are truly hemolytic. The classification of hemolytic streptococci by the Lancefield method is generally accepted today by most workers especially in the practical consideration of epidemiological problems.

In the Bergey classification, the streptococci are grouped on the basis of their action on blood agar; serological reactions; bile solubility; and only secondarily on the basis of sugar or carbohydrate fermentation. A diagnosis in practice is made mainly according to the source of material and action on blood-agar medium. The finding of deep colonies with a wide zone of hemolysis, which upon microscopical examination reveal the presence of Gram-positive cocci in chains of varying length (chains best seen in spreads of liquid subcultures), are interpreted as positive findings (presumptive test) of beta hemolytic streptococci. Observations of acid formation in lactose, mannitol and salicin media and in other carbohydrates are made only occasionally, but various cultural characteristics and serological observations can be determined to confirm, when desired, the specific identity of the streptococcus thus isolated (confirmatory test).

Under the heading *Streptococcus pyogenes*, the author is placing all streptococci which cause suppurative lesions or severe human infections and produce hemolysis when grown on blood-agar media. Flagella and spores are not observed. Growth is obtained when grown at body temperature. They do not grow at 10° C. and but infrequently at 45° C. Growth is not obtained in media containing 6.5 per cent NaCl, or 0.1 per cent methylene blue or at a pH of 9.6 alkaline reaction, thus revealing that they are not tolerant to these substances. They have low thermal death points and possess a weak reducing action. Various important biological properties are found among many of the strains belonging to **Group A hemolytic streptococcus** which corresponds roughly to the *Streptococcus pyogenes* described here. Among the latter are: (1) the ability to produce fibrinolysin, which is capable of liquefying *human* blood clots (or fibrin). The determination of fibrinolysis is an outstanding characteristic of these strains and observation of fibrinolytic activities is a helpful procedure to differentiate human pathogenic strains from nonpathogenic ones. (See page 77.)

(2) The presence of filterable hemolysin can be demonstrated. (See page 76.) At least two types are produced: (*a*) one sensitive to heat (thermolabile) and acid but oxygen-stable, and the other (*b*) resistant to heat (thermostable) and acid but sensitive to oxygen (oxygen-labile). The latter is antigenic and the former is nonantigenic.

(3) Leucocidin is produced. It is thermolabile and by destroying white blood cells inhibits phagocytosis.

(4) An erythrogenic toxin is produced by certain strains which upon injection is capable of producing a skin rash in susceptible humans. This erythrogenic or rash-producing toxin is relatively heat-stable and is antigenic.

(5) Other strains produce a so-called "spreading factor," which alters the permea-

bility of tissues. The human nasopharyngeal tract is probably the principal habitat for strains of this species.

Few, if any, pathogenic organisms can lay claim to as many diseases and affections among humans as are to be observed caused by hemolytic streptococci (Group A) as the main and primary cause. The list, though a long one, is probably not complete. *Hemolytic streptococci (Group A)* may be the primary cause of infection in erysipelas, puerperal (childbed) fever, epidemic sore throat, bronchopneumonia, circumscribed and extensive acute abscesses as carbuncles, suppurative and inflammatory conditions in different organs and tissues, as periostitis, osteomyelitis, synovitis, endocarditis, peritonitis, otitis media, mastoiditis, meningitis, tonsillitis, sinusitis and empyemia, septicemia, pleurisy and skin affections.

Some workers have differentiated these strains of hemolytic streptococci (Group A) into various types and varieties. The observation of specific pathological properties possessed by these species has led to the subdivision into disease-specific types, an undesirable classification to employ and for which there appears no or little justification. Accordingly hemolytic streptococci found in the throats of scarlet fever patients are known also as *Streptococcus scarlatinae*, just as the streptococcus causing infectious bovine mastitis is known as *Streptococcus mastitidis*, and Small's streptococcus of acute rheumatic fever is known as *Streptococcus cardio-arthritidis*. The latter was physiologically and serologically identified by Sherman and associates (*J. Bact.*, 1943, **45**, 249) as *Streptococcus salivarius*. George and Gladys Dick demonstrated that the hemolytic streptococci of scarlet fever produce a soluble (extracellular) toxic substance, capable of giving a definite skin reaction in man (*Dick Test*). Evans (*J. Bact.*, 1937, **34**, 21), however, has put forward claims for recognizing *S. scarlatinae* as a separate species from *S. pyogenes* on the ability of the former to ferment salicin. Focal infection, a name given to a systemic or local disease caused by infectious material, which is disseminated from a focus of infection, as the teeth, tonsils, intestinal tract, etc., is often due to streptococci. As secondary invaders, streptococci produce considerable annoyance and frequent complications, especially in tuberculosis, influenza, pneumonia, measles, scarlet fever, smallpox, etc. From all of the streptococcus lesions a septicemia may arise if the infection gains any headway. Hemolytic streptococcus septicemias are very dangerous and usually fatal.

Group B Hemolytic Streptococci.—Strains belonging to this group are associated with bovine mastitis and correspond to *Streptococcus mastitidis*, the designation formerly applied or *Streptococcus agalactiae*, the name used more frequently today. The latter possesses limited and variable hemolytic power, produces a low pH in dextrose broth (less than 4.8 (usually 4.5) in 1 per cent dextrose medium), hydrolyzes sodium hippurate into benzoic acid and glycocoll, produces chromogenesis (color ranging from yellow to brick-red), and curdles milk media. For further references, see P. A. Hansen, *N. Y. (Geneva) Agr. Expt. Sta., Tech. Bull.* **232**. Although *S. agalactiae* is not regarded as a human pathogen, the possibility of its occurrence in human infections must be recognized. Its isolation from the human nose, throat, vagina, uterus and from feces has been reported. Probably a harmless saprophyte and only infrequently responsible for mild clinical infections in man, an occasional serious and fatal disease in humans by strains of this species is possible and has been reported (Hare, *J. Path. and Bact.*, 1935, **41**, 499–520).

Group C.—In the present state of our knowledge there are to be found here at least three clearly defined biochemical groupings which appear to deserve consideration under headings as three separate species: (1) *Streptotoccus equi*, the cause of equine distemper or "strangles" in horses. Strains of this species do not ferment lactose, trehalose or sorbitol, do not lyse human blood clots, are unable in general to cause the production of agglutinins when inoculated into animals, and possess a high virulency for white mice and a low or no virulency for rabbits and guinea pigs. Sodium hippurate is not hydrolyzed. For further details see Edwards (*Kentucky Agr. Expt. Sta. Bull.* **356** (1935)) and Evans (*J. Bact.*, 1936, **31**, 423; 1937, **34**, 21). (2) The "animal pyogenes" streptococcus includes clearly defined strains, especially characterized by the ability to ferment sorbitol and lactose and an inability to ferment trehalose (a unique observation among strains of hemolytic streptococci). Thus the common hemolytic streptococcus of animal infections is differentiated from the true *Streptococcus pyogenes*, the hemolytic streptococcus of human infections in that strains of the former do and of the latter do not ferment sorbitol. *Streptococcus dysgalactiae*, the cause of acute bovine mastitis is the important species of interest. (3) The Lancefield serological technique recognizes a hemolytic streptococcus designated as the "human C" type. Some question regarding this as a species distinct from *S. pyogenes*. The former does and the latter does not ferment glycerin and the former grows and *S. pyogenes* does not grow on media containing methylene blue. Differences with respect to active fibrinolytic powers, possible capsule formation and active fermentative powers on carbohydrates are also of value to consider these as distinct groups. Strains of "human C" streptococcus have been obtained from humans but, though they may at times cause erysipelas, they are generally of low virulence and are not important as causative agents of human disease.

Group D contains strains which are found mainly as harmless parasites. On the basis of our present knowledge nonhemolytic species are also placed in this group. Some of the members of the so-called *enterococci* discussed below are included by some workers in this group.

Group E includes a few strains of hemolytic streptococci obtained from the bovine udder and milk. They are regarded as being nonpathogenic, though *S. uberis* does cause a mild bovine mastitis, which may produce, at times, serious damage. For further details, see Plastridge and Hartsell (*J. Infect. Dis.*, 1937, **61**, 110).

Group F represents the species designated as the *minute hemolytic streptococcus* reported by Long and Bliss (*J. Exp. Med.*, 1934, **60**, 619). These strains produce very small "pinpoint" colonies, at times barely visible, but always surrounded by a zone of true hemolysis. They occur as harmless human parasites, have been isolated from the human throat, vagina and feces, and may at times be the primary cause of disease.

Group G includes hemolytic streptococci that are widely distributed, having been found among humans in the throat, nose, vagina, skin and feces and from normal and diseased animals. It appears that these strains are of little importance as potential producers of disease in humans.

Groups H and K.—Hare (*J. Path. and Bact.*, 1935, **41**, 499) segregated a new Group H and only provisionally suggested Group K, which contain species isolated from human sources. No evidence has as yet been presented that they are pathogenic.

The "Viridans" Streptococci

Under this heading are included all streptococci which produce on blood agar colonies surrounded by a greenish discolored zone, the so-called *alpha hemolysis*. Serological methods have not as yet proved of value for the classification of these types, and grouping within this division is based at present on physiological characteristics. The recognized types display many properties in common, such as: inability to cause true (beta) hemolysis, possess relatively high maximum growth temperature (45° C.), do not produce ammonia from peptone (as is produced by hemolytic streptococci and enterococci), possess weak reducing properties and a limited tolerance to high concentrations of salt, alkali and methylene blue, and generally survive (except *S. salivarius*) 60° C. for thirty minutes. The different species included are: *S. salivarius* (found in human throat), *S. bovis* (found in intestine of cow), *S. equinus* (found in intestine of horse), and *S. thermophilus* (found in dairy products). *S. mitis* is today regarded by many as being identical with *S. salivarius*. For further details concerning this as well as the other groups of streptococci, see Sherman (*Bact. Revs.*, 1937, **1**, 3). Green producing streptococci (*S. salivarius*) (*S. mitis* or *S. viridans*) have been encountered in certain infections in man, especially subacute bacterial endocarditis. The so-called *Borgen streptococcus* regarded by Borgen as possessing a causative relationship with ulcerative colitis is at present considered identical with *S. bovis* or at least closely related. Sherman and associates (*J. Bact.*, 1943, **45**, 249), in a study on nonhemolytic streptococci of the human throat, identified the predominating species as *Streptococcus salivarius* and the others as members of the *S. mitis group*. The former species was found to occur also in large numbers in the human intestine. A nutrient agar, containing 5 per cent saccharose and 0.02 per cent sodium azide, was found useful as both a selective and differential medium for the *S. salivarius*.

Indifferent Streptococci

This group includes the so-called *nonhemolytic streptococci* (*S. anhemolyticus*) and those designated as the gamma type or indifferent streptococci. The important species and varieties will be considered here as the *lactic-acid producing* streptococci and the enterococci.

Lactic-Acid Producing Streptococci.—This is a misleading designation as lactic acid is produced by most all streptococci. However, inasmuch as the commonly observed milk-souring bacterium has been spoken of as the *lactic-acid streptococcus*, this term is frequently used and has even acquired a familiar technical meaning. Lactic-acid streptococci include the *S. lactis* (isolated from milk, cheese and certain plants, the so-called *S.* or *Bact. acidi lactici; S.* or *Bact. lactis; B. guntheri*) and *S. cremoris* (found in dairy products). These species have not been found to be the cause of infections in man or animals. Lactic-acid producing streptococci are readily differentiated from the beta and alpha hemolytic streptococci by their ability to grow at 10° C. and in the presence of methylene blue (sterile milk containing 0.1 per cent concentrations), and they possess strong reducing powers. *S. lactis* and *S. cremoris* differ from each other in their fermentative reactions on arabinose, mannitol and xylose and the former does and the latter does not produce ammonia from peptone and hydrolyzed sodium hippurate. *S. cremoris* does not grow as well as *S. lactis* on artificial media, is less acid-tolerant, will not grow at 40° C. or in media containing 4 per cent salt or possessing a *p*H of 9.2 or higher. It is of interest to note that, in litmus milk, *S. lactis* produces color reduction before curdling and the color change is complete.

Enterococci.—This term is used commonly to designate the streptococci found in the intestinal tract of warm-blooded animals, so-called *fecal streptococci*. The outstanding species is *S. fecalis*. *S. liquefaciens* and *S. zymogenes* regarded by some as a Group D streptococcus, are either variants of *S. fecalis* or at least very closely related, in the same manner that *S. fecalis* itself is subdivided by some workers also into a hemolytic variety. *S. durans* is another nonpathogenic intestinal streptococcus which produces hemolysis. The enterococci as a class grow at a temperature from 10° C. to 45° C. and in the presence of 6.5 per cent NaCl, 0.1 per cent methylene blue and at a *p*H of 9.6. They possess strong reducing powers (except *S. durans*) and survive a temperature of 60° C. for thirty minutes. In addition to that noted above, they are differentiated from each other by observing differences in fermentative powers, hemolysin production and proteolytic action (especially gelatin liquefaction). *S. liquefaciens* liquefies gelatin and this characteristic is displayed at times by certain strains of *S. zymogenes*. These are the only known proteolytic gelatin-liquefying streptococci. Though the enterococci or intestinal streptococci are to be regarded as saprophytes and generally are nonpathogenic, they may occasionally be found in cases of human infections. Some species have been isolated in cases of subacute bacterial endocarditis. For details on enterococcic infections, see Rantz and Kirby (*Arch. Intern. Med.*, 1943, **71**, 516).

Anaerobic Streptococci

Pathogenic obligate anaerobic streptococci have been isolated from different infections in humans. They are usually nonhemolytic and are gas producers. Schott-müller named those strains producing a fetid gas in blood media as *S. putridus* or *putrificus*. Other species reported are *S. anaerobius*, *S. foetidus*, *S. lanceolatus*, *S. intermedius*, *S. parvulus* and *S. micros*. Many of the facultative anaerobic streptococci are erroneously labeled as anaerobes having been isolated by anaerobic culture, but are later found to grow aerobically. The various obligate anaerobic types have received very little detailed attention and at present are not clearly defined nor readily differentiated and classified. Anaerobic strains have been isolated from the blood in cases of puerperal sepsis.

Saprophytic nonpathogenic bacteria occurring in the form of chains of cocci to short rod forms have been found especially in acid fruit juices, fermenting vegetables and in dairy products. These species are now grouped under the genus *Leuconostoc*.

Neurotropic Streptococci

Rosenow and associates and other workers have reported the frequent isolation of a neurotropic type of streptococcus in cases of epidemic encephalitis, epizoötic encephalitis in the fox, and of epidemic equine encephalomyelitis. In a consideration of the relation of these neurotropic streptococci to encephalitis and the encephalitic virus Rosenow (*Proc. Staff Meeting Mayo Clinic*, 1942, **17**, 551) expresses the opinions that "the streptococcus is a source of what is now considered virus and that virus represents the filterable phase of the streptococcus."

Therapy

Antitoxic and antibacterial sera have been used in the therapy of streptococcic infections. Generally speaking, the antistreptococcus sera have given unsatisfactory results. The various streptococcic antitoxins and especially scarlet fever streptococcus antitoxin and sera from convalescent cases have proved more valuable and these preparations are indicated in the therapy of those streptococcic infections in which a rash-producing toxin is responsible for many of the clinical symptoms. Immunity to streptococcus infections is usually of low order, except in those instances in which the causative streptococcus produces an erythrogenic toxin. Accordingly active immunization with bacterial vaccines as a prophylactic measure against streptococcic infections is usually unsatisfactory. On the other hand, active immunization with toxin (or toxoid) against erythrogenic-toxin producing streptococci (as in scarlet fever) is an effective procedure and is to be advocated. Within the past five years the treatment (and even the prevention) of streptococcal infections has been revolutionized by the introduction of the sulfonamide drugs. Properly administered under medical supervision sulfanilamide in particular is a highly effective chemotherapeutic agent in the control of Lancefield Group A hemolytic streptococcal infections. It is about two-thirds as effective in Group C infections and only of slight value in Group B cases. It has no effect against species in Group D and against the enterococci and is only of indifferent value in some of the viridans infections. See pages 327.

THE DIPLOCOCCUS OF PNEUMONIA

Diplococcus Pneumoniae (*Pneumonococcus, Diplococcus or Micrococcus Lanceolatus*).—The diplococcus of pneumonia occurs as spherical or oval cocci, usually united in pairs, but at times shorter or longer chains, resembling the streptococcus, are to be found. The individual cocci vary from 0.6 to 1.25 μ in diameter. The distal ends of each pair of cocci are pointed or lancet-shaped. The adjacent ends of the cocci are frequently bluntly rounded. A wide capsule surrounds each coccus that may be found singly and the pairs of cocci as ordinarily observed. The capsules of pairs of organisms making up a chain are continuous and may appear as a capsule surroun ing the whole chain. On culture media, the organisms upon microscopic examination often appear elongated and almost bacillary in shape, and unless special media are employed, the capsule may not be apparent. Flagella and spores are not present. It stains with the ordinary aniline dyes, the capsule being visible as a colorless halo surrounding the colored organisms. It is Gram-positive. It grows with or without oxygen, best on blood or blood-serum agar (pH 7.6 to 7.8) at 37.5° C. and will not develop below 20° C. Some strains produce smooth, sticky or mucoid colonies. Pneumococci produce acid in most sugar media, and milk is acidified and coagulated. Due to the protective influence afforded by the capsular material, pneumococci may retain their virulence for long periods of time. There are occasions when it is practically impossible or at least difficult to distinguish between some strains of pneumococci occurring in chains and strains of streptococci, and especially when typical morphology and capsule formation in the former organisms are lacking. Under such conditions the following tests are employed as of special value in differentiation: If cultivated in inulin-serum water medium, streptococci leave the latter unchanged. Acid production and coagulation are the result when pneumococci are inoculated in this medium. Pneumococci form dry blackish colonies or they will appear flat and greenish with no (alpha) hemolysis on blood agar, while pathogenic streptococci will produce hemolysis or green discoloration on this medium. Living cultures of pneumococci are bile-soluble (in proportion of 1:10), while streptococci are insoluble. Sterile solutions of sodium taurocholate (10 per cent) may be used instead of oxbile. Harris and McClure (*J. Lab. Clin. Med.*, 1942, **27**, 1591) suggest the use of an 0.2 per cent aqueous solution of sodium lauryl sulfate (Duponol WA flakes), a detergent and wetting agent, to replace the more expensive 1 per cent sodium desoxycholate in solubility tests for differentiating pneumococci from other microorganisms producing discoloration on blood-agar medium. Pneumococci usually display greater pathogenic properties for mice. Decisive differential importance may be attached to specific agglutination tests. (See Agglutinins.)

As with other pathogenic bacteria, so with the pneumococci, we are able to distinguish several types and varieties. Cultural differences, as observed with the several varieties of streptococci, have not given a satisfactory basis for differentiation. The most satisfactory means of differentiating pneumococci is by the use of immunological (serological) reactions (specific agglutination tests). On the basis of specific agglutination with the serum of immunized animals (see Agglutinins), three fixed types of pneumococci are recognized, Types I, II, III and Group IV. The latter represents a heterogenous (mixed) group of organisms frequently differing from each other in serological reactions and all of them are not agglutinated by the antipneumococcic sera prepared separately from Types I, II or III. Group IV contains strains which are the least pathogenic of the four types and to this group belong most saprophytic pneumococci commonly found in the nose, throat and mouth of healthy individuals. Types I and II are frequently found causing (slightly over 50 per cent of all cases of) acute lobar (fibrinous or croupous) pneumonia in man (characterized by inflammation of the parenchyma of the lungs). Types II and III are, however, the most virulent. If pneumococci are found in sputum or other body fluids causing lobar pneumonia or any pneumococcus infection, it is possible to determine the specific type to which the particular pneumococcus belongs. Subsequent investigations, especially by workers at the New York City Health Department Laboratories, resulted in the extension of the serological differentiation of Group IV, and 29 additional types were classified as being in this heterogenous "Group IV," and designated as types IV to XXXII, continuing the numbers and expansion from the recognized types of I, II and III. Due to more recent observations, this numerical classification has undergone revision and further expansion. In fact 55 types appear to deserve consideration, and possibly dividing the latter into 40 groups and 15 subgroups. Though the numerical classification of 32 types can no longer be regarded as complete, it is not being supplanted for the present. Further study is necessary before adopting a revision of the present classification.

Pneumococci contain two types of antigens. One, the somatic antigen, of protein origin is present in the cell substance and, being group-specific, it is immunologically the same in all types. The other, a complex polysaccharide (specific soluble substance (SSS)) differs chemically in each type and, due to this chemical difference, it is type-specific and serves to differentiate immunologically the different types of pneumococci from one another. Treatment with type-specific serum has resulted in the necessity of typing all pneumococcus pneumonia cases. Many techniques have been introduced for typing the pneumococci in pneumonia sputum but, of all of the procedures, the Neufeld (Quellung) Method (*Prevent. Med.*, 1937, **7**, 39) (see page 505) has been widely acclaimed and is used because of its simplicity, accuracy and ease in obtaining a quick report. Typing is essential to the specific serum treatment in pneumococcus infections. The pneumonias of infants and children differ from those of adults in the types of pneumococci usually envolved. In adults the frequency of the types are I, II, III, V, IV, VIII and VII. These types are responsible in adults for approximately 80 per cent of all pneumococcus lobar pneumonias. In children the following types are observed most often: I, IV, V, VI, VII, XIV, XIX. In fact, Nemir and associates (*Am. J. Dis. Child.*, 1936, **51**, 1277) point out Type XIV is the most common type among cases in infants; its frequency decreases as age increases: and that there is a change in the distribution of types depending upon the age of the children.

In practice bacteriological control is necessary in lobar pneumonia, regardless of the treatment to be instituted. It is important to know the organism causing the infection; and if a pneumococcus, the type which is present, and also whether there is a bacteremia. Sputum should be collected on swabs from the posterior pharynx obtained for a bacteriological examination, and typing and a blood culture should be made. If sulfonamides are to be used, typing of sputum should not be omitted; in fact specimens should be obtained, before the administration of these drugs, for the latter may exert an effect on the pneumococci (*Quart. Bull. N. Y. City Dept. Health*, 1940, **8**, 73), so that if chemotherapy is ineffective, it may be impossible to use type-specific serum.

The causative agents of lobar pneumonia are generally more specific in character and occur usually in pure culture. Statistics reveal that the pneumococcus (see specific types mentioned previously) is responsible for 96.8 per cent of all cases of lobar pneumonia, the streptococcus in 2.4 per cent, and less than 1 per cent of all cases are caused by either the *Klebsiella pneumoniae*, *H. influenzae*, or the staphylococcus. Bronchopneumonia, so-called lobular or catarrhal pneumonia, may be caused by many different organisms. The latter may be either the pneumococcus, streptococcus, *K. pneur oniae*, *H. influenzae*, *E. typhosa*, *P. pestis*, *P. tularensis*, and the virus of psittacosis. Each of these organisms produces its own characteristic pathologic lesion frequently with its own peculiar clinical symptoms. Minor respiratory infections predispose to pneumonia and the prevention of the latter is closely bound up with the control of all infections, acute and chronic, of the respiratory tract. In rarer instances, the inhalation of dust containing fungi or their spores, especially molds and yeasts, may invade the lungs. The so-called *Valley* or *San Joaquin Fever*, caused by *Coccidioides immitis*, is a pulmonary infection of this type, which, at times, is of some public health concern. There are certain types of pneumonia, the so-called *noninfectious pneumonias*, in which different predisposing factors are of importance and the infecting organism plays only a secondary role. Examples are the postoperative pneumonias, more common after inhalation anesthesia. Aspiration pneumonia may be postoperative in type due to the aspiration of vomitus, but occurs more frequently during periods of unconsciousness, epileptic seizures, drowning and other accidents, and among infants especially when using, improperly, oily nasal drops. Recently a *contagious bronchopneumonia* has appeared in this country. The causative agent is undetermined, but it is believed to be a filterable virus. The disease is highly communicable and the clinical symptoms resemble closely that of psittacosis. For other details concerning *pneumonitis* or *virus pneumonia*, see page 245.

The pneumococcus may also cause other primary affections, as inflammations of the endocardium, pericardium, pleura and meninges. As a secondary invader, producing complications and sequelae of pneumonia, we find that meningeal and middle-ear infections are common. Almost any organ or tissue may be attacked by the pneumococcus, and if a lowered resistance or the causes affecting predisposition prevail, an infection will be the result. Specific serum therapy and the use of ethylhydrocuprein (Optochin) and cinchona and its alkaloids are of value in pneumococcus infection. Workers at the Mellon Institute (*Science*, 1942, **95,** 458) have and are working not only with the cinchona alkaloids, but also with hydroxyethylapocupreine and other synthetics in the treatment of pneumococcic infections.

Since the introduction of the sulfonamides and especially sulfapyridine, sulfadiazine and sulfamerazine, which have been found so effective in the treatment of all kinds of pneumococcus infections and in pneumonia caused by all types of pneumococci, there has been a marked reduction in the use of immune serum in treatment. Though the use of these chemotherapeutic agents is the treatment of choice to be instituted wherever practical as soon as possible, there are many indications for combined therapy (chemoserotherapy). Chemoserotherapy is advisable in all pneumonia cases with bacteremias, in postoperative patients for whom nausea and vomiting would be dangerous, and for all patients who do not respond to these drugs or to whom the sulfonamides cannot be given. For further details on all phases of pneumonia and the pneumococcus, see White, *The Biology of the Pneumococcus*, 1938 and Lord and Heffron, *Pneumonia and Serum Therapy*, 1939, both issued by the Commonwealth Fund, New York City.

Pneumococcus Mucosus (*Streptococcus Mucosus of Schottmüller;* **Diplococcus Pneumoniae, Type III.**—The so-called *Streptococcus mucosus* (*capsulatus*) or *Pneumococcus mucosus* is described by many as an incitant of lobar pneumonia and a variety of other conditions as well as occurring as an apparently harmless inhabitant of the mouths of normal individuals. Capsular substance is markedly developed and inulin-serum media is promptly coagulated. Typical lancet-shaped forms may not be present and the individual cocci may vary from 0.6 to 0.8 μ in diameter. The optimum temperature for growth is 37° C., but it also will grow at room temperature. Due to the regularity of the former characteristics and because of specific agglutination with Type III antipneumococcus serum, this organism is regarded as a Type III pneumococcus.

ANAEROBIC DIPLOCOCCI

Several obligate anaerobes, members of the *Diplococcus* genus, have been isolated from various sources. Among the latter are: *Diplococcus morbillorum*, found in the nose, throat, eyes, ears, blood and mucous secretions from cases of measles. It is not soluble in bile. *Diplococcus constellatus* was isolated from pus in cases of acute appendicitis and in chronic cryptic tonsillitis. Inulin is not acidified. *Diplococcus plagarumbelli* is commonly found in septic wounds, is nonpathogenic, more resistant to heat than other diplococci, and acidifies and coagulates milk strongly. *Diplococcus paleopneumoniae* is highly pathogenic and was found in lesions of bronchopneumonia, osseous abscess, and in the buccal-pharyngeal cavity of man and rodents. *Diplococcus magnus* is nonpathogenic, commonly found on butcher's meat in the process of putrefaction and occurs as large spheres possessing a very marked alkalizing power.

GRAM-NEGATIVE COCCI

The family *Neisseriaceae* consists of obligate parasites found in two genera: *Neisseria*, consisting of 11 species of paired Gram-negative cocci with adjacent sides flattened and *Veillonella*, consisting of 2 species of anaerobic cocci of small size, occurring in masses, rarely in pairs or short chains.

Neisseria Intracellularis (*Meningococcus; Micrococcus, Streptococcus or Diplococcus Intracellularis Meningitidis*).—This is a Gram-negative, biscuit-shaped (flattened adjacent sides) diplococcus, but at times it may be found occurring singly, in groups of fours (tetrads), or in masses. Small degenerated forms are observed occasionally. Like the gonococcus, the meningococcus, when found present in body fluids, may be observed within the pus cells, and spoken of as being intracellular. When found outside of the pus cell, it is spoken of as being extracellular. The individual coccus is from 0.6 to 0.8 μ in diameter, though the individual cells of a pair may vary markedly in size (and in intensity of staining). Flagella, spores and well-defined true capsular substance are absent. Growth occurs upon media to which blood, blood serum, ascitic fluid or other natural fluids are added and when incubated at a temperature between 25° and 38° C., best at body temperature, and under a reduced oxygen tension (microaerophilic). As a rule, the smooth translucent colonies produced when freshly isolated on solid media are very characteristic and give a positive "oxidase test" (see page 120). It is weak resistant, being readily destroyed by heat, disinfectants, sunlight and even drying and freezing. Attempts have been made to type this organism, just as in the case of the pneumococcus. By immunological (specific agglutination) tests, distinct types or groups of the meningococcus have been found to exist. No attempts are, however, made in routine work to type the meningococcus.

Serological classification, however, is important in the case of meningococci isolated from carriers and from patients during epidemics. Briefly summarized, meningococci fall into two broad serological groups—I and II. The latter are further divided into subgroups or types. Group I contains Types I and III which are identical in most respects immunologically, chemically, clinically, epidemiologically and in their pathogenicity. Group II is apparently also composed of subgroups and types. Types II and IV of Gordon and Murray (*J. Roy. Army Med. Corps*, 1915, **25,** 411) are listed in Group II. However, strains of Type IV are rarely encountered in the United States, so that in this country Group II at present is the designation used for all strains which are agglutinated by a specific Type II serum. The relation of the Gordon and Murray Type IV to the present Groups I and II is not understood, and only intensive study in the future will establish its relationship. Furthermore it must be borne in mind that most strains of meningococci show a degree of overlapping which makes it difficult to classify them into distinct types. The meningococcus contains a group-specific carbohydrate common to all types of meningococci and related bacteria. In addition Types I and III and Group II possess a type-specific polysaccharide (*J. Exp. Med.*, 1933, **58,** 361; 1935 **61,** 753).

Meningococci are differentiated from other Gram-negative cocci by the lack of pigment production, growth at or only slightly below body temperature, by the specific agglutination (at some time) with 1:100 and 1:50 dilutions of antimeningococcic serum and by fermentation tests on sugar media, especially dextrose, maltose, lactose and saccharose. Meningococci ferment dextrose and maltose with the production only of acid. Saccharose, levulose or lactose is not fermented. For further details on meningococci, see Branham (*Bact. Rev.*, 1940, **4**, 59) and *Diag. Proc. and Reag.* (A. P. H. A., 1941).

Toxin production by the meningococcus has been and is the subject of much discussion, especially since Ferry and associates (*J. Immunol.*, 1931, **21**, 293) revealed that bacteria-free filtrates contain soluble toxic substances. The opinion held by most workers at present is that the apparent exotoxins obtained by Ferry and his associates and used for preparing a so-called antitoxin are in reality endotoxins released by the spontaneous autolysis of the bacteria. Kirkbride and Cohen (*J. Immunol.*, 1937, **33**, 375) reveal no qualitative differences between the antibacterial and so-called antitoxic meningococcic (serum) preparations.

The membranes lining the brain and spinal cord (pia mater, dura mater and arachnoid) are complexly known as the meninges. An inflammation of this is known as meningitis. The meningococcus is the cause of primary or epidemic meningitis (also known as cerebrospinal meningitis, the only variety of meningitis occurring in epidemic form). This occurs most frequently in children and young adults. Other than the definite clinical symptoms, blood cultures may be of value but an accurate diagnosis is best made by obtaining the spinal fluid and finding the meningococcus in the latter directly or after culturing. In obtaining the spinal fluid, sterile precautions are observed, and a sterile lumbar needle is thrust into (puncturing) the spinal canal, a little to one side of the third or fourth lumbar space (therefore the expression, lumbar puncture, used when spinal fluid is to be obtained). Owing to the fact that meningococci often undergo rapid autolysis, spinal fluid should be examined as soon as possible after collection. In the detection of suspected carriers, examinations of nasopharyngeal secretions are made, as the nasopharynx is the normal habitat of the meningococcus. Care in taking the cultures and the use of a suitable culture medium enhance the chances of obtaining a higher percentage of positive findings. The use of antimeningococcus serum in the treatment of this disease may be of value if used early. It is administered directly into the spinal canal, first removing an amount of fluid equivalent to the amount of serum to be injected. Intravenous administration of the serum is also practiced. Some workers advocate injection by the intravenous route only. Whenever possible, it is advisable to culture the meningococcus from the spinal fluid obtained from the patient under treatment, and to use only a lot of antimeningococcus serum which is capable of agglutinating the specific strain of meningococci. The introduction of the sulfonamide drugs has changed the therapy of meningococcus infections. Though these drugs alone are highly effective both as prophylactic and as therapeutic agents in meningococcus infections, the present trend is to advocate and use combined therapy of the sulfonamides and serum (chemoserotherapy) for treatment. Organisms in primary infections in other parts of the body may find their way into the meninges, causing a secondary meningitis. Such organisms may be the pneumococcus, streptococcus, tubercle bacillus, staphylococcus, influenza bacillus, typhoid, colon and plague bacilli. Apparently the most important measures to be considered in connection with the control and prevention of epidemics of meningococcus meningitis are: (1) prompt recognition of cases and of carriers of the disease; (2) prompt reporting to the health authorities; (3) avoidance of overcrowding; (4) maintenance of high standards of bodily vigor; (5) sterilization of dishes and eating utensils; (6) optimum of fresh air and sunshine for carriers and convalescents. See also Awe, *et al.* (*Naval Med. Bull.*, 1943, **41,** 625).

Considerable interest is anticipated in the recent announcement that seven strains of *Neisseria*, possessing all of the known biologic characteristics of Group I meningococci, were isolated from the genito-urinary tract of seven patients with clinical symptoms of gonococcal infection. (Carpenter and Charles, *Am. J. Pub. Health*, 1942, **32,** 640.) Eight cases of meningococci conjunctivitis were recently reported with subsequent cure by the use of sulfonamide therapy (*Arch. Ophth.*, 1944, **31,** 245). This infection may be the first stage of meningitis and its early recognition and treatment are important.

Neisseria Gonorrhoeae (*Gonococcus; Micrococcus or Diplococcus Gonorrhoeae*).— This is a Gram-negative, aerobic diplococcus, the sides where they are in contact (in juxtaposition) being flattened (coffee-bean- or biscuit-shaped). When found in pus, masses of pairs are found occurring within the pus cells (intracellularly) (especially during the acute stage) and some may be observed outside (extracellularly) (during the pre-acute and chronic stages). They are confined to the cytoplasm of the cell and do not invade the nucleus when found in pus cells. Spores, flagella and a capsular substance are absent. Growth will take place between 25° and 39° C. on media containing natural fluid. Different media have been advocated for isolating the gonococcus. A chocolate agar prepared with a meat infusion tryptic digest agar as the base appears to be one of the most suitable of the various media for such isolation (*J. Path. and Bact.*, 1934, **39,** 221). Difco "Proteose No. 3 Agar" combined with "Bacto Hemoglobin" assures a preparation which can be quickly prepared in small or large quantities, making available a fresh, moist suitable medium. Growth is improved during incubation by replacing about 10 per cent of the air in the container with carbon dioxide. When no typical colonies are observed by direct inspection (convex, slightly opaque colonies, 1 to 3 mm. in diameter, with undulated margins), or the growth is admixed with other freer-growing bacteria, the culture or segment of a plate is subjected to the *óxidase test*. This test facilitates the recognition of members of the genus *Neisseria*, as they all produce the enzyme *oxidase*. In the test, the colonies are flooded with 1 cc. of a 1 per cent aqueous solution of dimethyl (or tetramethyl) paraphenylene diamine hydrochloride, and evidence of change in color of the colonies is noted for a period of fifteen minutes. The color changes by the dimethyl compound (pink, maroon and finally black) and (lavender followed by purple) when using the tetramethyl compound identify the colonies as *Neisseria*. Gonococci produce acid in glucose only and do not attack other sugars. *N. gonorrhoeae* is easily destroyed by drying, sunlight, heat and disinfectants, and is not found outside of the human body. This organism is the cause of gonorrhea, a readily transmissible inflammation of the genital mucous membranes (of humans only) (known also as specific urethritis or specific vaginitis), the most common and most important of the prevalent venereal diseases (so called, because the disease is usually contracted by illicit sexual intercourse). In addition to the genital organs, the gonococcus may invade the eyes, in particular the conjunctiva, causing gonorrhea ophthalmia, which unless treated promptly will result in blindness. Ophthalmia neonatorum, inflammation of the eyes of the newborn, is caused in most cases by the gonococcus. Infection takes place as the head of the child passes down the birth canal. Gonococcal meningitis also is known to occur (*J. A. M. A.*, 1938, **110,** 1804). One of the great dangers in connection with gonorrheal infections is the indifference of the public and those who are diseased to this and other venereal affections. If they could only realize the serious secondary involvements and manifestations that may result there might be better cooperation. General measures should be practiced to control the spread of all venereal infections which are prevalent to such an alarming extent. This consists in education in matters of sexual hygiene, repression of prostitution, elimination of the use of common toilet articles, provisions for accurate and early diagnosis and treatment, personal prophylaxis, etc.

In the routine diagnosis of gonococcal infections, culturing is to be advocated and practiced when smears are doubtful or negative (and especially in the release of patients under treatment). A positive oxidase test, followed by a confirming Gram stain (Gram-negative) and, if desired, further confirmed by observing the reactions on carbohydrate media (dextrose, maltose, levulose, saccharose and lactose) presents sufficient evidence for the identification of the gonococcus. The fact that bacteria are coffee-bean shaped, Gram-negative diplococci and are from a genital source of infection is sufficient evidence to give a presumptive diagnosis of gonorrhea, especially if the clinical evidence and history are positive. Others consider that cultures and fermentation tests are necessary. This is essential in the isolations of suspicious organisms, in cultures taken especially from females, and in all medicolegal cases. Peizer (*J. Bact.*, 1942, **43,** 733) states that horse, beef and sheep bloods are not suitable enrichment agents in sugar fermentation tests for identifying the gonococcus, as in their presence maltose and glucose agar may be acidified. She recommends as enrichments human, rabbit and guinea-pig sera, ascitic fluid, or fractionally sterilized soluble starch. More recently, Cantor and associates (*J. Bact.*, 1942, **44,** 237) described a microscopic alkali-solubility test for the identification of colonies of *N. gonorrhoeae* and differentiating them from colonies of normal flora *Neisseria* species. This method minimizes the amount of work and the time entailed in rendering a report, inasmuch as culturing for sugar-fermentation tests is eliminated. The laboratory diagnosis involves the preparation of primary cultures. "Oxidase-positive" colonies can be selected, but these or other suspicious colonies are emulsified on a slide. The suspension is so prepared as to show not more than a perceptible turbidity. A loopful of $N/10$ hydrochloric acid is added. The mixture is air dried, heat fixed and stained by Gram's method. The smears are then examined, comparing them with controls which are carried along and treated at the same time. Gonococci are completely soluble in $N/10$ and $N/5$ alkali; meningococci are partially soluble in $N/10$ but completely soluble in $N/5$ alkali; other species of *Neisseria* are insoluble. Corbus and Corbus (*J. A. M. A.*, 1941, **116,** 113) advocate a cutaneous test as a valuable diagnostic adjunct. The complement-fixation test and other serological tests have as yet not proved of much practical value.

Gonococcic vaccine and antigonococcic serum have but limited use as prophylactic or therapeutic agents. Many different antigenic preparations are being used with but little success. The widespread acceptance of the sulfonamide drug therapy as effective agents in gonococcic infections has modified greatly the use of all pre-existing types of treatment. The beneficial action of these drugs is said to be due to the fact that gonococcic infections are true bacteremias rather than merely localized involvements. Sulfanilamide, sulfapyridine, sulfathiazole and sulfadiazine have been used orally, with different workers claiming one or the other as the best choice, and others regarding all of them equally effective. Oral chemotherapy with the sulfonamide drugs is to be combined with local treatment, as the merits of combined treatment are definite. Loveless and Denton (*J. A. M. A.*, 1943, **121,** 827) have reported the use of sulfathiazole successfully as a prophylactic against gonorrhea and chancroid. Recently, penicillin has been employed with effective results. For further details, see the literature obtainable from the United States Public Health Service on "Venereal Disease Information," "The Gonococcus and Gonococcal Infection," one of the A. A. A. S. symposia publications and Stokinger and associates (*J. Bact.*, 1944, **47,** 129).

Neisseria Catarrhalis (*Micrococcus Catarrhalis*); **Neisseria Sicca** (*Diplococcus Siccus; Micrococcus Pharyngis Sicci*); **Neisseria Flava; Neisseria Perflava.**

DIFFERENTIATION OF THE VARIOUS SPECIES OF NEISSERIA

Species	Fermentation				20° C. growth on agar	Agglutinated by anti-meningococcic serum	Other growth characteristics
	Dextrose	Maltose	Saccharose	Levulose			
N. gonorrhoeae	A	—	—	—	—	—	Small, convex, transparent colonies with undulated margins
N. intracellularis	A	A	—	—	—	+	Small, round, translucent colonies with a tendency to confluence
N. catarrhalis	—	—	—	—	+	—	Large, opaque colonies with an irregular wavy border; difficult to emulsify
N. sicca	A	A	A	A	+	—	Large, firm, wrinkled colonies; difficult to emulsify
N. perflava	A	A	A	A	+	—	Greenish-yellow colonies, adheres to medium
N. flava	A	A	—	A	—	—	Yellow pigment, small, and adheres to medium
N. subflava	A	A	—	—	±	—	Greenish-yellow adheres to medium
N. flavescens	—	—	—	—	?	—	Golden-yellow pigment

A indicates acid production.

Neisseria Subflava.—The latter four frequently designated as the *Micrococcus catarrhalis type or group* are aerobes found in the mucous membranes of the respiratory tract of healthy and diseased individuals. Their importance, and especially that of *Neisseria catarrhalis*, which is found frequently in the nose and throat, is in the fact that they may be mistaken for the meningococcus. The last three named organisms are as their names indicate, chromogenic bacteria, the pigmentation best observed by transmitted light. For differentiating purposes, if necessary, the worker depends entirely upon cultural characteristics and especially upon the use of agglutination tests. Culturally, they grow more readily than the meningococcus on the ordinary media and at times even at room temperature. The fermentative powers on various sugar media are characteristic. But above all, careful agglutination tests with an antimeningococcic serum (diluted 1 to 100) are of great differential value. Only the meningococcus will be agglutinated by the specific serum in the dilution mentioned, while the other Gram-negative coffee-bean-shaped diplococci will not be affected. See accompanying table. *Neisseria catarrhalis* has been suggested as an index of swimming pool pollution and as a possible index of the bacterial quality of air (see Jennison and associates (*J. Bact.*, 1942, **43**, 100)). It is of interest to note that these workers found many strains of *N. catarrhalis* giving negative *oxidase* reactions.

Some workers claim that *N. catarrhalis* may excite catarrhal inflammation and even more serious affections. This organism seems to be a secondary invader in many respiratory infections and, as such, it was found extensively in some localities during the 1918 influenza pandemic. Recent reports by different workers reveal that *N. sicca* appears to be a pathogen, and more of a clinical entity than has been suspected (see *J. A. M. A.*, 1918, **71**, 1739; 1924, **82**, 1850; and *Science*, 1932, **75**, 488). *Neisseria flavescens* was found as the causative agent in an epidemic of cerebrospinal meningitis in Chicago (see Branham, *U. S. Pub. Health Repts.*, 1930, **45**, 845). Recently Carpenter (*Science News Letter*, Nov. 7, 1942, 291) reported on the ability of *N. flava* to produce disease. Three cases of suspected gonorrhea revealed the absence of the gonococcus and *N. flava* was isolated.

Chapter IX

COMMONLY OBSERVED PATHOGENIC AND NONPATHOGENIC BACTERIA

BACILLI (NONSPORE-FORMING)

The Diphtheria Bacillus and Diphtheroids

THE DIPHTHERIA and diphtheroid bacilli (*corynebacteria*) and the tubercle and acid-fast bacilli (*mycobacteria*) are considered here with the true bacilli merely as a convenience and due to the long-established custom still in vogue by most workers. The Bergey classification places all of these organisms in the same order with the higher bacteria and not with the lower forms of bacteria.

Corynebacterium diphtheriae (*Diphtheria Bacillus; Klebs-Loeffler Bacillus*).— This is a Gram-positive, nonacid fast, slender rod, straight or slightly curved, varying in size from 0.3 to 0.8 by 1 to 6 μ. It decolorizes more readily than most Gram-positive bacteria; decolorization therefore should not be carried too far. *C. diphtheriae* occur singly and in pairs, infrequently in chains of three or four, often lie at various angles to one another forming V or Y shapes, and a palisade arrangement may also be apparent. The individual organisms are markedly pleomorphic, also are not usually uniformly cylindrical throughout their entire length and appear swollen at one or both ends, or swollen in the middle portion and pointed at the ends. Spores, flagella and a capsule are absent. Of great aid in identifying this organism is the characteristic irregularity of staining, best obtained when using Loeffler's methylene-blue solution. In some strains, a granular or beaded appearance is observed, the beads, granules or oval bodies stained deeply are found near the ends or in the center, and the intermittent spaces are practically unstained or at best only slightly stained. In other strains, instead of occurring as beads or granules, the bodies appear as stained bars or striations. These are the "metachromatic" granules or the so-called "polar" or "Babes-Ernst" bodies. In addition to the beaded or granular and barred or striated types, a type of diphtheria bacillus which stains solidly is recognized by some workers, although its exact relation to clinical diphtheria is not definitely known. Many observers, however, regard these solid types as nonpathogenic, and group them with the pseudo-diphtheria bacilli or diphtheroids. The granular or beaded forms predominate in clinical diphtheria. A distinction of these forms was attempted at one time by some workers in the use of Westbrook's system of typing the diphtheria bacillus, when examining cultures from suspected throats (see Gorham (*J. Med. Research*, 1901, **6**, 201)). In older cultures, clubbed forms and turnip- or top-shaped and even involution forms may be observed. The Neisser or Albert as well as other staining methods have been advocated for noting more readily metachromatic granules and then using this as an aid in distinguishing virulent and nonvirulent diphtheria bacilli. These methods, however, do not supply more, and at times even as much, information as given when

124

staining with Loeffler's methylene-blue solution.   In fact, they tend to mislead when studying organisms in original cultures.

The diphtheria bacillus is aerobic and facultatively anaerobic and grows best on Loeffler's blood-serum medium, or in suitable media possessing an alkaline reaction and preferably when free access of air is available.   Loeffler's blood-serum medium should always be employed, particularly for diagnostic purposes, in making cultures from throats and nasal passages of individuals suspected of having diphtheria.   These cultures are made from swabbings of the exudate or membrane.   Thin smears are always made on slides at the same time.   If diphtheria bacilli are found on the latter, an immediate diagnosis can thus be made.   The slides may reveal a Vincent's angina infection.   The absence of diphtheria bacilli on the slides does not exclude the possibility of diphtheria, as bacilli may appear in culture within eight to twenty-four hours.   The optimum temperature is 37° C. and it will not grow below 19° C.   Pai's egg medium (*Chinese M. J.*, 1932, **46**, 1203) has been recommended as a substitute for

	Hiss's Serum Water plus 1% of			Virul	
	Dex-trose	Sac-charose	Dex-trin		
C. diphtheriae	AC	...	AC	Virulent	
C. pseudodiphthericum (C. hoffmannii)	...	...	...	Nonvirulent	
C. xerosis	AC	AC	...	Nonvirulent	
C. ulcerans	AC	...	AC	Virulent for animals; not for humans	Liquefies gelatin; coccoid forms
C. pyogenes	AC	AC	AC	Virulent for animals; not for humans	Produces a weak solid toxin immunologically distinct from diphtheria toxin

Loeffler's medium.   The former to which no serum is added (*J. Infect. Dis.*, 1936, **59**, 22) may be useful ni small laboratories, where serum is impracticable either due to the expense or is otherwise not obtainable.   This medium is easy to prepare and is said to be as reliable as Loeffler's medium with respect to the morphology and virulency of *C. diphtheriae*.   The diphtheria bacillus grows readily in milk and does not ferment the lactose present.   Liquefaction of gelatin or of coagulated protein does not occur. Indol is not formed, but nitrates are reduced to nitrites.   All strains produce acid but no gas from levulose and dextrose.   Some strains produce acid in maltose, galactose, glycerin, glycogen, starch and dextrin.   Saccharose is never attacked by true diphtheria bacilli, though most diphtheroids do ferment this sugar.

A highly poisonous true exotoxin is produced by this organism in suitable fluid media and in the tissues, and it is this toxin which represents the principal disease-producing agency of the organism.   The production of toxin *in vitro* is markedly influenced by the composition of the medium and environmental factors, such as *p*H (7.4 to 8.2), temperature (33° to 36° C.), aerobiosis, period of incubation (7 to 10 days), exposure to light, etc.

Investigations by McLeod and associates (*J. Path. and Bact.*, 1931, **34**, 667) bring new light upon the recognition of differences in toxigenic power by the study of other biological properties.   They have succeeded in demonstrating by means of a special chocolate medium containing 0.04 per cent of potassium tellurite that there are two types of the diphtheria bacillus associated, respectively, with grave and severe varieties of clinical diphtheria, one which is highly toxigenic, producing very quickly large quantities of toxin, and the other type which is only moderately or feebly toxigenic. These forms they designate as *Bacillus diphtheriae gravis* and *Bacillus diphtheriae mitis*, respectively. There are cultural and biological differences between the two groups. The *intermediate types* lie between the latter. On tellurite media, the *gravis type* produces irregular striated *rough* colonies predominantly gray in color with a black granular center. The *mitis type* produces small, round, *smooth* flat disks, which appear black by reflected light and reveal a narrow grayish margin by transmitted light. The *gravis* type does and the *mitis* type does not ferment starch and glycogen, produce a pellicle within four days when grown on ordinary infusion broth and affect the pH of the latter, so that it will revert to a reaction of pH 7.6 or over in ninety-six hours. The *mitis* type does and the *gravis* type does not produce hemolysin (using human erythrocytes in the test). The relation of the *gravis* type of *C. diphtheriae* to severe and fatal diphtheria as observed in Europe and noted by the above-mentioned workers has received wide attention. It has been difficult to assess the significance of the presence of the different types with varying degrees of severity in clinical diphtheria. Recently, Frobisher (*J. A. P. H, A.*, 1942, **32,** 709) presented interesting data concerning the properties of strains of *C. diphtheriae* obtained from various parts of the United States. Among the presentations by him is found the following: "The gravis type of *C. diphtheriae* is not an important health problem in the United States *at present*, but may become so at any time." See also editorial (*J. A. M. A.*, 1943, **122,** 176). It is important to note that smears from colonies on tellurite media are frequently not characteristic and typical of the microscopical observations as described above. The diphtheria bacillus has about the same resistance as other nonspore-forming bacteria. In a dry state and at low temperatures, it may live for long periods of time. Crosbie and Wright (*Lancet*, 1941, **1,** 656) noted its ability to persist in floor dust for periods as long as fourteen weeks *in vitro* and five weeks on the floor.

The pharynx is the site usually invaded by the diphtheria bacillus, causing the contagious disease, named diphtheria, because of the characteristic (leathery) false membrane that forms. The larynx may also become involved, producing laryngeal diphtheria or membranous and diphtheritic croup. Nasal diphtheria or membranous rhinitis is at times frequently found. Middle-ear affections, infected wounds of the skin, and even infections of the vaginal tract and other mucous membranes may be caused by this organism. Reiss (*Lancet*, 1943, **244,** 381) reported recently nine bacteriologically verified cases of cutaneous diphtheria. Suspected clinical findings should always be confirmed by a bacteriological examination of the secretions from the affected parts. The greatest problem in epidemics or in the spread of diphtheria is the detection of carriers. It has been shown by many workers that almost 1 per cent of the population may be diphtheria carriers. These individuals not feeling sick are not confined to bed, but in their daily routine come in contact with many individuals, and as such they may become a menace. The disease may be disseminated by personal contact with diseased persons or convalescent cases, by articles soiled with infected discharges, by human and animal carriers or through infected milk and milk products.

Diphtheria is not a natural disease of lower animals and true diphtheria occurs in them only in rare instances.   Through its toxin, lower animals are susceptible to the action of *C. diphtheriae* when they are inoculated with the latter.   Cats, dogs, pigeons and guinea pigs are highly susceptible.   Rabbits are less susceptible than guinea pigs. Rats and mice are relatively refractory.   Frobisher recently pointed out in studies of the virulence of members of the genus *Corynebacterium* that "7 to 14 day old chicks are, in many respects, more desirable subjects for testing the virulence or toxigenicity of diphtheria bacilli, and for measuring the potency of toxin, than are guinea pigs and rabbits."   It is well to remember that the ability of diphtheria bacilli to produce clinical diphtheria depends upon their ability not only to produce toxin, but also upon their invasive properties.   Furthermore, the presence of antitoxin in the one attacked and the association of other bacteria are other factors to be considered.

In a bacteriological investigation of a suspicious diphtheria, at least two, and possibly three, kinds of evidence are necessary.   In frank cases of clinical diphtheria the clinical symptoms supply more information as to the gravity and extent of the disease than is possible in laboratory findings.   In such cases the presence of morphologically typical organisms in a typical clinical lesion, found on direct smear and by culture on Loeffler's blood-serum medium, is sufficient *presumptive evidence* of the existence of true diphtheria.   *Final* or *completed evidence* of the identity, type and virulence may await later findings after the organism has been isolated in a pure culture.   In the meantime on the grounds of the presumptive evidence or even clinical symptoms alone, the diagnostician should administer antitoxin.   Whenever suggestive clinical symptoms are present, the case should be treated as one of diphtheria.   Negative bacteriological findings by direct smear and especially by culture must be given consideration in proportion to the assurance that the swabbing technique was properly performed (the swab reached the exudate), a suitable culture was properly inoculated, and that the microscopic examination was adequate and performed by a capable and experienced worker.   Cultures made from suspicious or doubtful cases, especially in those instances where the clinical symptoms are not marked and lesions are absent, and those prepared from swabs obtained from "convalescent" carriers (in so-called *release cultures*) and especially *healthy* carriers, require more conclusive evidence for verification or confirmation than microscopic and simple culturing methods.   *Completed* evidence is needed.   It is well to remember that the latter techniques supply information as to the presence or absence of diphtheria or diphtheria-like organisms and that the clinical symptoms indicate whether clinical diphtheria exists.   The presence of diphtheria bacilli without frank clinical signs does not mean that the case is necessarily one of diphtheria.   The *completed evidence* for identifying an organism as being *C. diphtheriae* consists in supplementing the *presumptive evidence* (typical organisms found on direct smear and on simple culturing) with isolating the organism in pure culture (preferably from tellurite medium) and demonstrating that (1) it produces acid but no gas in dextrose, (2) does not attack saccharose, and (3) gives a positive virulency test (see Fraser, *A. P. H. A. Year Book*, 1936–1937).   The pathogenicity test is performed by injecting a pure culture subcutaneously or intracutaneously into suitable animals, and using suitable controls.   This *completed evidence* as to identity and virulence may be further supplemented as to type if the latter information is desired.   Demonstration of the presence or absence of the several important differentiating characteristics (see page 126) will indicate whether the organism is a *gravis* or a *mitis* type.

Various optional and rapid methods for culturing the diphtheria bacillus from lesions have been recommended. The use of a swab impregnated with animal serum, or a swab placed into sterile tubes containing a few cc. of sterile serum has been advocated as yielding rapid results at a lower expense. Various formulas of tellurite-blood-agar medium have been described for the isolation of *C. diphtheria* directly from lesions and used for routine rapid diagnosis of diphtheria. In most quarters these methods for the isolation of *C. diphtheriae* directly have found little favor, as the chances of getting false negative findings are greater. Also, as mentioned previously, a tellurite medium is only of value as a differential medium for the observation of typical colonies. The microscopy of the latter is not characteristic, so that it either becomes necessary to transplant the typical colonies on Loeffler's medium (and thus lose twenty-four hours' time) or initially inoculate both the tellurite and the Loeffler's medium (resulting in an added expense).

A highly potent diphtheria antitoxin, possessing temporary protective and especially curative properties, is available. Valuable tests for determining the presence or absence of an immunity to diphtheria (*Schick Test* and *Reh Test*) are being employed. Diphtheria toxoid (plain and alum precipitated), Floccules, T-A Mixture and other diphtheria preparations are used successfully as prophylactic agents to create a more lasting immunity to diphtheria. For a consideration of the foregoing and other data concerning biological products in diphtheria, see pages 485–489. For other details concerning diphtheria, see Forbes (*Diphtheria, Past and Present; Its Aetiology, Distribution, Transmission and Prevention*, London, 1932), Mueller ("Nutrition of the Diphtheria Bacillus," *Bact. Revs.*, 1940, **4**, 97) and Frobisher ("The Diphtheria Bacillus," *Diagnostic Procedures and Reagents, A. P. H. A.*, 1941).

The Diphtheroid Bacilli

Corynebacterium Pseudodiphthericum (*Pseudodiphtheria Bacillus; Bacillus Hoffmanni*).—This, a nonpathogen, is found in throats of normal and diseased individuals.

Corynebacterium Xerose (*Bacillus Xerosis*).—This is found in normal and diseased conjunctiva. It may at times produce a low-grade chronic conjunctivitis.

Corynebacterium Hodgkinii (*Bacillus Hodgkinii*).—This is found in lymph glands in Hodgkin's disease and is nonpathogenic.

Corynebacterium Segmentosum (*Bacillus Segmentosus*).—This, a nonpathogen, is found in nasal secretions.

Corynebacterium Acnes (*Bacillus Acnes*).—This bacillus has been isolated from sweat glands, hair follicles and from acne pustules. It is a nonpathogenic microaerophile.

Corynebacterium Hoagii is found in the air and is frequently a contaminant of cultures, producing a pink coloration. It also has been isolated from the throat.

Corynebacterium pyogenes (*Bacillus or Bacterium pyogenes*) is found in different pyogenic processes in cattle, sheep and swine, especially in cases of mastitis and arthritis. For further details concerning this species and *Corynebacterium renale*, see Marchant (*J. Bact.*, 1935, **30**, 95). The latter species has been found in certain cases of pyelitis in cattle. Some workers do not but many do regard *C. renale* (*B. pyelonephritis bovis*) as a separate species.

Corynebacterium equi has been recovered from cases of purulent pneumonia in foals and from various lesions in swine. For further details, see Karlson and associates (*J. Infect. Dis.*, 1940, **67**, 243).

Corynebacterium ovis (*C. or B. pseudotuberculosis; Preisz-Nocard bacillus*) produces the so-called pseudotuberculosis or caseous-lymphadentis in sheep. In foreign countries, this organism has also been isolated from cases of ulcerative lymphangitis of horses.

There are a large number of bacteria which because of their morphological resemblance to the true diphtheria bacillus have been loosely termed *pseudodiphtheria bacilli*, more frequently known as *diphtheroids*, and placed in genus *Corynebacterium* of the Bergey classification. Their chief importance is in connection with their presence in nose and throat cultures of suspected cases of diphtheria, convalescent cases ready to be discharged, or diphtheria carriers. The diphtheroids are also to be found in urethral and vaginal discharges and skin affections; in fact they may be said to be ubiquitous. They are all usually Gram-positive, do not produce spores, flagella or capsules. As a rule, they are shorter, thicker, more uniform in size, do not curve as the true diphtheria bacillus, and they grow more readily on ordinary culture media. They may also show differences in their fermentative activity on sugars. Some, as the acne bacillus, are microaerophilic. None of them produces an extracellular toxin. Some of them may display chromogenesis. They tend to stain solidly, though in some instances the ends may be more deeply stained than the remainder of the organism. Neisser's stain for diphtheria bacilli is employed by some workers for its differentiating value, but is not always successful. Whenever in doubt as to whether an organism is a true diphtheria bacillus or one of the diphtheroid bacilli, inoculations of the organism are made into guinea pigs. The true diphtheria bacillus is virulent and pathogenic for guinea pigs and the diphtheroid bacilli are nonvirulent and nonpathogenic.

Fusiform Bacillus

Fusiformis Dentium (*Bacillus Fusiformis; Vincent's Bacillus; Vincent's Fusiform Bacillus*).—The genus *Fusobacterium* consists of Gram-negative, slender, anaerobic rods, usually nonmotile and with tapering ends. They stain with more or less distinct granules. The exact relationship between the many different strains has not been clearly established. The *F. plauti vincenti* is a Gram-negative, anaerobic rod, with pointed or blunt ends, fusiform, from 0.5 to 2 by 3 to 10 μ. Stained preparations show an irregularity in staining and several deeply stained granules may be apparent. *F. plauti vincenti* is nonpathogenic for experimental animals when in pure culture, but in mixed culture produces abscesses. These *fusiform* bacilli occur in association with the so-called spirochetes or spirilla of Vincent (*Borrelia vincenti*) in fusospirochetosis or Vincent's angina, gingivitis or trench mouth, dental caries and allied infections, ulcerative stomatitis, gangrene and in wounds. They are rarely found in the healthy mouth. The constancy of the presence of these two anaerobic organisms in the affections mentioned suggests a symbiotic relationship and their etiological connection with these conditions. A diagnosis is generally made in direct smears due to the preponderance of the number of these organisms when present. Culturing is rarely resorted to, as growth on laboratory media is obtained only when special precautions are taken. For treatment of affections by these organisms, arsphenamine has given good results, when administered locally or intravenously. For further details, of this species and other fusiform bacilli, see Dack (*Bact. Rev.*, 1940, **4**, 227). See also page 187.

Acid-Fast Bacilli

Mycobacterium Tuberculosis (var. **Hominis**) (*Tubercle Bacillus, Human Type*).— This is the cause of tuberculosis in man.

Mycobacterium Tuberculosis (var. **Bovis**) (*Bacillus Tuberculosis, Bovine Type*).— This bacillus is the cause of tuberculosis in cattle and which is transmissible to man and domestic animals. See also page 133.

Mycobacterium Avium (*Bacillus Tuberculosis, Fowl, Avian or Bird Type*).— This bacillus is the cause of tuberculosis in chickens, pheasants, turkeys, and transmissible to pigeons and birds. Ducks and geese are exempt. See also page 134.

Mycobacterium Piscium (*The Ichthic Type of the Tubercle Bacillus*).—This bacillus is the cause of nodule- and tumor-like formations in carp. It is infectious for carp, frogs, turtles and lizards, but not for guinea pigs and pigeons. These strains other than their acid-fastness have little resemblance to the mammalian types of tubercle bacilli. They grow rapidly and luxuriantly on the commonly observed culture media, best at 20° to 24° C., growth ceasing at 37° C. or above. They are regarded as harmless saprophytes and are only of interest mainly because of claims made from time to time that an immunity can be produced in man against tuberculosis by their injection. See Friedman and Aronson (*J. Infect. Dis.*, 1929, **44**, 222).

The *human type of the tubercle bacillus* appears as slender rods, usually slightly curved, from 0.2 to 0.6 by 0.5 to 4 μ. They occur singly, in pairs and in occasional threads, in heaps, small or large bundles or in compact masses in which the individual bacilli tend to lie parallel or form an acute angle with each other. Club-shaped forms and branching are observed under exceptional conditions. They may stain irregularly, showing beaded or banded forms. Unstained spaces due to vacuoles may give the organism an appearance of a chain of cocci or even may be mistaken for spores. Owing to the presence of a waxy substance, it may require heating or a long period of time to make the ordinary aniline stains permeable, but when once stained it is very difficult to decolorize even by the use of alcohol and strong acids. This alcohol- and acid-fast characteristic is utilized in the Ziehl-Neelsen and Pappenheim methods of staining (see page 45), commonly employed in practice when staining material to detect the presence of tubercle bacilli. Recently Richards and Miller (*Am. J. Clin. Path.*, Tech. Suppl., 1941, **11**, 1) described a procedure for the detection of acid-fast bacteria by using the fluorescent stain, *auramine*. This method appears most promising, and may replace the widely used Ziehl-Neelsen method due to its convenience and greater ease in detecting the presence of tubercle bacilli in materials. Van Dyke (*Am. J. Clin. Path.*, 1943, **13**, Tech. Sect., 6) in a comparative evaluation of the Ziehl-Neelsen and the fluorescent methods concluded that the latter procedure was the more efficient as to a saving of time and the larger number of positive findings for tubercle bacilli in sputum. Observations were reported by Sister John (*Am. J. Med. Tech.*, 1941, **7**, 256) which reveal that after the administration of sulfonamide drugs, the sputum may contain crystals which are acid-fast and which may resemble rather closely *M. tuberculosis.* These crystals are seen as long, slender, acid-fast rods, some-times curved, at times short and straight, and sometimes in bristling clumps. It may be advisable to discontinue these drugs before sputum examinations for tubercle bacilli are reported conclusively as positive by staining techniques only.

In the "Fluorescence Method" (*Am. J. Clin. Path.*, Tech. Suppl., 1941, **11,** 1), the smears are prepared; air-dried; and stained for 2 to 3 min. in Auramine Solution (Auramine O (C.C.), 0.1 Gm., 3 per cent aqueous phenol, 100 cc.); washed in tap water; washed for 3 to 5 min. in a freshly prepared acid alcohol (Ethyl Alcohol (70%), 100 cc., Conc. HCl, 0.5 cc., NaCl, 0.5 Gm.); and dried. It is then examined under a monocular microscope, using an 8-mm. dry objective and a 20 × ocular with a low-voltage, high-amperage microscope lamp, supplied with a blue (ultraviolet trans-mitting) filter, and a complementary yellow filter for the ocular. The background is almost black; acid-fast bacteria are bright yellow and fluorescent; other organisms are barely visible.

M. tuberculosis is strictly parasitic, an obligate aerobe, nonmotile, nonspore-bearing, Gram-positive and possesses a thin capsular or enveloping substance, which is only detectable under special conditions. A true soluble toxin is not produced. Chemi-cally and immunologically, the body of *M. tuberculosis* is distinctive in the lipoids, proteins and carbohydrates present. For details of the constitution and antigenic fractions present, see Long (*Proc. 8th Amer. Sci. Congress,* 1942, **6,** 253). Much (*Beitr. klin. Tuberk.,* 1907, **8,** 85) has described nonacid-fast, Gram-positive granules (so-called *Much granules*) in tuberculous lesions in which acid-fast bacilli could not be found. He claims that these granules are viable, virulent and infective, and give rise to typical acid-fast bacilli. Their exact significance is not clearly understood. Growth in all media is slow, requiring several weeks (4 to 6) for development. Glycerin or some natural fluid must be present in the media. Among the special culture media employed for isolating the tubercle bacillus are to be found: Dorset's, Petroff's, Bordet-Gengou's, Corper's, Petragnani's and Lowenstein's (pages 56 and 61). Wooley's potato egg medium (*Am. Rev. of Tuberc.,* 1931, **24,** 596) and Schwabacher's egg-yolk saline medium are recommended. Most strains of the human type grow more abun-dantly on these media and on glycerin medium than do the strains of the bovine type Those strains growing freely (as the human type) are termed *eugonic* and those growing feebly (as the bovine type) are termed *dysgonic.* The human type can be grown in the simpler synthetic media, of which Long's Medium (*Am. Rev. of Tuberc.,* 1926, **13,** 393) is the best known. For an evaluation of different media for diagnostic cultures of tubercle bacilli, see Corper and Cohn (*Am. Rev. of Tuberc.,* 1942, **46,** 560). Tem-peratures below 30° C. and above 42° C. inhibit growth.

Recently nonacid-fast forms of the tubercle bacillus were studied by means of different improved counterstain techniques. For further details, see the differential triple stain for demonstrating and studying these forms in sputum, tissue and body fluids as presented by Alexander-Jackson (*Science,* 1944, **99,** 307).

Laboratory aids for demonstrating the presence of the tubercle bacillus in body fluids or tissues is by means of stained smears (using alcohol- and acid-fast methods of staining) made directly from the fluids or after treatment by digestion and concentra-tion methods, by culturing or by guinea-pig inoculation. The use of the latter pro-cedure and then observing the presence of tubercles containing the organisms in these animals at the end of from four to six weeks after injection or after they succumb give conclusive and valuable findings. Many methods of sputum digestion have been presented. In these procedures, different reagents are added which digest the albuminous and most cellular elements, leaving the tubercle bacilli relatively unaffected. Centrifugalization concentrates the bacteria present, so that a sediment is obtained free of all bacteria but rich in tubercle bacilli if the latter are present. This sediment can be used for staining and direct microscopy and for culturing. Uhlenhuth and Xylander (*Ber. Klin. Wchnschr.*, 1908, **45**, 1346) suggested the well-known *Antiormin* as the digestant. Lowenstein (*Wien. Klin. Wchnschr.*, 1924, **38**, 231) used a 6 per cent sulfuric acid solution. Petroff (*J. Exp. Med.*, 1915, **21**, 38) recommended a 3 per cent NaOH solution and Corper (*J. Lab. & Clin. Med.*, 1930, **15**, 348) employed a 5 per cent oxalic acid solution. MacNamara and Ducey (*J. Lab. & Clin. Med.*, 1935, **20**, 976) recommended a digestion method in which pepsin was used as the digestant and Petroff and Schain (*Quart. Bull., Sea View Hosp.*, 1940, **5**, 183) used "Tergitol 08." All of these digestants have been tried in the author's laboratory. The "Tergitol 08" technique yielded the most satisfactory results. Of the others, the following are listed in the order of their efficiencies: Antiformin (sodium hypochlorite), 3 per cent sodium hydroxide and 5 per cent oxalic acid digestants.

Due to the presence of a waxy substance in the organisms and the mucus usually present in tuberculous material, tubercle bacilli have a somewhat greater resistant power than possessed by most other nonspore-forming pathogens. Cold has little effect. In dust, at ordinary room temperature and away from direct sunlight, tubercle bacilli may survive for many months. In sputum, they may remain viable for several weeks and even months. Bichloride of mercury and hypochlorite solutions are unsuitable for the destruction of tubercle bacilli in sputum. A 5 per cent solution of phenol may require at least six hours. The addition of an excess of alkali and the use of boiling temperatures will kill this organism in sputum within one to two minutes.

The human type of the tubercle bacillus is not pathogenic for fowl but it is pathogenic for guinea pigs and rabbits. This type produces generalized tuberculosis in guinea pigs but not in rabbits, while the bovine type produces generalized tuberculosis in both animals.

The *tubercle* is the characteristic lesion of tuberculosis. The localization of *M. tuberculosis* in a tissue area results in an accumulation around the bacteria of a variable number of round epithelial-like cells ("epithelioid cells"), the latter being formed due to the action of the various metabolic products of the tubercle bacilli upon the fixed connective tissue cells. Large characteristic giant cells are intermingled with these epithelioid cells and tubercle bacilli may be present in the former. A large number of leukocytes, predominantly lymphocytes, surround this area and between the cells there are present varying amounts of a fibrinous matrix of a coagulated exudate. The tubercles appear at first as small, nonvascular, translucent, whitish-gray nodules. The latter coalesce, giving rise to larger nodules, which are more opaque and yellow in color. As the process continues, a caseous degeneration of the central portion of the nodule occurs. The caseated nodule becomes calcified, preceded by the formation of a fibrous capsule, if the lesion or nodule heals.

Practically every organ and tissue of the human body may be invaded by the tubercle bacillus. The lungs, of course, are the common seat of infection (pulmonary tuberculosis), but it is possible to have tuberculosis of the larynx, intestines, urinary bladder, kidneys, lymphatic glands (known as scrofula), skin (known as lupus), bones (known as white swelling), mesenteric glands (known as marasmus or *take off*), spine (Pott's disease) and membranes lining almost any part of the body, including the meninges, joints, etc.   The organism enters the body chiefly through the nose and mouth and in contaminated food and drink.   The *white plague*, as this malady is also known, is communicable.   Though rarely hereditary, it is a household disease so that those living in the same home where a careless tubercular patient is found are more apt to contract this condition.   Familial and race predispositions are apparent.   The several predisposing causes common to respiratory infections will also assist in bringing a tubercular focus into activity with the result of active tuberculosis.   In tubercular infections there is always found associated with the tubercle bacillus one or more varieties of organisms, the predominating ones being the pneumococcus, staphylococcus, streptococcus, influenza and other bacilli.   There is no doubt that these organisms exert an unfavorable influence and aggravate the existing condition.   One may, therefore, be inclined to regard "consumption" (as the layman speaks of tuberculosis) as an affection in which the symptoms are not caused by the tubercle bacillus alone, but that a great part of the unfavorable progress of the disease may be attributed to these secondary invaders.

It is not always possible to find tubercle bacilli in sputum or other material, even though a tubercular infection exists.   Careful clinical findings and an accurate history, Roentgen-ray, tuberculin testing and other laboratory tests may be required before a correct diagnosis is made.   It should, however, be emphasized that tuberculosis can be arrested if treatment is applied early.   This consists in a carefully regulated regimen, in which rest, fresh air and sunshine, proper and sufficient nourishing food and contentment are employed.   The most noteworthy advance, however, has been made in the use of collapse therapy.   Among the large number of chemotherapeutic agents employed in treatment, most favorable results are reported on the use of gold thiosulfate. *Promin*, a sulfonamide compound, and related compounds, *diamino diphenyl sulfone and Diasone*, have been recently recommended.   Steinbach and Duce (*Proc. Soc. Exptl. Biol. Med.*, 1942, **49**, 460) report that in experimental tuberculosis in guinea pigs, promin exerted a retarding effect on the course of the disease; and Zucker and associates (*Am. Rev. of Tuberc.*, 1942, **46**, 277) conclude that promin administered to humans by the intravenous drip method is ineffective.   Vitamins and enzymes from earthworms are receiving some consideration.   For a consideration of the epidemiology of tuberculosis, see Pinner (*Am. Rev. of Tuberc.*, 1940, **42**, 382) and Godfrey (*Am. Rev. of Tuberc.*, 1941, **43**, 1).   For social and economic factors in tuberculosis etiology, see Emerson (*Proc. 8th Amer. Sci. Congress*, 1942, **6**, 243).

The *bovine type of the tubercle bacillus* is highly pathogenic for all mammals except man.   This type is shorter and more plump than the human type and grows but feebly on any culture medium.   Growth of the bovine type is not necessarily enhanced by the addition of glycerin to the medium nor does it produce a yellow to red pigment on serum media as is produced by the human type.   Antigenically the human and bovine types are not distinguishable.   It is more pathogenic for rabbits than the human type and it is nonpathogenic for fowls.   Calves and cats are resistant to the human strains, but subcutaneous injections of bovine strains produce generalized tuberculosis. Children are the ones especially infected with the bovine type; adults only infrequently.   It is thought that infected milk may be the cause of bovine infections. Pasteurization of milk and obtaining the latter from tuberculin-tested cows, proved to be free of tuberculosis, will probably entirely eliminate this as a source of danger. Griffith and Smith (*Lancet*, 1940, **2**, 291) reported finding approximately 7 per cent of bovine type tubercle bacilli in the sputum of 977 cases in Northeast Scotland.

The optimum temperatures of growth for the *avian type* is 40° C. (range 30° to 44° C.). Human and bovine types will not grow above 41° C. The avian type is pleomorphic and is culturally distinguished from the mammalian types by the production of only a very slight growth on solid media, the absence of pellicle formation in fluid media and it will grow below the surface of broth. Pheasants, turkeys, pigeons and chickens suffer from tuberculosis caused by the avian type. There is no danger to man from this type of tubercle bacillus. The mouse and the rabbit are mammals in which avian strains can cause a generalized tuberculosis.

Other Acid–Fast Bacteria

Mycobacterium lacticola is the species name being employed at present and used broadly to include the following which were previously listed as individual species: *M. smegmatis* (*smegma bacillus*), found on the genitalia of man and in urine and feces; *M. butyricum* (*butter bacillus*), isolated from butter; *M. stercussis* (*dung bacillus*), found in cow manure; and *M. graminis*, isolated from plant dust. *M. phlei* (*timothy hay bacillus*) has been isolated from timothy grass, dust and milk.

The so-called *Lustgarten bacillus*, reported in 1884 as the cause of syphilis, was probably the *M. smegmatis*.

The above are some of a number of acid-fast bacteria (grouped under the genus *mycobacterium*) which occur as harmless saprophytes. Sufficient evidence has not been presented to regard many of them as individual species, with the result that the present designation (*M. lacticola*) is being employed to include all of them, until definite presentations will entitle each one to species rank. Their importance lies in the fact that they may be present in materials under examination and which are suspected of containing tubercle bacilli. The fact that most of these acid-fast organisms are shorter, thicker and usually solidly stained, are nonalcohol-fast, nonpathogenic, grow at low (room) temperatures on ordinary media within a few days, and display different morphological characteristics, is taken into consideration as an aid in differentiating them from the tubercle bacillus. For further details, see Gordon (*J. Bact.*, 1937, **34**, 617) and Gordon and Hagan (*J. Bact.*, 1938, **36**, 39).

Mycobacterium Paratuberculosis (*Johne's Bacillus; Scrapie Bacillus*).—This is a plump, pleomorphic rod which in many ways resembles the tubercle bacillus. It is difficult to cultivate in primary cultures and has been grown only in media containing dead acid-fast bacteria. A synthetic medium (free from acid-fast bacteria) was used successfully by Dunkin (*J. Comp. Path. & Therap.*, 1933, **46**, 159) and Watson (*Canad. Pub. Health J.*, 1935, **26**, 268). The Johne's bacillus, apparently an obligate parasite is the cause of Johne's disease, which affects the intestinal mucosa in cases of chronic enteritis of cattle. The chronic diarrhea is produced in sheep as well as in bovines. At one time this disease was thought to be a type of intestinal tuberculosis, which it resembles only remotely. Its presence is detectable by the use of the *Johnin test*, similar to the tuberculin test. This organism, unlike the tubercle bacillus, is nonpathogenic for guinea pigs and rabbits. Infection with *M. paratuberculosis* has not been recorded.

Mycobacterium Leprae (*Leprosy Bacillus*).—*Mycobacterium leprae* has a close morphological resemblance to the tubercle bacillus, except that it is shorter, less slender and rarely bent or curved. Staining and many other characteristics are like that of tubercle bacilli, although *Mycobacterium leprae* generally stains more solidly and it does not stand decolorization as well. Material, smears from tissue pulp or scrapings obtained from infected areas, when stained, will usually reveal the presence of large numbers of bacilli, generally grouped together in masses or bundles like a packet of cigarettes tied together in the granulation tissue cells. They are especially demonstrable in nasal and skin lesions. In some cases of nodular leprosy during the febrile stages, the bacilli can be detected in the blood after treating the latter by concentration methods. Successful cultivation on culture media or pathogenic results when inoculated into laboratory animals have not been successful. The negative results are important as methods of differentiation from tubercle bacilli. The evidence appears to be that most of the organisms isolated from the tissues of lepers, though some of them appear acid-fast, are in reality saprophytes. *M. leprae*, an obligate parasite in man, is the cause of the chronic disease, leprosy, characterized by the presence of a spreading nodular infiltrate in the skin (face and other parts of the body) and mucous membranes (so-called tubercular or nodular leprosy) or by changes or lesions of the nerves (so-called anesthetic leprosy). The one point above all others which may be relied upon to exclude a diagnosis of leprosy with reasonable certainty is the absence of thermal anesthesia.

Leprosy, one of the oldest of known diseases, occurs in all climates, among all races and both sexes. The disease is, however, more commonly found in countries with moist tropical climates. Leprosy is more prevalent among males than females. Most cases are contracted during childhood or adolescence. The natural mode of infection is not known and nothing is known concerning the distribution of leprosy bacilli outside of the human body. The contagiousness of leprosy is not as great as that of other bacterial diseases. Though the communicability of leprosy from man to man is generally accepted, intimate contact *alone* does not necessarily result in infection. Intimate and prolonged contact with infected individuals, among whom the standards of personal hygiene are low, will result in the contraction of leprosy.

Chaulmoogra and hydnocarpus oils and their derivatives are used in treatment, with the indications that they possess only slight value in this disease. Davison and Grasset (*Leprosy Rev.*, Oct., 1941) and McKean (*Internat. J. Leprosy*, April–June, 1941) discuss the limitations to the diphtheria toxoid treatment of leprosy, originally suggested by Collier. The *Montel Method*, using 1 per cent aqueous methylene-blue solutions (*Indian Med. J.*, June, 1941) and vaccinotherapy (*Med. Bull.*, Jan. 17, 1942), using the *Waudremer vaccine*, are methods of treatment employed in special cases.

The only sure means of eradicating leprosy known today is segregation. The use of the modern leprosarium is proving a most effective aid in arresting the disease and in replacing the unwarranted popular fear of leprosy by a more general enlightened attitude. The only leprosarium in the United States, the finest and most modern in the world and which serves as a center for the dissemination of knowledge concerning leprosy, is located at Carville, Louisiana. For the story of this national institution, see Faget (*Pub. Health Rep.*, 1942, **57**, 641). (See also *Internat. J. Leprosy*, 1936, **4**, 141; 1940, **8**, 501). It is well to emphasize that caution is needed in the interests of both patient and public health, when making a diagnosis of leprosy. The actual diagnosis

is made by clinical evidence and the demonstration of the presence of acid- and alcohol-fast bacilli in lesions of suspicious cases is *only* confirmatory.   In anesthetic or nerve leprosy, the diagnosis at present is always made independently of the bacteriological findings, as the bacilli are found but infrequently in the living subject.   For limits of bacteriologic diagnosis, see Hoffman (*J. Trop. Med. & Hyg.*, 1940, **43**, 234, 243). For further details, see also *Tuberculosis and Leprosy, The Mycobacterial Diseases* (one of the A. A. A. S. symposia publications), and Pardo-Costello and Tiant (*J. A. M. A.*, 1943, **121**, 1264).

M. Leprae Murium, morphologically indistinguishable from *M. leprae,* is the cause of a natural disease in wild rats (rat leprosy).   In spite of the similarity of human leprosy to rat leprosy, the accepted opinion today regards these organisms as separate species and the diseases as distinct from each other.   Rats are not susceptible when injected with human leprous material.   It has been suggested that the relationship between the two species is comparable to that of the human and avian types of the tubercle bacillus.   For further details, see Lowe (*Internat. J. Leprosy*, 1937, **5**, 311, 463) and Fite (*Nat. Inst. Health Bull.* **173,** 1940).

The Colon-Typhoid-Dysentery Group and Closely Allied Bacilli

Coliform Bacteria.—There is a large number of bacilli that may be found in the colon or other parts of the intestinal tract of man and other animals.   Many of them are nonpathogenic.   They are short, rather plump, nonspore-bearing rods, aerobic and facultative anaerobic, grow on ordinary media producing almost identical characteristics, do not (with but few exceptions) liquefy gelatin, and are Gram-negative.

It has been a common custom for several decades to group together many of these Gram-negative bacilli, especially those found in the intestinal tract and which also are closely related biologically and in many other characteristics.   A casual but apparently convenient reference is made by the use of such explanatory terms as: *colon group, colon-typhoid group, colon-typhoid-dysentery group, coli-aerogenes group, typhoid-paratyphoid group,* etc.   The convenient use of such grouping and subdivision is apparent, but to the beginner it may be misleading.   It must be remembered that the important forms, at either extreme, are easily distinguished from one another, but between these extremes are intermediate forms which display wide variations and which defy definite classification and grouping.   An important distinction between the more frequently found Gram-negative nonpathogenic and pathogenic intestinal rods is made on the basis of lactose fermentation.   The correlation between lactose fermentation and pathogenicity, though not absolute, is sufficiently marked to possess considerable practical importance.   The *coli-aerogenes* or *Escherichia-aerobacter* group as the terms continue official in Standard Methods of Water Analysis and in Examination of Dairy Products, respectively, constitute the lactose-fermenting Gram-negative rods.   It is the lactose-fermenting bacteria (species of *Aerogenes* as well as of *Escherichia*), which are used as a measure of the pollution of water or as a sanitary index.   In such instances the term *coliform* bacteria rather than *E. coli* is the more suitable term.   In 1937, Jordan, in an editorial statement (*J. Am. Water Works Assoc.*, 1937, 1999) advised that his policy would be to substitute the term *coliform* for *B.* or *E. coli* or "colon group" in papers submitted to him.   The editions of Standard Methods of Dairy Products issued since 1937 also carry this term.   From the sanitary standpoint, all of

the coliform bacteria must be regarded as possibly fecal in origin, until methods of further differentiation or classification are practiced. In the confirmatory test, to differentiate the *coliform* or *Escherichia-aerobacter* group, eosin-methylene blue agar plates are inoculated with some of the growth from positive lactose broth tubes which reveal the presence of gas. After incubation at 37° C. for twenty-four hours, minute amounts of the growth of several suspicious colonies are inoculated into separate tubes of Koser's Citrate Medium which are incubated at 37° C. Absence of growth after twenty-four hours is a positive test for *E. coli*. Into tubes of Modified Eijkman Lactose Medium, there is placed a loopful of growth from the primary lactose broth culture which reveals fermentation, and the inoculated tubes are incubated at 45.5° C. (±0.2° C.). Any quantity of gas production within forty-eight hours is a positive test for *E. coli*.

The incubation in the modified Eijkman test, unlike incubation as is usually carried out, must be carefully and closely controlled. Below 45° C., bacteria of the coliform group other than *E. coli* will grow, while temperatures above 46° C. will inhibit *E. coli*.

Among the various tests mentioned under *Escherichia* and *Aerobacter*, the following tests have proved most useful for differentiation and classification of the different species: indol production, methyl-red reaction, Voges-Proskauer reaction and citrate utilization. This has resulted in the introduction by Parr (*Am. J. Pub. Health*, 1936, **26**, 39) of the IMVIC, a mnemonic, which fixes in order the four tests commonly used in classifying coliform bacteria. The *imvic* group of tests are used frequently in conjunction with other biochemical and serological aids.

The importance of coliform bacteria in pathological processes is apparent by the existence of a very large literature on the subject. In human pathology, these organisms are frequently the cause of affections of the genito-urinary and gastro-enterological tracts. In veterinary medicine, the coliform bacteria have received recently considerable attention. They are frequently involved as secondary invaders that complicate infection. In plant pathology, the species of *Erwinia* and even other genera, recognized as causative agents of diseases among plants, are very closely related to the coliform bacteria. In other abnormalities encountered here, coliform bacteria are suspected as the etiological factors. Coliform bacteria appear then as a ubiquitous group of bacteria with variable and changeable forms, each of which apparently adapts itself to certain environments and predominates there. For further details on coliform bacteria, see Parr (*Bact. Revs.*, 1939, **3,** I) and on coliform mutants, see Parr and Simpson (*J. Bact.*, 1940, **40**, 467).

Escherichia Coli (*Colon Bacillus; Bacillus Coli Communis; Bacterium Coli*).— The colon bacillus exhibits considerable variations in morphology. Short, oval and coccus-like (coccoid) forms may be present. The rods are generally short, with rounded ends from 0.4 to 0.7 by 1 to 4 μ, occurring singly, in pairs and rarely as short chains. Flagella are present. It is aerobic and facultatively anaerobic and grows on ordinary media at room and body temperatures (range from 10° to 45° C.). Gelatin is not liquefied. Milk is acidulated and coagulated. Many of the sugars are fermented with both acid and gas production. Indol is produced, and nitrates are reduced to nitrites. It is M-R (methyl-red) positive, V-P (Voges-Proskauer) negative and does not utilize citric acid or citrate as the sole source of carbon for its food supply. Uric acid is not and uracil is utilized as the sole source of carbon (*J. Bact.*, 1938, **35,** 19). Catalase is

produced. Trimethyleneglycol is not produced from glycerin by anaerobic fermentation (*J. Bact.*, 1932, **23,** 167). *E. coli* is a weak resistant organism. Most strains are quickly destroyed by the commonly used disinfectants and at 60° C. in a water bath for thirty minutes. It is nonspore-bearing, does not possess a capsule, is Gram-negative and under some conditions bipolar granules are apparent. This organism is normally an inhabitant of the intestinal tract of man and all vertebrates. Each gram of feces contains millions of these organisms. The presence of *E. coli* in water and foodstuffs, etc., is regarded by sanitarians as indicative of sewage contamination. Due to its presence in defecated matter, this organism is eventually distributed and becomes practically ubiquitous in all thickly populated areas. The colon bacillus may gain entrance to other parts of the body and exert a marked pathogenic effect. It may cause infection of the kidneys, gallbladder, urinary bladder, liver, appendix, anus, genitals, and even invade the circulation in agonal stages of disease, causing a bacteremia. A case of *E. coli* meningitis was recently reported (*Arch. Pediat.*, 1944, **41,** 75).

Escherichia Coli var. **Communior** (*Bacillus Coli Communior*).—This bacillus resembles *Bacillus coli* in every way, differing solely in its behavior toward saccharose and when specific agglutination tests are made. It ferments saccharose but not salicin. It is found in the intestinal canal of normal animals, rarely causing disease.

Escherichia Coli var. **Acidi Lactici** (*Bacillus Acidi Lactici*).—The lactic acid bacillus resembles the *E. coli* and is now given the above species name. It differs from the latter in being nonmotile, does not ferment dulcite, saccharose or salicin, and in specificity in agglutination tests. It is found normally in the intestinal tract of man and animals, in water, milk and cheese. It has no pathogenic significance.

Escherichia freundii is widely distributed in nature. It is found in soil and water and to a varying degree in the intestinal canal of man and animals. Most strains differ from *E. coli* strains in that they produce H_2S in peptone iron agar (*Am. J. Pub. Health*, 1934, **24,** 505; 1937, **27,** 1240), utilize citric acid as a sole source or carbon, produce trimethyleneglycol from glycerin by anaerobic fermentation and will not produce gas in sugar media when incubated at 44° C.

Aerobacter Aerogenes (*Bacillus Lactis Aerogenes; Bacillus Aerogenes*).—The *Bacillus aerogenes* is in many ways similar to *Bacillus coli*, differing in being nonmotile, may at times be found possessing a capsule, and in fermentative powers on sugars and specific immunological reactions. It is widely distributed, being found normally in the intestinal tract, and therefore present in sewage, water, etc. It is constantly present in milk and is one of the chief causes of the natural souring of milk and cream. It is probably nonpathogenic, but at most only slightly. The presence of *E. coli* in water, milk, etc., is regarded as indicative of sewage contamination. Differentiation of *Escherichia coli* and *Aerobacter aerogenes* may at times be necessary because of this accepted difference in sanitary significance. The latter is Voges-Proskauer-positive; methyl-red-negative; indol negative; and will grow in a citrate medium. *E. coli* displays a complete opposite reaction in all four instances. *A. aerogenes* also utilizes uric acid as the sole source of carbon, hydrolyzes sodium hippurate, reduces nitrates to nitrites and does not produce trimethyleneglycol from glycerin by anaerobic fermentation. Burkhardt and associates (*J. Am. Vet. M. Assoc.*, 1943, **103,** 381) reported recently the isolation of *A. aerogenes* from 10 cows in an outbreak of acute mastitis.

Aerobacter Cloacae (*Bacillus Cloacae*).—This bacillus is found in the intestinal canal, sewage, soil, water, etc. It resembles *E. coli*, differing mainly in its property

of liquefying gelatin and in not producing indol. Sodium hippurate is not hydrolyzed. Milk is slowly peptonized. It is nonpathogenic to man.

Proteus Vulgaris (*Bacillus Proteus Vulgaris*).—The *Bacillus proteus vulgaris* is a short and plump or long and slender rod from 0.5 to 1 by 1 to 3 μ, occurring singly, in pairs, and rarely in chains. Flexible filaments may be found. It is Gram-negative, nonspore-bearing, motile, does not possess a capsule, aerobic and facultatively anaerobic, grows well on ordinary media, best at room temperature, and rapidly liquefies gelatin medium. It possesses specific agglutination properties. Litmus milk is slightly acidified, then becomes alkaline and is quickly peptonized. Hydrogen sulfide is produced from sulfur, thiosulfates, cysteine and cystine or compounds containing these molecules, and urea is decomposed. The latter two characteristics are important distinguishing points from other Gram-negative gelatin liquefiers. Where this organism is present, a putrefactive odor will be found. *Proteus vulgaris* is normally found in putrefying material, especially decaying meat and cheese. It is also found in water, sewage and soil. Next to *E. coli* it has been found the most frequent cause of cystitis and pyelitis. It has been found associated with other bacteria in suppurative processes. There are indications that this organism, or decomposition products formed by it can produce symptoms characteristic of "food poisoning."

Proteus vulgaris tends to spread in a thin, opaque film when grown on the surface of agar medium due to the marked active motility possessed by this organism. Occasionally, however, only discrete colonies are found. The latter are nonmotile strains and are designated as the O colonies. The spreading type is designated by the letter H. The O type contains antigens present in the body cell and differing from those present in the H or flagellar antigen. It is the latter which confers a type specificity upon the bacterium. Certain *Proteus* strains (the so-called X strains) are agglutinated by the serum of patients having typhus fever. The agglutination of these X strains of *Proteus* comprises the well-known *Felix-Weil Reaction*, which is employed as an important diagnostic aid in typhus fever. They first isolated the X_1 and X_2 strains from the urine of typhus fever cases. These strains agglutinate but weakly. The X_{19} strain which they isolated later and which is used at present in the test is strongly agglutinated by the serum of typhus patients (up to 1:50,000). The reaction is nonspecific. However, the X strains contain an antigen common to the *rickettsiae* causing typhus fever.

Proteus morganii, the *Morgan bacillus*, does not liquefy gelatin and does not attack lactose, saccharose, maltose or dextrin. This organism has, therefore, been placed at times in different genera because of its characteristics resembling various species of the coliform bacteria. More recent investigations (*J. Path. and Bact.*, 1936, **42**, 183; 1939, **49**, 457), however, suggest its closer relationship to members of the *proteus* genus. This organism has been isolated from normal and diarrheal stools. It has been of some concern in outbreaks of summer diarrhea of infants and in certain cases resembling paratyphoid fever.

Eberthella Typhosa (*Typhoid Bacillus; Bacillus Typhosus*).—*Bacillus typhosus* is a short plump rod, 0.5 to 0.8 by 1 to 3 μ, possessing rounded ends. It is found singly, in pairs, rarely in chains, and is inclined to involution forms. It is motile, nonspore-bearing, aerobic and facultatively anaerobic, is nonacid-fast, nonencapsulated, and grows on all common media. It is Gram-negative and bipolar staining may be found occasionally among some strains. It grows readily on the commonly employed nutrient media, over a relatively wide pH range (5.0 to 8.6, optimum pH 6.8 to 7.0) and at a temperature between 10° and 40° C., optimum 37° C. Gelatin is not liquefied; indol is not produced. Nitrates are reduced to nitrites and hydrogen sulfide is formed. It has no effect on lactose and other sugars, producing only acid but never forming gas in the presence of many of them; it does not coagulate and produces only a slight transient acidity in litmus milk; and the final differentiation is based upon specific agglutinative properties. With few exceptions, most strains are weak in resistance. The typhoid bacillus is by preference a parasitic organism found only in man. Elimination of this organism in urine and feces by those diseased, convalescent cases and carriers may result in the contamination of water, vegetables, oysters, etc. This organism is the cause of typhoid or enteric fever, an acute general infection, usually caused by infected water, milk or food. In the tropics, the chances of infection are greater due to the enormous prevalence of fly vectors and on account of such predisposing causes as the debilitating effects of the tropical sun, over-exertion and over-fatigue. Recently, Sirois (*Canad. Pub. Health J.*, 1942, **33,** 168) reported on an epidemic of 68 cases of typhoid fever with seven deaths, due to infected raw milk.

A diagnosis is generally made by clinical symptoms confirmed by the *Widal Test* or *Gruber-Widal Test* (agglutination test for *E. typhosa*) and, better still, by a bacteriological examination of the blood (blood culture), as typhoid fever, in the early stages, is accompanied by a bacteremia. In most instances, little or no multiplication of the bacteria takes place in the blood stream.

Eberthella typhosa produces both smooth (S) and rough (R) colonies of which the individual organisms in each may be motile or nonmotile. The organisms producing S colonies are more toxic, more virulent, more antigenic, produce a larger yield of antibodies and contain a common somatic or so-called "O" antigen, which appears to be composed of lipoid combined with polysaccharide, representing the so-called endotoxin of the typhoid bacillus. Its agglutinin produces, macroscopically, a granular or fine agglutination. The O antigen has not been isolated from R strains. All motile typhoid bacilli possess, in addition, a thermolabile, flagellar or H antigen and its agglutinin produces macroscopically a floccular or large and flaky agglutination. H agglutinin is type specific while the O agglutinin is group specific. Investigations have revealed the necessity of testing for the presence of H and O agglutinins in suspected cases of typhoid fever (see *J. Hyg.*, 1928, **28,** 55; 1930, **29,** 380; 1932, **32,** 143 and *J. Lab. & Clin. Med.*, 1935, **20,** 638). In preparing antigens for the agglutination test for the different types of agglutinins, specific for *E. typhosa*, suitable strains of the latter must be selected. For the flagellar antigen, a formalin-treated suspension of a smooth, actively motile strain of *E. typhosa* is prepared. For the somatic antigen, an alcohol-treated suspension of a smooth nonflagellated strain of *E. typhosa* is used (for technique of test, see page 506). The macroscopic or tube agglutination method is replacing the microscopic slide agglutination technique. The interpretation of the test is of importance. In its use, formerly as a slide agglutination procedure, agglutination of typhoid bacilli by patients' serum in a dilution of 1:40 or more, after excluding any recent immunization with typhoid vaccine, was considered positive indicating typhoid infection especially if clinical symptoms of enteric fever prevailed. Since this simple application of the test, the technique has developed into a more extensive but more exacting procedure. The routine method for the agglutination test in the diagnosis of enteric fevers in use at the present time employs at least six suspensions, which include the H and O antigens of the three species of bacteria responsible for enteric fever—the typhoid, paratyphoid A and paratyphoid B bacilli (*E. typhosa*, *Salmonella paratyphi* and *S. schottmuelleri*).

In addition to the formalin-treated suspensions of actively motile S strains and alcohol-treated suspensions of nonflagellated S strains of each of these three latter species, other suspensions may be added. A group suspension may be added so as to detect the possible presence of other species of *Salmonella*, or suspensions of other antigens diagnostic for brucellosis or tularemia may be included upon request.

In the interpretation of findings in agglutination tests, an explanation of the findings is needed so as to be able to assign positive or negative values to such tests. In the case of tests for typhoid, negative agglutination findings indicate that the patient does not have the infection for which the tests were performed or the blood was obtained before the appearance of agglutinins in the serum. Agglutination indicating positive findings have the following significance: Agglutination of typhoid bacilli, both granular (somatic or O) and floccular (flagellar or H), in a dilution of 1:80 or higher, indicates infection with *E. typhosa*. Agglutination with H antigen only, in a dilution of 1:80 or higher, with little or no agglutination with O antigen, occurs very rarely with sera from typhoid fever cases. These findings, however, are observed with specimens from those who were recently immunized with typhoid vaccine or who had typhoid fever in the past (and not necessarily carriers at the time of the test) or who are typhoid carriers at the time of the test (and with or without a past history of infection). Agglutination with the O antigen (*E. typhosa*) only in a dilution of 1:80 or higher, with little or no agglutination of the H antigen, may be encountered in enteric infections in which the latter are caused by organisms antigenically related to *E. typhosa* and rarely in infections due to other bacteria (the so-called *anamnestic reaction*). In all cases of typhoid infection, the titer (agglutinin content) for *E. typhosa*, both H and O antigens, is high and this also rises with the progress of the disease.

Felix and Pitt (*Lancet*, 1934, **2**, 186) detected a new antigenic factor in freshly isolated, actively virulent cultures. This substance was suggested due to the fact that freshly isolated living typhoid bacilli were not agglutinated by an anti-O serum. A *Vi antibody* was produced which possessed a powerful protective action. The O and H antigens are not affected by the Vi antibody and the latter is incapable of neutralizing the endotoxin produced by the organism, this being the function of the O antibody. The Vi (virulence) antigen, though a factor found in virulent organisms, is not *per se* responsible for the virulence. The latter is due to a combination of both the Vi and the O antigens. Experimental evidence indicates that antisera prepared from "natural Vi" antigen or "formolized Vi" antigen may be of value as a therapeutic agent (*Brit. J. Exp. Path.*, 1934, **15**, 346; 1935, **16**, 422). The fact that Vi antigen is sensitive to heat and certain chemicals would appear to challenge the effectiveness of typhoid vaccine as prepared today. Extensive experiments, however, have proved the value of the latter (see also *J. Hyg.*, 1936, **6**, 559). The serum of patients and convalescents may contain the Vi antibody, but it is present in variable amounts and, at present, is being studied to determine its value as a diagnostic aid.

Craigie and Yen (*Canad. Pub. Health J.*, 1938, **29**, 448, 484) introduced a bacteriophage typing technique and demonstrated the existence of several types of Vi antigen. Many workers regard this typing technique as of considerable practical value. The technique, however, has not been standardized nor used sufficiently to warrant as yet recommending it for routine use. The procedure requires special care and attention in its performance and it is possible that the establishment of central typing laboratories would be helpful in epidemiologie investigations of typhoid fever. Levin (*Northwest Med.*, 1941, **40,** 77) reveals that type constancy in individuals was striking and presents evidence which indicates that proof instead of conjecture in epidemiologic problems is possible by typing. The Vi factor plays a leading role in the so-called *binomial* theory of typhoid fever. Manwaring (*California & West. Med.*, 1940, **55,** 206) believes that the "binomial" theory of typhoid fever, proposed by F. Magrassi et al. (*Boll. atti accad. med. Roma*, 1938, **64,** 7; *Arch. ges. Virusforsch.*, 1940, **1,** 324), "may take its place as one of the most important basic contributions to medical science of the present generation." The theory, based on experimental evidence, is that typhoid fever is not a simple bacterial infection but is a synergic disease caused by a nonpathogenic typhoid bacillus in adherent symbiosis with a typhoid virus (Vi antigen). This theory has not been accepted as yet by most workers. Positive blood cultures are obtained most frequently during the first week of the disease. The Widal or Gruber-Widal test may not begin to yield positive findings until after the first week or ten days of illness and usually is positive after the second week of the disease. Typhoid fever gives rise both to the H (flagellar) and O (somatic) agglutinins. The O agglutinins are more common as the response is more marked, appear earlier and are of greater diagnostic significance. *E. typhosa* is found in feces more frequently from the twelfth to the twentieth day, and about 25 per cent of the patients excrete the bacilli in the urine after the second week. Samples of feces and urine may be examined at these stages of the disease. A positive diazo reaction of the urine appears in over 95 per cent of all cases in about the fourth or fifth day and disappears after the second week. There is no specific treatment for typhoid fever. Neither vaccines nor serums are effective in treatment. There is no convincing evidence as yet to indicate that chemotherapy is successful. Though the case fatality in typhoid fever is about 10 per cent, the greater hazard is the complications which set in after the acute phase. The gallbladder may become infected. Cystitis may occur and inflammatory and suppurative processes may develop in other parts of the body. Almost any organ can be and is attacked occasionally in some cases. Secondary and mixed infections are not uncommon. An attack of typhoid fever confers, in most instances, a certain degree of immunity but two or more attacks in the same individual are possible and have been reported. Recently, Reitler and Marberg (*Tr. Roy. Soc. Trop. Med. & Hyg.*, 1943, **36,** 305) used colloidal metallic tin and tin stearate in the treatment of typhoid fever cases and typhoid carriers and found tin displayed a bactericidal effect both *in vitro* and *in vivo* against *E. typhosa*.

Patients with typhoid fever should be isolated in flyproof rooms and sanitary precautions should be observed. Those who have been exposed should be preferably immunized with typhoid vaccine. Disinfection of all bowel and urinary discharges and articles (bedding, clothing, utensils, etc.) soiled with them coming from diseased patients or carriers should be practiced.

General measures to be observed in the prevention of epidemics of typhoid fever, dysentery and other gastro-intestinal diseases consist in the sanitary disposal of human excreta; treatment of water supplies; pasteurization of milk; sanitary supervision of shellfish and of all food and ice supplies; all food should be cooked adequately and only food which can be peeled (as apples, bananas, etc.) should be eaten raw; periodic medical examination of cooks and all food handlers and the exclusion of typhoid carriers; prevention of fly breeding; prophylactic immunization with typhoid vaccine or bacterin; isolation of diseased individuals and carriers.

In most chronic typhoid carriers, the focus of infection is usually the gallbladder, and the bile harbors the bacilli. Feces, urine and duodenal drainage are examined in suspicious carriers for *E. typhosa*. Cholecystectomy has so far been the only reliable method of cure. Recently, however, iodophthalein has been given (*J. A. M. A.*, 1942, **118**, 964) in 40 oral doses of 4 Gm. each three times a week to 65 typhoid carriers maintained on a low fat diet with sufficiently encouraging results to warrant further trial of the drug. Others have tried the sulfonamide drugs and the use especially of sulfaguanidine and succinylsulfathiazole is warranted to definitely determine their alleged efficiency or inefficiency as reported by different workers.

Shigella Dysenteriae (*Bacillus Dysentery, Shiga*); **Shigella Paradysenteriae** (*Dysentery Bacillus, Flexner; Dysentery Bacillus, Hiss; Dysentery Bacillus, Strong; Dysentery Bacillus, Sonne (Groups I and II);*) *Shigella Ambigua* (*Bacillus Ambiguus; Bacillus Dysenteriae "Schmitz"*) and *Shigella Sonnei* (*Bacillus Dispar; Shigella Paradysenteriae* var. *Sonnei; Group III Paradysentery Bacillus of Sonne*).—Dysentery, a symptom complex, namely, the existence of a diarrhea with the passage of blood and mucus from the bowel, and which is caused by different pathogenic agents, may be divided into the acute and chronic forms. Amoeba are the agents causing the chronic type known as amoebic dysentery. The latter runs a course, clinically, quite different from the acute type which is caused by various closely related bacilli and known as bacillary dysentery. Amoebic dysentery is usually common and a serious menace in tropical and subtropical countries. Bacillary dysentery, though found in warm regions, is more common in temperate climates.

The Shiga dysentery bacillus and the several paradysentery varieties are generally regarded as the causative agents of bacillary dysentery. They resemble the typhoid bacillus in many ways. They are, however, nonmotile and differ also in their fermentative powers on carbohydrates and specific agglutination reactions. The species of *Shigella* associated with epidemic and endemic bacillary dysentery do not liquefy gelatin, do not utilize citrate, are Voges-Proskauer-negative, do not produce NH_3 or H_2S, form acid in litmus milk and acid but no gas in dextrose, and display variable results in the reduction of nitrates to nitrites. Differentiation between the various distinct types of dysentery bacilli and other species of *Shigella* can be made by sugar fermentations (using lactose and mannitol, and aided by maltose, sucrose, dextrose, xylose, dulcitol, rhamnose and dextrin) and verified by specific agglutination reactions. On the basis of fermentation reactions, the first group consists of nonmannite, nonlactose fermenting bacteria comprising the Shiga and Schmitz (*B. ambiguum*) bacilli. Those which ferment mannite but not lactose are placed in the second group and are the paradysentery organisms usually spoken of as the Flexner, Hiss-Russell and the Strong Bacilli. The Sonne bacillus (*Shigella sonnei*) and dispar bacillus (*Shigella madanipensis*) comprise the third group. Of the various species, the Shiga bacillus and the Sonne variety of the paradysentery bacillus do not produce indol. The Shiga bacillus produces a powerful exotoxin and is probably the most virulent of the dysentery bacilli. In fact, the disease caused by this type is regarded as a true toxemia. For studies on Shiga bacillus toxins, see Olitzski and associates (*J. Immunol.*,

1943, **46,** 71). An antidysentery serum is available. Differentiation of *Shigella* species by the reduction of trimetylamine oxide has been reported (*J. Bact.*, 1944, **47,** 575).

In the human body, the dysentery bacilli are only found in the feces of diseased individuals and dysentery carriers. Invasion of the blood stream by dysentery bacilli is rare and the bacilli apparently do not invade other parts of the body. The use of the agglutination test with the patient's serum (serological diagnosis) is employed but infrequently. The clinical symptoms are usually sufficiently diagnostic in well-marked cases. Agglutinins do not appear in the blood in the early acute stage. Whenever the serological diagnosis of infections due to species of *Shigella* is employed, it is necessary to employ a standardized procedure using suspensions of antigen of known agglutinability of the many species of *Shigella* responsible for dysentery. This is time-consuming. Finally isolation of the offending agent or bacillus in freshly collected feces is the only method of diagnosis for a certain identification of the causative agent or of species of bacilli (in bacillary dysentery) causing the infection. It is important to examine the feces as soon as possible after collection, preferably using the particles containing blood, pus and mucus and suspending these in nutrient broth or isotonic salt solution. If an immediate examination is not possible, a preservative solution should be added, as suggested by Bangxang and Eliot (*Am. J. Hyg.*, 1940, **31,** 16). They employ a buffered saline solution (*p*H 8.5) containing 1 per cent sodium citrate and 0.5 per cent sodium desoxycholate.

Bacillary dysentery affects only human beings and is prevalent in all countries and climates. It occurs more frequently and in a more severe form in warmer areas or during warm months and in epidemics especially in places and under circumstances in which there is a lack of personal hygiene or proper sanitation is inadequate or deficient. In the United States, the Shiga, Flexner, Park-Hiss and Sonne dysentery bacilli are the types most commonly found. A polyvalent antidysentery serum is available. This is prepared by immunizing horses against the Shiga bacillus, its soluble toxin, and against the other types of dysentery bacilli. This polyvalent serum is required to show a high antitoxin content specific for the exotoxins of the Shiga bacillus and also a high agglutinin titer for the other types of dysentery bacilli used in immunizing the horses. At present, the use of dysentery vaccines cannot be recommended as a general prophylatic measure and their use as therapeutic agents is very limited.

Methods of transmission and prevention as given under typhoid fever apply for dysentery. Though Eaton and Bayne-Jones (*J. A. M. A.*, 1934, **103,** 1769, 1776, 1847, 1853, 1934, 1939), in a comprehensive study of bacteriophage therapy, concluded that its value in dysentery has not been proved, there is some evidence of the prophylactic and therapeutic value of oral polyvalent dysentery bacteriophage in bacillary dysentery, which has been presented recently. Enthusiastic reports have been forthcoming in the use of sulfaguanidine and succinylsulfathiazole in cases of bacillary dysentery (*U. S. Nav. M. Bull.*, 1942, **40,** 601; *Lancet*, 1942, **243,** 14; *South. M. J.*, 1942, **35,** 606; and *J. Lab. & Clin. Med.*, 1942, **28,** 162) and of carriers (*J. A. M. A.*, 1942, **119,** 615, 1489). For a detailed consideration of dysentery bacilli and allied species and all members of the genus *Shigella*, see Neter (*Bact. Revs.*, 1942, **6,** 1). In this country, at the Bronx Hospital in New York City there is a Dysentery Registry for the study and prevention of Bacillary Dysentery.

Shigella equirulis (*Shigella viscosa; Bacillus nephritidis equi; Bacterium viscosum* *equi; Bacterium pyosepticus equi*) is the cause of "joint ill" or "navel ill" and "pyosepticemia" in young horses. It is said to be the cause of certain cases of nephritis and purulent polyarthritis in young pigs. For further details, see Dimock (*J. Am. Vet. M. A.*, May, 1941). *Shigella alkalescens* resembles the paradysentery bacilli in many respects. One of its most characteristic reactions is in litmus milk when, following transitory acid production, an intense and lasting alkaline reaction results. Though its pathogenicity has geen regarded as uncertain, convincing evidence is accumulating that this species may cause dysentery or enteritis.

Shigella gallinarum (*Bacterium or Bacillus or Salmonella Gallinarum, Bacterium Sanguinarium*) is a short, almost coccoid, nonmotile rod, showing at times "peripheral staining," wherein the central portion is unstained and the poles and borders are stained. The organism is the cause of fowl typhoid, a disease different from fowl cholera, and identical with Moore's infectious leukemia of fowls. This organism is not known to infect man but by feeding or parenteral administration, it will attack rabbits, certain wild birds and all poultry and canaries. *Shigella gallinarum* is closely related to *E. typhosa* in many respects and is antigenically identical with *Salmonella pullorum*.

Salmonella Paratyphi (*Bacillus Paratyphosus A*); **Salmonella Schottmuelleri** (*Bacillus Paratyphosus B*); **and Salmonella Hirschfeldii** (*Bacillus Paratyphosus C*). —These are the causative agents of paratyphoid fever, a febrile infectious disease, which in all features resembles typhoid or enteric fever to a mild degree. The paratyphoid B bacillus occurs in almost 80 per cent of these infections, and is more commonly observed in Europe and temperate climates, while paratyphoid A infections are most commonly found in the East. The two diseases are identical as to the source of infection, modes of transmission, incubation periods, methods of control and symptoms. The methods given under *E. typhosa* to aid in the diagnosis of suspected cases of enteric fever and also of carriers are used for paratyphoid cases, and differential diagnosis is established by bacteriological and serological methods. Positive blood cultures, as in typhoid fever, are the surest means of making a definite diagnosis, especially if the patient had been immunized with triple vaccine. Positive blood cultures in paratyphoid fever generally continue over a longer period of time than in typhoid fever. These organisms are indistinguishable from the colon and typhoid bacilli as to morphology, staining and many of the general and cultural characteristics, etc. As a group, they are differentiated from the colon and typhoid organisms, and between themselves by their behavior in litmus milk, acid and gas production on various sugars, and specific agglutinative powers. For serological characteristics of *Salmonella* species and varieties, see Kauffman (*Ztschr. f. Hyg.*, 1937, **120,** 194). Serological relationships are used as the chief means of classifying species of bacteria in this genus.

Salmonella paratyphi and *S. schottmuelleri* are Gram-negative, motile rods varying from 0.6 to 0.7 by 2 to 4 μ in size, occurring singly and in pairs, do not liquefy gelatin, produce acid and gas in dextrose, levulose, galactose, maltose and mannite, do not attack lactose, saccharose, salicin and inulin, are aerobic and facultatively anaerobic, do not produce indol and grow best at 37° C. *Salmonella paratyphi* does and *S. schottmuelleri* does not produce nitrites from nitrates, while the latter produces and *S. paratyphi* does not produce hydrogen sulfide, and acid and gas from inositol. *S. schottmuelleri* produces acid and gas in xylose media, but *Salmonella paratyphi* differs

markedly from other *salmonella* species in its inability to ferment xylose.   The paratyphoid B type is also capable of producing "food poisoning" in man, by using raw
and improperly cooked meat, dairy products and other foodstuffs coming from infected animals or otherwise contaminated with this organism.   Jones and associates
(*Lancet*, 1942, **243,** 362) reported on a water-borne outbreak of paratyphoid B fever
occurring in 21 out of 34 cottagers at Brixworth, England, this being traced to an infected well which supplied the cottages.   Only four of the infected persons showed
typical clinical symptoms.   The others excreted the paratyphoid B organisms in the
feces and few had a diarrhea.

   Salmonella hirschfeldii (*Bacillus paratyphosus C*) has been found in enteric fevers in
man in British Guiana, Africa and Asia.   It is closely related biologically to *S. choleraesuis* (*Bacillus suipestifer*).   Outbreaks of paratyphoid C fever develop generally in
association with other diseases, such as malaria and relapsing fever.   The infection is
essentially a bacteremia without involvement either of the intestine or of the mesenteric glands.   *S. hirschfeldii* is readily isolated from the blood throughout the greater
part of the duration of the diseased condition caused by it.

   Salmonella Enteritidis (*Bacillus Enteritidis; Gärtner Bacillus*).—This bacillus is
well known as an old offender and an important factor in "food poisoning" in man
and produces marked gastro-intestinal disturbances and even septicemia in lower
animals.   This species and its varieties are widely distributed, occurring in both
domestic and wild animals, and are well known for their marked toxic effects.   A true
soluble toxin is not secreted.   An endotoxin, however, is present, which differs from
those present in other meat-poisoning bacilli in this group, in that it is very resistant
to heat, withstanding boiling temperature for long periods of time.   It is not uncommon to find that in *salmonella* food infections, it is these toxic products, frequently preformed, which are responsible for the gastro-enteric symptoms.   Morphologically,
culturally, and in many other respects, *S. enteritidis* can be distinguished from the
other closely related organisms in this group only with great difficulty.   Its marked
pathogenic effects for laboratory animals and agglutination tests may be of value in
differentiation.

   In the differentiation of species of *Salmonella*, observations are made of cultures of
the suspicious organism in media containing separately arabinose, inosite, trehalose,
zylose, tartrate and lead acetate.   *S. enteritidis*, though less commonly found than *S.
typhimurium*, resembles the latter culturally, but is said not to ferment inosite and
trehalose, while *S. typhimurium* does.   The two may be differentiated readily by serological (specific agglutination) tests.   These two species, but especially *S. typhimurium*, have been employed in commercial preparations, mice and rat virus products as "Ratin," for eradicating mice, rats and other rodents.   The use of these preparations is to be condemned, as some of the rats and rodents do not die, become healthy
carriers, and there exists the danger of the latter spreading virulent bacilli about our
premises.   The so-called *Danzig virus* cultures or *Bacillus of mouse typhoid* is usually
S. typhimurium, but some may be *S. enteritidis*.

   Salmonella centers, where *Salmonella* species are differentiated and identified, are
found in various countries throughout the world.   In this country, the National
Salmonella Center is located in Kentucky (see *Circ.* **50,** Ken. Agr. Expt. Sta., Lexing-
ton).   On the incidence of *Salmonella* species, see Edwards (*Proc. 7th World Poultry
Congress*, pp. 271–274).

Salmonella Pullorum (*Bacillus Pullorum*).—This bacillus is the cause of "white diarrhea" or septicemia in young chicks. It may infect the ovaries and eggs of adult birds, and is not regarded as a pathogen for man. *S. pullorum* does not differ from other members of the *Salmonella* group in the several characteristics, except that it is nonmotile and has but little effect in producing gas in many of the sugar media.

Salmonella Typhimurium (*Bacillus Psittacosis or Salmonella (Bacillus) Aertrycke; Bacillus Pestis Caviae*).—This was at one time regarded as the causative agent of pneumonia in parrots. Psittacosis in parrots and in man is now attributed by most workers to a filterable virus. Humans associated with sick birds are apt to contract this virus affection, which may occur as a severe and at times fatal pneumonia.

This organism is very similar to *S. schottmuelleri*, differing mainly in specific immunological reactions. It is a natural pathogen of rodents and especially mice, and it may cause outbreaks of disease among guinea pigs, domestic animals and in birds. *S. typhimurium*, together with *S. schottmuelleri*, *S. enteritidis* and *S. choleraesuis* are the important members of the so-called paratyphoid group, the paratyphoid-enteritidis group, the salmonella group or the Gärtner or meat-poisoning group, which may be responsible for the gastro-intestinal disturbances and symptoms accompanying food poisoning. *S. typhimurium* is the one most frequently isolated in food-poisoning outbreaks in this country. Milk, sausages, meat pies, jellies, custard fillings, etc., have been implicated. Among 50 *Salmonella* infections in infants and children reported by Bornstein and Schwarz (*Am. J. M. Sc.*, 1942, **204,** 546), nine showed symptoms of septic infection and 41 predominantly diarrhea. Eleven cases were found to be due to *S. typhimurium* and 25 to organisms of Group C *Salmonella*. Although these organisms are also predominant in adult infection, the relative order of importance is reversed. Other species of *Salmonella* were responsible for the other eight cases. *S. typhimurium* is considered the most common type in human infections in this country and probably causes in 90 per cent of the cases a rather harmless gastro-enteritis.

In general, food infections in man by species of *Salmonella* have a high morbidity rate and a low case fatality rate. Diagnosis depends upon clinical symptoms and, if possible, upon isolating the offending species of organism in the excreta of patients, rarely by blood culture, and when possible from the suspected food source. Agglutination tests of the patient's serum are rarely performed as they are only occasionally positive. Prophylactic measures against *Salmonella food infections* depend mainly upon sanitary supervision of slaughterhouses, food establishments, bakeries, dairies, control of food handlers and purveyors and adequate cooking.

Salmonella Choleraesuis (*Bacillus Suipestifer; Bacillus Cholera Suis*).—This bacillus is a common inhabitant of the intestinal tract of hogs. At first regarded as the cause of "Hog Cholera," it is now definitely established merely as a secondary invader in this widespread infection, the primary etiological factor being a filterable virus. There are several closely related varieties comprising bacteria designated at times as the *suipestifer group*. Due to its wide distribution in Nature, *S. chloraesuis* may infect meat and dairy products, so that this organism may be encountered in food poisoning, causing an acute gastro-enteritidis in man. It has the general characteristics of the organisms of the *Salmonella* genus, differing mainly in certain cultural characteristics (does not attack arabinose, inosite, dulcitol and trehalose and does not produce H_2S), and in specificity in agglutinin production. For further details, see Bruner and Edwards (*Kentucky Expt. Sta. Bull.* **404,** 1940). Schweiler (*Ann. Intern. Med.*, 1944,

20, 275) reported 3 cases infected by and Levine and Plattner (*Am. J. Clin. Path.,* 1944, **14,** 342) report on 3 cases of pneumonia by *S. choleraesuis.*

Salmonella abortivoequina is the cause of equine infectious abortion. Its characteristics correspond closely to that of *S. schottmuelleri.* This organism possesses a rather potent endotoxin. *Salmonella anatis,* though found among all species of domestic animals and even man, is especially highly pathogenic among young ducklings, producing a disease commonly known as *keel.* For further details, see Rettger and Scoville (*J. Infect. Dis.,* 1920, **26,** 217).

Alcaligenes Faecalis (*Bacillus Alcaligenes Faecalis or Faecalis Alcaligenes*).— This is found in the normal intestinal tract and is of interest because it closely resembles the typhoid bacillus, differing from the latter mainly in its inability to produce acid and even forming alkali in some of the sugar media and in specific agglutinative reactions. It is generally regarded as being nonpathogenic, though recently a case of bacteremia due to this organism, and successfully treated by the use of sulfadiazine, was reported (*Am. J. M. Sc.,* 1942, **204,** 719).

The Brucella Group

Brucella Bronchiseptica (*Alcaligenes or Bacillus Bronchisepticus; Bacillus Bronchicanis*).—This organism is closely related to the other species of *Brucella.* It, however, is motile, highly aerobic, does not produce H_2S and is distinguishable by agglutinin-absorption tests. *B. bronchiseptica* is found in the bronchial secretions and nasal discharges of dogs, and at times of cats, affected with distemper, but it is not regarded as the etiological factor of this affection. It has also been found in a respiratory condition of rabbits known as *snuffles* and may at times be the cause of outbreaks of bronchopneumonia in guinea pigs and other rodents.

Brucella Melitensis (*Alcaligenes, Bacterium, or Micrococcus Melitensis*).— *Br. melitensis* is a nonmotile, coccoid (0.3 to 0.4 μ) rod. It occurs singly and in pairs, is Gram-negative, nonacid-fast, nonspore-bearing, nonencapsulated, aerobic and facultatively anaerobic, grows at first rather slowly on ordinary media, and does not ferment any of the sugars or carbohydrates. Indol is not formed; nitrates are reduced, often with the complete disappearance of the nitrite; litmus milk is unchanged in twenty-four hours but later becomes alkaline; and ammonia is produced from urea. The presence of dextrose or liver extract favors growth; the optimum reaction is pH 7.4; the optimum temperature is 37° C., no growth occurring at 6° or at 45° C.; it does not require increased CO_2 tension. *Br. melitensis* is the cause of abortion in goats and of "undulant," "Mediterranean," or of "Malta fever" in man. Nicolle prognosticated well when he said: "that Mediterranean fever is in the course of evolution, and is tending to become chronic. It is a malady which on account of its manifestations and chronicity will become one of the most common and stubborn diseases. Mediterranean fever is a disease of the future."

In 1887, Bruce (*Practitioner,* 1887, **39,** 161; 1888, **40,** 241) isolated and named the causative agent of undulant fever as *Micrococcus melitensis.* When other workers revealed that it was a rod and not a coccus, it became known as *Bacterium* or *Bacillus melitensis.* The term *Brucella* (after the discoverer) is now usually applied to this organism and infections by species of this genus are known today as brucelliasis and brucellosis.

In 1897, Bang (*Ztschr. f. Tier Med.*, 1897, **1**, 241), of Copenhagen, isolated a small bacterium, the *Bacillus abortus*, from the uterine discharges of cows which had aborted. Bovine infectious abortion is frequently designated as *Bang's disease*. In 1918, the classic work of Miss Alice Evans (*J. Infect. Dis.*, 1918, **22**, 576, 580; *J. A. M. A.*, 1927, **88**, 630) brought together the two diseases—Malta fever in man, and infectious abortion in cattle. In 1924, Keefer (*Bull. Johns Hopkins Hosp.*, 1924, **35**, 6) reported a definite case of human infection with *Bacillus* (now known as *Brucella*) *abortus*. Carpenter (*J. Am. Vet. M. A.*, 1927, **70**, 459); (*J. A. M. A.*, 1931, **96**, 1212; 1932, **99**, 296) and others later succeeded in isolating the latter organism from the blood and various lesions of many patients. The infectious abortion of swine, caused by the *porcine strain, Brucella suis*, is also pathogenic for both man and cattle. In districts where hog raising is carried on, it is recognized that this animal and the porcine strain may be the source and cause of human infections. The following is the order of their relative pathogenicity for man: *Br. melitensis; Br. suis* and *Br. abortus*.

The results of the numerous investigations during recent years have led workers to the following conclusion: Brucellosis in man and animals is a widespread disease in this and other countries throughout the world. Though some workers regard the causative agent of infectious abortion in cattle and that of undulant fever in man as very similar, with serologic distinctions as the only difference, others regard the relationship as still an open question. In man, the *bovine, caprine* (*from goats*) and *porcine types* of brucellosis have been found. It is known that in some regions sheep are infected, and it is possible that a distinct *ovine strain* of brucella exists. Recently horses have also been proved to be sources of infection. Infected raw milk or its products, direct contact with the flesh or discharges from infected animals (either diseased or carriers), and improperly cooked meat from such animals are, in the light of our present-day knowledge, the principal sources of the infection in man. The possibility of untreated water, contaminated with the urine or discharges (or even with raw milk) of affected animals or carriers, and even insect vectors serving as a source of the spread of brucellosis, must be kept in mind. It is impossible to estimate the extent of brucellosis in man and in cattle, as exact statistical records are not available. Furthermore, it is known that the vast majority of cases that occur in man remain unrecognized. The same disease has been confused with other diseases. In many instances, due to the mildness of the infection, an exact diagnosis is not made. For other details, see the survey on undulant fever and Bang's disease presented by the author and associate (*Am. J. M. Sc.*, 1937, **194**, 678).

Diagnosis of the disease is made by finding the organisms in the blood (repeated blood cultures are made) very early in the disease or later they appear in the urine. Agglutination tests are also of value. An intradermal test is used, but this has its greatest value when negative. For complete details of diagnostic procedures in brucellosis, see *Diagnostic Procedures and Reagents* (A. P. H. A., 1941) and for a discussion and review on undulant fever, see Levitt (*M. Clin. North America*, 1943, **27**, 259).

Undulant fever or brucellosis is a term employed frequently to include not only Malta fever but all other febrile conditions caused by infection with a pathogenic species of the genus *brucella*. The bovine strain of *Br. abortus* is less pathogenic for animals than the goat or swine strain. The significant clinical features are a low-grade temperature, weakness and the absence of objective physical findings. As the organism causing undulant fever has its source in the cow's udder, no amount of cleanliness, inspection, sterilization of utensils, etc., will be of greatest value unless serological tests of the animals are included. The use of the *Bang test* on cattle to detect positive reactors is required if milk from these animals is to be sold as raw or certified raw milk. The latter should be obtained only from cattle giving negative Bang tests. Pasteurization of the milk kills all species of *brucella* and other vegetative forms of pathogenic microorganisms, and renders this product safe. Pasteurization must be the sheet anchor in the prevention of milk-borne undulant fever.

Brucella Abortus (*Alcaligenes or Bacillus Abortus*).—The morphological and cultural characteristics are identical with that of *B. melitensis* with the following exceptions: For isolation, first 25 and later 10 per cent carbon dioxide is necessary in the atmosphere. The browning of the medium in an agar slant is less marked. It is differentiated from *Br. melitensis* but not from *Br. suis* by the agglutinin absorption test as recommended by Wilson and Miles (*Brit. J. Exp. Path.*, 1932, **13**, 1).

Brucella species differ from each other in their behavior when grown separately under suitable conditions on liver infusion media containing thionin (1:200,000) and basic fuchsin (1:100,000). *Br. abortus* will grow only on the medium containing basic fuchsin. *Br. suis* will grow only on the medium containing thionin. *Br. melitensis*

DIFFERENTIATION OF SPECIES OF BRUCELLA

Species	CO₂ required for growth (10 per cent)	H₂S production (days)	Dextrose utilized	Amino N utilized	Growth in presence of			
					Basic fuchsin (1:100,000)	Thionin (1:200,000 to 1:400,000)	Pyronin (1:200,000)	Methyl violet (1:100,000)
B. melitensis	−	± (1)	+ +	+	+	+	±	+
B. abortus	+	+ (2)	+	+ +	+	−	+	+
B. suis	−	+ + (4)	+ +	+	−	+	−	−

will grow on each of the media though its growth is not very luxuriant. There also exists a difference in the H₂S metabolism of the three species. *Br. suis* produces it in abundance, *Br. abortus* to a lesser extent, and only in a slight degree by *Br. melitensis*.

Br. abortus is the cause of contagious abortion in cattle, one of the most widespread diseases in livestock. Other animals (mares, sheep, rabbits and guinea pigs) are susceptible to this infection. Though the organism is found mainly in the mucous membranes of the uterus, the male species have been found to harbor it in their seminal vesicles. The most important path of infection is by way of the alimentary tract as the result of ingesting contaminated food and water. Infection by way of the genital route is also possible. This species causes brucellosis (undulant fever) in man and Bang's disease in cattle.

Brucella Suis.—The morphological and cultural characteristics are identical with *Br. melitensis* and it is differentiated from the latter, but not from *Br. abortus*, by the agglutinin absorption test, as recommended by Wilson and Miles (*Brit. J. Exp. Path.*, 1932, **13**, 1). This species is the cause of abortion in swine and is infectious for horses, cows, dogs, monkeys and laboratory animals. It may cause undulant fever (brucellosis) in man. For other details, see above and also Huddleson (*Brucellosis*, Commonwealth Fund, 1943, New York City).

Bacilli of the Hemorrhagic Septicemia Group

Pasteurella Pestis (*Plague Bacillus; Bacillus Pestis; Bacillus of Bubonic Plague*). —This is an important member of the group of organisms, causing *hemorrhagic* · *septicemias* (*pasteurelloses*) from which man and animals suffer. The plague bacillus is a short, thick, round-ended bacillus, 0.5 to 0.7 by 1.5 to 2 μ, occurring singly, occasionally in pairs and infrequently in short chains. It shows distinct bipolar staining, is Gram-negative, nonmotile, nonspore-bearing, nonencapsulated, aerobic and grows well on ordinary culture media. Pleomorphic forms are apparent and are accentuated by cultivation on media containing 3 to 4 per cent sodium chloride. It grows best at temperatures between 30° and 35° C. Gelatin and coagulated serum are not liquefied. Milk is acidified slightly, but not coagulated. Indol is not produced and nitrates are not reduced. In flasks of bouillon left undisturbed after inoculation for five or six days, there is produced (especially if the surface of the medium is covered with a layer of oil) a pellicle from which long, delicate filaments or projections sprout or hang downward (stalactite formation). *P. pestis* is readily destroyed by heat, sunlight and disinfectants. The agglutination test is of value in identifying suspected organisms.

P. pestis is primarily the cause of plague in rodents. The rat is the chief offender, but mice, ground squirrels, chipmunks, prairie dogs and other rodents may harbor this organism. In Manchuria, it is the tarabagan or marmot; in South Africa, the gerbille; the cavy in South America; and the suslik in Russia. Barrera (*Proc. 8th Amer. Sci. Congress*, 1942, **6**, 291), in reporting on plague as it affects Argentina, found the latter in many rodents in areas far removed from seaports. Epizootics always occur during the winter months, affecting many rodents. During 1939, 9500 rodents were examined in an epizootic. Rats were not affected but 92 per cent of the rodents were *microcavia*. *Graomys* and *octomys barrerai* were also infected. During epidemics, domestic animals may suffer from pneumonic plague and become sources of infection.

While plague may be transmitted from animal to animal through the eating of infected carcasses or even through ingestion of infected food and drink, the common mode of transmission is by means of an intermediate host, the rat flea. *Xenopsylla cheopis* in India and *Ceratophyllus faciatus* in the United States and Europe are the intermediate factors, though other species may also serve as vectors. Fleas feeding on infected rats become themselves infected, and the plague bacilli present multiply rapidly The infected flea biting man or any animal deposits on the skin of the new host regurgitated material or feces or both, which contain the organisms, and the infection occurs in the man or animal bitten. There is some evidence to show that bedbugs may spread bubonic plague, and viable *P. pestis* have been found in human lice, but their role is either nil or a minor one as vectors.

In man, plague, the most dreaded of all scourges, manifests itself in three forms: (1) Bubonic (or glandular) plague, which is characterized by carbuncles, glandular swellings known as *buboes* (therefore the term bubonic) and hemorrhages from mucous surfaces and beneath the skin, which caused this disease to be known as *black death*. This type is spread by the bite of infected fleas. (2) Pneumonic plague, a highly fatal form, appears with the usual characteristics of an inflammation of the lungs or a typical bronchopneumonia. The sputum is usually laden with blood and *Bacillus pestis*. The pneumonic form of plague requires no vector, but contact with material soiled with the sputum and inhalation of the sputum spray because of close contact with infected individuals is the method by which this form is transmitted. Murdock (*U. S.*

Pub. Health Rept., 1940, **55**, 2172) reports on three outbreaks of pneumonic plague in Ecuador. (3) Septicemic plague commences with immediate overwhelming symptoms, hemorrhages under the skin are numerous (these turning black, therefore the name *black death*) and death occurs within a few days. There is an ambulatory form, so-called *pestis minor* (or mild plague) to differentiate it from the three forms of *pestis major*. In the former type, there is usually a primary vesicle or pustule at the site of the flea bite and this should be examined for *P. pestis*. In rodents, the disease is either acute or chronic and the diganosis of natural infection in rats is generally made microscopically. The important problem in the prevention of this disease is the extermination of plague-infected rats, ground squirrels and rodents, and the destruction of and protection against fleas. See also under Biological Products for the use of vaccines in the prevention and serum in the treatment of this disease.

As aids in diagnosis, material is obtained from the buboes by aspiration with needle and syringe or after incision. Direct smears may be valuable as a rapid presumptive diagnostic aid. Cultures and inoculations of guinea pigs also are made. Blood cultures are frequently positive, especially late in the disease. Agglutination tests on patients' blood serum are performed but infrequently, as agglutinins do not appear until the tenth day or later after infection. In pneumonic plague, the sputum, and in *pestis minor*, the material in the pustules are examined. In post-mortem examinations, the heart's blood and spleen are examined. Caution is to be observed in handling all animals suspicious of being infected with *P. pestis*. They should be freed of all ectoparasites, just before use, by dipping them into a suitable solution of a disinfectant to destroy both insect pests and pathogenic organisms. The operator, when handling such animals, must wear rubber gloves and a long-sleeved gown. The animals themselves should be kept at all times in jars or suitable cages covered with fine mesh netting.

Pasteurella Tularensis (*Bacillus or Bacterium Tularense*).—This is a small pleomorphic rod, 0.2 by 0.3 to 0.7 μ, and occurs singly. Coccoid forms may be present especially in older cultures. It is nonmotile, nonspore-bearing, gives the appearance of being surrounded by a capsular substance (especially in body fluids), stains best with crystal violet or carbol fuchsin, may reveal bipolar staining, is Gram-negative, aerobic, and requires for growth media containing blood, blood serum, egg yolk, or cystine to which has been added a piece of sterile rabbit spleen. Acid but no gas is produced in dextrose, maltose and mannite. This organism causes a plaguelike disease ("rabbit fever") in various rodents, especially squirrels and jackrabbits. The disease is transmissible to man by biting insects, especially horseflies. Evidence indicates that ticks, fleas, lice and mosquitoes may transmit this disease. The coyote has been found to be a carrier of this organism. The possibility of aerial spread of this dangerous infection was recently reported (*Science*, 1942, **96**, Supplement, 8). Nymphs and larvae of the common rabbit tick, believed to spread the disease among rabbits, were found on 29 kinds of birds. In man, the disease is known as tularemia, rabbit fever, deerfly, or *Francis' disease*. It is commonly contracted by hunters, cooks, market men, laboratory workers and others who are careless in handling infected rabbits, failing to use rubber gloves, or eating infected meat. Various clinical types are recognized, one the so-called *typhoidal type*, the other, which is more common, being known as the *glandular* or *ulceroglandular type*. Some workers differentiate between the glandular type, which reveals no primary lesion, but there is enlargement of the regional lymph nodes. In the ulceroglandular type, there is, in addition, a primary lesion which appears as a papule and later as an ulcer of the skin. The *oculoglandular* type occurs following infection by way of the eyes, and is rarely fatal.

Laboratory diagnostic aids for tularemia are: agglutination tests, cultural methods, animal inoculation and skin tests. The most frequently used procedure is the agglutination test, the macroscopic tube method being preferred. It is advisable to use agglutinable avirulent strains of *P. tularensis* in routine testing, as virulent strains of this and of *Brucella* species, have caused many accidental laboratory infections, due, it is believed, to their ability to invade even the unbroken skin. Agglutinins do not appear in the patient's blood until after the first week of illness. In suspicious cases, repeated tests should be performed and negative tularemia findings considered only if they persist beyond the fifteenth day of illness. Early in the disease the titer may be only 1:10 or 1:20, and it continues to rise. The agglutination test in tularemia is very reliable, but one must be familiar with its shortcomings. In human tularemia serums frequent cross-agglutination occurs between *P. tularensis* and either *Br. abortus* or *Br. melitensis.* In like manner, human brucellosis serums may show cross-agglutination of *P. tularensis.* Unless the history or clinical findings definitely point to one or the other of these two diseases, it is always advisable when performing agglutination tests in suspicious cases to set up tests against *P. tularensis* and *Br. abortus* and *Br. melitensis.* If the serum being tested contains agglutinins specific for *P. tularensis*, the latter will be agglutinated earlier and in a higher dilution. With such marked differences in titer, the serum can be classed by the higher titer as due to either one or the other. If a serum agglutinates all three organisms the same or almost the same titer, agglutinin absorption tests are to be performed.

Microscopic examinations of direct smears taken from patients are valueless. Though it may be possible to isolate *P. tularensis* from infected tissue or fluids of human cases, this procedure is rarely practiced. The best method is to inject subcutaneously into guinea pigs material taken from the primary lesion or from the enlarged glands or from the blood of the patient. As a rule, animals will die within a week or ten days if *P. tularensis* is present in the material injected. At autopsy, characteristic lesions are sought. Cultures and smears are made from the heart's blood, spleen, liver and lymph nodes, and injections made into other animals. Foshay (*J. Infect. Dis.*, 1936, **59,** 330) speaks highly of the value of intradermal skin testing. At present skin testing is being tried out, using a specific antiserum intradermal test and a bacterial antigen skin test. These tests may prove of great diagnostic value in human cases because of their ease in performance and apparent specificity.

Rabbit hunting is good sport and the meat is a valuable supplement to the diet during period of meat shortage, as occurs frequently during wartime. Contact with wild rabbits, however, requires the carrying out of simple precautionary measures to avoid contracting tularemia or *rabbit fever.* Rubber gloves should be worn at all times when cleaning rabbits, whether obtained by hunting or purchased on the open market. Care is to be observed in the cleaning process, so as to avoid getting a cut or break in the skin either with the knife or by other means. The gloves should be washed thoroughly with soap and hot water before taking them off. The rabbit meat is to be cooked thoroughly. Parker and associates (*J. Bact.*, 1943, **45,** 56) reported recently that epizootic tularemia in beavers and muskrats is widespread in the northwestern states, that water contamination with *P. tularensis* occurs by the affected animals, that the contamination may persist for considerable periods of time (at least seven months) and the importance of this to the fur industry and its consequential source of infection for humans, particularly trappers and game conservation officials, are apparent.

Foshay and associates (*Am. J. Pub. Health*, 1942, **32,** 1131) prepared a vaccine against tularemia by treating virulent strains of *Pasteurella tularensis* with nitrous acid. It has been employed in 2143 susceptible exposed persons during 1933–1941, and reports indicate that a useful degree of protection is conferred by this product.

Pasteurella Suilla (*Pasteurella Suiseptica; Bacillus Suisepticus; Bacillus of Swine Plague*).—This is the causative agent of swine plague or hemorrhagic septicemia of hogs. Infection with this organism in hogs is often accompanied by an infection with the hog-cholera virus, which has resulted in confusion, for at one time *P. suilla* was regarded as closely associated with the causative agent of hog cholera. The organism possesses many of the morphological, staining, cultural and general characteristics of the plague bacillus. It is pathogenic for mice, rabbits and birds. The natural disease of swine, characterized by a bronchopneumonia followed by septicemia with lymphadenitis, is generally fatal in young pigs. Isolated and rare cases of infection in man by this organism and other species of *pasteurella* causing hemorrhagic septicemia in lower animals have been reported.

Pasteurella Bollingeri (*Pasteurella Boviseptica; Bacillus Bovisepticus*).—This is the causative agent of hemorrhagic septicemia of cattle, a relatively frequent, highly fatal and contagious disease. To a lesser degree, this disease is found among domestic sheep and cattle. In some respects the symptoms of the disease resemble anthrax. Other than a septicemia, another form of the disease, known as shipping fever, is found associated with the shipment of stock. Whether this form is actually caused by *P. bollingeri* or whether the latter is a secondary invader and the primary cause is a filterable virus has not been proved. The organism possesses many of the characteristics of the plague bacillus, except that it is smaller and that bipolar staining is not as distinct.

Pasteurella Avicida (*Bacillus or Bacterium Avisepticus; Coccobacillus Avicidus; Bacillus Cholerae Gallinarum; Bacillus of Chicken Cholera*).—This is the causative agent of fowl cholera, a markedly acute disease with a high mortality and one of the most important diseases of fowl, affecting chickens, ducks, geese, pigeons, etc. Transmission occurs through the intestinal tract and the disease is characterized by diarrhea, drowsiness, prostration, general hemorrhagic infiltration and death. In its various characteristics the organism corresponds in general to the other members of the genus *pasteurella*.

Pasteurella Pseudotuberculosis (*Corynebacterium Pseudotuberculosis Rodentium; C. Rodentium; Bacillus Pseudotuberculosis Rodentium*).—This organism causes the so-called pseudotuberculosis of guinea pigs, the mode of infection being probably by way of the alimentary tract. Isolated cases in other rodents and rarely in man have been reported. This species differs from other members of this group in that it is motile when grown at 22° C. but not at 37° C. It frequently produces an alkaline reaction in milk and displays a relatively low pathogenicity for white rats.

Glanders Bacillus

Malleomyces Mallei (*Pfeifferella Mallei; Bacillus or Actinobacillus Mallei; Glanders Bacillus*).—The glanders bacillus is a small, slender rod, with rounded ends, at times slightly curved 0.3 to 0.8 by 1.5 to 5 μ, occurring singly, and occasionally in pairs and groups. Long threads of branching filaments may be found, at times vacuolated. It displays marked irregularity in (even bipolar) staining (due to the presence of lipoidal granules), is Gram-negative, nonacid-fast, nonmotile, nonspore-bearing, nonencapsulated, aerobic, will not grow below 20° C. or above 43° C. and develops best on media containing glycerin or blood serum. A characteristic growth is produced on potato medium. *M. mallei* is inactive biochemically, but produces variable amounts of acid in glucose, slight acid and slow coagulation in milk, slight liquefaction of gelatin, and small amounts of H_2S. Indol is not produced and nitrates are not reduced to nitrites. The relation of this organism to other bacteria is not clear, as is evidenced by the different generic names used at one time or another. *M. mallei* is not very resistant.

This organism is the cause of a rather common and one of the oldest of diseases in animals—glanders, ordinarily a chronic disease of the equine species. Horses, mules, asses, and to a lesser extent sheep, cats and more rarely dogs, contract the disease. Cattle and the house rat are immune. The common drinking trough and the insanitary conditions of stables are the probable potent sources of infection for animals. Three forms of the disease are recognized: Pulmonary, nasal and the cutaneous or *farcy* varieties. The term *glanders* is applied to the first two types, the pulmonary variety occurring frequently in an acute form. When the disease is limited to the upper respiratory tract and nasal mucosa, ulceration of the latter membranes occurs. When affecting the superficial lymphatic glands the disease is known as farcy or cutaneous glanders. Either the acute or chronic form may be contracted by man, especially those who are in habitual contact with the infected horse or articles soiled with discharges from equine or human cases. Doubtless many cases are mistaken for other diseases, which accounts for the high fatality rate of glanders among humans.

The recognition of the disease in man and animals is best verified by finding *M. mallei* in discharges, by the "Straus test" and by specific biological reactions (complement-fixation, agglutination and mallein tests). The *Straus Reaction* (*Compt. rend. Acad. Sci.*, 1889, **108,** 530) consists in injecting intraperitoneally fragments of diseased tissue, scrapings from ulcers, some of the nasal discharge or cultures. Male guinea pigs are used. On the second or third day, the testicles become red or swollen (positive test). Other symptoms also develop and death usually occurs within two weeks. Though not absolutely specific, this test is of value as an additional aid or where other procedures are inapplicable. The *Mallein Test* is of high diagnostic value. It is sharp, decisive and specific. The ophthalmic test is preferred to the subcutaneous or other methods of injecting mallein. In latent or occult cases, serodiagnostic tests (the agglutination or complement-fixation tests or both) supplement other diagnostic procedures.

General measures of control are to kill infected animals, properly disposing of carcasses, testing of horses by the mallein reaction to detect the disease early, abolition of the common drinking trough and the sanitary supervision of stables, blacksmith shops, etc. In human cases, the patient should be isolated and all discharges should be disinfected.

Malleomyces Pseudomallei (*Bacillus Whitmori; Bacillus or Actinobacillus Pseudomallei*).—This organism is the cause of a rare glanders-like disease of rodents, producing a highly fatal affection termed *meliodiosis*. The disease is communicable to other animals and occasionally to man.   Rats are the carriers of this infection.   The bacillus is closely related to *M. mallei* microscopically, culturally and serologically. It differs in the following respects: It is actively motile, grows luxuriantly on culture media, liquefies gelatin and attacks carbohydrates more energetically, occurs usually in very large numbers in the acute lesion; and in guinea pigs, it produces the Straus reaction and death of the laboratory animals occurs more quickly.

Malleomyces agliaceus is responsible for pseudotuberculosis in frogs.

Encapsulated, Gram-Negative, Respiratory Bacilli

Klebsiella Pneumoniae (*Pneumobacillus;   Friedländer Bacillus;   Encapsulatus Pneumoniae;   Bacillus Mucosus Capsulatus*).—This is a short, usually thick bacillus, varying from coccoid forms to long rods (0.5 to 1.5 by 0.6 to 5 μ), occurring singly in pairs or in short chains.   It is Gram-negative, encapsulated, nonmotile, nonspore-bearing, aerobic and facultatively anaerobic, grows readily on ordinary culture media and does not liquefy gelatin, but displays a characteristic, filiform growth in gelatin stab cultures.   A slimy growth is produced on artificial culture media and the colonies are mucoid in consistency.   It produces acid but no coagulation in litmus milk, acid and gas in media containing dextrose, lactose, saccharose, levulose and galactose, but does not attack other sugars.   Indol is not formed.   *K. pneumoniae* possesses the average resistance to heat and disinfectants, but is usually resistant to drying.

K. pneumoniae is closely related to the *coliform* bacteria, and the relationship between *klebsiella* and *aerobacter* especially is very close.   For some unexplainable reason, species of *klebsiella* are kept separated from the coliform bacteria, probably due to the fact that the former usually are encapsulated.   Perhaps if we keep in mind the close relationship of members of the Friedländer group and the coliform bacteria, we may be able to understand many characteristics of the individual species in each group.   Based on immunological reactions, Julianelle (*J. Bact.*, 1935, **30**, 535; 1938, **35**, 24) found that strains of *K. pneumoniae* may be divided into distinct types, A, B and C, to which the majority of strains belong.   These can be differentiated by agglutinin, precipitation and protection tests.   A heterogeneous group X contains all undifferentiated strains.   The strains comprising Type A are mainly from human sources.   Type B includes strains largely from the lower animals.   As in the case of the pneumococcus, type specificity is dependent on different polysaccharides in the capsular substance, and species specificity is dependent on a common nucleoprotein in the body or soma of the organism.   Recently Rakieten and associates (*J. Bact.*, 1940, **40**, 544) found that specific phages may be useful in classifying strains of *K. pneumoniae.*

The Friedländer bacillus is found frequently in the nasopharyngeal tract, especially in individuals suffering from respiratory infections.   It, however, may cause pneumonia, both lobar pneumonia and bronchopneumonia, which, though rare, is characterized by a high mortality.   It may be found associated with other bacteria, or by itself, causing (in rare instances) inflammations of other parts of the respiratory tract.

Klebsiella Rhinoscleromatis (*Bacillus of Rhinoscleroma;   Encapsulatus Rhinoscleromatis*).—This is almost identical with the Friedländer bacillus, differing only in its weaker fermentative powers, producing acid and gas from dextrose and only occasionally from lactose, but attacking other sugars but infrequently. Litmus milk is unchanged other than growth production. It is regarded by many workers as the cause of rhinoscleroma, a disease characterized by a slowly growing granulomatous inflammation located in the nose, mouth, pharynx or larynx. This disease is rarely found in this country, but is prevalent in southeastern Europe.

Klebsiella Ozaenae (*Bacillus or Encapsulatus Ozaenae*).—This is now regarded as being identical with *Escherichia foetida*, also known as *Bacterium foetidium*, *Perez bacillus* and *Coccobacillus of Ozaena*. It is almost identical with the Friedländer bacillus in all characteristics. In fact, some workers question whether this is a separate species. Slight differences in pathogenicity for mice and inability to form gas in some sugar media are cited as facts which at present are regarded as sufficient to consider this as a separate species. It is constantly present in ozena or fetid rhinitis, and is regarded by some as a secondary invader and by others as the caustive agent in this disease. It is infectious for house and field mice. For further details, see Julianelle (*J. Bact.*, 1935, **30**, 535).

Klebsiella granulomatis has been isolated from lesions of granuloma inguinale, but is not the causative agent of this venereal disease. The organism, especially in body fluids, may appear coccoid. One or more metachromatic granules may be apparent. Litmus milk is acidified and coagulated; and acid and gas are produced in most of the commonly used sugar media.

Hemoglobinophilic Bacilli

Hemophilus Influenzae (*Influenza Bacillus; Pfeiffer Bacillus; Hemoglobinophilic Bacillus*).—Bacilli that will not grow or at least not luxuriantly in pure cultures without the presence of hemoglobin (whole blood) are called hemoglobinophilic or hemophilic bacteria. These organisms are placed under the genus *hemophilus* in the Bergey classification. They are generally minute rod shaped cells, moderately thick, 0.2 to 0.3 by 0.5 to 2 μ, and occur singly, united in pairs; occasionally some species are pleomorphic or show long thread forms, occasional short chains may be seen. There may be a tendency to bipolar staining. They are nonmotile, nonspore-bearing, do not generally possess capsular material, are Gram-negative, aerobic, weak-resistant and have not been found outside of animal bodies.

The important member of this genus is the influenza bacillus or *Hemophilus influenzae*. This organism requires both factors X and V for its growth. The former is heat-stable and found in hemoglobin (or hematin) and the V factor is heat-labile and is found in yeast. For details on these growth-stimulating substances, see Avery and associates (*J. Exp. Med.*, 1921, **34**, 454; 1923, **38**, 73; 1924, **40**, 405). Chocolate agar is frequently used for culturing this organism. Recently a medium containing 3 per cent agar-beef-liver extract and 10 per cent of a staphylococcus filtrate was recommended (*Canad. Pub. Health J.*, 1943, **34**, 178). *H. influenzae* is aerobic and facultatively anaerobic and grows between 26° and 43° C., best at 37° C. Indol is produced by some strains and nitrates are reduced to nitrites. Its reaction to carbohydrates is variable, but mannitol and lactose are never fermented. In body fluids, it is found frequently intracellularly (in relation to pus cells). It is found in the nose and throat and sputum of patients suffering with respiratory diseases, especially tuberculosis. When causing disease it is probably more frequently a secondary invader than the primary cause. It has been known to be the causative agent in cases of broncho-pneumonia, various throat affections and meningitis. Occasional cases of otitis media, sinusitis and other localized infections are at times caused by this organism.

Hemophilus influenzae has been and is regarded by a few workers as the cause of the disease which we know as influenza, an acute communicable disease always endemic in many localities, becoming epidemic and even pandemic, and sometimes traveling under the name of grippe. It is characterized by a general nervous prostration, high fever and a catarrh of the mucous membranes of the respiratory tract, accompanied at times by bronchitis and pneumonia. Occasionally the gastro-intestinal tract may be the site of the important symptoms. As a result of innumerable investigations since the influenza pandemic of 1918, it may be stated that the causative agent of the latter remains unsolved, but it is supposed to be caused by a filterable virus. Though the influenza bacillus has been found in many cases during the pandemic, the majority of workers believe that this organism was not the initiating cause, and that if *Hemophilus influenzae* is found in influenza cases its role is to be considered as that of a secondary invader.

So-called *hog-flu* or *swine influenza* developed as a new epizootic during the last influenza pandemic. Shope and associates (*J. Exp. Med.*, 1931, **54**, 349, 373; 1934, **60**, 49; 1935, **62**, 561; 1936, **64**, 791) revealed that both infections were caused by immunologically related viruses, that swine are susceptible to at least some strains of human influenza virus, and that two agents which "act in concert," a filtrable virus and a bacillus, *H. suis*, produce swine influenza. This swine influenza bacillus, *H. influenzae suis* or *H. suis*, an important secondary factor, resembles *H. influenzae*, except that it is relatively inert biochemically. Mote and Fothergill (*J. Bact.*, 1940, **40**, 505) reveal the inability of human strains of *H. influenzae* to establish themselves in the respiratory tract of swine and suggest a possible biologic difference between human and swine strains of *H. influenzae*. There are other bacilli which closely resemble *H. influenzae*. Some are atypical forms and others are at present even designated as separate species.

The *Hemophilus conjunctivitidis* or the *Koch-Weeks' bacillus*, the cause of acute contagious conjunctivitis ("pink eye") and at one time regarded as a separate and distinct species, is believed to be identical with *H. influenzae* and is so listed in the Bergey classification.

Hemophilus Hemolyticus (*Influenza-like Bacillus*).—This is an influenza-like bacillus found in the upper respiratory tract of man. Some strains are somewhat larger and stain more evenly and heavier. This organism is nonpathogenic.

Hemophilus Pertussis (*Bordet-Gengou Bacillus; Bacillus Pertussis; Whooping Cough Bacillus*).— *Hemophilus pertussis* resembles somewhat the influenza bacillus. In morphology it is, however, more regularly ovoid, somewhat larger and displays a lesser tendency to pleomorphism and involution. It is Gram-negative and frequently displays a tendency to bipolar staining. Specific agglutinative powers and differential diagnosis by various cultural characteristics are employed to prove the distinctness of this organism from the influenza bacillus. No action is produced in carbohydrate media; indol is not formed and nitrates are not reduced. It is catalase-positive. To observe the latter, Farrel's technique is suggested (*J. Bact.*, 1935, **29**, 411). Litmus milk is slowly rendered alkaline. The evidence is strongly in favor of *H. pertussis* being the cause of pertussis or whooping cough, though *Br. bronchiseptica* and closely related organisms have also been implicated (*J. Bact.*, 1937, **33,** 71; 1938, **35,** 6). The infection is a communicable endemic and epidemic disease, characterized by catarrh of the respiratory tract and a characteristic spasmodic whoop. The disease, which is widely prevalent and peculiarly a disease of childhood and infancy, can be controlled by excluding the patient from school and public places, disinfection of infected discharges, personal cleanliness, etc.

H. Pertussis, though difficult to cultivate upon primary isolation, differs from *H. influenzae* and other hemophilic bacteria in that it does not at all times require for growth the essential factors V and X. Bordet-Gengou medium is the classic diagnostic medium used for the isolation of *H. pertussis* and if it is definitely acid (*p*H 5), the *H. influenzae*, if present, will not grow. Colony formation requires two to three days and by repeated passage on media containing decreasing amounts of blood, *H. pertussis* can be acclimatized to grow subsequently even upon ordinary nutrient agar. The isolation of this organism is of particular value in the early stages of the disease before paroxysms have appeared or in those atypical cases without paroxysms. Diagnostic procedures are generally not needed when the characteristic clinical symptoms of whooping appear. The direct microscopic examination of sputum is of little value, as other Gram-negative bacilli resembling *H. pertussis* may be present. Furthermore, infants do not expectorate their sputum, the latter may only contain saliva and mucus, or vomitus may be admixed. Where suitable specimens can be obtained, the sputum is washed in three or four changes of isotonic salt solution, and the thick tenacious, grayish portion is plated. The method of choice, however, is the "droplet method of inoculation" or "cough plate method" (*Am. J. Pub. Health*, 1934, **24,** 309). An uncovered Petri dish containing Bordet-Gengou medium is held 4 or 5 inches from the patient's mouth during expulsive coughing. If necessary, coughing is induced, by some method, generally by tickling the throat with a swab. The plate is covered as soon as possible after obtaining the specimen, and incubated at 37° C. for at least four to five days. Examine the plates twice daily to detect typical growth. The colonies are smooth, raised, glistening, almost transparent, not over 1 mm. in diameter, and surrounded by a characteristic zone of hemolysis (if less than 30 per cent of blood is present in the medium). *H. influenzae* darkens the medium and produces smaller and less opaque colonies. Brooks and associates (*J. A. M. A.*, 1942, **120,** 883) advocate a method of nasopharyngeal culture in the diagnosis of whooping cough. Agglutination tests are most convenient for testing for identification of suspicious colonies of *H. pertussis*. In patients during the natural disease, few agglutinins are produced and complement-fixing antibodies appear late in the disease; consequently the agglutination test and complement-fixation test are of limited diagnostic value. The opsonocytophagic reaction or test (*J. Clin. Investigation*, 1937, **16,** 749, 825) has been used in pertussis studies as a means of measuring the opsonins, this correlating with protection. Its exact significance requires further investigation. Skin tests with various antigens and antigenic fractions of *H. pertussis* for determining susceptibility to and as a possible diagnostic aid for whooping cough are being tried (*Am. J. Dis. Child.*, 1939, **57,** 1246), but these also must be studied further. Lesslie and Gardner (*J. Hyg.*, 1931, **31,** 423) used the agglutination and agglutinin absorptive procedures to classify strains of *H. pertussis* into "phases," I, II, III and IV. Freshly isolated strains are toxic for guinea pigs and fall into phases I and II. Old strains are nontoxic for guinea pigs and fall into phases III and IV. Bacterial vaccines and other biological products are being used in the prevention and treatment of this disease. See Biological Products.

Hemophilus Duplex (*H. Lacunatus; Morax-Axenfeld Bacillus; Diplobacillus of Morax*).—*Hemophilus duplex* is a short, thick, square- or round-ended rod, 0.5 to 0.8 by 2 μ, occurring usually in pairs, placed end to end, but not infrequently singly and in short chains. Involution forms are rarely observed. It is nonmotile, Gram-negative, aerobic and can be cultivated on blood-serum media at body temperature. Indol is not formed and nitrates are not reduced to nitrites. Various carbohydrates including mannitol are fermented. This organism is the cause of certain subacute inflammations of the cornea and conjunctiva, a catarrhal conjunctivitis, usually attacking both eyes, and especially noticeable about the angles of the eyes ("angular conjunctivitis"). As far as known it is only pathogenic for the human eye. Zinc sulfate (0.25 per cent) solutions are specifics.

Hemophilus Ducreyi (*Ducrey Bacillus; Bacillus of Chancroid; Bacillus Ulceris Cancrosı; Streptobacillus of Ducrey; Bacillus of Soft Chancre*).—This is a small, round-ended rod, 0.5 by 1.5 to 2 μ, occurring singly but showing a tendency to appear in short chains, in parallel rows or twisted together in irregular groups. It is nonmotile, Gram-negative and may show bipolar staining. It is delicate and can be cultured when special precautions and perseverance are observed. It is aerobic and facultatively anaerobic. Best growth is obtained on clotted rabbit, sheep or human blood heated to 55° C. for fifteen minutes, and in casein digest agar containing blood. Optimum temperature of growth is 37° C.

This organism is the cause of chancroid or soft chancre, one of the venereal diseases, observed as an acute inflammatory ulcerating sore, single or multiple, with irregular, crater-like margins, a somewhat indurated inflammatory base, and occurring usually on the genitalia or surrounding skin and displaying a tendency toward the formation of complicated suppurating inguinal adenitis. Infection generally results from illicit sexual intercourse. It differs from the syphilitic chancre in being painful, due to violent inflammation which it produces, in the lack of induration and in yielding quickly to treatment.

Every genital sore must be regarded as a potential case of syphilis. It is important that, in any genital sore in male or female, dark-field examination should be made of the aspirated fluid in accessible lesions on successive days until three negative findings for the absence of *Treponema pallidum* are obtained. During this period, withhold all local medication, applying only saline dressings. It is absolutely necessary

---

PLATE I

Fig. 1. *Streptococcus hemolyticus* (*pyogenes*). Methylene blue. (See page 107.)

Fig. 2. *Staphylococcus aureus*. Methylene blue. (See page 104.)

Fig. 3. *Diplococcus pneumoniae* (*pneumococcus*). Gram stain. (See page 114.)

Fig. 4. Neisseria gonorrhea from urethral discharge (acute gonorrhea). Gram stain (the Gram stain should always be used in diagnosing gonorrhea). (See page 120.) The meningococcus (*N. intracellularis*) possesses a similar morphology.

Fig. 5. *Mycobacterium tuberculosis* (tubercle bacillus) from sputum. Stained by Ziehl-Neelsen technic. Beaded forms. (See page 130.)

Fig. 6. *Treponema pallidum* from tissue section. Levaditi's stain. (See page 191.)

Magnifications are 1000 × in all illustrations. Color plates courtesy A. S. Aloe Co. and American Colortype.

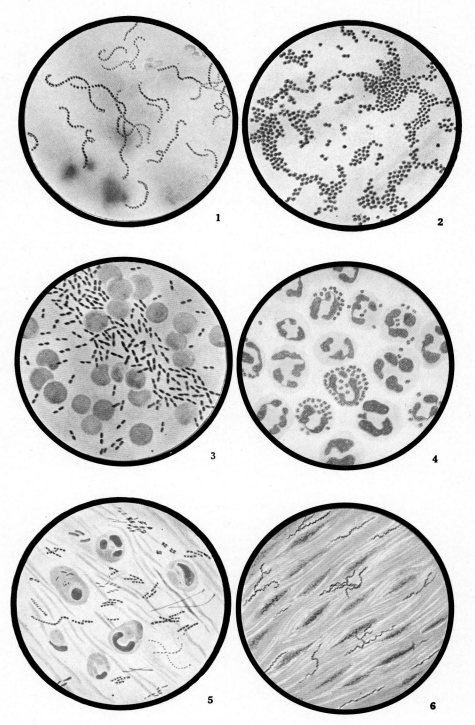

PLATE I
See facing page for explanation.

to rule out mixed syphilitic and chancroidal infection. The patient should be kept under observation for syphilis for two months. For smears or cultural isolation of *H. ducreyi*, it is best to use the pus aspirated from unruptured buboes if the latter are present. Gram's method and, still better, Wright's or other blood-staining techniques are used. The *Ito-Reenstierna intracutaneous test* is a specific test as an aid in the diagnosis of chancroid. The latter is relatively uncommon among clean people. It is readily prevented by prompt prophylactic treatment. Even simple washing with soap and water after coitus reduces the risk of infection with *H. ducreyi*. Practically all cases of chancroidal infection respond to treatment with sulfonamide drugs, locally as well as internally (by mouth). Kornblith and associates (*J. A. M. A.*, 1941, **117**, 2150) reported the successful use of sulfanilamide and sulfathiazole in 175 cases. Quaternary ammonium compounds (2 per cent solutions) were found most effective for the prevention of experimental chancroid in human volunteers by Greenblatt and associates (*Am J. Syph., Gonor., Ven. Dis.*, 1944, **28**, 165). For further details on chancroidal infection, see Greenwald (*J. A. M. A.*, 1943, **121**, 9).

Hemophilus gallinarum (*Bacillus Haemoglinophilus Coryzae Gallinarum*) has been isolated from chickens affected with infectious coryza and **Hemophilus haemoglobinophilus** (*Haemophilus ccanis*) is found, at times, in the penile "drippings" observed in dogs.

Noguchia granulosis is a hemoglobinophilic bacillus, somewhat longer than *H. influenzae* and has been regarded by Noguchi and others as the cause of trachoma. General confirmation, however, is lacking (See Weiss, *J. Infect. Dis.*, 1930, **47**, 107). This organism grows at 37° C. but its optimum temperature range is between 15° and 30° C. Motility is apparent at 15° but not at 37° C. It is differentiated otherwise from closely related Gram-negative rods by action on carbohydrates and specificity in agglutination reactions. It is nonpathogenic for the commonly employed laboratory animals.

Dialister pneumosintes is an obligate anaerobic Gram-negative, nonmotile, very short rod with pointed ends. It passes through Berkefield V and N filters. It has been isolated from filtered nasopharyngeal secretions of influenza patients during the early hours of the disease.

Chromogenic Bacilli

Pseudomonas Aeruginosa (*Bacillus Pyocyaneus; P. Pyocyanea; Bacillus of Green and of Blue Pus*).—This is a short, slender rod, 0.3 to 0.6 by 1.5 to 3 μ. The variations in size may be very marked at times, not only short and plump rods but occasionally threadlike arrangements may be observed. It occurs singly, but may be united in pairs and short chains. It is actively motile, nonspore-bearing, Gram-negative, aerobic and facultatively anaerobic, grows on ordinary media even at room temperature, producing a characteristic green pigment (if in free access of oxygen). Indol is generally not produced. Nitrates are not reduced to nitrites and nitrogen. Blood is hemolyzed. Most sugars are not attacked. Hydrogen sulfide is produced. Litmus milk is alkalinized and with the production only of a soft coagulum, the latter is followed by rapid peptonization and reduction of the indicator. *P. aeruginosa* liquefies blood serum and gelatin rapidly. This organism is widely distributed in Nature. It is found as a saprophyte in water, sewage, manure, etc. It is frequently found in the intestinal tract, upon the skin and in the upper respiratory tract of normal humans and animals. It is ordinarily only slightly pathogenic for man, but under certain conditions (as in general debility) this organism may become a dangerous source of infection. Suppurative lesions of various parts of the body, as in open wounds, old sinus and middle-ear infections and in intestinal disorders, caused by this organism, have been reported. The pus is usually tinged green. Favorable results in treatment by the use of sulfonamide compounds have been reported. Solomon (*J. Florida M. Soc.*, 1942, **29,** 174) recently reported definite value with the latter in the treatment of a patient with *P. aeruginosa* infection of the cornea.

There are many other fluorescent bacteria of the genus *Pseudomonas*, which are found for the most part in water, soil and in decomposing material. Bergey's classification lists 31 species. *P. aeruginosa* is the only species pathogenic for man. The other species are mainly saprophytes, but some of them may cause diseases in lower animals, reptiles, insects and possibly plants. The genus *Phytomonas* contains 137 species which are mainly pathogenic for plants. Many of them produce a water-soluble greenish pigment and the relationship with species of *Pseudomonas* is frequently questioned. Elrod and Braun (*J. Bact.*, 1942, **44,** 633) have isolated *P. aeruginosa* strains which grow equally well in plant as well as in warm-blooded animal tissues. They claim that this species is identical with *Phytomonas polycolor*, which is the cause of an economically important disease of tobacco.

Serratia Marcescens (*Micrococcus or Bacillus Prodigiosus; Bacillus or Bacterium Prodigiosum; Erythrobacillus Prodigiosus*).—This is a small coccoid rod, 0.5 by 0.5 to 1 μ, occurring singly and occasionally in chains. It is motile, Gram-negative, nonspore-bearing, aerobic and grows well on ordinary media, producing a bright red pigmentation, which usually develops best at room temperature. Gelatin is rapidly liquefied. It is V-P (Voges-Proskauer) positive. Indol is not produced; nitrates are reduced to nitrites. Hydrogen sulfide is produced from cystene or cysteine and compounds containing these substances, and from sulfur, but not from sulfites, sulfates or thiosulfates. The optimum temperature for growth is between 25° to 30° C. Pigment is not produced at 35° C. and growth does not occur at 37° C. The pigment is soluble in alcohol, benzol, chloroform, ether and carbon bisulfide. *S. marcescens* is a saprophyte found in water, milk, bread and other foodstuffs and in soil. Cultures of this organism are used to make Coley's Fluid (which see).

There are other species of *Serratia* which are found as saprophytes widely distributed in Nature, especially water, foodstuffs, etc. Six species are listed under Bergey's classification. *Ser. anolium* is of interest in that it is pathogenic for amphibians, reptiles and to some extent fish. It is nonpathogenic for warm-blooded animals.

Other Intestinal Bacteria and Group of Lactobacilli

There are many anaerobic nonsporulating Gram-positive and Gram-negative rods of medical importance which have been placed in different genera. Most of these species are as little known today as they were several decades ago. Unfortunately some workers even question their importance in medical bacteriology. Recent investigations, however, have shed some light on the relationship of the many forms. Many of the old genus names as *Bacteroides* are being discarded. The species are separated mainly on their cultural characteristics and behavior to the Gram-staining technique, supplemented by knowledge of their origin. The genus *lactobacillus* includes all Gram-positive rods, which are microaerophilic to anaerobic, produce very little surface growth on media, ferment carbohydrates with the formation of considerable quantities of lactic acid. They are usually capable of withstanding an amount of acid generally fatal to most nonsporulating bacteria. The term *acidophilic* or *aciduric* (acid-tolerant) is commonly applied to those bacteria producing large amounts of acid, which they themselves are able to withstand. King and Rettger (*J. Bact.*, 1942, **44**, 301) reviewed the intra- and extra-group relationships of many of the above species and found that potassium cyanide exerted a more pronounced poisoning influence on obligate anaerobes than upon those of the facultative aerobes. For characterization of species of genus *lactobacillus*, see Pederson (*J. Bact.*, 1942, **43**, 57).

Lactobacillus Bifidus (*Bacteroides Bifidus; Bacillus Bifidus*).—This is a nonmotile rod which from cultures (only) shows a bifid branching at the end, usually found singly, varying from 0.3 to 0.7 by 2 to 8 μ. Smears made from the intestinal contents when revealing the presence of this organism do not show the latter with bifid ends, but as a slender bacillus, with one end tapering and the other club-shaped. It is an obligate anaerobe (on primary isolation), grows on ordinary media and does not produce gas in any of the sugar media. It is Gram-positive but some strains may reveal a Gram-negative body with Gram-positive granules scattered through them. It is nonpathogenic, and found normally in the stools of breast-fed infants, being abundant in the large intestines of the latter. There are many closely related organisms grouped in this genus, commonly found in the intestinal canal, and which differ from *L. bifidus* as to motility, indol production, action on milk and sugar media.

Lactobacillus Bulgaricus (*Bacillus Bulgaricus and probably Bacillus Acetogenes, Bacillus Dimorphus and Streptobacillis Longis*).—This is a large, square-ended rod, 1 by 4 μ, occurring singly, in pairs, frequently in long chains and often showing metachromatic granules. This organism is nonmotile, microaerophilic and grows best on milk, whey or malt media. The optimum temperature for growth is 45° to 50° C. Growth does not occur below 22° C. Milk, whey or preparations of the latter are more suitable media for growth. Indol is not formed. Nitrates are not reduced. It is Gram-positive, but in old cultures it may appear as a Gram-amphophile. It is nonpathogenic and has been isolated from various fermented milks, as "matzoon" and "yoghurt." There are probably many allied species, differing on the basis of carbohydrate fermentation, which have been isolated from other sources as human feces, milk, beer, silage, sour potato mash and other fermentations. The use of this organism in cases of intestinal putrefaction, etc., is considered in Chapter XIV (Useful Bacteria).

Lactobacillus Acidophilus (*Bacillus Acidophilus*).—This bacillus is a rather slender rod, frequently with tapering ends, from 0.6 to 0.9 by 2 μ long, and occurs singly and in pairs. It is nonmotile and Gram-positive, though in old cultures it may appear Gram-amphophilic. Polar granules may be observed, so that if found in smears from feces acidophilus bacilli may resemble the diphtheroids. It grows best under microaerophilic conditions on milk or whey media. The optimum temperature for growth is 37° C.; the maximum is 43° to 48° C.; and the minimum is 20° to 22° C. In anaerobic cultures the clubbed, involution characteristics of *L. bifidus* may be observed, so that some consider these two organisms very closely related. It is nonpathogenic and is found normally in the intestinal tract of healthy human infants and to a lesser degree in adults. On the basis of variations in carbohydrate fermentations, several types of this organism have been distinguished. Acidophilus therapy in the treatment of intestinal disorders is considered in Chapter XIV (Useful Bacteria).

Lactobacillus Boas-Oppleri or *Boas-Oppler Bacillus* is in many ways similar to *L. acidophilus* (and is so designated in the Bergey classification), though it is somewhat longer, and occurs more frequently in long chains. This organism is nonpathogenic and is found in small numbers in normal gastric contents, but is present in great abundance and in long chains in gastric carcinoma (cancer). The significance of this is not known.

Lactobacilli and Dental Caries.—Dental caries denotes an injury to the teeth produced by acids formed locally by bacteria attacking carbohydrates in a stagnant environment. Hardness or softness and cleanliness or uncleanliness of teeth are not responsible *per se* for this affection, although poor hygiene may accelerate the process and the latter may be controlled by the calcification of the teeth by nutritional methods. Dental caries also is reduced if fluorides or iodoacetic acid or some other waterborne constituent (not identified as yet) are present in the water supply or added to the diet. It appears that enamel containing more fluorine acquires antienzymotic properties and is more resistant to the acids formed, inasmuch as the solubility is decreased. Dental caries is directly related to the starch and sugar intake, to certain intrinsic factors of the affected individual, and to the *Lactobacilli* content of the saliva. *Lactobacillus acidophilus* counts of saliva collected after activation by chewing paraffin, are employed as a true index of caries suceptibility of an individual. Scrivener (*Dental Survey*, 1943, **19**, 344) recommends either the bacterial-count or the color-reaction methods for determining caries-susceptibility. In the bacterial-count method, 0.1 cc. of saliva, diluted 1:20 with saline, is plated, using tomato agar (*p*H 5) and incubating at 37° C. for three days. Counts over 400 per cc. indicate caries-susceptibility. In the color-reaction technique, 0.2 cc. of saliva is added to a tube of brom cresol green dextrose agar, which was liquefied and cooled to 54° C. and the mixture incubated at 37° C. for twenty-four hours. A change to a yellow color indicates caries-susceptibility. The name *Lactobacillus odontolyticus* is used at times for strains found in dental caries. Recently Hammond and Weinmann (*J. Dent. Research*, 1942, **21**, 509) established a correlation between the degree of caries and the ability of the saliva to stimulate phagocytosis (opsonin content). Caries-positive patients possessed saliva which was not capable of stimulating many leukocytes to take up the oral *lactobacillus* test organism. Turner and Crane (*Science*, 1944, **99**, 262) reveal a relationship between the incidence of dental caries and the rate of starch hydrolysis by saliva. Individuals with extensive caries yield saliva which hydrolyzes starch very rapidly as compared to those without caries in whom the saliva hydrolyzes starch very slowly.

Lactobacilli and Microbiological Assay of Vitamins.—Different species of *lactobacilli* are employed today for the microbiological assay of several of the different vitamins. *Lactobacillus casei* is used in the assay of riboflavin (vitamin B_2 or G), and in the assay for pyridoxine (vitamin B_6) and pantothenic acid. *Lactobacillus arabinosus* is used in the assay for niacin (nicotinic acid). The strain of *L. casei* is Number 7469 and that of *L. arabinosus* is Number 8014 of the American Type Culture Collections (obtainable at the Georgetown University Medical School, Washington, D. C.). These microbiological assays have been proposed for immediate U. S. P. status by supplement. The characteristics of these two strains of *lactobacilli* are being studied and the present confusion concerning their exact nomenclature might possibly be cleared in the not too distant future. Tittsler and associates (*J. Bact.*, 1942, **43**, 56) described the characteristics of the strain of *Lactobacillus casei* used in microbiological assays and point out that the latter does and members of the *L. acidophilus-bulgaricus* group fail to grow in the medium employed in the assay procedure. See also Light and Clarke (*J. Biol. Chem.*, 1943, **147**, 739) for additional studies on *L. casei* in microbiological assay.

Other Gram-Positive Nonspore-Bearing Rods

A number of saprophytic, nonpathogenic Gram-positive nonspore-forming rods are occasionally encountered. Species of the genus *Microbacterium* produce catalase and include *M. lacticum*, isolated from cheese and milk; *M. mesentericum*, isolated from decayed red beets; and *M. flavum*, found in cheese and butter. *Kurthia zopfiii* and *K. zenkeri* (regarded by some as identical) are found in decomposing materials.

Listerella Monocytogenes.—This is a nonacid-fast, Gram-positive, motile rod, from 0.5 by 1 to 2 μ in size and occurs singly, frequently in V-shaped or parallel pairs and occasionally in short chains. Spores and capsules are absent. Staining is uniform, though a beaded appearance is apparent at times. This organism is aerobic and facultatively anaerobic and the optimum temperature is 37° C. It grows on media containing natural fluids or extracts as liver-extract agar, egg media and blood agar. Growth on the latter is with a zone of hemolysis around the colonies. Seastone (*J. Exp. Med.*, 1935, **62**, 203) reports characteristic growth in semisolid media. The colonies are small, grow along the stab, followed by irregular cloudy or granular extensions into the medium. Growth does not spread through the entire medium. The colonies appear transparent by transmitted light and milk-white by reflected light. *L. monocytogenes* is relatively inactive biochemically. Acid but no gas is produced promptly in media containing dextrose, salicin and rhamnose, slowly from saccharose, dextrin, soluble starch and glycerin, irregularly and slowly from lactose and maltose, and no action on the other sugars. Indol and hydrogen sulfide are not produced, gelatin is not liquefied, and nitrates are not reduced to nitrites. It possesses the resistance of the commonly found bacteria, the thermal death point being 58° to 59° C. in ten minutes. Most strains are serologically related. Tentatively named as above in the Bergey classification, this organism appears closely related to species of the *erysipelothrix* genus (Barber, *J. Path. and Bact.*, 1939, **48**, 11). Pirie (*Science*, 1940, **92**, 383) has suggested *Listeria* as the name for the genus, as the generic name. Listerella has been applied previously to a mycetozoan.

Infections with this organism are known frequently as *listerellosis*. It is the cause of "circling," a disease of sheep (*J. Am. Vet. M. A.*, 1937, **91**, 73) and this or possible related species have been isolated from bovine encephalitis, abortive ovine fetuses (*Vet. Jour.*, 1940, **96**, 327), from chickens with myocardial disease, rabbits with a large mononuclear leukocytosis, and a plaguelike affection of the South African gerbille. The pathogenicity of this and related species for man is uncertain. Nyfeldt (*Folia Haematologica*, 1932, **47**) has suggested its relationship with *infectious mononucleosis* or *glandular fever* in man, but the evidence is not conclusive. For further details, see Julianelle (*Ann. Int. Med.*, 1940, **14**, 608).

Other Gram-Negative Nonspore-Forming Aerobes

Actinobacillus Lignieresi.—This is a Gram-negative, nonmotile, nonspore-forming aerobe and facultative anaerobe. Growth is favored by the presence of CO_2, in the atmosphere, and no growth is apparent under obligate anaerobic conditions. It grows well on common culture media incubated at 37.5° C. Media of slightly alkaline reaction to which blood serum is added are best suited for its propagation. Preparations from cultures on solid media reveal the presence of minute rods varying from 0.4 to 1 by 2 to 3 μ, but in liquid cultures chains or filaments as long as 15 μ or more may be found. In thick, pasty pus obtained from abscesses there are found small grayish-white granules, which when examined microscopically reveal the presence of rosettes of radiating clubs without the presence of a mycelium. This organism is of interest in veterinary rather than in human medicine as the cause of a disease in bovines simulating actinomycosis. Cattle, goats and sheep are affected. Isolated cases have been reported in man. This disease, *actinobacillosis*, is characterized by the appearance of granulomata and abscess formation, affecting principally the lymph nodes and soft tissue, and in many ways resembles actinomycosis, except that the bony structures are not attacked.

Actinobacillus Actinoides (*Actinomyces Actinoides; Bacillus Actinoides*).— *Actinobacillus actinoides* may cause outbreaks of pneumonia in calves. It is non-pathogenic for man and other animals. This organism is microaerophilic, will grow at 37.5° C. or at room temperature (under reduced oxygen tension) on media to which are added calf serum and a piece of sterile guinea pig spleen. It appears as a slender pleomorphic rod changing to spherical or coccoid forms in old cultures. In certain cultures rosettes composed of filaments and clubs may be observed. When stained the organism is Gram-negative.

Anaerobic Nonspore-forming Bacilli

Bergey's classification lists 23 species of Gram-negative, anaerobic nonspore-forming rods in the genus *Bacteroides*. These species have been encountered in a variety of infections in humans and from the intestinal tract of normal and diseased mammals. Some of them grow only if the medium is enriched with ascitic fluid or other natural proteinaceous material; and in few instances, the organisms will grow only after one or two weeks' incubation. *Bacteroides vulgatus* has been isolated most frequently from adult human feces. *Bacteroides fragilis*, *Bacteriodes funduliformis* and *Bacteroides serpens* have been isolated from cases of acute appendicitis, pulmonary gangrene, septicemia, meningitis, mastoiditis, peritonitis and abscesses of liver and urinary tracts. Smith (*J. Bact.*, 1943, **45,** 54) noted that three out of five strains of *Bacteroides funduliformis* isolated by him produced pleuropneumonia-like (L) type colonies as variant growth forms. Waring and associates (*Laryngoscope*, 1943, **53,** 717) reported a case of septicemia (with recovery) due to *Bacteroides funduliformis* and Ballenger and associates (*Ann. Otol. Rhin. and Laryng.*, 1943, **52,** 895) reported a case of bacteroides meningitis with recovery.

Bacteroides Fragilis (*Bacterium Fragilis; Bacillus or Fusiformis Fragilis*).—This is a small, slender, straight, round-ended or occasionally slightly curved rod. It is non-motile, anaerobic or microaerophilic, stains somewhat unevenly and is Gram-negative or occasionally Gram-amphophilic, nonspore-forming, and grows on the common laboratory media but feebly. It takes about three or four days for growth to appear and after seven or eight days the bacteria are no longer viable. Nitrates are not reduced, gelatin not liquefied, hydrogen sulfide and hemolysis (on blood agar) not produced and acid is produced in lactose, dextrose, saccharose and maltose. This organism has been found in cases of appendicitis, infections of the urinary tract, septicemias with metastatic abscesses, and in lung, pelvic and hepatic abscesses.

Bacteroides Melanogenicus (*Bacterium Melaninogenicum*).—This is a very small, anaerobic, nonspore-bearing diplobacillus or diplococcoid bacillus. On blood-agar plates, grown aerobically, the colonies assume on the fourth or fifth day a typical coal-black appearance. The pigment is similar to but not identical with melanin. It is difficult to isolate and maintain this organism in pure culture. Whether this organism is a secondary invader or a pathogen is not known. It has been found in the tonsils, mouth, infected abdominal wounds, kidneys, feces, and isolated especially from stools in cases of chronic amebic dysentery.

Bacteroides Funduliformis (*Bacterium or Fusiformis Ramosus*).—This is a small slender rod, straight or slightly curved, some cells showing variable thickness, swellings and branching V forms. It is nonmotile, nonspore-forming, not encapsulated, Gram-positive, anaerobic and grows only at 37° C. requiring three or four days for the display of growth. Indol is not produced, gelatin is not liquefied, hemolysis is not produced, and milk is coagulated. Acid is produced in dextrose, lactose, saccharose, maltose, galactose and mannitol. This organism was found in humans and isolated from the blood, and in infections of the urinary tract, liver abscesses, osteomyelitis, chronic otitis media, mastoiditis, pulmonary gangrene, gangrenous appendicitis, intestinal ulceration, putrid pleurisy and cavernous tuberculosis.

Bacteroides Serpens (*Bacterium Serpens*).—This is a small, stout, round-ended, straight rod, motile, an obligate anaerobe, Gram-negative, nonspore-forming, and nonencapsulated. Indol is produced; milk is acidified and coagulated with the production of gas; brain medium is blackened; and acid and gas are formed from dextrose, lactose, maltose, galactose and levulose. Pus containing this organism in mixture with other bacteria displays more virulency upon injection into laboratory animals than pure cultures alone. *B. serpens* admixed with *B. funduliformis* was found in a fatal case of mastoiditis.

Chapter X

COMMONLY OBSERVED PATHOGENIC AND NONPATHOGENIC BACTERIA

BACILLI (SPORE-FORMING)

Spore-bearing Aerobic Bacilli

THE GENUS *bacillus* is a very large one, consisting of Gram-positive, aerobic, motile, spore-bearing rods, mostly saprophytes and which frequently decompose protein material. The on'y important pathogenic species is *B. anthracis*. The nonpathogenic species lead a saprophytic existence and are found widely distributed in dust, soil, water, hay, etc., and are represented by *B. subtilis*. They accordingly are frequently found as contaminants in laboratory cultures, all materials, on our bodies; and occasionally mild localized lesions, such as conjunctivitis may occur.

Burdon and associates (*J. Bact.*, 1942, **43**, 717) recommend classifying the common aerobic spore-forming bacilli into a fat-negative group and a fat-positive group by means of Sudan black B. The organisms are grown on glycerin infusion agar or glucose infusion agar for twenty-four to forty-eight hours. The bacteria from the slant are emulsified directly in a filtered 70 per cent alcoholic solution of Sudan black B (saturated solution), allowed to dry at room temperature and then counterstained with a 1 per cent aqueous solution of safranin. The smear is washed with water, dried and examined. The fat appears as bluish-gray or bluish-black granules, ranging in size and found against a background of pink-stained cytoplasm. The amount and the distribution of the stored fat is characteristc and fairly constant for the particular species of the fat-positive bacilli. Among the latter are found especially the large-celled spore formers, namely *Bacillus mycoides*, *B. megatherium*, *B. anthracis*, *B. subtilis* Michigan, *B. brevis* and *B. circulans*. The small-celled spore formers are generally fat-negative, namely, *B. mesentericus*, *B. subtilis* Marburg, *B. subtilis* Ford, and *B. vulgatus*. The species within the fat-positive and fat-negative groups, respectively, are then differentiated by inoculating deep butt-slants, made with 1.5 per cent agar, containing brom cresol purple as the indicator (*J. Bact.*, 1942, **44**, 163). Inoculation is made into the butt as well as over the slant, the medium containing separately a different sugar. The commonly used carbohydrates are employed. Differentiation of individual species is readily made, and quickly revealed on the butt-slants, where it is possible to observe more clearly the relative vigor of fermentation, the speed and extent of reversion to a neutral or alkaline reaction after an initial acid change, and the appearance of zones of acid reaction in definite locations in the medium.

Bacillus Subtilis (*Hay Bacillus*).—*B. subtilis* is a short, thick, straight, round-ended rod, 0.6 to 1.2 by 1.5 to 3 μ occurring singly, sometimes in chains of long rods, and infrequently thread forms are found. All forms except the threads are actively motile. A thin capsular substance may at times be apparent. Centrally located or excentric spores are present. It is Gram-positive and grows well on ordinary culture media between 10° and 60° C. A heavy tenacious pellicle is formed in liquid cultures. It is aerobic and facultatively anaerobic. Gelatin and blood-serum melia are liquefied. Milk is not coagulated, but becomes alkaline and is slowly peptonized. Indol is not formed. Starch is hydrolyzed and nitrates are reduced to nitrites. It is V.-P. positive. Vegetative forms are weak resistant but the spores are capable of withstanding even boiling temperatures for several minutes. *Bacillus subtilis* is a nonpathogenic saprophyte, widely distributed in Nature and found in hay, straw, soil, dust, vegetable matter, milk, water, etc. It is found frequently as a contaminant in the laboratory and as a secondary invader in chronic suppurative lesions. For this reason, and due to the fact that it is similar in some respects to the *Bacillus anthracis*, one should be familiar with the morphology of this organism, one of the commonly found aerobic, spore-bearing, Gram-positive, saprophytic soil bacilli, the others being *Bacillus mycoides*, *Bacillus megatherium*, *Bacillus graveolens*, *Bacillus mesentericus*, etc. (these frequently placed in the so-called *Bacillus subtilis* group).

Bacillus Anthracis (*Anthrax Bacillus*).—The anthrax bacillus is a large straight rod, with square and infrequently slightly concave ends, from 1 to 1.5 by 4 to 10 μ, occurring singly, in pairs or short chains if found in body fluids and practically always in long chains if in cultures. In the latter, long and flexible filaments may be observed which are united in twisted or cordlike bundles as in a bamboo fishing rod. On artificial culture media spores are formed. Oxygen is necessary for the formation of the latter, this accounting for the fact that spores are absent in bacilli found in tissues and blood of those infected. Sporeless varieties of *Bacillus anthracis* are occasionally encountered. Spores when present are located centrally. In preparations of tissues and blood an enveloping or capsular substance may be seen at times, especially if special techniques for staining capsules are employed. These are rarely seen in preparations from artificial media, though they are observed occasionally if the organism is grown in milk or media containing blood serum or other albuminous material. The capsular or mucin-like substance does not contain a polysaccharide as is found in most encapsulated bacteria, but is a polypeptide composed exclusively of *d*-glutamic acid. *Bacillus anthracis* is nonmotile, aerobic and grows on ordinary culture media best at 37° C., but will develop between 12° and 45° C. Milk is coagulated, becomes slightly acid, and is peptonized. Starch is not hydrolyzed, nitrates are not reduced to nitrites, and blood serum is partly liquefied. Gelatin is liquefied. In gelatin stabs, before liquefaction occurs, the growth assumes a picture of a small inverted "pine, fir or Christmas tree." On potato, a grayish-white furry growth is produced, with an abundance of spores. The vegetative forms are of the same resistance as most other nonspore-bearing bacteria, but the spore forms are extremely resistant to chemical and physical agents, especially in the dry state. Dry heat at 140° C. requires an exposure of at least three hours, and live steam for at least eight minutes is necessary to destroy spore-bearing anthrax bacilli. Bichloride of mercury (1 to 1000 or 1 to 2000, to which has been added 0.5 per cent hydrochloric acid) is the most effective of the disinfectants. *Bacillus anthracis* is the only spore-bearing, aerobic, Gram-positive bacillus which is pathogenic for man. It can always be differentiated by demonstrating its pathogenicity by subcutaneous inoculation of guinea pigs. It is also virulent for mice and rabbits.

This organism is the cause of anthrax, charbon or splenic fever, a disease, the first shown to be caused by a specific microorganism and primarily an important affection of the herbivora.   Cattle and sheep (except the Algerian race) are especially attacked, and occasionally horses, hogs, goats and dogs are affected. Sheep are perhaps most susceptible, then come cattle. In these animals anthrax develops rapidly, is very contagious and highly fatal. Hogs, cats, dogs and some wild animals become affected occasionally. Man, though not as susceptible as the lower animals, may contract anthrax, while birds and fowl are practically immune. Small rodents are sensitive to inoculation. Upon subcutaneous injection, rabbits, guinea pigs and white mice, in the order named, are very susceptible and usually fatally affected. In man, the infection may occur through the skin, the intestines or occasionally by inhalation through the respiratory tract.   External anthrax in man is similar to this form of the disease as found in animals, mainly sheep and infrequently cattle. The disease appears as a "malignant pustule," usually resulting from a cut or an abrasion, becoming inoculated with the spores of *Bacillus anthracis*, which in the case of animals may be by contact with contaminated soil and infected animals or material coming from the latter. In man it may be by contact with contaminated hides, wool, meat of infected animals or hair, as shaving brushes, etc. A malignant anthrax edema, characterized by the absence of papule and vesicle forms and by extensive edema, occurs in the eyelids, and the head and neck may become involved. Internal anthrax, known also as intestinal anthrax (*Mycosis intestinalis*) which is less common in man, may occur by infection through the stomach and intestines resulting probably from the eating of raw or improperly cooked infected meat or unboiled milk of diseased animals, etc. Cattle and sheep are affected chiefly with this form. The pulmonic form of internal anthrax known also as *wool-sorters' disease*, which is occasionally found in man, is an occupational disease, caused by the inhalation of contaminated dust, usually present in improperly ventilated plants where wool, hair, etc., are sorted and cleansed. Pulmonary anthrax and the gastro-intestinal form are highly fatal.

The detection of the anthrax bacillus in cases of human infections is usually not difficult. The material collected is the pus or fluid from malignant pustules, blood in septicemia, sputum in pulmonary infection, and rarely the spinal fluid in meningeal involvement. Film preparations for microscopic study and cultures in Nutrient Agar and Broth are made. If the material is laden with other bacteria, heat the liquid cultures (or portions of the body fluids before treatment) at 65° C. for thirty minutes and transplant on agar plates. Inoculate a rabbit, guinea pig or white mouse subcutaneously with some of the material or, preferably, with a small portion of the final culture. If anthrax bacilli are present, the animal will die in from ten to seventy-two hours. A diagnosis of anthrax is warranted if the findings reveal a Gram-positive, spore-bearing, nonmotile, square-ended bacillus, producing characteristic colonies on agar medium and a fatal septicemia in animals. The control of anthrax in the lower animals through the immunization of the susceptible ones and the use of anti-anthrax serum in the treatment of anthrax in man are considered on page 474. Good results have been reported in man with the use of arsphenamine and other arsenicals, but chemotherapy should be supplemented preferably with specific antisera. In tanneries and in wool and hair-processing plants, it is advisable to mop or spray the floors at least once daily or as often as required with a 2 per cent formaldehyde solution or other suitable bactericides. It is important to be vigilant as to plant hygiene and the handling of all materials. The rules and regulations promulgated by the Committee on Industrial Anthrax (*A. P. H. A. Year Book*, 1941-1942, 114) should be strictly enforced. Wool, hair, skins and hides can be and, wherever possible, should be disinfected.

Spore-bearing Anaerobic Bacilli (Clostridia)

Genus Clostridium.—This group comprises a large number of species of bacteria, all rods, which form endospores in the so-called clostridium or plectridium forms. They are anaerobic or occasionally microaerophilic, usually Gram-positive, frequently decompose proteins or ferment carbohydrates actively through the agency of enzymes. Some of these are the anaerobic nitrogen-fixing bacteria and the butyl alcohol and acetone-producing bacteria. Others are commonly found as inhabitants of the gastro-intestinal tract of man and lower animals, and, their spores being highly resistant, survive for long periods of time in soil, dust, etc. It is these species, essentially saprophytic forms, which often become parasitic and pathogenic to man and lower animals, after they find their way into the bodies of the latter through the agency of contaminated material. Those of special interest are *Cl. botulinum* causing *botulism; Cl. tetani* causing *tetanus* or *lockjaw* and the gas-gangrene group of bacilli. For the cultivation of anaerobes, see page 79, and for a comparative study of materials suitable for the cultivation of *Clostridia*, see Vera (*J. Bact.*, 1944, **47**, 1).

Clostridium Tetani (*Bacillus Tetani*).—This is a slender, round-ended rod, 0.3 to 0.6 by 2 to 8 μ, occurring singly, in pairs, and at times long chains and filaments or thread forms are to be found especially in old cultures. It forms a round spore, larger in diameter than the cell and usually situated at the extreme end of the rod, and giving the latter an appearance of a tack or drumstick. *Clostridium tetani* is an anaerobe, motile, nonencapsulated, Gram-positive and grows on ordinary media (preferring the presence of carbohydrates), best at body temperature. Spore production is not inhibited but even accelerated, when grown in carbohydrate media, as is the case with most of the fermentative *clostridia*, especially those associated with gas gangrene. Tetanus spores are very resistant to environmental influence. Gelatin is liquefied and brain medium is slightly blackened. Many of the commonly used sugar media and milk are not fermented. Hemolysis occurs on blood agar. Indol is not formed and nitrates are not reduced to nitrites. It does not display active proteolytic properties. *Cl. tetani* produces a highly potent exotoxin (upon injection but not feeding), which has a particular affinity for nerve tissue. Ten serologic types, are distinguishable by the agglutination test. (See Maclennan, *Brit. J. Exp. Path.* 1939, **20**, 371.) In the United States, England and France, Types I and III predominate. The division into types has not as yet assumed practical significance and the toxin formed is identical in all instances. The pathogenicity of *Cl. tetani* depends entirely upon the exotoxin and for which an antitoxin is prepared, the latter being of considerable value if employed immediately after infection and before clinical symptoms of tetanus set in.

Cl. tetani produces tetanus or lockjaw, a disease known for many centuries and characterized by spasms of the voluntary muscles. Man and almost all domestic animals are susceptible (in order of their susceptibility are horses, sheep, goats, cattle, dogs and cats). Cold-blooded animals are not susceptible to tetanus. This disease differs from most infectious diseases in that a diseased animal does not necessarily play the only important role in the spread of the infection. The normal horse may spread tetanus bacilli as freely and as widely as an animal sick with tetanus. Though an anaerobe, this organism seems to grow better in symbiosis with aerobes, as in an infected wound.

The tetanus bacillus is present in the superficial layers of the soil, especially in fields which have been fertilized with manure probably because its normal habitat is in the intestines of the herbivorous animals (cows, horses, sheep, fowl, etc.). It is present in the intestinal tract of man, but occurs there only as a saprophyte. It is found also at times in the dust of rooms, gelatin, catgut, and occasionally in court plaster. Considering the wide distribution of the bacilli, tetanus infections are of comparatively infrequent occurrence. The nature of the wound and the simultaneous presence of other microorganisms appear to be important factors resulting in the occurrence of tetanus. Injuries causing crushing and considerable destruction of tissues, especially deep, lacerated wounds (as frequently occur in compound fractures and gunshot wounds), especially when grains of gunpowder, splinters of glass, metal or wood are embedded, are the most likely to be followed by tetanus infection. It is frequently associated with the organisms causing gas gangrene. Tetanus has been observed not infrequently after childbirth, as a result of an infection of the umbilical cord (*tetanus neonatorum*), or following induced abortion or intrauterine manipulation, following intestinal operations particularly hemorrhoidectomies, and in rare cases it has developed from the infection of necrotic mucous membranes following diphtheria and ulcerative lesions of the throat. At times very little local evidence of the disease can be observed, and it should be borne in mind that when an external wound is not visible there may be an internal one.

After the entrance of tetanus bacilli into a wound a definite period of incubation elapses before the symptoms appear; in man this may be from three to fourteen days in acute cases, and four or five weeks in the so-called chronic form of tetanus. During this incubation period, the bacilli are multiplying and producing the toxin which is the cause of the clinical symptoms. Tetanus bacilli are localized almost entirely at the point of inoculation, but the symptoms are due to the toxin being absorbed into the central nervous system. The tetanus bacillus produces two toxins: *tetanolysin* (produces some lysis of erythrocytes) and *tetanospasmin* (produces toxic spasms). Only the latter is of importance. Once tetanus toxin is firmly united with nerve cells, it is practically impossible for the antitoxin to effect its neutralization.

Because of the long incubation period in lockjaw, the time in which the antitoxin would exert the most curative effects has largely passed before the occurrence of symptoms. Therefore, in man, the most important use of tetanus antitoxin is as a prophylactic agent. It should be borne in mind that the antitoxic effect passes off in about ten days, and that a single immunizing injection of tetanus antitoxin may not always be sufficient. In the first World War the compulsory routine use of tetanus antitoxin injections to every wounded soldier at the first possible moment after an injury followed by a second injection ten days later resulted in the almost complete abolition of tetanus among the wounded troops. More recently, however, tetanus toxoid, plain and alum precipitated, has come into use. This is a most satisfactory prophylactic agent to be used in advance of an injury as a precautionary measure against tetanus. It is to be used among those who are subject to injuries and are in surroundings where tetanus infection is likely to occur. Tetanus anti-toxin, though of little value in the treatment of clinical tetanus, should, however, be used here and also for the prevention of the infection in those wounded individuals who have not been actively immunized with the toxoid. Patients given the anti-toxin prophylactically are to be vaccinated with the toxoid at the same time. New-houser (*Milit. Surgeon*, 1941, **88,** 371) reports that in the several million soldiers in France, England, Canada and Italy, who received active immunization against tetanus during the previous four years, no case of tetanus has been found to date. The technique for injection recommended is three 1-cc. doses of plain toxoid at in-tervals of three to twelve weeks, followed by a fourth injection at six to twelve months. With alum-precipitated toxoid two injections of 1 cc. each at intervals of six to eight weeks, followed by 1 cc. at the end of one year and thereafter at the time of injury, are advised. See also under Tetanus Antitoxin and Tetanus Toxoid.

The examination of material, body fluids, and wounds for the presence of *Cl. tetani* is most frequently a detailed and complicated procedure. Direct microscopic exam-ination of film preparations is carried out, but it has little value as a diagnostic aid. Cultural observations after inoculating the specimen in cooked meat media and on blood-agar plates are made. The presence of spores in the meat medium necessitates heating the latter at 75° to 80° C. for thirty minutes and then inoculating blood-agar plates. Animal inoculation to note pathogenicity must be carried out. Injections are made subcutaneously into the thigh of a guinea pig, using separately a portion of the original material or of a heated (as above) culture or, wherever possible, of a por-tion of a bouillon culture of pure *Cl. tetani* previously isolated. Control test animals receive the same injection but are also injected intraperitoneally with tetanus anti-toxin. Unprotected animals usually die within four days. The detection of tetanus toxin serves as an additional aid. Ten day old bouillon filtrates of the suspension of organism are injected as above, using control animals, or similar toxicity tests are made using the spinal fluid obtained from the patient.

Clostridia Associated with Gas Gangrene

Gas gangrene is a condition affecting chiefly muscles, in which there occurs a rapidly spreading necrosis with edema and gas production. It usually follows dirty, lacer-ated wounds especially those involving fractures and untreated extensive traumatic wounds and it occurs more frequently in warfare and less frequently in civil life. In such wounds, pyogenic and nonpathogenic aerobes and anaerobes are carried by the missiles contaminated from the soil, clothing or skin into the tissues. The latter are destroyed to a variable degree and such devitalized or dead material furnishes culture media for the growth and development of bacteria. If surgical aid is not given quickly, the contaminating organisms penetrate into the deeper tissues and exert their effects. Gas gangrene is essentially a local infection, the blood stream being invaded by bacteria only shortly before death. It is apparent that gas gangrene is rarely caused by only one organism. It is a mixed infection and the isolation and incrimination of the predominating species encountered in such wounds is not a simple task. Much of our present knowledge of the bacteriology of wounds, which obviously is still incomplete, is the result of the intensive studies of the war wound infections, which occurred during World War I. For a detailed consideration, see "Notes on the Diagnosis and Treatment of Gas Gangrene" (M. R. C. Memor. No. 2, H. M. Stationery Office, London, 1940, including scheme suggested by Comm. of London Sector Pathologists).

The exact role played by the aerobes and anaerobes and especially by species of *Clostridia* in gas gangrene is not definitely known. It is important to note that the clinical diagnosis of gas gangrene, frequently a complex condition, may be verified or confirmed by bacteriological examination and identification of *Clostridia* predominating in the infected wounds. On the other hand, bacteriological findings alone without clinical observations and data are not to be relied upon for a diagnosis of gas gangrene. The organisms frequently found associated with gas gangrene are aerobic cocci (most all species); anaerobic cocci (especially hemolytic and nonhemolytic microaerophilic and anaerobic streptococci); aerobic spore-bearing and nonspore-bearing Gram-positive bacilli; Gram-negative rods of the coliform group, *Eberthella*, *Shigella*, *Proteus*, *Salmonella* and *Pseudomonas;* and species of *Clostridia*.

Species of Clostridia.—On the basis of pathogenicity, the species of *Clostridia* associated with gas gangrene in man may be divided into the following groups:

Those which are pathogenic for man and their occurrence in order of virulency are *Cl. perfringens* (*welchii*), *Cl. septicum* (*Vibrion spetique*), *Cl. novyi* (*Cl. oedematiens*), *Cl. bifermentans* (*sordelli; oedematoides*), *Cl. histolyticum*, *Cl. fallax* and *Cl. sporogenes* (*Cl. oedematis maligni*). *Cl. chauvei* is pathogenic for lower animals and the following are *per se* probably nonpathogenic for man: *Cl. aerofoetidium*, *Cl. lentoputrescens* (*Cl. putrificum*) and *Cl. tertium*.

On the basis of their biochemical reactions, the species of *Clostridia* are divided into those which attack sugars, *saccharolytic anaerobes* and those which attack proteins, *proteolytic anaerobes*. The separation between these two groups is *not distinct and clear cut*. There is overlapping, in that some species possess both properties but, when classified, are grouped depending upon the characteristic which is most prominent. Most species of *Clostridia* pathogenic to man are saccharolytic. With the exception of *Cl. histolyticum*, the proteolytic species are nonpathogenic. The *proteolytic clostridia*, though nonpathogenic, aggravate existing wound infections by their marked action in decomposing protein. However, they have no invasive powers and, being nonpathogenic, will not cause envolvements without the presence of the saccharolytic pathogens. The latter multiply and exert their effects in devitalized tissue.

All of the pathogenic *Clostridia* associated with gas gangrene produce true exotoxins so that a toxemia may exist. The *Cl. perfringens* (*welchii*) occurs most frequently (in about 75 per cent of all cases) followed most frequently by *Cl. novyi* (*oedematiens*) in about 25 to 35 per cent, *Cl. sporogenes* in 27 per cent of cases, *Cl. septicum* (*Vibrion septique*) in from 10 to 15 per cent of all cases.

The danger of gas-gangrene infections in civil life is probably not so widely recognized as it deserves. From a survey of the frequency of its occurrence in New York State, it would seem probable that this type of infection is found as commonly as is tetanus (*New York State J. Med.*, 1938, **38**, 1022). Traumatic injuries caused by automobile and railroad accidents may develop gas gangrene. Certain cases of appendicitis, intestinal obstruction, peritonitis, puerperal sepsis and various postoperative infections may develop infections caused by bacteria producing gas gangrene.

For methods of bacteriological diagnosis, see page 533. Lyons and Owens (*J. Bact.*,

1942, **43**, 685) recommend Wilson and Blair medium as a useful diagnostic aid in the early recognition of certain *Clostridia* in wounds. In treatment, proper surgical prophylaxis must be practiced, aided by chemoserotherapy. The use of the sulfonamide drugs (parenterally, orally and locally) are highly advocated. Along with the latter, gas-gangrene antitoxins should be administered as early as possible and in adequate dosage.

The exotoxins of the species of *Clostridium* commonly found are used for preparing specific antitoxins. The individually prepared antitoxins are mixed to make available a polyvalent anaerobic antitoxin or polyvalent gas-gangrene antitoxin. Treatment should be started with a mixed antitoxin and in special cases, where a monobacterial infection has been proved or specific bacteria found by bacteriological examination, additional injections can be given of serum corresponding to the bacterial flora present. The dosage of the mixed antitoxin advocated is *Cl. perfringens* antitoxin, 3000 units; *Cl. septicum* (*Vibrion septique*) antitoxin, 1500 units; *Cl. novyi* (*oedematiens*) antitoxin, 1000 units.

The subcutaneous route may be used if the antitoxin is given shortly after the injury; if delayed, the intramuscular route (or even intravenous) is preferable. If the wound is extensive or heavily contaminated or if prophylaxis has been delayed, repeat this dose at intervals of from four to seven days. If the wound is slow in healing or the possibility of infection exists, another prophylactic dose should be repeated within a week. Obviously the possibility of tetanus should be considered. Tetanus antitoxin if administered may be present in the combined antitoxin mixture, all antitoxins to be given in one injection or the tetanus antitoxin may be administered separately. A *Tetanus Gas Gangrene Antitoxin Mixed* is also marketed.

Clostridium Perfringens (*Clostridium Welchii*).—*Cl. perfringens* (*welchii*) is a thick, usually square-ended rod, 1 to 2 by 4 to 8 μ, at times the rods are round-ended, occurring singly, in pairs, and less frequently in short chains or long threads. It is encapsulated, nonmotile, an obligate anaerobe, Gram-positive and possesses oval spores, found centrally or excentric. Spores are usually absent in animal tissues. *Cl. perfringens* grows on ordinary media at body temperature. It can grow at 50° C. The growth in broth is at first turbid, then peptolytic action occurs and there is a clearing of the turbidity with the production of a viscid sediment. Milk is acidified and coagulated, and the coagulum is broken with profuse gas formation, but digestion does not occur. Gelatin is liquefied but not blackened; blood serum is not liquefied. Acid and gas are produced from most sugars; indol is not formed, but nitrates are reduced to nitrites. It produces an exotoxin, which is a complex substance and highly toxic. On the ability to ferment glycerin and inulin, four types of *Cl. perfringens* (*welchii*) are distinguished, but such biochemical types are not recognized. *Cl. welchii* strains from cases of gaseous gangrene differ immunologically and different types have been suggested on the basis of different fermentation tests, but all strains found in human infections produce the same exotoxin. Reports presented by Wilsdon (Inst. Animal Path. Cambridge; 2nd Report of the Director, 1931, p. 53) have apparently created the impression that four different types of exotoxin are produced by *Cl. welchii*. Toxicogenic bacilli closely resembling *Cl. welchii* have been found among lower animals. The toxins from these bacilli appear to be related immunologically. These organisms are the *B. agni* (the lamb dysentery bacillus), the *Bacillus paludis* (causing "struck" in sheep) and *B. ovitoxicus* (causing an enterotoxemia in sheep).

Wilsdon has suggested that these three organisms be designated as *Cl. welchii*, Types B, C and D, respectively, and the gaseous gangrene *Cl. welchii* as Type A. The general acceptance among workers for the present, however, is to employ the designation *Cl. welchii* only to Type A or the gas-gangrene bacillus. For a consideration of the relationship of these types, see Dalling (*Vet. Record*, Dec. 12, 1936). This organism is widely distributed in Nature, found normally in the feces of man and animals and accordingly may be commonly found in fertilized soils, sewage, water, etc. During the World War this organism was the cause of the majority of cases of gas gangrene. Chronic intestinal infections have occasionally been reported as caused by this organism. Besides the exotoxin, *Clostridium welchii*, one of the most active members of the saccharolytic groups of anaerobes, produces large quantities of gas, and the mechanical effect of pressure on the tissues and blood vessels, produced by the latter, is an important part of the injury and harm caused by the infection.

For isolation and identification of this organism, the following are important aids: morphology and cultural characteristics; stormy fermentation of milk with coagulation but no digestion; inoculation of two guinea pigs one of which received a prophylactic dose of perfringens antitoxin; and the intravenous inoculation of a rabbit, which is killed ten minutes later and kept at 37° C. for eighteen hours. The heart blood and liver will yield *Cl. perfringens* if present. For further details, see pages 533 and 534.

Clostridium Sporogenes (*Clostridium Oedematis Maligni; Bacillus Oedematis Maligni*).—This is a long, narrow, round-ended rod, 0.6 to 1 by 2 to 8 μ, occurring singly but usually in pairs joined end to end and frequently in long chains or filaments. It is motile, usually Gram-positive, but may appear as a Gram-amphophile, and grows on ordinary media, preferring the presence of carbohydrates or albuminous material. It is an obligate anaerobe and spores are usually centrally located. Hemolysis is produced on blood agar. It is actively proteolytic; meat medium, brain medium and blood serum are blackened and digested; and gelatin is liquefied and blackened. Like other spore-bearing bacteria, *Cl. sporogenes* is very resistant. It is a widely distributed soil organism and has been found in the intestinal tract of man and animals. In pure culture, it is a harmless saprophyte. An exotoxin is not produced. This putrefactive anaerobe and probably others enhance the pathogenicity of nonputrefactive pathogens. In man, this organism is frequently found in war wounds, the latter becoming infected through contaminated soil or other infectious material.

Cl. parasporogens, recognized by some as a distinct species, is probably a variety of this organism. Its main differences are the absence of wooly colonies in deep agar and the production of specific agglutinins.

PLATE II

Fig. 1. *Corynebacterium diphtheriae* (Klebs-Loeffler or diphtheria bacillus). Old culture showing clubbed forms. Gram stain. (See page 124.)

Fig. 2. *Clostridium perfringens* (*B. welchii, B. aerogenes-capsulatus*). Gas bacillus from gas gangrene. Gram stain. (See page 177.)

Fig. 3. *Clostridium tetani* (*B tetani*). Fuchsin-methylene blue spore stain. (See page 173.)

Fig. 4. *Vibrio comma*. (Spirillum of Asiatic cholera.) Gram stain. (See page 184.)

Fig. 5. *Escherichia coli* (*Bacillus coli*). (Colon bacillus.) Gram stain. (See page 137.)

Fig. 6. *Hemophilus influenzae* (Pfeiffer's bacillus). Gram stain. (See page 157.)

Magnifications are 1000 × in all illustrations. Color plates courtesy A. S. Aloe Co. and American Colortype.

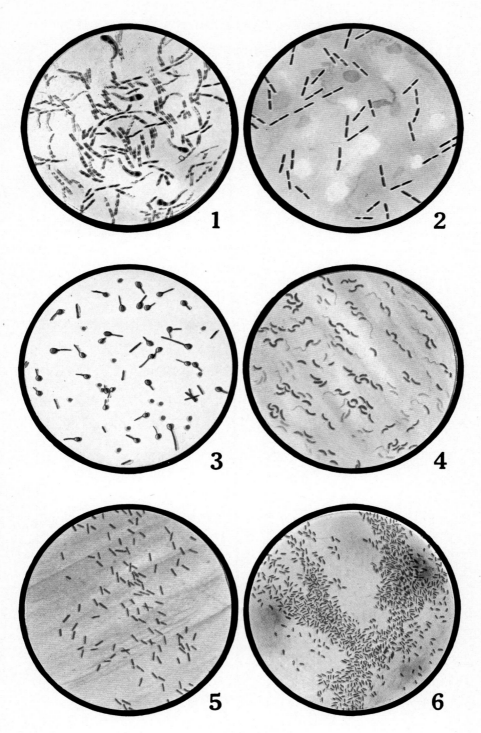

PLATE II
See facing page for explanation.

Clostridium Novyi (*Cl. or B. Oedematiens*).—This is a large, relatively stout rod (1 by 2.5 to 10 μ) resembling somewhat *B. anthracis*, occurring singly or in chains. Spores are oval and either central, excentric or subterminal; the rods are distinctly swollen at sporulation. It is sluggishly motile, an obligate anaerobe, Gram-positive, feebly hemolytic. It produces an exotoxin and a specific antitoxin is available. Though *Cl. novyi* produces a toxemia, septicemias do occur. Lesions in infected guinea pigs are characterized by a clear gelatinous exudate with little necrosis and no gas. Meat and brain media are not darkened, though the former may be bleached or turned slightly pink. Nitrates are not reduced and indol is not formed. Gelatin is liquefied, but coagulated egg and serum are not affected. Hydrogen sulfide is produced. Acid production is slight, but gas production is marked with many sugars. Lactose and saccharose are generally not attacked; this serves as a differential aid. This organism may be responsible for infection in wounds and is in part the cause of *black disease*, an acute infection in sheep. This condition is an infectious necrotic hepatitis brought about by the invasion of the immature liver fluke *Fasciola hepatica* joined by the toxin production of *Cl. novyi* in the necrotic liver tissue.

Clostridium Septicum (*Vibrion Septique*).—It is a large slender, pleomorphic, motile, nonencapsulated, obligate anaerobe. Clubbed or valvular rods and filaments are found even in young cultures. Indol is not produced; nitrates are reduced to nitrites; gelatin is liquefied; most commonly used sugars except saccharose are fermented. It is hemolytic, produces a powerful exotoxin and may invade the blood stream, producing a septicemia. When injected into guinea pigs, the latter die; and upon autopsy in the liver, there will be found characteristic long, filamentous forms of this species. This observation is a valuable aid in the isolation and identification of *Cl. septicum*. An antitoxin is produced which is specific.

Clostridium Fallax (*Bacillus Fallax*).—This is a saccharolytic, slender, motile, Gram-positive, anaerobic rod, 3 to 6 μ in length, with subterminal spores, which are not formed readily. It does not liquefy gelatin nor digest coagulated serum. Acid and gas are produced slowly in milk and carbohydrate fermentation is variable. It is slightly pathogenic and produces a soluble exotoxin.

Clostridium Histolyticum (*Bacillus Histolyticus*).—This is a Gram-positive, short, round-ended, motile bacillus, 0.6 by 3 to 5 μ, with oval spores, which are subterminal or terminal, but which do not form in the body. It is anaerobic and facultatively aerobic and actively proteolytic. Gelatin is liquefied and meat, brain, coagulated egg, coagulated serum and milk are digested. Nitrates are not reduced; indol is not formed; sugars are not fermented. It produces an exotoxin which stimulates the production of an antitoxin. Infection with this organism alone is rare; mixed infections are generally observed. A characteristic aid in identification is noted when *Cl. histolyticum* is injected into guinea pigs. Digestion of the tissue is rapid even down to the bone which may be exposed. In spite of the marked local lesion, the test animals show no general reactions and may remain well. The exudate contains no gas or putrid odor.

Clostridium Bifermentans (*Cl. Oedematoides; B. Sordelli*).—This is a large, sluggishly motile, Gram-positive bacillus, with oval central or subterminal spores. Indol is produced; nitrates are not reduced to nitrites. Milk is digested with the production of gas. Sugars with the exception of dextrose are not fermented. Gelatin is liquefied. Different strains vary in their display of toxicity and pathogenicity. The more virulent and more toxic strains are generally referred to as *B. sordelli*.

Clostridium tertium (*Bacillus tertius*), **Clostridium aerofoetidum** (*Bacillus aerofoetidus*), and **Clostridium lentoputrescens** (*Clostridium putrificum; Bacillus putrificus*) are nonpathogenic, proteolytic anaerobes which may also be found in mixed infections in gas gangrene. Other *Clostridia* reported occasionally are: Cl. **Capitovalis** (a mildly proteolytic species) and **Cl. Paraputrificum** (saccharolytic but nonproteolytic).

Other Pathogenic Clostridia

Clostridium Chauvoei (*Bacillus Chauvoei; Bacillus of Blackleg or of Symptomatic Anthrax*).—This bacillus is a large, round-ended rod, 0.5 to 1 by 3 to 8 μ, occurring usually singly, at times in pairs, end to end, in short chains, but never in long filaments. It is motile and an oval spore, located centrally or excentrically, is found under all conditions. The spores are very resistant. It is usually Gram-positive but may appear as a Gram-amphophile. It is an obligate anaerobe, growing on ordinary media, but preferring the presence of bovine serum or other natural fluids, and develops best at 37° C. It can grow at temperatures as high as 50° C. Gelatin is liquefied and gas bubbles are present. Blood serum and egg are not liquefied. Milk is acidified and coagulated, but the coagulum is not digested. Inulin, salicin, mannitol and dulcitol are not but most of the other sugars are fermented. Brain medium is not blackened nor digested. Indol is not formed; nitrates are not reduced, but H_2S is produced. Exotoxins are formed when grown in suitable media under favorable conditions. *Cl. chauvei* is a soil organism. It is pathogenic for cattle but not man, producing in the former a highly fatal disease, known as *blackleg, black-quarter, quarter-ill* or *symptomatic anthrax*. The disease affects principally young cattle, between one-half and three years of age, they becoming infected by pasturing on contaminated soil. In the disease the thighs assume a dark color, thus the name blackleg, and for years this malady was considered merely as a variety of anthrax, until differentiation was made in 1875, when the etiological factor was isolated. The guinea pig is the most suitable (laboratory) animal for inoculating purposes.

Clostridium Botulinum, Types A and B (*Bacillus Botulinus*).—This bacillus is a large, straight, round-ended rod, 0.3 to 1 by 3 to 8 μ, occurring singly and occasionally in short chains. Involution forms are but infrequently observed. An oval spore is usually found near the end. It is an obligate anaerobe, motile and Gram-positive. It will grow at body temperature on ordinary media. Williams and Reed (*J. Infect. Dis.*, 1942, **71,** 225) reported recently that incubation temperatures between 24° to 27° C. resulted in the recovery of more positive cultures than when incubated at 31° to 37° C. Milk is acidified but not coagulated. Gelatin is liquefied. The *Cl. botulinum* strains do not but *Cl. parabotulinum* strains do liquefy blood serum. The latter strains do and the *botulinum* strains do not blacken and digest meat medium and brain medium.

The toxic species of *Cl. botulinum* have also been divided into a *nonovolytic* (*Cl. botulinum*) and a putrefactive or *ovolytic* (*Cl. parabotulinum*) group (see Meyer and Gunnison, *J. Infect. Dis.*, 1929, **45,** 96, 106, 119, 135). The *Cl. parabotulinum* includes those strains commonly referred to as *Memphis* and *Canton* (or Type A) and

Nevin (or Type B). Growth of these types is more readily obtained than with the *Cl. botulinum* strains and they usually are proteolytic. Types A and B are differentiated only by immunological tests on animals. The powerful exotoxins which both types produce, and which are not destroyed by gastro-intestinal secretions, are capable of forming antitoxins. Botulism, a form of food poisoning, is produced by this powerful soluble toxin. The ingestion of infected material—in particular, meat, sausages, canned or preserved fruits and vegetables, and pickled food products—have been the cause of these outbreaks. The disease is characterized by a marked disturbance of the central nervous system, resulting in great muscular weakness, and unless sufficient antitoxin is administered *previous to the onset of symptoms* (just as in tetanus), death is the result.

Quortrup and Holt (*J. Bact.*, 1941, **41**, 363) report the existence of potential botulinus-toxin-producing areas, especially in certain duck marshes involved in harboring *Cl. botulinum* Type C toxin. The common aquatic and emergent vegetation found in this oxygen-deficient area appears to serve as an ideal medium for growth and toxin production. Raking and aerating proved successful as control measures, as evidenced by a marked reduction of duck sickness. They also demonstrated that aerobic bacteria were capable of destroying and inactivating preformed botulinus toxin.

In cases of botulism, the bacteriological examination consists in examining the suspicious food and making direct smears, cultures and animal inoculations. The most conclusive evidence is supplied by the injection and feeding of guinea pigs and mice, using as controls at the same time animals which are treated with heated material or heated cultures and other animals injected with the material and are given at the same time an inoculation of a mixed-type botulism antitoxin. If several animals are used and each is injected separately with a type-specific antitoxic serum, additional data as to the specific type of *Cl. botulinum* involved are obtained.

Chapter XI

SPIRILLA

THE TRIBE *Spirilleae* is one of the two tribes of the family *Pseudomonadaceae* and it contains four genera. Two of the latter consist of cellulose-digesting bacteria and the other two genera are: *Vibrio* and *Spirillum*. The *Vibrio* genus contains 21 species, the latter being mainly short, bent rods, single or united in spirals, aerobic, nonspore-forming, usually Gram-negative, and most of them are saprophytes. The genus *Spirillium* consists of four species, the latter being rods of varying thickness and length and the appearance of either long screws or spiral turns, and most of them are found in putrid or stagnant water.

Vibrio Comma (*Spirillum of Asiatic Cholera; Comma Bacillus*).—The comma bacillus is a curved rod, 0.4 to 0.6 by 1.5 to 3 μ, with rounded ends which do not lie in the same plane. The degree of curvature may vary from the slightly bent comma-like forms to S forms, and threads showing even three turns may be apparent. Involution forms are rare. It is actively motile, nonspore-bearing, Gram-negative, weak resistant, aerobic, and grows on all ordinary media. Growth occurs between 14° and 42° C., the optimum temperature being 37° C. Acid but no gas is produced from dextrose, galactose, levulose, maltose, mannitol and saccharose. It does not ferment lactose, inulin, arabinose or dulcitol. Growth upon gelatin is characteristic. The latter and coagulated blood serum are rapidly liquefied. Indol is formed and nitrates are reduced to nitrites. Hydrogen sulfide is produced.

Balteanu (*J. Path. & Bact.*, 1926, **29**, 251) showed that the antigenic structure of all vibrios consisted of H and O antigens. Gardener and Venkatraman (*J. Hyg.*, 1935, **35**, 262) found that all vibrios contained a common H antigen but that they can be differentiated into six groups on the basis of a specific heat-stable O antigen. Groups II to VI, inclusive, contain only nonpathogenic cholera-like vibrios. Group I contains all true cholera vibrios together with some strains isolated at El Tor. The latter are actively hemolytic to goats' blood and are apparently noncholerigenic. True cholera vibrios are nonhemolytic, so that they are referred to as belonging to Group I, nonhemolytic. Recent extensive cholera research has been aimed at differentiating the pathogenic and nonpathogenic vibrios. The identifying characteristics for authentic cholera organisms as used today are: fermentation of saccharose and mannite but not arabinose; no hemolysis, using goats' blood; and agglutination with O-group I serum. For further details, see Linton (*Bact. Revs.*, 1940, **4**, 261). *Vibrio comma* is present, mainly in the intestinal canal of diseased patients and carriers, where it thrives and produces an endotoxin. It causes cholera, essentially a disease of man, which is usually contracted by the ingestion of these organisms in infected water and milk, uncooked food, or any contaminated material. Flies play an important role in spreading the infection. Cholera is a gastro-intestinal disease endemic in Oriental countries and occurring occasionally in epidemic form. The present geographical limitation is the result of the strict enforcement of sanitary measures, port sanitation and quarantine regulations. The general methods of control advised for all gastro-intestinal infections are effective if practiced here. Diagnosis is confirmed by a bacteriological examination of the feces. In the case of suspected carriers who are constipated, rectal swabs are made and from the cultures prepared, the presence or absence of *V. comma* is noted. Chopre and associates (*Indian M. Gaz.;* through *J. A. M. A.*, 1942, **119,** 530) report on the effective use of sulfaguanidine in cases of cholera. The use of biological products in the treatment of this disease and effective prophylactic agents are considered in Chapter XXXIX.

Vibrio Metschnikovii (*Spirillum Metschnikovii*).—This is almost identical with *Vibrio comma*, though the curved rods are usually shorter and thicker. Chubby and almost coccoid-like types are occasionally found. This organism, found in the intestinal tract and blood of diseased birds, produces a rapidly fatal, cholera-like disease in chickens. The fact that this organism is much more pathogenic for guinea pigs and especially pigeons than *Vibrio comma* is employed as a means for the differentiation between the two organisms.

Vibrio fetus is a microaerophile, requiring media enriched with natural fluids (blood, blood serum, etc.) for initial isolation. Isolated from cases of abortion in cows, this organism, however, is more common as a factor in producing abortion in sheep. In cases of infection, it is found in the urine exudate, the chorion and in various tissues of the fetus.

Vibrio jejuni is the cause of an infectious diarrhea of cows, known commonly as *winter dysentery*. On account of the appearance of liquid, dark-colored feces, the affection is also known as *black scours*. For further details on vibrios associated with intestinal disorders of cows and calves, see Jones and associates (*J. Exp. Med.*, 1931, **53,** 845, 853).

Vibrio massauah; Vibrio septicus; Vibrio proteus (*Spirillum or Vibrio of finkler and prior; Spirillum finkleri*); **Vibrio berolinensis** and **Vibrio schuylkiliensis** are a few of several vibrios which have been isolated from stools, polluted water and other sources. Many of them termed *cholera-like vibrios* are practically identical morphologically and frequently culturally with *Vibrio comma*. Most of them are essentially saprophytes, usually harmless or at most but slightly pathogenic. Their importance lies in the fact that it may become necessary at times to differentiate between the true Vibrio of Asiatic cholera and these nonpathogenic organisms. Most of them do not give the cholera-red reaction. Some of them display differences in fermentative reactions as compared with *V. comma*. All of them differ from the latter immunologically and are not lysed nor agglutinated by anticholera serum.

Spirillum Volutans (*Vibrio Spirillum*); **Spirillum Serpens** (*Vibrio Serpens*); **Spirillum Undula** (*Vibrio Undulum*).—These with other members of the genus *Spirillum* are motile, Gram-positive, rigid rods of various thickness and length, with one to three twists or wavelike undulations. They grow on ordinary media, are aerobic, nonspore-bearing and are usually found in water, especially stagnant pools and in other putrid infusions.

Spirillum Minus (*Spirochaeta or Leptospira or Spirillum Morsus Muris or Borrelia Muris*).—This is a short, rather thick, 2 to 5 μ in length, Gram-negative relatively rigid spiral organism, each spiral about 1 μ in length. The tapering ends are provided with polar tufts of flagella. Futaki and associates (*J. Exp. Med.*, 1916, **23,** 249) who found this organism in the blood and lymph glands of human cases of rat-bite fever, were able to culture this organism, but others have been unsuccessful. Distinct diseases, designated as rat-bite fever, may follow after being bitten by rats. Scharles and Seastone (*New England J. Med.*, 1934, **211**, 711) isolated an organism from a patient having clinical Haverhill fever, and traced it to a bite of a rat. The disease more frequently designated rat-bite fever is caused by *Spirillum minus* and occurs sporadically all over the world, especially in Japan, where it is known as *sodoku*. It follows a bite inflicted by an infected rat, or, more rarely, by a mouse, cat or dog. The usual history is that the wound heals well, but from one to three weeks later, the wounded area becomes inflamed, a skin eruption appears, the glands are enlarged and, if untreated, a relapsing fever will last for many months. Diagnosis is established by finding the organism in the local lesion—in material aspirated from a regional lymph node, and occasionally in the blood. Mice and guinea pigs, especially the latter, inoculated with the blood, exudates or tissue of suspected cases, will reveal the organisms in their blood. Arsphenamine and other arsenic compounds usually effect a prompt cure. For the prevention of the disease, measures aimed at reducing the rat population, the interposing of barriers to prevent their contact with man, and the prompt and energetic treatment of wounds infected by rats are the necessary requisites. For a comparison of the spirochetal (sodoku) and bacillary (Haverhill fever) forms of rat-bite fever, see Witzberger and Cohen (*Arch. Pediat.*, 1944, **61**, 123)

SPIROCHETES AND ALLIED ORGANISMS

The name spirochete was and still is used by many workers to denote elongated motile, flexible organisms, possessing one or more spiral turns. They present various characteristics similar to species of the genus *spirillum*. The latter, however, have rigid bodies and true flagella. Spirochetes, though motile, do not possess flagella. They move about through the rotation of the screw-shaped cell. Terminal projections, or filaments resembling flagella, have been described in some spirochetes, but it is thought that they occur either due to the shrinking of the cytoplasm or the protrusion of the axial filament. For many years and still today the exact biological status of spirochetes has been in dispute. Due to the fact that they possess certain characteristics closely resembling the protozoa and others that of bacteria, they have been classified among the former by protozoologists and among the bacteria by bacteriologists. Unfortunately their detailed study has been neglected by both groups of workers. Others have suggested classifying them in an intermediate group, regarding these organisms as a sort of connecting link between the bacteria and protozoa.

At present, the majority view is to place the spirochetes among the bacteria. Like the latter, they multiply by transverse fission; there is no anterior-posterior polarity; well-defined nuclei are not apparent; and they possess about the same or usually less resistance to heat, chemicals and other destructive agents as do the vegetative forms of bacteria. In most cases, they are difficult to cultivate on artificial culture media; and they do not stain readily with the stains commonly employed when staining bacteria. They are more frequently examined unstained. Inasmuch as the fractility of their protoplasm is low, the hanging-drop method is unsuitable; and the technique of dark-field illumination and examination is most frequently used. To demonstrate them in stained preparations, special methods of staining are most frequently necessary. In few instances for certain pathogenic species, animal inoculation is significant for diagnosis or confirmation of diagnosis.

As far as is known, no cycle of development takes place in the intermediate host. Spirochetes vary in size from 6 to 500 μ in length. The production of antibodies is similar to that of bacteria, though the antigenic characteristics of the spirochetes are more readily altered by environmental changes. There are spirochetes which are free-living, others which are commensal and those which are parasitic and pathogenic. Spirochetal diseases respond most frequently to chemotherapeutic agents, which are compounds of arsenic, bismuth, antimony or mercury.

Nomenclature and classification of the many species of spirochetes are uncertain, incomplete and unsatisfactory. Various classifications have been suggested and are used. Until a more convenient and more useful division is made available, that given in the Bergey classification is suggested.

Though the name spirochete is frequently employed for all members of the family *Spirochaetaceae* in the Bergey classification, this term is limited to species of the genus *Spirochaeta*. Members of the latter are free-living forms (found in fresh and salt water), with no apparent periplast membrane but possessing an axial fiber. The genus *Saprospira* contains species (free-living in foraminiferous sand) which possess a distinct periplast membrane, chambered bodies, are of large size, and an axis filament is not apparent. In species of these two genera, a crista or ridge is absent and the cells are altered but not disintegrated upon the addition of 10 per cent bile salts or saponin. They are nonpathogenic to higher animals.

The *Cristispira* contains species characterized by the presence of a crista or ridge, a bandlike membranous appendage wound (spirally) about the body of the cell; the body is divided by transverse septa. The crista is frequently dissolved but the body of the cell is only altered upon the addition of 10 per cent bile salts or saponin. The species in this genus are of large size, nonpathogenic to higher animals but are parasitic in the alimentary canal of oysters and shellfish (lamellibranchiate mollusks).

The genus *Borrelia* contains species, which are flexible and snakelike, terminate in a fine terminal filament, vary in size from 4 to 20 μ, stain with aniline dyes, are disintegrated completely by 10 per cent bile salts, and their usual habitat is in the blood of animals. The pathogenic species are those which cause relapsing or recurrent fevers. Species of the genus *Treponema* include numerous nonpathogenic and few pathogenic, aerobic and anaerobic tissue parasites. They are from 6 to 20 μ in length, shaped like a corkscrew, possess a number of primary spirals, an indefinite axial fiber, and the ends or extremities are sharply pointed. They are slowly disintegrated by 10 per cent bile salts; first resist, then are immobilized and finally are disintegrated in a few hours by 10 per cent saponin. The important species is the *Treponema pallidum*, the causative agent of syphilis. Species of the genus *Leptospira* are from 6 to 14 μ in length, possess many (10–20) closely set, regular, wound spirals, with an indefinite axial filament, and tapering, flexible ends bent in a semicircular hook. Bile salts do but saponin does not disintegrate species of this genus. The important species is *Lept. icterohaemorrhagiae*, which causes infectious jaundice or Weil's disease.

Borrelia Vincenti (*Spirochaeta Vincenti; Spirillum of Vincent; Treponema or Spironema Vincenti*).—This is longer than the "fusiform" bacillus, averaging 0.3 by 12 to 25 μ, and appears as slender bodies, made up of a variable number of undulations, shallow and irregular in their curvatures. It is Gram-negative, nonspore-bearing and anaerobic. Growth on culture media is obtained only when special precautions are taken. This organism, found in the oral cavity, stains with difficulty but does not display metachromatism, at times observed in the bacilli with which it is usually associated in *Vincent's angina* and allied infections. It has not been definitely determined whether there exists an essential symbiotic relationship between the fusiform bacillus and *Borrelia vincenti* alone or whether other species of spirochetes enter into such symbiotic relationship with the fusiform bacillus. There are some investigators who still hold the view that the bacillus and spirillum of Vincent are simply different phases in the life of one organism. A large number of drugs, administered both topically and internally, especially oxidizing agents and arsenicals, have been used with varying results in the treatment of Vincent's infection. Some believe that a vitamin deficiency plays a role in this condition. Hydrogen peroxide solution, sodium perborate, zinc peroxide and chromic acid are among some of the oxidizing agents used. The topical application of powder zinc peroxide to the affected tissues is highly successful. Local applications and intravenous injections of neo-arsphenamine and bismuth compounds and even antimony and potassium tartrate have been used. Smith (*South M. J.*, 1942, **35**, 299) advocates at least six intramuscular injections of *Fuadin*.

Vincent's angina occurs more frequently than suspected or diagnosed, though McCarthy (*J. A. M. A.*, 1941, **116**, 16) asserts that this affection is decreasing. As a secondary infection, invasion by the etiological factors of the nose, middle ear and even conjunctiva occurs occasionally. Lung abscesses, bronchiectasis and fuso-spirochetal pneumonitis are some of the more serious complications (see Field, *J. A. M. A.*, 1940, **114**, 1073). Though fusospirochetal organisms are found normally in secretions beneath the prepuce and about the clitoris, genital lesions occur but infrequently. However *venereal fusospirochetosis* does occur. Known as *balanitis gangrenosa, erosive* or *ulcerative* or *gangrenous balanitis*, this affection, though rare, is important, because of its destructive course if unrecognized and treated as chancroid. As with the latter and all genital sores, the lesions may mask syphilitic infection; and all cases require careful watching subsequently for syphilis. For further details on balanitis gangrenosa or venereal fusospirochetosis, see Reasoner (*New York State J. M.*, 1927, **27**, 767) and von Haam (*Am. J. Trop. Med.*, 1938, **18**, 595).

Borrelia Recurrentis (*Spirochaeta Obermeieri; Spirochetes of European Relapsing Fever; Spironema Recurrentis*).—This is a long, delicate, spiral thread, undulations varying from 4 to 10 or more in number, cylindrical or slightly flattened, 0.35 to 0.5 by 8 to 16 μ, with pointed ends. It is motile, flagella are absent, stains but faintly with aniline dyes. *Borrelia recurrentis* is Gram-negative, is an anaerobe and can be cultured on special media when unusual precautions are taken. Bile salts, in 10 per cent concentrations, will completely disintegrate the organisms; saponin, in 10 per cent concentrations, will immobilize them in thirty minutes and within a few hours will break them up.

Borrelia recurrentis is the cause of European relapsing fever. Spirochetosis (African, European and other forms of relapsing fever) is communicated in most cases by blood-sucking arthropods. Relapsing fever is the name given to a group of closely related diseases, found in tropical and subtropical areas, and characterized clinically by a sudden onset, fever, severe frontal headache and muscular pains. The infection produces fever for five to seven days; falls by crisis to normal; an afebrile period follows which lasts for about one week; the symptoms and fever recur; and from five to ten such periods or relapses may result until the condition finally subsides. Relapsing fever is either louse-borne or tick-borne. There is also the Spanish variety or Mediterranean form which, though maintained by ticks (soft- and hard-shelled ticks), is spread in epidemic form by lice. Though there are slight differences between the relapsing fevers in different parts of the world, the treatment is the same in each instance. Arsphenamine and other arsenicals are generally used, though bismuth salts and other compounds are also employed at times. Various names have been given to the several species isolated in the relapsing fevers, but some workers regard all of them as varieties of *Borrelia recurrentis*. The human body louse (*Pediculus humanus*), by its bite, and probably the common bedbug (*Cimex lectularius*) (more as mechanical carriers) are regarded as the transmitting agents of European relapsing fever. The causative agents are found in peripheral blood during the paroxysms and can be stained or observed by the dark-field technique. They also have been observed at times in sweat and in tears and have been found capable of passing through the unbroken skin and intact mucous membranes. Diagnosis depends upon finding the *Borrelia* in fresh blood film preparations preferably by dark-field illumination. If organisms are absent or few in number, the injection of mice with blood from the patient will produce in twenty-four hours large numbers of organisms in the animal's blood.

Borrelia Duttonii (*Spirochetes of African Relapsing Fever*).—*Borrelia duttonii* has, with but slight differences, the same characteristics as *Borrelia recurrentis*. It is usually smaller in size, and frequently shows a long regularly curved, delicate projection at each extremity. This organism is the cause of West African relapsing fever. Transmission to man occurs through the intermediation of a species of tick (*Ornithodorus moubata*).

There have been other species of *borrelia* reported as the cause of relapsing fevers in different parts of the world (Persian, American, Algerian and relapsing fever in India). Immunological reactions seem to have been demonstrated as the only reliable means of differentiating these several species. Cooper (*Med. J. Australia*, 1942, **1**, 635) reports on tick-borne relapsing fever among soldiers in Tobruk. He found that intravenous doses of arsenic were of little benefit in the tick-borne variety.

Borrelia kochii, the cause of African relapsing fever, is morphologically similar to *Borreiia duttonii*. Serologic differences have been demonstrated. *Borrelia novyi*, the cause of American relapsing fever, resembles *B. recurrentis* morphologically, but differs serologically. In the United States, relapsing fever occurs mainly in the western states and is transmitted by bites of infected ticks of the genus *Ornithodorus*. The only effective control measures are those directed against ticks (and other blood-sucking arthropods) and rodents. The reservoir of the disease is in burrowing rodents such as ground squirrels and chipmunks as well as opossums and armadillos. Personal cleanliness and attention to the sanitation of environments are important aids. For a consideration of tick-borne relapsing fever in the United States, see Davis (*U. S. Public Health Repts.*, 1940, **55**, 2347) and A. A. A. S. Symposia publications on "Relapsing Fever."

Borrelia Refringens (*Spirochaeta Refringens*).—This is a long, thick spiral, 0.5 to 0.8 by 15 to 35 μ, with several irregular, wide flat spirals. In other characteristics it resembles the members of this genus. It is a saprophyte, found in the mouth and more frequently around the genitalia of man. This organism is of interest, inasmuch as it may be found with and mistaken for *Treponema pallidum*, the causative agent of syphilis.

Borrelia Gallinarum (*Spironema Gallinarum; Spirochaeta Gallinarum; Spirochaeta Anserina*).—This is a long, spiral organism, 0.3 by 8 to 20 μ, with but few turns and about 1.5 μ intervening between the coils. In other characteristics, it resembles the members of this genus. It is the causative agent of a septicemic disease in fowls, especially chickens, geese and ducks. The infection is transmitted by the bites of certain species of ticks, especially *Argas miniatus*, *A. persicus* and *A. reflexus*.

Leptospira Icterohaemorrhagiae (*Spirochaeta or Treponema Icterohaemorrhagiae*). —This is a wavy, cylindrical thread, from 0.3 by 6 to 10 μ and infrequently up to 20 and even 25 μ, with irregular undulations, usually composed of two or three large irregular and four or five smaller waves. It is actively motile, flagella are absent, stains with difficulty with the usual aniline dyes and is Gram-negative. It has tapering ends which are frequently hooked either at one or both ends, resembling the letters J, C, S or L. *L. icterohaemorrhagiae* will grow only when special media are used and prefers a microaerophilic environment. The optimum temperature for growth is 25° C. Bile salts, 10 per cent concentration, dissolve it readily, but it is resistant to saponin (10 per cent concentration). This organism is the cause of *infectious* (or *epidemic*) *jaundice*, *icterohemorrhagic fever* or *Weil's disease* or *leptospirosis icterohaemorrhagica*. It appears that the infection is common to rats wh ch do not suffer from it. It has been found in the kidney and blood of wild rats. The disease is transmitted to man, spirochetes gaining entrance through the skin or by mouth from material contaminated by rat urine. Workers in contact with contaminated sewage have been infected. The disease occurs sporadically or in small localized epidemics but when sanitation is defective and personal cleanliness is poor, as may occur in warfare, extensive epidemics occur. The disease may occur as a severe infection with jaundice, or as a mild pyrexial infection without jaundice, or as a latent infection without clinical symptoms. It may be that infected soil plays a part in the transmission of this disease. Infection from man to man, though rare, may occur. The diagnosis is confirmed by dark-field examination and by injecting the blood (during the first week), or urine (after the first week), or bile of suspected cases into guinea pigs. Characteristic lesions are produced and the blood and liver contain the organisms. Packchanian (*U. S. Pub. Health Rept.*, 1940, **55,** 1389) has suggested the use of various species of deer mice as more suitable laboratory animals. Preventive measures consist in the proper care of water supplies and the protection of food supplies from rats. Thorough cooking destroys the *leptospira*. Convalescent sera contain specific agglutinins and lysins so that agglutination and *Pfeiffer's phenomenon* (breaking up the organisms in the animal's body) can be demonstrated. A satisfactory chemotherapeutic agent has not been found as yet. Immune serum, human or animal, has given favorable results in treatment. Immunization with killed *leptospira* is apparently of some value. Methods of prevention are directed mainly against the rat, protection of food from them, attention to badly drained areas, avoidance of bathing in contaminated waters and the use of gum boots or waders for sewer workers and miners in wet mines. In the first reported case of Weil's disease in Wisconsin (*Wisconsin M. J.*, 1943, **42,** 408), rats infected with the *leptospira* were captured at the meat-packing plant where the patient was employed. See also Balkin (*New Orleans M. and Surg. J.*, 1944, **96**, 351).

Dogs are susceptible to infection with *leptospira*, either identical with or closely related to this species, and man may acquire the disease from infected animals. Peterson and Christensen (*Compt. rend. Soc. Biol.*, 1939, **130**, 1507) described another species, *Lept. sejroe* as the cause of human infection in Denmark, the symptoms being milder than those cases infected with *L. icterohaemorrhagiae*.

Leptospira Icteroides.—*Leptospira icteroides* is similar but slightly smaller than *Leptospira icterohaemorrhagiae*, from 4 to 9 μ, and tapers toward the ends to sharp points. It resembles the latter organism in most of the other characteristics. At one time it was regarded as the cause of yellow fever, a disease peculiar to man, and transmitted under natural conditions only by the bite of a species of mosquito (*Aedes calopus*). Noguchi's investigations brought to light other facts concerning this disease, the important one being that there are probably more than one transmitting agent and even causative factor of yellow fever, depending upon where the disease is contracted.

Leptospira Hebdomadis.—This is similar to *Leptospira icterohaemorrhagiae*, but is differentiated from it by serological tests. It is the cause of one form of *seven-day fever* (Nanukayami), occurring in Japan. It is said to be carried by a species of field mice (*Microtus montebelli*).

There are other similar infections caused by *leptospira* which produce symptoms as are caused by the above species of *leptospira*. "Hasami" or "autumn" or "harvest" or "Akiyami" fever, a mild infection, known in Japan, is similar epidemiologically to seven-day fever but clinically, the disease resembles infectious jaundice. The causative agent is *L. autumnalis*. Two species, Types A and B, are recognized. The latter is considered identical with *L. hebdomadis*. Type A is more virulent and resembles *L. icterohaemorrhagiae*, but serologically is different from both species.

Leptospira canicola (more frequently) and *L. icterohemorrhagiae* (less frequently) are the etiological agents of canine leptospirosis, one of the forms of canine enzootic jaundice or "yellows." Veterinarians and others in contact with infected dogs may contract canicola fever.

For further considerations on leptospirosis in man and animals, see Anigstein (*Vet. Med.*, 1943, **38**, 221).

Treponema Pallidum (*Spirochaeta Pallida*).—This is a delicate structure, ranging usually in size from 0.25 to 0.4 by 4 to 16 μ. It is characterized by the regularity of its spirals, these not only being regular, but close together, with a deeply cut angle, and, like a corkscrew, remain sharp when the focus is changed. The spirals are about 1 μ apart and the number of these curves may be from 3 to 20 and even more. The ends are pointed. Flagella are absent. It is actively motile, stains with difficulty, if at all, with the aniline dyes, is Gram-negative and an anaerobe. Special techniques of staining and special media for culturing are necessary. *T. pallidum* is readily killed by drying, is very fragile and dies quickly outside the body. Experimental infection can be produced in monkeys, rabbits and mice by intratesticular, corneal or intradermal inoculation. The rabbit is the animal of choice. This organism is the cause of syphilis or lues, one of the important venereal diseases and a disease appearing spontaneously only in man.

Syphilis or lues is a communicable chronic infection acquired during sexual contact or transmitted by a diseased parent (congenital). There are many cases on record of so-called innocent syphilis. Physicians, nurses, dentists and attendants are not infrequently inoculated innocently. Cases are known where the initial lesion of syphilis started on the lips, tongue and even tonsils, such infection having taken place through kissing infected individuals and the use of the common towel or other material which may have contained discharges from luetic patients. The disease may be congenital and either parent may be responsible for hereditary transmission. However, classed as a venereal disease, it is most frequently acquired by illicit sexual intercourse. It usually progresses through a number of stages. The incubation period in acquired syphilis is from four to six and usually about three weeks. The infection manifests itself by the appearance of the initial sore, the chancre or hard sore. This may be located anywhere on the body, but is always found at the point where infection entered. The *Treponema pallidum* is present in this primary lesion, and any suspicious sore should be examined so as to definitely exclude a luetic infection. It is a better and safer practice to regard any genital sore or any indolent lesion anywhere on the body, which fails to heal within two weeks (especially if on lips, tonsils, breasts or fingers), as possible primary syphilis until it is proved to be otherwise. The diagnosis of primary syphilis is made on careful laboratory examinations. No determining weight should be given to specific clinical characteristics without laboratory findings, which, if properly performed, will prove the diagnosis. Antisyphilitic and local treatment should not be given until repeated dark-field examinations of the surface serum as well as that of the aspirated serum from the chancre base or from the lymph node are made.

In preparing specimens from lesions for the detection of the presence of *Treponema pallidum*, the lesions are cleansed of surface crust, bacteria and pus by application with cotton or gauze. If any local antiseptic was used, the latter is washed off and a dressing with saline solution is applied for one or two days prior to the examination. Rubbing the lesion between the gloved finger and thumb or with a dry cotton applicator will provoke the exudation of serum and thus material can be obtained from the deeper layers or tissues (without drawing blood). This is prepared for microscopic examination without fixation, and dark-field illumination is employed (see page 31). By such technique, the *Treponema pallidum* stands out as silvery white, actively motile coils or spirals against a dark background. As the focus is changed, the silvery spirals remain sharp and white. If a dark-field of surface serum and aspirated serum is negative, repeat at least three times on consecutive days before local treatment is instituted. If facilities for dark-field examination are not available or if the chancre fluid cannot be examined as soon as collected, specimens are obtained in sterile capillary tubes. The latter are 1 mm. in diameter, about 2 to 3 inches long, and similar to those used for smallpox vaccine. Hold the tube in a horizontal position and by touching the fluid which exudes from the lesion, the tube will fill by capillary action. The ends are sealed by pressing into wax (equal parts of petrolatum and paraffin). This can be placed in a stoppered test tube, waxed or sealed, and shipped in a mailing outfit. The chancre fluid can be stained by Giemsa's method or by one of the methods used for staining blood. In the *Nigrosin* and *India ink* methods, a loopful of chancre fluid is mixed on a slide with a loopful of a 10 per cent aqueous solution of nigrosin or with India ink, allowed to dry, and examined by ordinary illumination with the oil-immersion lens. White spirals are seen against a black background, but these methods are inferior to the dark-field technique. Gilbert and Bartels (*J. Lab. & Clin. Med.*, 1924, **9**, 273) employ a modification of Fontana's Method (*Derm. Wochnsch.*, 1912, **55**, 1003) and report highly satisfactory results. The spirochetes appear dark brown or black against a dark maroon background.

Lues, if detected as soon as the primary lesion is apparent and treated properly, is curable. If treatment begins later, it is questionable whether a cure is effected, this depending upon the patient, mode of treatment, etc. If untreated, the organisms spread to the glands near-by, which soon enlarge. The fluid obtained by glandular aspiration is most desirable for dark-field studies. This entire period lasting from six to ten weeks after the appearance of the chancre is known as the *primary stage*. Immediately thereafter the so-called *secondary stage* is ushered in. Here the organisms in the blood stream give rise to general constitutional symptoms and eruptions on the skin and mucous membranes. Sore mouth and sore throat, patchy loss of hair, iritis or neuroretinitis and vague bone pains may occur. Spirochetes are present in the skin and mouth lesions. The disease is most infectious in the late primary and secondary stages and patients in these stages are more frequently the cause of the spread of innocent syphilis. There is no distinct or definite time elapsing between the secondary and tertiary stages. In the *tertiary stage* the organisms become localized in certain tissues, particularly the brain and spinal cord, and lead to the formation of nodules (known as gumma) which have a tendency to become soft and cheesy. This stage, where the nervous system is mainly affected and cardiovascular involvements occur, may last for many years, to be followed by any one of a series of conditions, including tabes, paresis, locomotor ataxia, certain types of epilepsy, etc. In tertiary and late syphilis, the symptoms of many different diseases may be simulated, so that this disease has well earned the designation of *Great Imitator*. All syphilitic infections are *latent* at some time and subsequently a breakdown occurs and clinical manifestations develop.

The disease other than the clinical symptoms should be definitely diagnosed by confirming the finding of the causative agent by examining the serum or fluid from initial sores; by performing during all stages repeated serological (flocculation (Kahn and Kline) and complement-fixation (Wassermann, Kolmer, etc.)) tests on suspected patient's blood serum; and performing serological tests on the spinal fluid during the late stages, when the nervous system is attacked. In addition, other tests, such as *Lange's colloidal gold test*, the *mastic test* and the *luetin test*, are employed during various stages.

As a prophylactic especially for the male, a 30 to 35 per cent colloidal calomel ointment is used as an aid in reducing the incidence of syphilis. The use of arsphenamine, neoarsphenamine, mapharsen or other organic arsenicals in conjunction with bismuth or mercury preparations has been and is being employed in the treatment of syphilis. It is important that the treatment in all cases should be thorough and under the direction of expert workers and trained personnel. In advanced stages, when paresis or general paralysis prevails, remarkable progress in arresting the disease has been made by artificially inoculating with plasmodia causing malarial fever, and allowing the paretic patient to recover spontaneously from the malarial attack without giving quinine. Inasmuch as the value of malarial therapy depends upon the production of fever, physical means are now employed to elevate body temperature. The so-called *artificial fever therapy* has been and is being used effectively in the treatment of neurosyphilis. Intensification of chemical treatment, aided by artificial fever, has recently received considerable attention. Massive dose chemotherapy (*Bull. New York Acad. Med.*, 1941, **17,** 135) and other experimentations ("Venereal Disease Information," U. S. Public Health Service Suppl. No. **16,** 1942) may make available in the near future treatment which will abolish the disease, at least in the early stages, in a very short period of time. For further details, see "Syphilis" (an A. A. A. S. Symposia publication) and the many pamphlets and publications on this and other venereal diseases issued by the U. S. Public Health Service, "Venereal Disease Information."

Treponema Pertenue (*Spirochaeta Pertenuis*).—This is a long, slender spiral, usually 0.3 to 0.5 μ by 10 to 12 μ, with pointed ends and numerous undulations (6 to 20), resembling the *Treponema pallidum* in many respects. It is stained by the usual methods employed to stain blood films. Culturing on laboratory media is difficult, and it is questionable whether this has been accomplished. Monkeys and rabbits can be infected by inoculation with material from lesions in human cases. This organism is the cause of *yaws* or *frambesia tropica* and *gangosa* (a form of yaws), common in and limited to the West Indies and tropical countries. The extent of its occurrence is apparent in Rutter's (*Tr. Roy. Soc. Trop. Med. & Hyg.*, 1941, **34,** 429) recent report on the incidence and treatment of yaws in the Western Solomon Islands, where at least half of the population suffered from acute yaws lesions. The disease in man is highly communicable and is characterized chiefly by a generalized papular eruption. It is nonvenereal and distinct clinically from syphilis. The initial lesion is located usually extragenitally, often on the leg and at times at the site of a pre-existing wound. It is frequently observed in childhood. The source of infection is discharging skin lesions and where the organisms are found in large numbers; and transmission occurs in most instances by direct contact. It is possible that biting and nonbiting flies act as transmitting mechanical vectors. The Wassermann test and flocculation tests are also employed as an aid in the diagnosis of suspected cases of yaws; in fact, positive findings are given more frequently by these tests here than in luetic infections. Maltaner (*Am. J. Trop. Med.*, 1941, **21,** 145) obtained 41 positive Wassermann and flocculation tests in an examination of 44 cases. In the early stages, the organisms are to be observed by dark-field technique, in fresh preparations made from the liquid expressed from the lesion or from fluid aspirated from enlarged lymph glands. Arsphenamine and other luetic chemotherapeutic agents are also more specific for yaws than for syphilis.

The causative agents, clinical features, common serological reactions and response to the same chemotherapeutic agents of yaws and syphilis are similar in so many respects that some observers still speak of yaws as a modified syphilis. Yaws, however, is a much milder disease, is not acquired congenitally; mucous patches are absent; and the central nervous system and viscera are not attacked (tabes and paresis being rare).

Treponema Microdentium; Treponema Macrodentium; Treponema Mucosum; Treponema Calligyrum; and Treponema Minutum.—These vary in width and length, in the number of spiral curves and in their rate of motility. They are species of *treponema* that are nonpathogenic. The first two are found in the mouth (especially under the gums) and in the throat *Treponema mucosum* possesses pyogenic properties and is found associated with amoeba and other bacteria in pyorrhea alveolaris and dental affections. The latter two are nonpathogenic, have been isolated from smegma and are found around the genitalia of man.

Various mouth spirochetes, known under the following names, *S.* or *T. dentium*, *S.* or *T. acuta* and *S.* or *T. tenuis* are probably the same as the other mouth spirochetes described under the above names. *S.* or *T. refringens* is a nonpathogenic species which may be found around the genitalia and may be mistaken by the novice for *T. pallidum*. *T. refringens* is coarser than the latter; the number of turns are fewer and less regular; it is more actively motile when in motion and does not keep its corkscrew shape as well as *T. pallidum* when at rest. *T. cuniculi* is also similar in appearance to *T. pallidum* and causes rabbit spirochetosis or so-called rabbit syphilis. The localized infection produced by it resembles superficially that caused by inoculating *T. pallidum* into rabbits, so that experimental work with rabbits may be complicated by this spontaneous disease, transmitted by coitus or by contact.

PART II

THE HIGHER BACTERIA, FUNGI, RICKETTSIAE AND FILTERABLE VIRUSES

Chapter XII

THE HIGHER BACTERIA

THE ORGANISMS which are included under the heading Higher Bacteria (as given on page 15) are generally filamentous forms. In their size, structure, gross appearance and cycle of development they possess characteristics which place them in an intermediate position between the lower forms of bacteria (true bacteria) and the molds or true fungi. They are classified by many workers in what is in reality a heterogeneous group, the *Chlamydobacteriaceae*. In the system of classification adopted by the Society of American Bacteriologists these higher forms are included in several orders under the class *Schizomycetes*, among the important ones being the order *Actinomycetales*. In this order are also found several families, genera and species, and among these we find organisms like the acid-fast bacteria (genus, *Mycobacterium*) and the diphtheria and diphtheroid bacilli (genus, *Corynebacterium*). To some observers there does not seem to be a close enough relationship between the latter bacteria and these higher forms to consider grouping them under one heading. The two genera, *Mycobacterium* and *Corynebacterium*, are listed under one family, *Mycobacteriaceae*. In the same Order with the latter is the family, *Actinomycetaceae*, which includes the following genera: *Leptotrichia, Erysipelothrix, Proactinomyces* and *Actinomyces*. The Order, *Chlamydobacteriales* contains one family, *Chlamydobacteriaceae*, in which are listed the following genera: *Sphaerotilus, Clonothrix, Leptothrix,* and *Crenothrix*. Many of the species among the latter are alga-like bacteria, unbranched or show true or false branching, and it is possible that some of them may eventually prove to be species of *Actinomycetales*. There is still confusion as to the position where the group should be placed and how to designate and classify the subdivisions in this group. Bergey's classification has not met with consistent support. Arrangement and grouping as employed by some are followed, depending upon the importance of the species in agriculture or in medicine, the type of diseases produced if pathogenic, etc. Most workers place all of the pathogenic thread organisms under the genus *Actinomyces*, which in turn is classified with the true fungi and grouped with *Fungi Imperfecti*. This practice is highly advocated and is preferred.

The term *leptothricia* is used to designate those species which are almost straight

197

threads and show no branching forms. This term is not to be confused with the former generic term *leptothrix*, which has been discarded, but this name (*leptothrix*) is employed now for a genus in the family *Chlamydobacteriaceae* containing 8 species of iron bacteria.

The term *Cladothrix* used formerly also has been discarded. *Streptothrix* and *Nocardia* are other terms which have been discarded. Both have been replaced by the term *Actinomyces*, which includes forms that show true branching.

PATHOGENIC AND NONPATHOGENIC HIGHER BACTERIA

Leptotrichia Buccalis (*Leptothrix Buccalis*).—This is a saprophyte commonly found as an inhabitant of the human mouth. It is Gram-negative, aerobic and facultatively anaerobic, nonmotile and occurs as rods varying from 1 to 1.5 by 1.6 to 2 μ. It may be found in long chains, occasionally with partition walls. Most workers regard this organism as being nonpathogenic.

Actinomyces

In the Bergey classification 62 species are listed. Most species are plant parasites or nonpathogenic saprophytes of soil origin. A few species are pathogenic to animals. They are all usually Gram-positive and nonmotile and are divided into two distinct groups, the aerobes and anaerobes, although some microaerophilic species are known. The aerobic species may be acid-fast or nonacid-fast. The plant parasites and saprophytic nonpathogens are generally aerobic. The species parasitic for animals are usually microaerophilic or anaerobic. Occasionally chromogenesis may be observed. They usually grow in the form of a much-branched mycelium, which may break up into segments which function as conidia.

Actinomyces Hominis (*Ray Fungus*) **and Actinomyces Bovis** (*Discomyces, Streptothrix, Cladothrix, Sphaerotilus or Oospora Bovis; Streptothrix Actinomyces; Cladothrix or Nocardia Actinomyces*).—Whether there is a difference between *Actinomyces hominis*, which is regarded as the causative agent of actinomycosis in man, and *Actinomyces bovis*, which is regarded as producing the disease in lower animals, has not been definitely settled. In the Bergey classification, they are listed as separate species. Most workers, however, regard *A. hominis* as a variant of *A. bovis*. Occurring chiefly in domestic animals, principally the bovine species, the disease is of relatively frequent occurrence in man to regard it as of clinical importance. Actinomycosis may affect any portion of the body, but in cattle the head region, particularly the tongue and lower jaw, are most frequently involved. Where the tongue affection has become chronic the organ eventually becomes swollen, hard and nonflexible, thus giving rise to the term *wooden tongue*. When the disease affects the maxillae it is commonly referred to as *lumpy jaw*. The symptoms and characteristics of the disease as found in man are different. Generalization of the infection and its occurrence in other areas is more common in man than in cattle. In chronic cases in which the lungs and pleura are involved the disease may simulate tuberculosis. Oral administration of potassium iodide has proved of value in actinomycotic affections. X-ray is administered to accessible lesions. Local applications and the internal administration of thymol are highly advocated. Few isolated reports on the use of the sulfonamide drugs have been very encouraging. Transmission of this infection by direct or indirect contact has not been satisfactorily established. It is believed that the organism commonly gains entrance to the body through the agency of awns of infected bearded grain, such as barley, oats and wheat. The latter is the so-called exogenous theory. Those who support the endogenous theory have recently presented varied evidence. Slack (*J. Bact.*, 1942, **43**, 193) isolated *anaerobic actinomyces* in 14 per cent of the cases from 100 pairs of tonsils and in 18 per cent of the cases from 100 samples of pyorrhea pus. One of the strains isolated gave a progressive, fatal actinomycosis with sulfur granules in 5 animals upon inoculation.

The causative agent when present in tissue processes or in the pus from discharging lesions forms small gray or grayish-yellow granules, visible to the naked eye. Ordinarily, these granules are soft and easily crushed between slides or cover slips. Granules from old lesions are frequently quite hard, due to calcification. Microscopically, these granules are found to be made up of a dense network of branching threads or filaments, which measure individually about 0.4 to 0.6 μ in thickness. They radiate from a central point, which appears as a dense and opaque core, and they terminate at the periphery in characteristic club-shaped endings. Clubs are more commonly found in bovine than in human lesions. Inside of the network there are often seen coccoid or sporelike bodies. These have been variously interpreted as either real cocci, which are secondary invaders, or as products of degeneration, probably occasionally spores (though most workers question this), or merely the ends of clubs that appear first when focusing. The *A. bovis* possesses branching filaments with branching hyphae; the *A. hominis* possesses a straight mycelium with straight hyphae showing branching. These species stain with the ordinary aniline dyes and are Gram-positive. Efforts to obtain pure cultures from open lesions in which secondary invaders are present is a difficult task. The organism grows rather slowly, requiring several days' incubation at 37.5° C. It will also develop at room temperature. Culture media of slightly alkaline reaction to which is added glucose or blood serum are best suited for the growth of this organism. Though some strains will grow in the presence of oxygen without difficulty, most strains are microaerophilic or even thrive best under anaerobic conditions. Deep stabs in glucose agar usually produce growth, with pigmentation (yellowish becoming dark), the pigment being insoluble. Gelatin is slowly liquefied. Litmus milk is not coagulated but is slowly peptonized. The organisms of actinomycosis must be classed among the more resistant organisms. They will remain viable for years, even if in a dry state, and survive boiling for several minutes. They are extremely resistant to chemical disinfectants, but of the latter, bichloride is most effective, a 1 to 1000 solution destroying the organisms within ten minutes.

Actinomyces Madurae (*Nocardia, Discomyces* or *Streptothrix Madurae*).—*Actinomyces madurae* is the cause of the pale or white variety of mycetoma or Madura foot, a disease in many ways similar to actinomycosis. As the name implies, this disease usually affects the foot, caused by the penetration of the organisms into the tissues. Occasionally the hand and rarely other parts of the body may be affected. Mycetoma is primarily a disease of warm climates affecting man only. This affection occurs in endemic form in India, especially in Madura. It is observed more commonly among males and is rarely seen before puberty. The affected part usually shows a swelling, finally softening and discharging a slightly purulent fluid in which are present characteristic minute granular bodies. According to the color of these granules in the diseased tissue, different varieties of this malady have been described: (1) white, pale yellow or ochroid granules, the most common type and which most observers believe is caused by *Actinomyces madurae;* (2) a less common black variety, in which black gunpowder-like grains are to be found; (3) a rare red variety of mycetoma. The distinguishing feature in the clinical observation of these varieties is the color of the granules. The black and red varieties of mycetoma have associated with them organisms very different from actinomyces. The granules, consisting of *Actinomyces madurae,* show practically all the characteristics of *Actinomyces hominis* or *Actinomyces bovis* as to appearance, staining, etc. The cultural features are somewhat different. It grows well under aerobic conditions. The treatment is the same as given on page 198.

There are other species of fungi which give rise to the same symptom complex as observed in cases of Madura foot or maduromycosis caused by *A. madurae.* Among such species are found *Madurella mycetomi* and other species of *madurella, indiella, glenospora, monosporium (scedosporium), allescheria, aspergillus* and *penicillium.*

Actinomyces Farcinicus (*Oospora, Streptothrix or Nocardia Farcinica; Discomyces Farinicus; Bacille du Farcin*).—*Actinomyces farcinicus* is of interest only in veterinary medicine, producing a farcy-like disease of cattle, known as *bovine farcy,* and which resembles chronic tuberculosis. The disease, occurring but infrequently at present, is transmissible to cattle, sheep and guinea pigs but not to monkeys, horses, dogs or rabbits. *Actinomyces farcinicus* isolated from material from the affected lymph nodes and vessels appears as slender branching filaments, 0.25 μ in thickness. Its growth on the ordinary culture media reveals, in addition to long filaments, small, ovoid forms. It is an aerobe and facultative anaerobe, definitely acid-fast and Gram-negative. Starch is not hydrolyzed, as occurs with the species of *actinomyces* considered above. Though rather resistant to desiccation, this organism is quickly destroyed by heat and chemicals.

Actinomyces Gedanensis and Actinomyces Candidus.—These and other species of *actinomyces* have been isolated from abscesses in man and lower animals. *Actinomyces gedanensis* and *A. gypsoides* have been isolated from sputum of some patients suffering from chronic lung disease. *Actinomyces candidus* has been isolated from lung tissue in pulmonary tuberculosis and others have been isolated from other diseased conditions.

Actinomyces Asteroides.—This, an acid-fast aerobe, grows well on media at 37° C., producing a brick-red pigmentation with star-shaped colonies. Clubs and granules are not found, but long, branched filaments are observed microscopically. This organism has been found in a brain abscess, in peritoneal exudates and in various pulmonary affections, giving rise to so-called *pseudotuberculosis.* It has also been found in maduromycosis. Guinea pigs are readily infected and animal inoculation is of value for purposes of diagnosis.

Actinomyces Foersteri (*Streptothrix or Nocardia or Oospora Foersteri*).—This species generally remains localized in the lumen of the lachrymal duct, undergoes calcification, and a calculus is produced. Secondary infections may set in. It is readily cultured under microaerophilic and still better under anaerobic conditions.

Actinomyces Necrophorus (*Bacillus Necrophorus; Corynebacterium or Bacterium Necrophorum; Bacillus Filiformis; Fusiformis or Streptothrix Necrophorus; Spherophorus Necrophorus; Bacillus Diphtheriae Vitulorum*).—This organism is of considerable importance in veterinary medicine. It is responsible for several affections ("necrobacilloses") among domestic animals. These various conditions are characterized by necrotic and diphtheritic inflammatory processes. *A. necrophorus* causes diphtheria in cattle with multiple sclerotic abscesses, gangrenous dermatitis in horses and mules, multiple necrotic foci in the livers of cattle, sheep, horses and hogs, and other localized processes in different animals. The role played by this organism may be secondary or contributory in some instances rather than primary. Infection by this bacterium in man has been reported. It is found in soil and is probably a normal inhabitant of the mucous membranes of man and animals. Infections occur when it enters the body through minor wounds, abrasions, etc. *A. necrophorus* occurs characteristically as long, beaded filaments, 0.8 to 1.5 by 80 to 100 μ. It is pleomorphic. Short and even coccoid forms may be found. Branching can be demonstrated in cultures. The morphology varies somewhat with the kind of medium used. A soluble ectotoxin is produced. It is nonmotile, an obligate anaerobe, Gram-negative and grows best on media containing natural fluids, or a fermentable carbohydrate or 0.05 per cent cystine or 0.1 per cent cysteine. Acid is produced from dextrose, maltose and levulose. Lactose, saccharose, mannite and glycerin are not fermented. Gelatin and coagulated egg albumin are not liquefied. Indol is produced. Litmus milk is unchanged. It is weak resistant. In the Bergey classification, this organism is not included under the genus *actinomyces*, family *actinomycetaceae*, but it is placed under the family *bacteriaceae*. For further details, see Dack (*J. Bact.*, 1940, **4**, 227).

Erysipelothrix Rhusiopathiae (*Bacillus Erysipelatus Suis; Bacillus Rhusiopathiae Suis*).—This organism, also known as *A. thuillieri* and *Erysipelothrix porci*, is the causative agent of swine erysipelas (red fever), a highly important disease of continental Europe, which also exists in this country, confined mainly to the corn belt area. The disease manifests itself in three different forms: (1) septicemic or acute type, which occurs frequently and is the most fatal form of the disease; (2) chronic type, which is characterized chiefly by heart lesions with their usual secondary conditions; (3) urticarial type, or so-called *diamond-skin disease*, which is the mildest and less serious form. The control of this disease in countries where it is prevalent is rendered difficult because many normal hogs have been found to be carriers, harboring the organism in their throats and intestinal tract. Hogs are usually infected through ingestion of contaminated food or water and only occasionally through tissue injuries. Man may contract this disease by accidental inoculation in contact with infected animals and their products, and he is usually infected through tissue injuries, rarely by other means. *Erysipelothrix rhusiopathiae* is a small slender rod, 0.2 to 0.4 by 0.5 to 2 μ, usually straight, but slightly bent forms may be observed. It occurs singly and in chains, and minute characteristic granules may be seen occasionally in some of the rods when stained by Gram's method, It is nonmotile, nonspore-forming, Gram-positive and will grow scantily on ordinary culture media. It is microaerophilic, and its growth in gelatin media is quite characteristic. It is very resistant to drying and to the action of pickling fluids, but is quickly destroyed by heat and the commonly employed disinfectants in their usual strengths. An agglutination test is available as an aid in diagnosis. Satisfactory results have been obtained in the treatment and prevention of swine erysipelas with biological products. For further details, see Grey and associates (*Am. J. Vet. Research*, 1941, **11**, 74).

Chapter XIII

FUNGI

THERE ARE FOUR great divisions in the plant kingdom (the first three divisions collectively are sometimes known as cryptogams):

1. Thallophytes:
   - (a) Algae—different colored algae; diatoms.
   - (b) *Fungi—bacteria* (lower and higher forms); slime molds; *true fungi* (molds, mildews, yeasts, smuts, mushrooms and *imperfect fungi* [as celery blight, etc.]).
   - (c) Lichens.
2. Bryophyta:
   - (a) Hepaticae or liverworts.
   - (b) Musci or mosses (black, true and peat mosses).
3. Pteridophyta:
   - (a) Lycopodineae or club mosses.
   - (b) Equiesetineae or horsetails.
   - (c) Filicineae or ferns.
4. Spermatophyta (sometimes called phanerogams or seed plants):
   - (a) Gymnospermae or gymnosperms—plants with naked or uncovered seeds. They include plants of the pine family (such as pines, spruces, firs, hemlocks, junipers), yew family, etc.
   - (b) Angiospermae or angiosperms—plants with covered seeds, the latter enclosed within the seed vessel or fruit wall.
     They include the two subgroups:
     1. Monocotyledons, represented by the cat-tails, the grasses and cereals, sedges, lilies, daffodils, palms, bananas, orchids, etc.
     2. Dicotyledons, represented by an array of plants which include most of the familiar trees and shrubs, except the conifers, garden plants, many weeds, etc. Asters, beans, cherries, chestnuts, maples, poplars, oaks, willows and violets are striking examples.

THE TRUE FUNGI

The term fungi in its broadest sense (general term) includes all thallophytes (no differentiation into roots, stems and leaves), which are characterized by the total absence of chlorophyll or its analogues. They, therefore, possess no independent power of manufacturing their food supply, but as *parasites* they obtain their nourishment from other plants or animals (the *hosts*), or as *saprophytes* they may exist by obtaining their nourishment from decaying vegetable or animal matter. Some may adapt themselves to both modes of existence. The bacteria (a subgroup of fungi) are unicellular and reproduce by simple fission. These are the simplest types in this group. Most of the members of the other subgroups reproduce infrequently by the sexual method and generally by means of spores, and in the narrower sense (especially among bacteriologists) the term fungi is usually (or specifically) applied to those forms (that reproduce by such process). These are also known as true fungi (*eumycetes*).

The eumycetes (true fungi) are further subdivided into:

I. *Phycomycetes* or *alga-like fungi* (molds, blights, mildews, rots).

II. *Ascomycetes* or *sac fungi* (yeasts, powdery mildews, morels, etc.).

III. *Basidiomycetes* or *basidia* or *club fungi* (smuts, mushrooms, puff-balls).

IV. *Deuteromycetes* or *fungi imperfecti* (imperfect fungi) (includes an assemblage of varied forms of fungi, the life histories of many of them being imperfectly understood).

The *true fungi* are the most complex of the plant organisms considered in bacteriology. The unicellular types, as the common yeast (*Saccharomyces cerevisiae*), grow and develop in easily dissociated masses. Each individual cell combines the function of nutrition, converting the food substances (which diffuse into the cell through the readily permeable cell walls) into needed life-sustaining substances with that of reproduction. Their method of multiplication is by budding, and not by fission. Otherwise they act much as do bacteria. Most of the other members of true fungi are made up of many cells, usually cylindrical, joined into filaments. From the latter spores (smaller rounded cells) develop. From these filaments and spores the various species build up a structure which differs and is characteristic for each species. The macroscopic (gross) and microscopic observations and the type of spores produced which will be mentioned are employed as the means for the identification and classification of the many species. Before giving these characteristics it will be well to consider and define some of the terms not mentioned in any of the preceding chapters and which are used to describe the morphology, the methods of reproduction, etc., of the members of this group. The attempt here will be only to cover those terms which will be necessary to use in this chapter.

The entire body or vegetative portion of a fungus is known as a *thallus*. This is composed of individual filaments or threads, known as *hyphae*. A network or mass of vegetative hyphae intertangled without definite arrangement or intertwined in tangled threads, is known as a *mycelium*. Frequently the latter term is applied to the entire thallus, but it is never applied to a single filament, only to a collective mass of hyphae or fungous substance. The hypha may appear as a long continuous tube (unicellular) with several nuclei present or multicellular, each cell separated by *septa*, and they then appear as chains of cylindrical cells. The hyphae spread out on or through decaying matter or invade tissues of living organisms. In the higher forms of fungi the hyphae become consolidated into false tissues and assume definite shapes characteristic of the several species. Three kinds of hyphae may be found: (1) submerged (or rhizoidal); (2) aerial (or sporangiophores); (3) occasionally stolomferous hyphae. The first type penetrates and grows down into the substratum and is equivalent to structures as seen in other plant life, being analogous to the roots of higher plants. The aerial hyphae project into the air. Hyphae which have special functions are often differentiated from the rest of the mycelium.

Reproduction is the power possessed by an organism to divide and multiply (produce offspring). When there is only a separation of a cell or cells from an individual, and each separated or free cell forms a new organism, the process of multiplication is termed *asexual or vegetative reproduction*. When there is a union of cells through a direct contact of the protoplasmic contents of these cells giving rise to new individuals the process is spoken of as *sexual reproduction*. Most of the fungi commonly observed in bacteriology reproduce asexually. There are two kinds of sexual reproduction— *fertilization* and *conjugation*. A union of two gametes (sexual cells) (formed by the blending of the protoplasm and the union of the nuclei), alike in character, gives rise to a product known as a *zygote* or *zygospore*. The fusion of these two undifferentiated cells is that sexual method of reproduction known as *conjugation*. Fertilization is that process of sexual reproduction in which there is a union of two unlike gametes (fertilization of a female cell by a differentiated male cell). The product is known as an *oospore*. A *spore* is an asexual or sexual reproductive cell possessing usually a highly resistant cell wall. These cells are analogous to the seed of a higher plant. It will be observed that the meaning of the term spore as used here and generally in botanical studies is *entirely different* from the term spore (or endospore) used in describing bacteria and commonly employed in bacteriology. (See page 13.)

The spore does not divide until it becomes separated from the thallus. Usually after a period of dormancy, if it has not perished due to adverse conditions, the spore (meeting favorable conditions) germinates and produces a new thallus and so the species is continued. Spores differ in their mode of origin, in the numbers produced by each species and in their arrangement on or within the thallus. We may have asexual spores (produced asexually) and sexual spores (produced by sexual reproduction).

Some species of fungi have hyphae which form fruiting branches, called *conidiophores* which support or bear specialized cells (containing chains of spores). These are known as *conidiospores* or *conidia*, and are asexual in origin (characteristic of *penicillium* and *aspergillus*). The *conidia* are structureless, are much smaller than mycelial cells, appear spherical or elongated and pyriform and readily detach into the immediate surroundings. *Aleuries* are similar to conidia, are attached to the parent cell by a broad base and become detached when the mycelium disintegrates. A large class of fungi is characterized by the occurrence of *basidiospores* in the life history. These are spores produced on special types of sporophores (fruiting bodies), known as *basidia* (singular *basidium*). Along the course of hyphae of some species, thick-walled spores, known as *chlamydospores* or *brand spores*, are formed as resisting structures, which withstand unfavorable conditions. They are round to spindle-shaped and contain many metachromatic granules. Those occurring along the course of a hypha are termed *intercalated;* if at the tips, *terminal chlamydospores;* and *lateral* if they extend on a short stalk from the side of a hypha. Certain fungi (*trichophyton*) reveal these spores in the form of bundles, or they become markedly enlarged and elongated into spindles, the so-called *Fuseaux*, usually septate and divided into chambers when fully developed, but at times, especially if immature, the partitions are incomplete. Each chamber becomes an individual chlamydospore.

In some species of fungi (*black fungi*) the mycelium forms hardened masses, known as *sclerotia*. These hard bodies are distinctive of the individual species. *Ascospores* are special types of spores formed after a process of division, when each cell divides into 2, 4 or 8 parts, each of which becomes nearly dry and all are held within a thick wall or membrane, known as the *ascus*. Their production not only serves as a method of reproduction but of resisting adverse conditions (characteristics of several types of yeasts). The following are other terms employed at times in describing and classifying fungi. *Buds* are round or oval cells protruding from the parent cell, from which they finally become abstricted. Actually they are spores (*blastospores*), which are the reproductive cells (as in *yeast*). A *sporangium* is a comparatively large sac enclosing an indefinite number of nonsexual spores at the end of a hypha (as in *Mucor*). *Zygospores* (see page 204) are sexual formations, developed by the fusion of two structures which are identical morphologically. They are spoken of as *homothallus*, if both are members of the same fungus plant; and *heterothallus*, if from two different plants. *Macrocondia* refers to those reproducing asexual spores, which are of large size; *microcondia* (*aleurospores*), if they are small in size. *Pectinate* bodies refer to the comblike structures formed by some fungi and *sterigma* to a short-stalk bearing chains of conidia (as in *Aspergillus*). *Pleomorphism* among fungi refers to the marked variations in morphology and culture which they may undergo under different living conditions. Diseases caused by fungi frequently terminate with the word *mycoses*.

It is important to mention again that the classification of the true fungi is not wholly satisfactory. There is still entirely too much confusion; exact relationships between groups are not as clear as they might be. Pleomorphism is common among some of the members, making exact identification at times difficult. From the bacteriological standpoint there are only a few fungi that are of known importance, so that an exact classification at this time is not of very great consequence, though the one given on page 202 and further groupings as on the following pages will be found useful and as satisfactory as any method. It is also well to remember that fungi occur widespread in Nature and only to a minor extent in disease in man. A classification to include all fungi, medical and botanic species, must be based mainly on the characters of the reproductive elements and the classification of the botanist must be employed. But from the standpoint of medical mycology, classifications of fungi are generally based on characteristics exhibited in animal tissues and in culture and only infrequently in Nature at large. As it happens, the most important subclass of true fungi is the *Hyphomycetes*, or *Fungi Imperfecti*. Here are included practically all the fungi pathogenic to man. For further details, see Lewis and Hopper (*An Introduction to Medical Mycology*, Year Book Publishers, Inc., Chicago, Ill., 1939), Henrici ("Yeasts," *Bact. Revs.*, 1941, **5**, 97; *Molds, Yeasts and Actinomyces*, Wiley and Sons, New York City, 1930), Stovall and Almon ("Pathogenic Fungi," *Diag. Proc. and Reag.*, A. P. H. A., 1941), Dodge (*Medical Mycology*, C. V. Mosby Co., St. Louis, Mo., 1935) and Swartz (*Essentials of Medical Mycology*, Grune and Stratton, N. Y. City, 1943). Recently, a diagnostic and registry center for the study of fungus diseases of man has been opened at Duke University Medical School. The service is available to all scientific workers (*Science*, 1944, **99**, 95).

Finally it is important to note that fungi play other roles apart from infection in human beings and few species are of value to man. Yeasts are of value in the baking and fermentative industries. Molds are useful in the manufacture of cheeses and in the production of various chemicals. Their specificity in attacking particular carbohydrates is utilized biochemically as an aid in the identification of the different urinary sugars. Certain mushrooms (*Agaricus campestris*) are used as delicacies, though some species (*Amanita muscaria* and *A. phalloides*) are poisonous. Ergot (*Claviceps pur-*

purea) is a fungus belonging to the Sac-Fungi, which parasitize the fruits of the rye plant and other grasses belonging to the grass family. Agaricus, the dried fruit body of the fungus *Polyporus officinalis*, and found on species of larch, spruce and pine trees, was used formerly as a purgative and antihydrotic (to lessen perspiration). Many fungi produce diseases of plants, grains, fruits, etc., which mean spoilage and economic waste. Just to mention a few, there are such conditions, as the white "rust" of mustards which occurs upon the radish, horse-radish, turnip and mustard, the onion mildew, the late blight of potato, and the downy mildew of the cucumber and of the grape. The brown rot of stone fruits affects the peach, plum, prune, cherry and apricot, and at times it may be found on apple, pear and quince. Corn smut, wheat rust and the leaf blight of tomato are fungous diseases which cause considerable losses. The rust of asparagus and carnation and the root rot of tobacco are a few other examples in which the fungi are found parasitizing higher plant life. Food spoilage by fungi in the home, dairy plant and in all food industries and their occurrence as contaminants in the laboratory are known too well to require consideration here. In veterinary medicine, there occurs the epizootic lymphangitis of equines, caused by *Blastomyces farciminosus* and the ringworms, favuses and thrush similar to diseases in man. In the following pages, only the important species of interest will be considered.

PHYCOMYCETES

Phycomycetes or Alga-like Fungi.—This is a small group of fungi showing a close affinity with the green algae. These produce a mycelium composed of unicellular hyphae. They reproduce by spores as well as by sexual reproduction. The spores (in asexual reproduction) develop on the tip of a hypha, which enlarges to form a spherical, caselike structure, known as the *sporangium*. The latter contains numerous small, brownish, multinucleate spores. The septum or partition wall, which separates the sporangium from the supporting hyphae, bulges into the latter, appearing as a dome-shaped structure and is known as the *columella*. Sexual reproduction is less frequent. Some species produce no exospores but numerous chlamydospores. There are orders, suborders and several families in this group. Most of them are only of interest to the bacteriologist because they occur frequently as contaminants of foodstuffs and media, etc., found in the laboratory. Though some of them are slightly pathogenic, their importance in human and animal pathology is not great.

Rhizopus Nigricans (*Mucor Stolonifer*).—This is known as the *black mold* or *black bread mold* and is frequently found in bread and jellies, and is a common laboratory contaminant. The source of this mold is the spores, which are found in the air, water, etc. There are three types of hyphae involved. The first type penetrates the medium, and by means of enzyme action changes the carbohydrates of the medium into soluble sugars and absorbs these for nourishment. Here and there, hyphae rise vertically and when mature end in a little globular head filled with microscopic brownish spores. The third type of hyphae grows along the surface of the medium and when its tip comes into contact with the medium forms a new cluster of subterranean hyphae and also aerial hyphae producing spores. Thus, it is possible for a rapid spread of the fungus on the nutrient medium. The stalk of each aerial hyphae is separated from the globular head containing the spores by means of a transverse partition. When the spores are ripe, the head breaks open and they are scattered. Some, falling to the surface of the medium, germinate and form new plants.

Mucor mucedo resembles *Rhizopus nigricans* in many respects, but differs mainly in that it forms sporangiophores singly instead of in clusters. It is found constantly as an inhabitant of horse manure, also on fleshy fruits, bread, etc. Two species of mucor (*Mucor mucedo* and *Mucor corymbifer*) have been found in nasopharyngeal and external ear affections; other infections (eye, lung and occasionally generalized) by species of *mucor* have been reported.

ASCOMYCETES

Ascomycetes or Sac Fungi.—The mycelium is composed of septate filaments. The most distinctive peculiarity is that the life history in many of the species is characterized by the appearance of a sac, called an "ascus," in which "ascospores" are formed. In other members of this group there is found a mycelium made up of septate filaments, and reproduction is by means of conidia, which are frequently borne on characteristic structures. There are several genera in this group which are important in bacteriology. The following may be considered together. The individual species reproduce by budding, and asci when present do not appear to have a sheath.

Saccharomyces.—*Saccharomyces* or *yeasts* are fungi with nuclei in which the usual and dominant growth-form is unicellular of spheroidal, elliptical, oval or sausage shape. Thread forms are occasionally observed. The size of the individual yeast cells vary, occasionally even in those of the same species, and obtained from the same culture. Old cultures frequently show cells averaging from 1 to 2 μ in diameter, while cells ranging from 12 to 20 μ in diameter are commonly found in young cultures. At times, in some species, giant cells often attaining a diameter of 35 to 45 μ are observed. The individual species are usually characterized by a fairly definite average in range of size and shape. At times the individual yeast cells may appear microscopically as fat globules, or even as erythrocytes or red blood cells, so that if the single, discrete nucleus (which is usually present) and budding are not observed certain reagents may be needed for distinguishing and identifying these cells. Young cells of the several species of yeasts stain with the commonly employed dyes and they are Gram-positive. Older forms do not always stain characteristically, usually irregularly. Spores may be stained by any of the techniques used to stain bacterial spores. Henrici employs the following procedure: Apply 5 per cent aqueous solution of chromic acid for five minutes; then steam with carbol fuchsin for five minutes; decolorize in 1 per cent aqueous sulfuric acid for two minutes; and counterstain with Loeffler's methylene-blue solution for one minute. Spores appear colored red, vegetative cells and asci blue. Yeasts usually grow on ordinary media, best on the latter to which is added glucose or maltose and when a slightly acid reaction is present. The characteristics of growth of yeasts in suitable liquid media noting the formation of a pellicle or mucoid scum, is frequently an important diagnostic aid. Among the observations on solid media are that the growth is smooth or wrinkled, mucoid or tenacious, white, creamy, buff, or possessing definite color. Sabouraud's culture medium is frequently employed for pathogenic yeasts. Beer wort is an ideal medium, but it is of variable composition. For commercial purposes the "so-called industrial yeasts" are readily grown by sowing the cells in Pasteur's solution or a dilute saccharine solution containing the latter, beer wort or grape juice, etc.

Pasteur's Solution.—Calcium phosphate, 0.1 Gm.; magnesium sulfate, 1 Gm.; potassium phosphate, 1 Gm.; ammonium tartrate, 5 Gm.; saccharose, 75 Gm.; distilled water to make 500 Gm.

Most members of this group are very resistant organisms. Yeasts reproduce by budding. In the latter process a small protuberance of the cell wall commences to form on the parent cell. This grows larger and a portion of the cytoplasm and nuclear material passes into it. The result is a daughter cell, which may eventually assume the size of the parent cell. Adhering to the latter, it appears as a bud, but it eventually separates from the parent cell. Ascospores may be formed. Yeasts have until recently been considered *parthenogenetic* (devoid of sexuality). But Guilliermond (*Botan. Rev.*, 1940, **6, 1**) and Winge and associates (Comp. rend. trav. lab. Carlsberg, 1935, **21,** 77; 1937–1939, **22,** 99, 235, 337, 357) have presented data of wide significance concerning our knowledge of sexuality in the yeasts. Their observations are accepted by many workers and that is the fact that spore-forming yeasts are not entirely parthenogenetic. A true mycelium with cross walls and a so-called pseudomycelium, a branched structure resembling closely true mycelium, are observed occasionally.

In an attempt to identify species of yeasts, microscopical, morphological, staining and cultural characteristics are needed. Important observations are: size and shape of vegetative cells; whether multiplication is by fission or budding; if buds are present, whether they are found at ends (bipolar) or at any place on the cell (multipolar); whether a pseudo or a true mycelium is present; etc.

Most species of commercial yeasts are generally found capable of breaking down some sugar with the production of alcohol and carbon dioxide. According to the sugar or sugars fermented, yeasts have been differentiated into several species. This process of splitting sugars (fermentation) is due to the fact that the protoplasm of the yeast cells produce two kinds of enzymes: one, an extracellular enzyme, *invertase*, which hydrolyzes cane sugar (saccharose) to dextrose and levulose, and an intracellular enzyme, *zymase*, which decomposes dextrose into alcohol and carbon dioxide. Another extracellular enzyme, *maltase*, is produced; this changes maltose into dextrose. The two most important species of yeasts found in the fermentation industries are *Saccharomyces cerevisiae* and *Saccharomyces ellipsoideus*. These two names have been employed for nearly all of the industrial yeasts, though more recently *S. ellipsoideus* is designated as a variety of *S. cerevisiae* (*i. e., S. cerevisiae* var. *ellipsoideus*). Industrial brewery yeasts are divided by some into *top yeasts* and *bottom yeasts*, the former being carried to the top in the fermentation process, and the bottom yeasts tend to sediment and the fermentation takes place at the bottom of the tanks. Wine yeasts are frequently separated into "normal-fermenting" and "cold-fermenting types." Specific strains of industrial yeasts are used for the special flavors or other particular desirable characteristics they may possess.

Compressed yeast (so-called bakers' yeast, yeast cake, etc.), known also as *Cerevisiae Fermentum Compressum*, consists of the moist living cells of *Saccharomyces cerevisiae* or of other species of *saccharomyces*, combined with a starchy or absorbent base. In addition to being used in the fermentation industries, yeast is employed as a leavening agent in baking, as a therapeutic agent in internal medicine, of value for its content of vitamin B complex and for making fermented milk or artificial koumyss.

Torula or False (Pseudo) Yeasts.—The term *torula* is employed by some observers to various uncultivated yeasts. They are usually spherical cells, reproduce by budding, do not produce spores or a mycelium and possess but slight fermentative power. These yeasts have been the subject of a confused literature and different names applied to the unacceptable *Torula*. For details, see Lodder (*Mycopathologia*, 1938, **1**, 62, 98). See *Med. Chin. N. A.* (July, 1944, p. 950) on torula infection.

The *Rhodotorula* is a genus which contains many species of red or pink yeasts. The latter are abundant on leaves and straw and occur as air contaminants. They are usually of little practical importance, though Pederson and Kelly (*Food Research*, 1938, **3**, 583) report their presence causing discoloration of sauerkraut. Schnegg and Weigand (*Zentr. Bakt. Parasitenk.*, 1936–1937, **95**, 154) found pink yeasts in solutions of boric acid purchased in drugstores.

Pathogenic Yeasts.—Practically all species of yeasts encountered have been assigned as the causative agent of different diseases. Moreover, the same species have been reported under different names. With the more exact knowledge of classifying yeasts in use today, it is evident that only few species of truly pathogenic yeasts are encountered. They may be divided into those species causing deep-seated infections and those which produce superficial infections of the skin and mucous membranes.

Cryptococcus (or Blastomyces).—These cells reproduce by budding, but ascospore formation is not observed. They are regarded as separate genera by some workers. Diseases caused by species of *blastomyces* are known as blastomycoses.

Cryptococcus Gilchristi or Gilchristia Dermatitidis (*Blastomyces Dermatitis, Blastomyces Gilchristi, Saccharomyces Hominis, Zymonema Gilchristi, Mycoderma Dermatitis, etc.*).—Round, and occasionally oval, doubly contoured, budding yeast-like cells from 8 to 20 μ in diameter and surrounded by a hyaline capsule. Granules of various sizes and often vacuoles may be found. Pairs united and appearing like a figure 8 are frequently observed. A single bud is observed. In cultures grown aerobically, a mycelium is usually formed. The infection with this organism is usually known as blastomycosis (occasionally oidiomycosis) or blastomycetic dermatitis. The skin infection by this organism generally follows a uniform course, which extends frequently over several years. Cases of generalized blastomycosis, which usually terminate fatally, have been reported. In the majority of the latter the lungs are involved (probably the seat of primary infection), giving rise to a condition resembling (and frequently erroneously diagnosed clinically) pulmonary tuberculosis.

Torulopsis Neoformans (*Cryptococcus or Torula Hominis; Torula Histolytica, Saccharomyces or Blastomyces Neoformans*).—The cells are round or short, oval, averaging 4 to 6 μ in diameter, occurring singly or in pairs, cause no fermentation on sugars, produce a yellowish to a light tan with a slightly rosy cast, and a smooth, pasty, moist, thick growth on agar medium. Capsules are present if in infected tissues. This organism is the cause of *torulosis* (*European blastomycosis*) and appears to have a predilection for nerve tissue. Lesions in various organs and cutaneous envolvements may occur. This probably is the same species isolated from spinal fluid and labeled as *Cryptococcus meningitidis*, causing torula meningitis. More recently the name *Debaryomyces hominis* has been suggested.

Histoplasma Farcinimosum (*Cryptococcus Farcinimosus; Grubijella Farcinimosa; Blastomyces or Saccharomyces Farciminosus*).—*Histoplasma farcinimosum* is an oval, doubly contoured, budding yeastlike cell, 3 to 4 μ in diameter. Granules may be present. It is Gram-positive and aerobic. The growth is exceedingly slow, requiring at times one month before appearance on any of the media, though potato medium and egg medium yield more luxuriant growths in a shorter length of time. Few investigators have maintained that this organism is protozoan in character, though most observers regard this as a member of the yeasts. It is the primary etiological factor of a disease in equines known as *epizootic lymphangitis*. The latter runs a long, chronic course and is characterized by a purulent inflammation of the superficial lymph vessels and glands. Few cases of this disease have been reported in man. The lymph vessels and nodes are mainly envolved.

Histoplasma Capsulatum.—This species grows more readily in cultures and reveals differences in spore production and the development of multiple budding forms. In tissue, the cells are somewhat larger and are not elongated. It affects man, occasionally producing a subacute disease, with fever, leukopenia, anemia and envolvements of the liver and spleen. A case presenting the clinical syndrome characteristic of vegetative endocarditis in which the causative agent was *H. capsulatum* was reported by Broders, *et al.* (*J. A. M. A.*, 1943, **122,** 489). These authors consider in detail the history and other characteristics of histoplasmosis.

Attempts have been made to differentiate other species of true yeast and yeastlike organisms. The task is a difficult one. Many studies to systematize and classify the members of this and closely related genera (so-called yeastlike forms) are being made. None of these attempts have been completely satisfactory. The exact relationship of some of these yeastlike forms is not definitely known. The present grouping here is only a tentative one, and we must await further study and investigations to guide workers so that the proper classification will be made.

Coccidioides.—The members in this genus do not show buds. They reproduce by the formation of endospores; a mycelium is produced in most cultures. Sugars are not fermented.

Coccidioides Immitis (*Coccidioides Pyogenes; Oidium* or *Geotrichum Immitis; Oidium Coccidioides; Mycoderma Immite*).—*Coccidioides immitis* causing coccidioidal granuloma is somewhat similar to *G. dermatitidis* (*Cryptococcus gilchristi*), but differs from it in that it is characterized by endogenous spore formation. In guinea pigs, inoculation with *C. immitis* produces extensive pathology, while with *Gilchristia dermatitidis,* these animals are refractory. The parasite does not show buds and is usually very large (30 to 60 μ). This organism has been isolated from soil, vegetation, and from internal organs of slaughtered cattle and sheep. The infection in man is either cutaneous or pulmonary, occurring through an injury to the skin or inhalation of infected dust. The disease, also known as *Valley Fever, Desert Rheumatism* and *San Joaquin Fever*, occurs endemically in California, Texas, Arizona and the Chaco region of the Argentine. As an aid in diagnosis, a skin test reaction to *coccidioidin* is said to be specific (see Hurwitz and Associates (*California and West. Med.*, 1938, **48,** 1)). The organism can be found in pus removed from skin lesions and from sputum and spinal fluid. Culturing and animal inoculation are aids. Thymol, in doses of 1 to 6 Gm. daily, is of value in treatment. Antimony and potassium tartrate, given intravenously, are also used. Emmons (*U. S. Public Health S. Repts.*, 1943, **58,** 1) recently established the fact that this disease occurs in rodents; the latter constitute a reservoir of importance in the epidemiology of the disease, and he suggests the examination and culturing of the lungs from samples of the rodent population (particularly species of *Perognathus*) as a quick and dependable method to determine whether coccidioides is present in a specific locality. Goldstein and McDonald (*J. A. M. A.*, 1944, **124,** 557) presented recently a detailed report on 75 cases of primary pulmonary coccidioidomycosis.

Paracoccidioides.—*P. brasiliensis, P. tenuis* and *P. cerebriformis* have been encountered in cases of paracoccidioides, especially in South America. *P. brasiliensis* is the species observed most frequently. This was confused for a long time with *C. immitis.* It is, however, smaller, 25 to 35 μ in diameter, spherical, and does not reproduce by endosporulation but by the extrusion of multiple gemmae through the capsule. The infection produced in man is found around the mouth, face and lymph nodes. The skin, intestines and even the lungs, liver and meninges may become envolved.

Other Genera

Various genera grouped under the *ascomycetes* are included together due to the fact that they show a tendency to form *perithecia.* The latter are receptacles containing asci.

The Dermatophytes

The term *dermatophytosis* is used frequently to indicate eczema-like eruptions due to fungi and includes such conditions as athlete's foot, eczema marginatum, eczematized ringworm, parasitic eczema, epidermophytosis, and tinea cruris. The sulfonamide compounds, present in lotions, have been recommended in the treatment of epidermophytosis. The important groups considered here are: *Microsporum, Trichophyton, Achorion* and *Epidermophyton.*

Microsporum.—The fungi of this genus are made up of organisms which develop small spores or segments (2 to 3 μ) and, instead of in chain formation, they are found closely grouped about the hair in an irregular, mosaic-like appearance and usually form a white sheath around the hair and extending several millimeters above the epidermis. Cultures of members of this genus grow slowly and reveal a downy surface and white color. Conidia, chlamydospores or a "fuseaux" may be observed. The last named are large, elongated-chambered bodies, regarded as chlamydospores by some and as specialized conidia by others. The several species have been divided into two groups, one affecting man only and one capable of producing ringworm in man and animals. The following are the important species:

Microsporum Audouini (Trichophyton Microsporon; Trichophyton Audouini).—This is the cause of a common and highly contagious affection of the scalp in children, especially those living in the western European countries. The hairy scalp is almost exclusively the affected part. Closely allied species are *Microsporum tardum, Microsporum umbonatum* and *Microsporum velveticum.*

Microsporum minimum, closely related to *Microsporum audouini,* and the type species of the microspora of animal origin, produces one type of ringworm in horses. Closely related species are *Microsporum lanosum,* found in ringworm of dogs, but which also causes ringworm in man; *Microsporum felineum,* reported as causing ringworm of cats; *M. equinum* in horses; etc.

Trichophyton or Megalosporum.—The species of this genus cause the affections commonly known as *herpes tonsurans* or ringworm. Man, cattle, horses and other domestic animals are attacked. The spores (from 4 to 12 μ in diameter) occur in chain formation and are found in and around the hair. The parasite rarely penetrates deeper than the epidermis and its appendages. The term *Trichophyta megalospora* is frequently employed to designate the large ringworm fungi, while if the spores are similarly arranged but are smaller in size (2 to 4 μ) they are termed *Trichophyton microspora*. The following designations are made at times by some workers. If the fungus is found only within the hair it is known as an *endothrix*. When found, mainly on the outside or on the surface of the hair, it is known as an *ectothrix*. If found both within and without (on the surface of) the hair, species are known as *neo-endothrix* or *ectoendothrix*.

For cultivation, potato and, better, Sabouraud's media are employed. Crater-like growths with fine marginal rays possessing often a yellowish color are produced. The spores or segments are always found in distinct mycelial filaments. Members of this genus cause ringworm of the hairy parts of the body, known also as *tinea tonsurans*, *herpes tonsurans* or *sycosis*. There are various, constant minor differences in many species which enabled workers to include several varieties under this genus.

The following produce endothrix infections: *T. acuminatum* (*T. sabouraudi*), *T. crateriforme* (*T. tonsurans*) and *T. violaceum*. These species infect man, producing ringworm of the scalp (*tinea capitis*), glabrous (smooth parts of) skin (*tinea circinata*) and nails (*onychomycosis*). The two important species producing ectoendothrix or neo-endothrix infection or ringworm of the scalp, beard and glabrous skin are *T. cerebriforme* and *T. plicatile*.

Species causing ectothrix infection are *T. gypseum* and its variants (*asteroides*, *farinulentum*, *lacticolor* and *persicolor*), all members of the *microides* group, so named because of the small-sized spores and *T. niveum* and its variants, the important one being *radians*, characterized by the production of a snowy white compact growth. *T. interdigitale* is most frequently found as the cause of athlete's foot on the Atlantic seaboard. Some workers regard this species as a variant of *T. gypseum*.

Emmons (*J. Bact.*, 1944, **47**, 107) directs attention to the fact that the name *Trichophyton rosaceum* is erroneously used for species of *Fusarium*, "a saprophytic fungus not etiologically related to dermatophytosis." Shaw and Von Gutfeld (*Virginia M. Monthly*, 1944, **71**, 256) report survival periods of the following fungi adherent to cotton strings: *Trichophytum gypseum* and *Microsporon lanosum* remained alive for 346 and 235 days, respectively, while the survival period for *M. audouini* was 276 days.

Weak solutions of free iodine and even vapors of iodine have been used successfully in the treatment of ringworm affections. Thallium salts, especially thallium acetate, practically every known antiseptic and x-rays have been used for tinea of the scalp. Sodium thiosulfate and hypochlorite (0.3 to 0.5 per cent) have been employed as remedies in the treatment and prevention of athlete's foot or ringworm of the feet. The use of "hypo" baths (10 to 15 per cent sodium thiosulfate solution) is a most useful prophylactic procedure in swimming pools and gymnasia. Individuals coming from the showers immerse both feet, to ankle height, in the solution present in a rubber, wood, enamel, tile or metallic container. Sprinkling the feet and footwear and floors of showers, locker rooms, etc., with a powder containing 20 per cent sodium thiosulfate in boric acid is also practiced. Recently propionic acid and propionates have been recommended for the treatment and prevention of athlete's foot. *Sopronol* is used as a powder (sodium propionate 10%, and urea 5%), an ointment (sodium propionate 10%) and as a liquid (sodium propionate 8.2%; propionic acid 1.8%; urea 5%; and *n*-propyl alcohol 25%). Quaternary ammonium compounds are also being used.

Mention may be made here that *herpes tonsurans* is a condition different from *herpes simplex* (cold sores) and *herpes zoster* (*shingles*). The latter two are affections of man due probably to filterable viruses.

Achorion.—Fungi in this genus are closely related to members of the genera *trichophyton* and *microsporum*. The mycelial segments developing among members of this group are usually longer than those of members of the latter two genera. Organisms of this genus are responsible for the affection known as *favus*. The disease, which chiefly affects the hairy scalp, may invade the nails and even the body. In favus a minute, dry, yellowish honeycomb-like incrustation or scab (known as a scutulum or favus cup) develops around the hair, at the mouth of the follicle. Favus is not as contagious as ringworm. Microscopically, the organisms show great irregularity of spores and mycelium; the hyphae, varying in thickness and length, appear wavy instead of straight as in genus trichophyton. They are frequently branching and dense, appearing as a feltlike mat. Members of this genus grow more slowly than the ringworm fungi, though they liquefy gelatin more rapidly. Some investigators regard this infection (favus) as due to a single highly pleomorphic fungus. Others recognize several distinct species (about nine varieties).

Achorion Schoenleinii (*Oidium Schoenleinii; Oospora Porriginis*).—This is the common etiological factor in favus of man and capable of producing this disease in other animals, especially cats. The scalp and occasionally the nails are affected.

Achorion Gallinae (*Lophophyton Gallinarum; Epidermophyton Gallinarum*).— *Achorion gallinarum* is commonly found as the cause of favus in chickens. Its growth, which develops more slowly on artificial media than some of the other species, is characterized by the production of a bright red color.

Achorion Quinckeanum.—This causes favus in house mice and is readily transmitted to man.

Achorion gypseum, named by some workers *Microsporum fulvum* or *gypseum*, is the cause of dog favus, and children may become infected.

Endodermophyton.—Species of the genera *Epidermophyton* and *Endodermophyton* do not attack the hairs. The characteristics of the fungi of this latter genus are the production of a mycelial network at the superficial epidermal layers of the skin. In cultures mycelial filaments alone are produced and conidia are not observed. The important species are *Endodermophyton concentricum* and *Endodermophyton indicum* obtained from scales of *tinea imbricata*, an important tropical ringworm. The former species in particular is considered as the causative agent of *tinea imbricata, a widespread mycosis* in the eastern tropical countries.

Epidermophyton.—Species of this genus are commonly found in temperate and tropical regions, producing eczema-like affections of the hands and feet. The genus differs from trichophyton in that when causing disease the hair or hair follicles are never invaded.

Epidermophyton Inguinale (*Epidermophyton or Tinea Cruris; Trichophyton Cruris*). —A ringworm fungus, producing eczema-like lesions of volar surfaces in man, is seen as long interlacing filaments made up of oval or oblong cells, with double contours. Conidia are not observed, but many blunt fuseaux are borne on aerial hyphae. In a disease known as *dhobie itch* or *washerman's itch,* an affection probably better known in Europe and other areas than any other tropical skin disease, this fungus is most frequently found. It is worse during hot, damp weather and may be responsible for considerable suffering. This species is one of the group of related fungi (*E. inguinale, T. gypseum, T. interdigitale* and *T. purpureum*) producing dermatophytosis, the general ringworm disease, which usually affects intertriginous positions, producing tinea axillaris in the axillae, tinea cruris in the groin, and athlete's foot or ringworm of the toes. The last two species named are included by some workers in the genus *epidermophyton.* In addition to this species, *Epidermophyton perneti* and *Epidermophyton rubrum* have been observed.

Molds

In the next important subgroup of ascomycetes there is to be considered the blue and green molds. These belong to a family in which the asci are frequently completely inclosed by a receptacle or investing membrane, the *perithecium.* The two genera of importance are *penicillium* and *aspergillus.* In *penicillium* vertical branches with strings or chains of conidia are found, the entire structure frequently resembling a broom. (The conidia form the loose green powder characteristic of *penicillium.*) In *aspergillus* the conidiophores are not septated and the upper portion of the latter (from which the conidia arise) is globular.

Penicillium.—Though members of this genus may at times form perithecia, chains of spores are characteristically observed. Most of the organisms of this genus live a saprophytic existence. They are chiefly of interest to the bacteriologist because they (the commonly found species is *Penicillium glaucum*) frequently appear as contaminants in the laboratory, being capable of invading cotton plugs, penetrating and even growing through these into the culture medium or contents. A number of species of *penicillium* are useful in the industries. *Penicillium roqueforti* is employed as the principal ripening agent in Roquefort and other commercially marketed cheeses and *Penicillium camemberti* in the ripening of Camembert cheese. *Penicillium brevicaule* has been recommended for the detection of arsenic. In the presence of the latter it produces diethylarsine. *Penicillium crustaceum,* the common blue-green mold, has been found occasionally as the cause of chronic catarrh of the Eustachian tube and in gastric hyperacidity. *Penicillium montoyai* (*Penicillium pictor*) causes the grayish-violet type of pinta (see also below). Certain strains of *Penicillium notatum* and of other species are responsible for the production of penicillin (see page 337).

Aspergillus.—The fruiting hyphae of most members of this genus are not ramified, but terminate in oval or globular heads from which a number of branches bearing conidia (and known as sterigmata) project in all directions. Under certain conditions perithecia are produced. The conidia are usually colored. These species are saprophytes and, being air-borne, are frequently found as contaminants. Caution is necessary in incriminating species of *penicillium, aspergillus,* and other contaminants as being the etiological factors in various diseases and infections.

Aspergillus Oryzae.—*Aspergillus oryzae* secretes diastase and, due to the presence of this valuable digestive ferment, this fungus is employed in the production and manufacture of various preparations, used extensively especially in Japan. Some species are pathogenic. When found as disease producers (*aspergillosis*) they commonly produce a mycotic pneumonia.

Aspergillus Fumigatus.—This is most commonly found producing pulmonary mycosis (mycotic pneumonia or pneumomycosis) in birds, horses, cattle and other animals. Man may become infected.

Aspergillus Niger (Aspergillus Nigricians; Monilia Pulla).—*Aspergillus niger*, a common saprophyte, affects corks, imparting a disagreeable taste to bottled beverages. It may produce occasionally affections of the ear and rarely of the lungs in human beings. It has brown or black conidia.

Aspergillus Repens and Aspergillus Flavus.—These also have been found in affections of the ear.

Aspergillus Pictor (Trichophyton Pictor).—This species has been reported by some workers as the cause of a skin affection (known as pinta or caraate) found in Central America. It produces the pure violet pinta.

FUNGI IMPERFECTI (DEUTEROMYCETES OR IMPERFECT FUNGI)

The term *hyphomycetes* is used by some observers synonymously with the term eumycetes (true fungi). The former term is, however, used more frequently by workers as a general heading which comprises the imperfect fungi. This class includes an assemblage of many and varied forms of organisms, the life histories of which are imperfectly understood or not definitely known. Under some systems of classification most of the fungi which have definitely been shown to cause disease are placed in this group. The following important genera and species are given:

Genus Monilia (Oïdium)

Species of this genus usually possess very simple sporophores. Yeastlike cells showing evidence of budding and mycelial threads are observed. Some workers consider this genus the same as *endomyces* (a genus grouped under the *ascomycetes*), though others separate the two genera due to the fact that members of the latter genus show asci and internal spores, which are not observed among the members of the genus *oidium*.

Monilia Albicans (*Oidium Albicans; Saccharomyces* or *Endomyces Albicans; Monilia Candida*).—This fungus is observed as a mass of simple or branched mycelial filaments of various sizes, at the ends of which or lying free oval yeastlike cells with or without buds are found. Growth on the commonly found media is obtained readily. Profuse growth is obtained on media of an acid reaction. Potato medium and especially turnip medium (made like potato) yield a rapid growth. The characteristic "inverted pine trees" is produced in gelatin stabs. Corn meal agar is ideal for showing the branching mycelium, globular masses of spores and chlamydospores. This organism is the cause of *thrush* or *mycotic stomatitis* (a localized disease of the mouth, occurring most frequently in young children, infants and the aged, who generally are found to possess a low vitality). Its occurrence in nursing infants is attributed to the improper cleansing of the nipples. It is probable that infection of the upper digestive and respiratory tracts, as well as the skin, may be due to this organism. Adults and lower animals are occasionally attacked. In rare cases, this organism may cause a mycosis in the vaginal tract, especially of pregnant women. Sodium perborate, mercurials and 1 per cent aqueous gentian violet are used in treatment. Turner (*Med. J. Australia*, 1942, **1**, 628) advises treating thrush with diluted hydrogen peroxide. He warns against the use of borax in the treatment of thrush in infants, since it has been shown that the continued administration of small quantities of borax caused serious disturbances of health.

An organism, formerly known as *M. psilosis*, but now regarded the same as *M. albicans*, has been found constantly present in the mouths and in the feces of patients suffering from *sprue*. It is recognized by some workers as the cause of this disease, which occurs in the tropics and is characterized by a catarrhal inflammation of the alimentary canal. Peculiar ulcerative lesions are present in the mouth and on the tongue. There is a progressive wasting and anemia and the stools, which are frequent, are pale and frothy. Other observers hold that this fungus becomes implanted in a weakened system causing *sprue*, which originates as a food-deficiency disease, though Ashford, who reported on this affection, does not hold this view. This worker is convinced that *M. albicans* is the cause of sprue, a disease which he found in Puerto Rico to be far more common and more fatal among American residents than tuberculosis.

Two cases of acute pulmonary moniliasis, confirmed by positive blood cultures, were recently reported by Hamkin (*Connecticut M. J.*, 1942, **6**, 264). Other workers have incriminated different yeastlike species as etiological factors. *Oidium pulmoneum* (*Monilia* or *Oospora pulmonea*; *Mycoderma* or *Geotrichum pulmoneum*) has been isolated from cases of a tuberculosis-like disease affecting the lungs as well as from a cutaneous mycosis simulating blastomycosis. In tissue, budding and mycelium are observed. In cultures as with all species of *Oidium*, yeast cells are not produced. *Oidium brasiliense* is the cause of a pulmonary disease occurring in Brazil, in which the symptoms are practically identical with tuberculosis.

Genus Sporotrichum

Members of this genus possess an irregular septate mycelium (slender, branching hyphae, about 1 μ thick), and they reproduce through the development of true conidia. True conidiophores are absent, and the conidia are formed at the sides and end of the hyphae. They grow readily on the ordinary media (best when slightly acid). Careful examination of material from lesions will reveal the presence of yeastlike forms only, and these generally sparingly. Mycelial growth, as found in cultures, is not found here. The important species are *Sporotrichum schencki* and *Sporotrichum beurmanni*, the latter being pathogenic for rats and mice, while the former possesses little or no pathogenicity for these animals. Both of these are, however, considered now by many observers as one species. *Sporotrichum schencki* shows the characteristics peculiar to this genus. It is the most common cause of human sporotrichosis, a chronic affection, characterized by the formation of gummatous-like swellings which are limited to the skin, the subcutaneous tissues and lymphatics. The lesions have been mistaken for tuberculous and syphilitic lesions, which they closely resemble. This or closely allied species are capable of producing lymphangitis in horses.

Horses, dogs, cats, rats and rabbits are also spontaneously affected by members of this genus. Many species are saprophytes, found on all types of vegetation, and it is possible that the latter serve as intermediary hosts at the site of a local injury. An agglutination test, using spores as the antigen, is of value as a diagnostic aid. Dilutions of the patient's serum, 1:200 to 1:800, giving positive agglutination, are useful in differential diagnosis. The use of iodides internally and iodine externally has given satisfactory results in treatment.

Malassezia Furfur (Microsporon Furfur)

Malassezia furfur is a fungus characterized by a profusion of mycelial threads, interspersed by large (3 to 8 μ in diameter), coarse, doubly contoured, round spores occurring in groups or clusters. Growth on culture media is obtained with difficulty. This fungus differs from the various species of favus and trichophyton in being semi-saprophytic. It invades only the most superficial layers of the skin, but does not produce marked pathogenic lesions. The vegetative elements of this fungus is much more numerous in the affected portions than is the case with the more parasitic species, yet the infection is not nearly so contagious as those diseases caused by the latter. In spite of this slight contagiousness, the dermatomycosis caused by this fungus is found very frequently, especially in the tropical and semitropical countries. This is, perhaps, due to the fact that the spores of this organism are widely distributed and many individuals are susceptible and easily infected. The dry, scaly skin eruption (which appears usually on the covered parts of the body) or dermatomycosis caused by *Malassezia furfur* is most frequently known as tinea versicolor or pityriasis.

Pityrosporum Ovale

Pityrosporum Ovale (*Pityrosporum Malassezi; Saccharomyces Ovalis; "bottle bacillus"*).—This is an ovoid, spherical or flask-shaped cell, with or without budding, Gram-positive, and varying in diameter from 2 to 10 μ. This organism is found mainly on the skin of man in the sebaceous glands and especially in great numbers in seborrhoeic dermatitis, but it is doubtful whether it causes the latter condition. It is probably the same species found in dandruff scales.

Actinomyces Minutissimus (Microsporon, Sporothrix or Nocardia Minutissimum)

Actinomyces minutissimus appears as minute twisted threads, 0.6 to 1.3 μ in diameter, possessing a narrow mycelium and small spores. The fungus cannot be cultured or only with difficulty. It is semisaprophytic and is generally considered as the cause of erythrasma, a superficial infection of the epidermis, appearing as round scaling patches which are red (though there is no inflammation) The latter are usually located in the axillae or groins. Due to the intolerable itching and scratching which results, the affection may spread along the inner surface of the thighs and other areas. The disease is common in the tropics, and the organism is found frequently in association with *M. furfur*. Applications of a 10 per cent solution of sodium hyposulfite are usually effective.

Chapter XIV

BACTERIA IN COMMERCE AND IN THE INDUSTRIES

INASMUCH AS disease-producing bacteria were studied with greater care and received the major attention of scientists at the beginning of the present-day bacteriological study, the general opinion soon prevailed that bacteria are harmful or objectionable, and are undesirable invaders. This is far from the actual fact. The useful bacteria are present in greater numbers, but the average individual does not come in contact with them, or is not familiar with the preparation of the many useful articles that are directly or indirectly the result of bacterial activity. The role of bacteria in commerce and in the industries is receiving more and more attention. Some of the applications of bacteria in various industries and pursuits have or will be touched upon in the different chapters. Space prevents a lengthy consideration of this subject. There are, however, several bacterial preparations which are used as medicinal agents. There are some important industries and pursuits, which are, in part or altogether, bacterial processes, or which depend upon the proper application of bacterial methods. These will be considered briefly.

SOIL BACTERIA

Bacteria are plentiful in the soil. Their numbers here depend upon several factors. Many of them are only accidentally present, due to contamination from the outside. Others and usually the majority of bacteria contained in soil pass their entire lifecycle chiefly or wholly in this environment, and are thus characterized as soil bacteria. Many of these varieties, some higher forms and fungi, which are normal soil inhabitants, fulfill definite functions, which most frequently are concerned with the continuance of the earth's food supply.

Nitrogen Fixation by Bacteria.—Nitrogen enters into the composition of all living matter. The constant withdrawal of nitrogenous substances from the soil by the plants would soon lead not only to a reduction, but to a complete absence of this element unless certain forces were replenishing the supply. Bacteria are supplied with the important function of constantly replenishing the nitrogen, and supplying this in a suitable form to be utilized by the plants. The nitrogen, which is supplied by bacteria, comes from one or two sources, either from the free nitrogen in the air, or from nitrogenous substances which are present in the soil, finding their way in there from animal excreta, decayed vegetable and animal matter, but are in a form which cannot be utilized by the plant. Bacteria change this nitrogenous matter into nitrogen compounds which can be assimilated by the plant.

There are bacteria in soil which possess the property of assimilating or fixing large quantities of atmospheric nitrogen. Most of these nitrogen fixers are aerobes, which function best between the temperatures of 50° to 104° F. Many factors other than temperature govern nitrogen fixation by these organisms. The pH and calcium, phosphorus, oxidizable carbon, iron and other (base) contents are important as influencing nitrogen fixation. The nitrogen-fixing organism first isolated is an anaerobe named *Clostridium pastorianum*. This is regarded by some as a strain of the butyric acid bacillus (*Bacillus amylobacter* or *Clostridium butyricum*). Other organisms have been found in normal soil which possess this property of nitrogen fixation. Many of them are aerobes, appearing as cocci, more often as large rods, and at times almost yeastlike in appearance, and are placed in the genus *azobacter*. The important species are: *A. chroococcum*, a motile chromogen (brown to black) which will not grow in peptone media and is found predominantly in soil and is world-wide in distribution; *A. agile*, a motile (and occasionally nonmotile) chromogen (soluble bluish-green pigment), found in water, showing occasional fluorescence and capable of growing in peptone-dextrose media; *A. vinelandii* and *A. beijerincki*. These four species fix nitrogen in a slightly alkaline environment. *A. indicum*, isolated by Starkey (*Science*, 1939, **89**, 267), fixes nitrogen in an acid environment. Two common molds frequently present, *Penicillium glaucum* and *Aspergillus niger*, and some of the commonly found spore-bearing aerobes possess, to a slight degree, this property of fixing the nitrogen of the air. For utilization of fixed nitrogen by species of *Azobacter*, see Horner and Allison (*J. Bact.*, 1944, **47**, 1).

Nitrogen Fixation by Nodule Bacteria.—For centuries farmers, the world over, found that legumes increase the productivity of the soil. Within recent days, it was found that the specific legumes and plants which augment the nitrogen content of the soil were those which had on their roots small knobs or nodule-like swellings, known as root tubercles or nodules. Wigand (1887) found that these tubercles contained bacteria. Hellriegel and Wilfarth (1888) demonstrated the relation between nodule formation and nitrogen fixation, and Beijerinck (*Bot. Ztg.*, 1888, **46**, 725, 741, 758, 782, 797) isolated them in pure culture. Many regard the tubercle as the result of bacterial action. The bacteria that are found associated with all tubercles possess certain constant characteristics. They have been known as *Bacillus* or *Pseudomonas radicicola*. The specific species isolated are now grouped under the genus *rhizobium*. The nodule bacteria are small, Gram-negative, motile rods, forming involution and branching forms as they grow older. They are obligate aerobes, growing best at 25° C. and several different related species or varieties are recognized. The varieties have been placed into two groups or species by some workers due to differences in immunological reactions, in that strains in the two groups infect different species of leguminous plants. Accordingly *Rhizobium leguminosarum* and *R. radicicola* are at times designated as separate species, though other workers regard them as varieties or strains of the same species. These bacteria present in the nodules on the plant make it possible for the legume to utilize atmospheric nitrogen. Only legumes which have these root tubercles or nodules (the habitat of these nitrogen fixers) are capable of fixing atmospheric nitrogen. Some of the common plants containing nodules are the lima bean, velvet bean, garden, navy and kidney beans, pea, peanut, cowpeas, partridge pea, soybean, alfalfa, sweet clover, red, crimson or white clover, trefoil and lupine. The tubercles or nodules of the *leguminosae* (pea or bean family) have been studied more carefully, but there are plants of other families that are also endowed with nodules. The latter apparently sustain the same relationship to the plant as observed with the leguminous nodules, and thus they can utilize the nitrogen from the air. The roots of members of the *myricaceae* (or bayberry family) and some species of the birthwort family, of the alders, and spruces are characterized by the appearance upon them of these nodules.

The exact relationship between plant and bacterium, as to whether the bacteria infect the plant producing an abnormality (nodules or tubercles), or whether the plant actually becomes a parasite upon the bacteria deriving the greater benefit from the relationship, is not definitely known. What we can see though is that there is a symbiotic relationship, and apparently of mutual benefit. The bacteria in the nodules obtain their food from the plant juices and in turn give the plant the nitrogen. The latter is obtained from the air and changed by the bacteria into a suitable nitrogen-bearing substance which can be utilized by the plant. In the Bergey classification, the following species of *Rhizobium* are recognized: *R. leguminosarum* (found in root nodules on *Lathyrus*, *Pisum* (pea), *Vicia* (vetch), and *Lens* (lentil)); *R. phaseoli* (found in root nodules on *Phaseolus vulgaris* (kidney bean), *P. angustifolius* (bean), and *P. multiflorus* (scarlet runner)); *R. trifolii* (on root nodules of species of *Trifolium* (clover)); *R. lupini* (on root nodules on *Lupinus* (lupine), *Serradella* and *Ornithopus*); *R. japonicum* (root nodules on *Soja max* (soy bean)); and *R. meliloti* (root nodules of *Melilotus* (sweet clover), *Medicago* and *Trigonella*). Virtanen and associates (*Nature*, 1938, **142**, 165) have recently introduced data which present a better understanding of the mechanism of the fixation of nitrogen by *Rhizobium*. Allison and associates (*Bot. Gaz.*, 1937, **98**, 433) report that the blue-green alga *Nostoc* also was capable of fixing atmospheric nitrogen.

Inoculation of Soil with Bacteria.—Many attempts have been made to enrich soil with nitrogen-fixing substances, so as to obtain fertile soil. Ordinarily bacteria present in the soil exert both positive and negative influences. The agriculturist attempts to treat the soil so as to reduce to a minimum the negative effects and raise to a maximum the positive effects of the microbiological activities present. Inoculation with *Rhizobium radicicola* is widely known and practiced. Success is only possible when these nitrogen-fixing bacteria are properly inoculated. It must be remembered that these bacteria do not persist in a soil indefinitely. Usually they disappear or decrease markedly within three years from a soil free from legumes.

Ammonification and Nitrification.—Bacteria in the soil are constantly decomposing organic nitrogenous substances so that they may obtain nourishment for themselves. It is only incidental that some of these decomposition products serve as food for higher plants.

The decomposition of nitrogenous substances by biological agencies with the production of ammonia is known as *ammonification*. Numerous bacteria, especially the Gram-positive aerobic spore-bearing rods of the *B. subtilis* group, and soil fungi play a prominent part in this process. From the agricultural standpoint, the process of ammonification is one which assists in making available food for plants. Ammonia and its compounds are not assimilated to any extent by plants, but as soon as these are produced, they are changed into nitrates and thus rendered utilizable by plants. This, a process of oxidation, and known as *nitrification*, is brought about by bacterial activities and accomplished in two steps. The ammonia compounds are oxidized or transformed first into nitrites and then into nitrates.

The nitrite-forming bacteria (four species are listed in Bergey's classification) are members of the genus *nitrosomonas*. The nitrite-forming bacteria (six species are listed) are at present grouped in the genus *nitrobacter*. These nitrifying organisms are widely distributed in soil and they occupy a unique position in relation to the bacterial kingdom and the higher forms of plant life. They are capable of growing and developing upon inorganic material solely. Though they do not possess chlorophyll, they seem capable of utilizing atmospheric carbon dioxide without the aid of sunlight, which they probably use for their carbon supply. Bacteria which possess the power of assimilating carbon dioxide in the absence of sunlight are known as *autotrophic* bacteria. The nitrifying bacteria, members of the *carboxydomonas* and certain sulfur bacteria are the only true autotrophic bacteria.

Denitrification.—Bacteria are normally present in the soil which under certain conditions are capable of reducing nitrates to nitrites and ammonia, nitrates and nitrites to oxides of nitrogen or the reduction may be complete with the production of free nitrogen, which is returned to the atmosphere. This process is known as *denitrification*. A rather large number of denitrifying bacteria have been described. These include many of the commonly known bacteria.

ROLE OF OTHER BACTERIA

Iron Bacteria.—Of interest to the geologist, chemist, etc., is a group of organisms living especially in swamps, stagnant and sewage-polluted and occasionally unpolluted fresh water, mud and soil, which possess the power of abstracting the iron and depositing this on the surface of their bodies, either in the sheath or in the protoplasm. These organisms are known as the *iron bacteria*. They are higher in the scale of evolutionary development than are the other bacteria mentioned in the previous chapters. They are filamentous, alga-like, with sheaths; and multiplication occurs usually by conidia. They are grouped in the following genera: *leptothrix*, *crenothrix*, *sphaerotilus* and *clonothrix*, all members of the Order *chlamydobacteriales* and *gallionella* of the Order *Caulobacteriales* (see Bergey classification). Some of the iron bacteria will grow in inorganic solutions containing ferrous carbonate, as in the case of the species *Gallionella ferruginea*. Other iron bacteria can live without iron, but when either organic or inorganic salts of the latter are present, a deposition of ferric hydroxide is produced. *Leptothrix ochracea* is an example of the latter group. There also are some species which attack only organic iron compounds, producing eventually deposits of ferric hydroxide.

There is no evidence that the iron bacteria are harmful but they may become a nuisance by attaching themselves to pipes in water mains, reservoirs, stone and woodwork, etc., and grow as long fine threads, eventually appearing as a mass of slimy material in which iron hydroxide is deposited. They may even clog up some pipes. Iron bacteria must have flourished in the water found in days of the past. There are all indications that they played an important part in the formation of iron deposits, many of which are being mined and used today. On this account these organisms are listed among the Useful Bacteria. For further details, see Dorff (*Pflanzenforschung*, 1934, Heft 16).

The Sulfur Bacteria.—Mention was made previously that some of these sulfur bacteria are autotrophic. This is in contrast with the iron bacteria, the hydrogen bacteria (*hydrogenomonas*) and the methane organisms (*methanomonas*) found in soil, which, while they possess the ability to secure their energy from simple compounds (the latter two genera by the oxidation of hydrogen and methane, respectively), they may also utilize complex organic matter to obtain their source of energy. The latter types are known as *heterotrophic bacteria*.

Sulfur, like nitrogen, is one of the important elements present in living matter. When organic matter decomposes, hydrogen sulfide is frequently one of the by-products. Many organisms are capable of reducing certain organic matter and even inorganic substances containing sulfur, producing hydrogen sulfide.

The "sulfur bacteria," however, are capable of oxidizing hydrogen sulfide to sulfuric acid. When this process is going on in soil, where these sulfur bacteria may be found, the acid produced acts upon the insoluble soil constituents, such as calcium and magnesium carbonate, calcium silicate and even tricalcium phosphate, making them soluble; and if appropriate conditions are present, many substances are thus made available for plant food. In fact, in certain soils, sulfur is added directly to the latter. This chemical is oxidized by the sulfur bacteria to sulfuric acid, which in turn renders certain plant food available, especially calcium and phosphorus. The sulfur bacteria are also found in sulfur springs, sulfur water, sea water, rivers, algal infusions, in sand, etc. For detailed characteristics, one can find the many species of sulfur bacteria grouped under the order *thiobacteriales*. Here are listed 3 families (*Rhodobacteriaceae, Beggiatoaceae, Achromatiaceae*), 2 subfamilies, 5 tribes, 32 genera and over 62 species. Most of these contain granules of free sulfur, or bacteriopurpurin (a red pigment) or both; and they usually grow best in the presence of hydrogen sulfide. Eight important autotrophic species are also to be found in the genus *thiobacillus* of the family *nitrobacteriaceae*.

Morphologically, some species of sulfur bacteria possess an appearance identical with the lower bacteria. Others are thread-forming filamentous forms and species of the family *Beggiatoaceae* resemble the blue-green alga *Oscillaria*. The purple and green sulfur bacteria possess a pigment which exercises a function similar to that of chlorophyll. They are dependent upon light for their maximum development. Valuable contributions have been presented by van Niel (*Cold Spring Harbor Symposia Quant. Biol.*, 1935, **3**, 138) demonstrating the photosynthetic activity of these purple and green sulfur bacteria. Sulfur bacteria are, at times, designated as *sulfide bacteria* if they derive their energy by oxidizing hydrogen sulfide to sulfur and *thionic or thiosulfate bacteria* if they derive their energy primarily through the decomposition of thiosulfate. *Thiobacillus thiooxidans* is the only species capable of oxidizing thiosulfate to sulfate and also elementary sulfur to sulfate.

Cellulose Bacteria.—Cellulose, a very resistant carbohydrate, is the essential constituent of the woody fiber of plants. Next to water, it is the most frequently found complex substance. Cellulose is insoluble in most solvents and resists the action of many powerful chemical reagents, but there are some snails, a few marine forms, fungi, and certain species of bacteria which are capable of decomposing or digesting this substance, through the agency of the enzyme *cellulase*. The genera *cytophaga, cellfalcicula, cellvibrio, clostridium, actinomyces* and other genera but especially *cellulomonas* contain many species. There are some 26 species belonging to the genus *cellulomonas*. They are mostly Gram-negative, aerobic, nonspore-forming, small rods, with rounded ends, isolated from soil, water and sewage.

In the soil, cellulose is to be found in large quantities in the residues of plants. Decomposition of cellulose by many of the cellulose bacteria results with the production of acids. The latter react with the insoluble minerals present in the soil and render them available as plant foods. In some instances, the decomposition of the cellulose and other organic matter especially by anaerobes may give rise to the production of carbon dioxide, hydrogen, methane, etc. A portion of these gases passes into the atmosphere. The remainder furnishes energy to some of the other soil bacteria which require these gases, such as the members of the *carboxydomonas*, *hydrogenomonas* and *methanomonas*. Cellulose bacteria are being used experimentally and in some instances in practice. Some investigators have attempted the synthetic production of manure by the use of these bacteria. Experimental work is being conducted in utilizing these ferments to decompose cellulose, producing an acetic-acid fermentation. The acid is then treated with chalk and the calcium acetate is separated. For further details, see Norman (*The Biochemistry of Cellulose*, 1937, New York City).

Pectin.—Pectins are closely related to cellulose and, as in the case of the latter, the term is a collective one used to designate a number of closely related chemical substances. Pectin fermenting organisms belong to the group of anaerobic soil bacteria and the amylobacter group which includes the butyric acid bacteria. They function through the agency of the ferment pectinase and play an important role in certain soft rots of plants, vegetables and fruits. The retting of flax depends upon the decomposition of the pectoses and pectins, which are present in the flax stem between the cellulose fibers. The dissolution of the pectin binders results in the separation of the fibers.

LACTIC-ACID BACTERIA, FERMENTED MILKS, AND MILK PRODUCTS

Milk will sour naturally. The fermentation which ensues results in the production of lactic acid due to the decomposition of the lactose. Many different species of bacteria are capable of producing this fermentation, but only a few species are responsible for the natural souring of milk and the subsequent production of lactic acid. The common lactic-acid bacilli are *Bacillus lactis* (*Aerobacter*) *aerogenes*, *Streptococcus lactis* or *cremoris* and *Lactobacillus bulgaricus*. The last three named organisms are more frequently found producing lactic-acid fermentation naturally.

There are other types of fermentation that may also take place spontaneously in milk. Alcoholic fermentation as a result of lactose fermenting yeasts is possible. In fact, kefir, koumyss, and other similar beverages, used for many years in the countries of eastern Europe and western Asia, possess the characteristic of both an alcoholic fermentation (caused by yeast), and a lactic-acid fermentation (caused by *Streptococcus lactis* or *Lactobacillus bulgaricus* or both). Butyric-acid fermentation and a variety of other fermentations which are of an abnormal character are met with in outbreaks of bitter milk. These are produced by various bacteria, especially by aerobic spore-bearing bacilli of the *subtilis-mesentericus* group.

The lactic-acid sour milk or buttermilks are of most interest, as in this case the sour end product is eagerly sought. In various parts of Europe and Asia these preparations have been in common use for many years. To control the general appearance and taste of the end product, the milk obtained from different animals is heated first and then a starter is added. "Koumyss," the most famous of all fermented milks, is prepared from heated mare's milk and to this is added some old or previously prepared koumyss. The fermentation is due to all three organisms: (1) *Streptococcus lactis;* (2) *Lactobacillus bulgaricus;* (3) a lactose-fermenting yeast. In addition to the lactic acid, the finished product contains from 1 to 2 per cent of alcohol and some carbon dioxide, which imparts an effervescence. *Kefir* is another fermented milk containing lactic acid and alcohol. *Leben* produced from the heated milk of cows, goats and buffaloes was and is used by the Arabs and Egyptians. In like manner other fermented milks are known in Europe, as *matzoon* in Armenia, *yoghurt* in Turkey and the Balkan states, etc.

Lactobacilli in Intestinal Disturbances.—A problem which has occupied investigators for many years is the function of the intestinal flora, intestinal disturbances and, in particular, intestinal putrefaction and gastro-intestinal autointoxication. Metchnikoff observed that Bulgarians, using fermented milks, appear to enjoy a somewhat long span of life. He concluded that the sour milk prevented putrefactive changes in the intestines, thus avoiding much illness and premature death. It became a common custom to advocate the use of fermented milk or buttermilk. This was soon replaced by feeding *Lactobacillus bulgaricus.* Liquid cultures of this organism are marketed and used. They are to be preferred to the tablets which are also available. Subsequent investigations showed that *L. bulgaricus* does not survive after ingestion, so that this organism cannot be and is not depended upon to change the bacterial flora of the intestinal tract. This led to the use of other bacteria, especially *Lactobacillus acidophilus.* The latter organism, normally an inhabitant in the intestinal tract, can become established here more readily. Various commercial preparations are available. Tablets (dry) of this organism are practically valueless, as they contain very few viable organisms, unless fresh. Even the liquid cultures, made from milk, milk whey or glucose bouillon, should be made freshly and used within a period of a few weeks. In acidophilus medication, broth cultures and concentrates are also employed. Among the latter are various candy-like preparations containing viable *L. acidophilus.*

The Role of Useful Bacteria in the Production of Milk Products

Among the milk products, sour cream, butter and cheese depend upon different bacteria for their production.

Butter.—The butter-making process consists in procuring clean milk of high quality, and separating the cream either by gravity or, still better, by centrifugal force, using the centrifugal separator. Before churning, the cream of proper richness (usually 30 per cent or more of fat) is allowed to "ripen." It has been shown that the changes taking place in the cream during this period are produced by the action of the bacteria originally present or introduced. At the end of the period of "ripening" the cream is thick and most frequently sour. There are different varieties of bacteria which participate in this process and determine to a large extent the quality of the end product. The important ones are probably different varieties of lactic-acid bacilli. In practice, preferably pure cultures of favorable bacteria or the so-called "starters" (a previously prepared batch of cream containing natural bacteria capable of producing the desirable qualities of ripening) are added to the pasteurized cream and the latter is allowed to "ripen." By this means it becomes possible to control those forms of fermentation which, otherwise, due to the presence of contaminating bacteria, would result in the production of the "souring" or "bittering" of butter and the production of undesirable flavors.

The pure cultures which are used by some manufacturers as the "starters" vary in different establishments. All are harmless, lactic-acid-producing bacteria. Many are nondisease-producing streptococci, apparently identical or closely associated with *Streptococcus lactis*. In butter cultures of high quality, associated organisms are present. The most common ones are *Streptococcus paracitrovorus* and *Streptococcus citrovorus*. Both of these organisms (nondisease-producing bacteria) produce volatile acid from lactic acid. It seems also important to control the conditions under which the best results are obtained with these cultures.

Cheese.—Cheese consists principally of the curd and fat removed in a mass from milk, which has been curdled by the action of rennet or by the natural souring of the milk. The conversion of milk products into cheese depends upon the action of enzymes and bacteria on the protein present. The enzymes involved are pepsin and galactase, while various lactic-acid-producing bacteria, as the *lactobacilli* and *Streptococcus lactis* also play a part. The cheese flavors are determined largely by the end products produced in such protein decomposition, which in turn are influenced by the bacteria present and the cultural conditions prevailing.

YEAST AND FERMENTATION

The yeasts which are commonly used or found in the fermentative industries are designated: (a) *Saccharomyces cerevisiae;* (b) *Saccharomyces ellipsoideus,* found naturally on grapes and used in wine making (they are also known by some as wild yeasts); and (c) *Torrula* or false yeasts; these are undesirable invaders, causing disagreeable tastes and unpleasant flavors, producing what is commonly known as diseases of beer and wines.

The *Saccharomyces cerevisiae*, either the top or bottom yeasts of beer or distiller's yeast, are more generally used. The latter is comparatively pure and is marketed as liquid, compressed or dried yeast. The compressed yeast usually mixed with flour or some starchy material is cut into small cakes, wrapped in tin foil, and kept cold until used. If properly prepared and kept, the organisms will remain viable for long periods of time. These so-called "yeast cakes" are also employed in bacteriotherapy. As therapeutic agents, they are said to be of value in some types of intestinal putrefaction. They are also said to act as a food, aiding digestion, and producing a natural laxative effect. For a consideration of yeasts, see page 207.

Bread Making.—The main biological leavening agent used in bread making today is yeast. The carbon dioxide which is produced, and in this instance is the desired product of fermentation (and not the alcohol), gives porosity to the bread. Not only are some of the starches changed by the action of diastase and yeast, but even the proteins in the flour are made more digestible. Flavors and aromas characteristic of the various flours are also produced.

Bacteria may serve as leavening agents. *E. coli* and *Cl. welchii* function in this capacity, though they find little use in practice in this country as starters. It is of interest to note that various kinds of objectionable fermentations may occur. *Ropy* and *slimy* breads are caused by the contamination with spore-forming bacilli of the *subtilis-mesentericus* group. See page 309, and for other data on rope and the estimation of rope spores, see Barton-Wright (*J. Soc. Chem. Ind.*, 1943, **62**, 33). Other undesirable bacteria may outgrow the yeast producing sour bread, and contamination with mold spores will produce moldy bread.

Wines, Beer and Alcoholic Fermentation.—Alcoholic fermentation may be induced in almost any kind of saccharine fruit juices resulting in the production of alcoholic beverages known as wines. The taste, odor, flavor, etc., of these preparations can be and are controlled by inoculating the juices with yeasts, and not depending upon the yeasts in the air to produce the fermentation. Not knowing which types of yeasts are in the immediate environment, one could not depend upon obtaining a uniform product at all times.

Starches are converted into dextrose. Saccharose is changed by yeast ferments to dextrose and levulose. The monosaccharides, dextrose and levulose are fermented by yeast with the production of alcohol and carbon dioxide. Any material containing from 12 to 15 per cent sugar, whether a fruit juice, malt or grain extract, diluted molasses, etc., is suitable for the starting point in alcoholic fermentation. The strains of yeast added are those responsible for high yields of alcohol and for the production of traces of other chemicals, which support the characteristic odor, taste, flavor and aroma (so-called bouquet). In some of the fermented alcoholic beverages, the fermentation is stopped before completion; in other instances, it is allowed to continue until all of the carbohydrate has been decomposed. When the alcoholic content during fermentation reaches 13 per cent, the fermentation process frequently stops. The distilled product of these vinous liquors forms the different spirits of commerce. Thus we have brandy (obtained from wine), whiskey (obtained from distillation of various grains), arrack (from fermented rice), rum (from fermented molasses), etc. Alcohol (ethyl) is made by distilling a crude grain spirit or molasses and redistilling and rectifying the distillate.

BACTERIAL FERMENTATIONS AND OTHER PRODUCTS

Vinegar and Acetic Acid.—The first step in vinegar production is to produce or make a weak (preferably 10 per cent or less) alcoholic solution. Wine, cider or a similar alcoholic liquid will be satisfactory. The alcohol is then oxidized into acetic acid. This oxidation can be effected by a purely chemical process. When vinegar is produced naturally, the aceti microorganisms are depended upon to produce the acetic acid from the alcohol. In the home, the "mother of vinegar," which is a slimy mass containing species of *acetobacter* (*A. aceti, A. xylinum, A. pasteurianum*, and especially *Acetobacter aceti* (*Mycoderma aceti*)), soon forms from these organisms present from the air. This mother of vinegar can be used as a starter for other batches. On a commercial scale, the same principle is applied, but the fermenting mixtures are supplied with various devices which permit the entrance of plenty of oxygen, so as to hasten the oxidation. The Quick or "German" and the Orleans methods are the processes used on a large scale. Pure cultures of *acetobacter* species are also used and appear to produce a better vinegar. The species of *acetobacter* are small, rod-shaped bacteria, occurring frequently in chains, and elongated, filamentous, club-shaped, swollen and even branched forms may appear as involution forms. As obligate aerobes, they are found on the surface of alcoholic solutions, securing growth energy by oxidizing the latter to acetic acid. The difference between the various species is, at times, slight and due frequently to the fact that the respective habitats, whether wine, beer, beer wort, other fermenting mash or vinegar are responsible for such changes. For further details, see Butlin (*The Biochemical Activities of the Acetic Acid Bacteria*, Chem. Research Spec. Rpt. 2, H. M. Stationery Office, London, 1936).

Though acetic acid is an important product of the hard wood destructive distillation industry, it can and is also produced by distilling vinegar. The commercial vinegars contain from 4 to 7 per cent acetic acid.

Lactic Acid.—Lactic acid is obtainable by various synthetic processes. It is also obtainable by the lactic fermentation of sugar. Numerous organisms are capable of converting sugar into lactic acid. The two main types of bacteria producing lactic acid are:

1. The *Lactobacilli*, including the following species: *L. leichmanni, L. delbrucki, L. acidophilus, L. casei, L. bulgaricus.*
2. *Streptococcus lactis.*

L. leichmanni and *L. bulgaricus* are used by themselves. *L. delbrucki* is used in conjuction with *L. bulgaricus* or *S. lactis*. When *Lactobacilli* are used, the temperature should be near 50° C. When *L. bulgaricus*, however, is used, the temperature of incubation should be 40° C. *S. lactis* is most suitable when whey is used as the raw material and the temperature should be 25° C. *L. delbrucki* cannot be used with whey, inasmuch as it does not ferment lactose. It does ferment dextrose, levulose, galactose, maltose, sucrose and dextrin, producing levo-lactic acid.

Acetone, Butyl and Isopropyl Alcohols.—There are manufacturers who produce acetone by fermenting a saccharine fluid, usually a diluted molasses, allowing the alcoholic fermentation to continue, wherein acetic acid is produced. To the mixture is added some milk of lime and the calcium acetate is obtained. The dry calcium acetate upon distillation yields acetone. In other processes, organisms, especially anaerobes as the *Bacillus granulobacter pectinovorum* (same as *Clostridium acetobutylicum*), are inoculated in a starch or corn-meal mash, the fermentation yielding acetone and normal butyl alcohol. Morikawa and Prescott inoculated *Bacillus technicus* in a rice mash which has undergone hydrolysis by the action of enzymes produced by *Aspergillus oryzae*. Gaughran and Thomas (*J. Bact.*, 1942, **43**, 37) state that 75 species of butyl-butyric anaerobes have been described. They studied 9 different species and concluded that any differentiation of the bacilli of the butyl-butyric group on the basis of morphology is impossible. In the early processes, various organisms as the butyl bacillus of Fitz, *Bacillus mascerans*, *Granulobacter pectinovorum* and *Clostridium acetobutylicum* were described and used in the manufacture. Recent studies and investigations, however, show that all these organisms which were usually incompletely described are either closely related or varieties of the same species, *Clostridium acetobutylicum*.

Clostridium acetobutylicum is a Gram-positive rod, 2 to 5 by 0.4 to 0.6 μ; ends rounded; and capsules are present in old glucose peptone cultures. It is anaerobic and motile. Subpolar endospores and sporangia are present in 5 per cent corn mash after forty-eight hours' incubation. In malt gelatin agar, polyhedral granular colonies are produced. It is nonpathogenic to rabbits and guinea pigs. While the organism is anaerobic, anaerobiosis is not absolutely necessary. It is viable for years in culture and very resistant to drying. *Clostridium acetobutylicum* will ferment: monosaccharides, disaccharides, polysaccharides and starches. Glucose, fructose, mannose, sucrose, lactose and starch are completely fermented with low acid production. Galactose, xylose, arabinose, raffinose, inulin, mannitol and melezitose are completely fermented with high acid production. Dextrin is incompletely fermented with partial decomposition of the product. Trehalose, rhamnose, melibiose and glycerol are not acted upon. In carbohydrate mixtures, the hexoses are completely removed before sucrose or lactose is acted upon. During fermentation, the organism secretes an enzyme or enzymes which hydrolyze starch to glucose. The latter passes into the cell and is oxidized to butyric and acetic acids. The acids are converted into butyl alcohol and acetone by reduction.

Butyric-acid Fermentation.—Many closely related anaerobic organisms, some of which are commonly observed, are capable of decomposing carbohydrates (and some even glycerin and lactic acid) with the production of butyric acid. Some of these species when producing the latter accompany the fermentation by the production of a disagreeable odor and flavor. This fermentation is objectionable and is frequently the cause of food spoilage.

Silage.—Silage (or ensilage) is a fermented product made in silos and used for cattle food. The silage produced in the almost one-half million silos in this country totals many millions of tons. Although corn is more extensively used, almost any farm product containing a sufficient quantity of sugar and a high water content can be siloed. Alcohols, acids and esters are produced, but lactic acid predominates in properly made silage, where organisms closely related to the *Lactobacillus bulgaricus* and *Lactobacillus acidophilus* are found in large numbers and many workers believe that these organisms are concerned in the curing process. Where the temperature produced in the process is too high, the butyric-acid organisms predominate and the finished product is apt to have an objectionable odor and taste. Molds develop only in the presence of oxygen; this will only occur if silage is not packed tight enough to exclude the air. For further details, see Nevens (Ill. Agr. Expt. Sta., 1936, *Circ.* **463**).

Cocoa and Chocolate.—Before the roasting of the beans of the cocoa tree, they are treated and allowed to undergo a process of fermentation, which removes a large amount of pulp and extraneous matter. It seems that yeast cells are concerned in this fermentation, which has a decided effect upon the taste, flavor and aroma.

Sauerkraut.—Lactic acid and other organic acids are produced in the fermentative process wherein shredded cabbage leaves are changed to sauerkraut, which is preserved by the lactic acid naturally produced. Acetic acid, alcohol, mannitol and carbon dioxide are also produced. The kind of cabbage and container, the temperature and the salt content influence the fermentative reaction. It is thought that species of *Leuconostoc*, primarily *Leuconostoc mesenteroides*, are responsible for starting and then the *lactic-acid bacteria* continue and complete this fermentative process. *L. plantarium* and *L. brevis* are found most frequently. With the increase of acidity, all bacterial growth eventually ceases. A product possessing an objectionable flavor and taste may result when putrefactive bacteria contaminate the sauerkraut and predominate. For the manufacture of a high-quality product, inoculation with pure cultures of desirable strains of bacteria is to be recommended. For further details, see Pederson (N. Y. State Agr. Expt. Sta., *Tech. Bull.* **168** (1930); **216** (1933) and *Bull.* **595** (1931); **613** and **614** (1932)).

Pickled Products.—Properly prepared immature cucumbers, beans, beets, onions aud other vegetables are pickled. These pickled vegetables are usually preserved in salt solution, with or without spices. They may be converted into sour pickled products by various processing methods. These vegetables develop characteristic flavors during aging which is due to fermentative changes caused by different bacteria. Fabian and associates discuss the types of microorganisms found in dill-pickle fermentation (Mich. Agr. Expt. Sta., *Tech. Bull.* **146**, 1935) and in the spoilage of pickles (*ibid.*, **157**, 1938).

In the production of pickled green olives, suitable varieties are selected. These are harvested, graded, treated with lye (1.6 per cent solution) to remove a portion of the bitter principle, washed with water to remove the alkali, placed in oak barrels for brining and fermentation and finally packaged. During brining and fermentation, care must be observed as yeasts and molds may develop and interfere with the flavor and keeping qualities. Cruess (*Fruit Products J.*, 1937, **17**, 12) advocates the introduction of pure cultures of species of *lactobacilli* as starters.

The Curing of Tobacco.—The texture and aroma of the tobacco leaves are markedly changed during the process of curing, which is a fermentative process due to bacterial activity and partly to the action of leaf enzymes. The bacteria most frequently found here are members of the genus *proteus*, *Bacillus subtilis*, *Bacillus mycoides* and closely related organisms. *Proteus vulgaris*, other Gram-negative rods, chromogenic bacilli, and, at other times cocci have been found predominating in some grades of tobacco. Marked differences are observed in the bacterial flora of good and poor quality tobacco; and experienced workers are capable of judging the quality of different kinds of tobacco by the bacteria associated with the latter. Species of the genus *Aspergillus* and other molds have been found. Various methods of improving inferior or ordinary tobacco so that it may resemble superior qualities are practiced. This consists mainly in inoculating the material with liquid cultures of one or more of several organisms which are isolated from tobacco of the finest quality.

Bacteria in Tanning.—The object of the tanning of hides is to treat the latter to prevent its decomposition but yet not to interfere with the property of being able to adapt it to the many purposes to which leather is put. In the making of leather from hides, the following steps are taken: (1) preservation (salting or curing); (2) disinfection (treatment with a disinfecting solution); (3) soaking and fleshing (removal of excess of tissue or flesh); (4) depilation (removal of the hair either by liming, sweating, use of acids, alkalies or enzymes or by carefully controlled bacterial decomposition); (5) bating (placing in a weak fermenting infusion of pigeon or fowl manure or a bran mash. If dog dung is used, the process is known as *purging*); (6) final tanning process (placing in the tan liquors). Bacterial processes play an important part in the finishing steps of preparing this product. For further details see Wilson (*Chemistry of Leather Manufacture*, 1939, New York City).

Retting of Flax and Hemp.—Flax raised for seed (which is pressed for the production of linseed oil) is of a different quality from that used for fiber. The latter produces less seed and is taller. It requires great care in cultivation and proper harvesting is very important. The fiber from hemp and flax is removed by a process of retting or rotting. This, a fermentation process, which is not allowed to last too long, dissolves the cementing substances known as pectins. The latter bind the bast fibers to the stock. In the water-retting of flax, the anaerobe *Granulobacter* *pectinovorum* (*Clostridium butyricum*) is said to accomplish the pectose fermentation. while the effects in the water-retting of hemp is attributed to the same anaerobe. Efforts to liberate the flax fiber by means of chemicals have not been successful. Pure cultures of pectose-fermenting bacteria in retting processes are, however, in use and the results are proving favorable.

Microbic Pest Exterminators.—There has been a tendency to attempt the extermination of agricultural pests, rats and other animal pests by inoculating food used as baits with virulent microorganisms, which will produce highly fatal and contagious diseases in these lower animals, but which will have no effect upon the food of humans and domestic animals. Most products of this character that are marketed have proved practically valueless. More experimental data are needed before such a procedure can be used effectively and without causing harm to anyone but the pests for which the preparation is used. The use of species of *Salmonella* in so-called *rat-virus* preparations or in *Ratin* with the thought of initiating an epidemic among rats and thus destroy them is to be condemned. There is always the danger involved that these viable organisms may infect man and pets around the home.

BACTERIA IN RELATION TO MISCELLANEOUS PRODUCTS AND INDUSTRIES

Bacteria of known origin are used today in research as an aid to identify individual sugars of unknown origin.

Bacterial processes undoubtedly play some role in the pulp and paper industry, but their exact status is not known. Evidence has accumulated to indicate that bacteria may have a marked effect on the keeping quality and behavior of rubber latex, textile fibers and wood. It is highly probable that cultures of bacteria may be used in the treatment of sewage, so as to increase the desired biological activity.

Citric acid is used medicinally, for the production of citrates, in the baking, confectionery, flavoring extract and soft drink industries, in calico printing, in dyeing, in engraving, in silvering and in the production of ink. Citric acid is produced on a commercial scale from cane sugar (saccharose) and technical glucose by the use of species of molds. Strains of *Aspergillus niger* are usually used though other species of *Aspergillus*, *Penicillium* and *Mucor* have been employed. For further details, see *Ind. Eng. Chem.*, 1934, **26**, 1142; 1935, **27**, 201; 1938, **30**, 255; 1939, **31**, 172.

Propionic acid is used in the manufacture of perfumes, as a solvent for pyroxylin and for the production of propionates (see page 308). There are many species of the genus *propionibacterium*. They are nonmotile, Gram-positive, nonspore-forming, catalase-positive, facultative aerobes. A large number of carbohydrates, including most of the common sugars, has been utilized for the fermentation. Different substances are required as the nitrogen source and as growth factors. The end products of propionic acid fermentation consist essentially of propionic and acetic acids in the ratio of 3 to 5 of propionic acid to 1 of acetic acid. For further details, see Werkman and associates (*J. Bact.*, 1933, **26**, 393; 1935, **30**, 652; 1937, **33**, 227; *Biochem. J.*, 1934, **28**, 745; 1936, **30**, 48, 618; 1938, **32**, 1262).

Kojic acid, first isolated as a by-product of the fermentation of steamed rice, can be produced by the fermentation of different carbohydrates by various species of *Aspergillus* and under favorable conditions, by several species of *Acetobacter*. The best yields are obtained from glucose and xylose. *A. glaucus* and *A. oryzae* are more frequently used. For further details, see Barham and associates (*Ind. Eng. Chem.*, 1936, **28,** 567; 1939 (*Anal. Ed.*), **11,** 31).

Gluconic acid in the form of calcium gluconate is widely used in medicine. Gluconic acid is produced by fermentation from glucose especially by species of *Acetobacter*, the acetic acid bacteria. Maltose and mannite can be used as the sugars and other organisms also have been employed. For further details, see Wells and associates (*Ind. Eng. Chem.*, 1937, **29,** 653), (*Chem. & Met. Eng.*, 1937, **44,** 188) and Porges and associates (*Ind. Eng. Chem.*, 1940, **32,** 107).

There are many different kinds of molds which are being used with many varieties of sugars in experimentations for the production of the following: gluconic, lactic, malic and oxalic acids, in addition to citric acid previously mentioned, fumaric acid (*Botan. Rev.*, 1938, **4,** 1938); mannitol (*J. Biol. Chem.*, 1932, **97,** 483); glycerol (*J. Ind. Eng. Chem.*, 1919, **11,** 842; 1937, **29,** 729); gallic acid (U. S. Dept. Agr., *Circ.* **216,** May, 1932); and for the production of various enzymes, vitamins and other substances. Leo and Burrie (*Ind. Eng. Chem., Ind. Ed.*, 1943, **35,** 354) recently considered the large-scale culturing of *Azobacter vinelandii* as a source of B complex vitamins, which was equal and at times superior to that found in yeast. There are many other possibilities in the practical utilization of bacteria in the arts and industries, and as additional experimentations are conducted, we will undoubtedly hear of many industrial processes in which bacteria will be found to play an important role.

Bacteria Attacking Petroleum and Other Products.—Various workers have pointed out, especially during the last fifteen years, that certain bacteria and molds are capable of attacking hydrocarbons and mineral oils. *Pseudomonas aeruginosa* and other species of *Pseudomonas*, species of *Achromobacter* and certain soil bacteria, described as *Radiobacter* or *Alcaligenes radiobacter*, have been implicated. For further details, see Stone and associates (*J. Bact.*, 1940, **39,** 91; 1942, **44,** 169), who consider organisms capable of attacking crude oil, lubricating oils, vaseline, asphalt and other petroleum fractions, producing an oxidative change characterized by emulsification and at times a decrease in the pH.

Cutting compounds circulating in machine shops have very high bacterial contents (10 to 50 millions per cubic centimeter). These bacteria in lubricating oil-water emulsions used in the cutting and grinding of metals are responsible for the development of objectionable odors in the compounds; they interfere with the emulsification of the mixture; and various skin infections among the workers are attributed to this bacterial contamination.

Lee and Chandler (*J. Bact.*, 1941, **41,** 373) discuss the nature, growth and control of these bacteria in cutting compounds and found that the addition of 1 per cent resorcinol was effective as a disinfectant. Gold and Weirich (*J. Bact.*, 1943, **45,** 37) also found species of *pseudomonas* occurring most frequently in a study of the normal bacterial flora of cutting oil compounds.

In the **canning industry,** different bacteria are encountered which are responsible for spoilage. *Clostridium thermosaccharolyticum* and *C. sporogenes* are two of the important spoilage organisms encountered. Stern (*J. Bact.*, 1942, **43,** 38) presents a comparative study of the growth of these bacteria in various anaerobic media.

Recently reports have been presented which indicate that bacteria and fungi play an important role in the deterioration of rubber and rubber products (both synthetic and natural). ZoBell and Grant (*Science*, 1942, **96**, 379) confirmed the findings of other workers, when they isolated species belonging to the genus *Actinomyces* or *Proactinomyces*. Rubber oxidizing bacteria belonging to the genera *Mycobacterium* and *Pseudomonas* were also found by them.

Chapter XV

THE RICKETTSIAE

THE *Rickettsiae* occupy a position intermediate between bacteria and viruses. As the latter, they depend on intracellular conditions. They also possess a more complex enzyme system than viruses. Accordingly they are capable of maintaining a certain degree of independent metabolic activity within the living cells of the host where they are clearly visible and can be studied with either dark or light field illumination. *Rickettsiae*, small bacterium-like coccoid short rods, live and reproduce only in anthropoid tissue, including lice, ticks, sand flies, mosquitoes, bugs, etc. They are often pleomorphic, stain poorly with aniline dyes and appear Gram-negative. Machiavello's basic fuchsin methylene blue stain (*J. Exp. Med.*, 1936, **64**, 673) is very suitable. They are nonmotile, nonencapsulated and usually nonfilterable.

Diseases caused by *Rickettsiae* are all transmitted by an insect (arthropod) vector. The infection is generally an acute one with symptoms of fever, headache, general aches, a cutaneous rash, and usually with nervous and mental symptoms. The etiological agent grows only in the cytoplasm of living cells and cannot be maintained like most pathogens on artificial media. The use of tissue culture methods and chick embryo inoculation is practiced. In man, usually the *Rickettsiae* live in the mesothelial cells of the vascular and reticulo-endothelial systems. The following are the important *Rickettsiae*: *R. prowazeki*, the cause of louse- and flea-borne diseases of the typhus group; *Dermacentroxemus rickettsi*, the cause of tick-borne diseases of the spotted-fever group; *R. tsutsugamushi* (*R. nipponica* or *orientalis*), the cause of mite-borne diseases of the tsutsugamushi or Japanese River fever group; and *R. ruminantium*, the cause of tick-borne "heartwater" disease in sheep, goats and cattle. The *R. wolhynica* (*R. quintana*) is probably the cause of the louse-borne disease of trench fever. *R. burneti* (*R. diaporica*) is the cause of the so-called *Q fever*. These diseases are dependent on the seasonal incidence, geographic distribution and life cycle of the vector. Accordingly tick-borne diseases (as spotted fever) occur in warm climates or during the warm season (spring and summer). Louse-borne typhus is more apt to be epidemic in cold climates or during the cold season (winter) when hygienic and sanitary standards are usually low. Flea-borne or murine typhus is confined to temperate regions, and though it may appear at any time, small epidemics occur more frequently during the summer. Infection with rickettsial diseases as with viruses generally confer a long lasting immunity.

For years as an aid in the diagnosis of rickettsial diseases in man, an agglutination test (the so-called Felix-Weil Reaction) has been used. In the latter the sera of infected patients yield positive agglutination with certain strains of *Proteus vulgaris* (especially OX-2, OX-19, and OX-K). The test is made just as the Widal test, preferably employing the macroscopic method, and using either dead or living organisms. The reaction is usually positive by the sixth day. The explanation of this reaction is doubtful. From our present knowledge of the causative agent of typhus fever, we may definitely assume that this is not a specific reaction, for the *proteus* organisms are not even secondary invaders in this disease. Possibly the reaction is a heterologous one. (See pages 139 and 235.) The relationship as Castaneda (*J. Exp. Med.*, 1935, **62, 289**) notes is perhaps a close antigenic relationship. With the exception of this possible common antigenic structure, the *Rickettsiae* and *Proteus vulgaris* possess nothing else in common. Pinkerton (*Parasitol.*, 1936, **28,** 453), in presenting some interesting data on the classification of the *Rickettsiae*, points out that in typhus fever, the agglutination titer to the OX-19 strain of *P. vulgaris* is usually high and low with the OX-K strain. The reverse is the case (low agglutination titer with OX-19 strain and high with OX-K strain) in tsutsugamuchi disease. In spotted fever cases, a low agglutination titer is generally observed with both strains. In mite-borne rickettsial infections, the agglutination titer is high to the OX-2 strain. For further details on the *Pathogenic Rickettsiae*, see *Bact. Revs.*, 1942, **6,** 37–78; *Virus and Rickettsial Diseases* (Harvard University Press, 1941); Dyer on *Rickettsial Diseases* (*J. A. M. A.*, 1944, **124,** 1165, 1188); and the complement-fixation test in the rickettsial diseases (*Pub. Health Rept.*, 1944, **59,** 402).

TYPHUS FEVER

It is perhaps best to speak of the typhus fevers, a group of closely related affections, which occur in various parts of the world. European or classical typhus, an acute highly contagious disease characterized by a high temperature and typical rash, which is easily distinguishable from any other commonly observed malady, is endemic in many countries, occurring frequently epidemically and is usually found where conditions of overcrowding and filth are present. It has been spoken of as *jail fever, camp fever, famine fever* and *hospital fever*. Famine, hardship, dislocation of social life, the lowering of sanitary and hygienic standards and crowded conditions, as occur frequently during wartime, account for epidemics during such period. The *R. prowazeki*, var. *prowazeki* is responsible for classic European or epidemic typhus. Transmission is from man to man by the agency of the body lice, *Pediculus humanus*, and possibly the head lice. The vector lice are themselves fatally infected. Typhus also is transmitted from rat to rat by the rat flea (*Xenopsylla cheopis*) and the rat louse (*Polyplax spinulosus*) and from rat to man by *X. cheopis*. The chief natural reservoirs of the disease are rodents and man. The disease is mild in rodents. Löffler and Mooser (*Schweiz. med. Wchnschr.* 1942, **72,** 755) have established the nasal route as a mode of transmission of laboratory cases of typhus fever.

A mild form of this disease appearing in cities of the Atlantic seaboard was thought to be a newly discovered malady, and named *Brill's disease* after the worker who first brought this to the attention of every one. There is endemic in the United States a disease which resembles typhus and gives a positive Weil-Felix reaction. The causative factor of this disease, the *R. prowazeki* var. *mooseri*, produces the so-called endemic or murine typhus and is carried by the rat flea. The rat mite also has been shown capable of transmitting endemic typhus. The rat is the reservoir. The *ship typhus of Toulon, the typhus of Manchuria*, and the *urban shop typhus of Malaya* have been identified with that of *tabardillo* in Mexico, all murine typhus, and the *Rickettsiae* in each have shown by immunological tests to be closely related to the species causing

Old World typhus. The North American strain appears to be originally derived from Old World sources. There are several differences between the two varieties of *R. prowazeki*, which are constant and important, such as the less luxuriant growth of the *prowazeki* variety in all methods, tissue culture, chick embryo and even in animals. The *mooseri* variety always induces an acute inflammation of the scrotal sac in male guinea pigs upon intraperitoneal injection and kills lice quicker when introduced *per anum*. Delousing methods and the eradication of lice, fleas and rats and general measures of personal hygiene and sanitation are the basis of prevention procedures to eliminate typhus fever. Typhus fever in the United States has been reported principally from the Southeastern States and California. A total of 2780 cases occurred in 1941. The case fatality rate for the United States in 1940 was 2.8 per cent. The control of the endemic type involves especially the eradication of rats, while the control of the epidemic type involves mainly frequent delousing procedures and scrupulous cleanliness. The disease can be prevented or at least modified by immunization, but so far no vaccine has been used extensively enough for a sufficient period of time to be of proved merit. The military personnel of this and other countries who are being sent to regions where louse-borne typhus is present are being vaccinated. At present, the approved typhus vaccine used in this country consists of a suspension of killed, louse-borne, epidemic typhus *rickettsiae* prepared by the Cox yolk-sac culture methods.

In an epidemic typhus area, a large-scale investigation has been carried out to test the effectiveness of a vaccine prepared at the U.S.S.R. Inst. of Experimental Medicine by a modification of the Weigl technique, the latter being the phenolized intestinal contents of lice infected by rectum with *R. prowazeki* obtained from the brains of infected guinea pigs. At the same time a test was made, under epidemic conditions, of the Cox vaccine prepared from fowl embryo cultures of *Rickettsiae prowazeki* and treated with phenol and formalin. It was established by animal and clinical tests that the Cox vaccine is most effective and simple to prepare. A complement-fixation test for the early diagnosis of typhus, performed at low temperatures has been devised in the same Russian laboratory and is stated to be very sensitive and strictly specific, giving results as early as the first and second day of illness (Levkevica, U.S.S.R. Inst. Exptl. Med. meeting, Aug., 1942; through *Brit. Med. J.*, 1942, **2**, 348). Castadena (*Science*, 1942, **96**, 304) reported recently on a bivalent typhus vaccine of high immunizing power which is prepared by adding epidemic typhus strains to monovalent "murine" vaccine. An initial dose of 0.5 cc. is followed by 2 subsequent doses of 1 cc. at weekly intervals. Laboratory workers require at least 5 doses to be fully protected. Treatment of typhus fever is symptomatic. Convalescent serum has been used but does not appear to be of great value. Plotz (*Science*, 1943, **97**, 20) reports that the complement-fixation test can be used now to distinguish between endemic and epidemic typhus, that mild cases of epidemic typhus actually exist in the United States and that man serves as the reservoir for epidemic typhus between outbreaks.

In the diagnosis of typhus fever great importance is attached at present to an agglutination test (Weil-Felix reaction), which the serum of typhus patients displays against certain organisms of the proteus group. These organisms are designated by them as OX-2 OX-19 and OX-K. The test is made just as the Widal test, preferably using the macroscopic method, and using either dead or living organisms. The reaction is usually positive by the sixth day. Animal inoculation is a simple procedure and should be utilized more frequently as an aid in the diagnosis of rickettsial diseases.

Sterle defibrinated or citrated blood, collected from the suspected case during the first ten days of illness during the height of fever is used for intraperitoneal inoculation of guinea pigs. From 2 to 6 cc. of blood or from autopsy (man) suspensions of fresh portions of brain or spleen are used. This animal is universally employed in rickettsial investigations and knowledge of the response of guinea pigs to the *Rickettsiae* is required for an interpretation of the findings. For a detailed consideration of typhus fever in Europe and the means of combating it, see Biraud (*Bull. Health Org. League Nat.*, 1943, **10**, 1).

SPOTTED FEVER

This comprises a group of diseases, which are tick-borne, are characterized by many similar clinical symptoms, though some differ immunologically and even in clinical observations.

Rocky Mountain Spotted Fever is the disease of this group which is encountered more frequently. At first considered limited to the Western United States in the Rocky Mountain region, cases of this disease have been reported in 42 of the 48 states of the Union. Clinically, Rocky Mountain spotted fever resembles typhus fever in many respects. An unfortunate practice has been the differentiation of the disease into an Eastern type and a Western type. Both are caused by *Rickettsia rickettsi* (*Dermancentroxenus rickettsi*), which in contrast to *Rickettsia prowazeki*, is found within the nucleus of the invaded cell. Both are immunologically identical and both are transmitted by ticks, but by different species. The wood tick, *Dermacentor andersonii*, is the carrier in the Western states and the dog tick, *Dermacentor variabilis*, is the vector in the Atlantic region. The incidence is greatest during the spring and summer months after the ticks have emerged from the ground and have entered into the adult stage. Other ticks may be potential vectors. *Amblyomma americanum* was reported recently as a vector (*U. S. Pub. Health Repts.*, 1943, **58**, 1491). The disease is innocuous for the ticks, and hereditary transmission occurs. Animals and usually native rodents bitten by infected ticks have a symptomless infection but may serve as temporary reservoirs for other ticks to feed on and become infected. In the United States for the past ten years, approximately 450 cases have been reported annually with a mortality of about 19 per cent. Confirmation of the clinical diagnosis is established preferably by guinea pig inoculation of the blood (see above). The Felix-Weil agglutination test is also used. A lasting immunity is conferred upon recovery. Among the prophylactic measures are the necessity for those whose duties may expose them to tick bites to wear heavy socks and high boots and to examine themselves frequently for the presence of ticks. The latter should be removed gently from the skin, preferably after first applying chloroform. The use of a pair of tweezers rather than the fingers is advocated, but if the latter are employed, the tick is not to be crushed between the fingers. Spencer and Parker (*J. Inf. Dis.*, 1935, **57**, 78) have prepared a vaccine which is a phenolized suspension of *Rickettsiae* made from the ground viscera of infected ticks. They advocate annual immunization and indicate that it has definite value. Vaccine made from tissue cultures and from the yolk sacs of infected chick embryos are also available. Baker (*Am. Inst. Med.*, 1942, **17**, 247) reports that the use of vaccine gives protection against the disease. The recommended dosage is 2 cc. repeated at an interval of from seven to ten days and 1 cc. for children. The degree and duration of protection varies with the individual and the virulence of the strain of organisms, but usually it affords either protection from the disease or the course of the disease is modified. In areas where the disease is prevalent and the mortality high, vaccination should be performed annually. At present the treatment of tick fever is supportive and symptomatic. There is no specific. Convalescent sera and blood transfusions have been used without beneficial effect. The sulfonamides have been tried, but are believed to be valueless. Tick vaccine should never be used for treatment of the infection. The intravenous administration of Neoarsphenamine dissolved in an aqueous solution of Metaphen is recommended by Baker as a definite therapeutic aid in the management of tick fever. For further details, see Topping (*U. S. Pub. Health Repts.*, 1940, **55**, 41; 1941, **56**, 2041; 1943, **58**, 757).

São Paulo Typhus, preferably called Brazilian spotted fever, is a tick-borne disease, occurring in Brazil, which is immunologically identical with Rocky Mountain spotted fever. The case fatality is very high, averaging about 70 per cent. *Amblyomma cajennense* is the transmitting agent and the etiological agent is identical with that causing Rocky Mountain spotted fever. For further details, see Monteiro (*Memories do Instituto Butantan*, 1931, **6**).

Fievre Boutonneuse is a tick-borne rickettsial disease prevalent in southern Europe and northern Africa. It is immunologically identical with Rocky Mountain spotted fever, but differs clinically in that a local nodule or small sore develops at the site of the tick bite (whence the name meaning button-like). The general symptoms are milder though an inflammatory reaction is produced in the regional lymph nodes, and the fatality rate is much lower. The animal reservoir of the infection is the dog, the tick vector is *Rhipicephalus sanguineous*, and the etiological agent is identical with that causing Rocky Mountain spotted fever. For further details, see Hass and Pinkerton (*J. Exp. Med.*, 1936, **64**, 601) and Plotz and Associates (*Proc. Soc. Exptl. Biol. Med.*, 1944, **55**, 173).

Kenya fever is identical with the other spotted fevers and is transmitted by the tick, *Rhipicephalus sanguineous*. A primary sore and adenitis are absent.

South African tick-bite fever is a rickettsial disease presenting clinical symptoms very similar to *Fievre Boutonneuse*, but it is immunologically distinct. The transmitting vectors are *Rhipicephalus sanguineous* and *Amblyomma hebraeum*.

The Tsutsugamushi Group.—The diseases in this group are mite-borne rickettsial infections, immunologically identical or closely related, and the animal reservoirs are mice and rats. The OX-K (*Proteus vulgaris*, Kingsbury) is agglutinated by the patients' sera in high dilution. In most respects including the high mortality, the several forms of the disease resemble epidemic typhus, but the infection is immunologically distinct from typhus and spotted fevers though the immunity conferred by an attack is less complete than in the case of the latter two diseases.

Tsutsugamushi disease, known also as *Japanese Flood or River Fever*, or *Kedani fever*, is caused by *R. tsutsugamushi* (also known as *R. nipponica*, *R. orientalis* and *R. akamushi*), which closely resembles *R. prowazeki* and *R. rickettsi*, though it is usually shorter and plumper than the latter. The disease is transmitted by the scarcely visible bright red-orange mite, *Trombicula akamushi*. *T. deliensis* may also serve as a carrier agent. The animal reservoir is the field mouse, *Microtus montebelli*. The disease generally occurs in Oceania (uncultivated areas along the banks of rivers in swamps and moist tropical jungles). There is a primary ulcer or painless sore at the site of the bite and an adenitis. Reinfection may occur, but second attacks are usually mild. See *J. A. M. A.*, 1944, **124,** 1095.

Mite Fever of Sumatra and *"Rural Typhus"* or *"Scrub Typhus" of Malaya* are almost identical with, but milder diseases than tsutsugamushi disease. The first-named infection is transmitted by *T. deliensis* and the animal reservoirs appear to be the house rat, *Mus concolor*, and the field rat, *Mus diardii*. *Rural Typhus* is to be differentiated from *shop typhus of Malaya*, which is murine typhus. It is transmitted by *T. akamushi* and *T. deliensis* and the animal reservoir is the rat.

Trench Fever.—*Trench or Wolhynian fever* became known especially during World War I and was responsible for much illness among the troops in certain areas. The *R. wolhynica* (*R. pediculi* or *R. quintana*) is probably the causative agent. It closely resembles *R. prowazeki*, though it is more oval, less pleomorphic, plumper and stains more deeply. Natural transmission is by infected body lice feeding on humans or through the infected feces entering through abrasions in the skin. The disease is characterized by relapses and these may occur as late as two years after onset. The disease itself is mild and rarely fatal. For comments concerning trench fever in the present war, see Kerger (*Deutsche med. Wchnschr.*, 1942, **68,** 814).

Q Fever.—This is a rickettsial disease found especially among workers in slaughtering houses and on dairy farms especially in Australia but also reported in Montana. In Australia, it is spread by the hard tick, *Ixodes humerosa* and in the United States by the soft tick, *Dermocentor andersonii*. The causative agent in the Australian cases is known as *R. burneti* and in the American cases as *R. diaporica*. Both organisms are identical or at least very closely related and they differ from the other *rickettsiae* in that they are filterable. Morphologically they resemble the *rickettsiae* of typhus and spotted fever. Vaccines prepared from infected mouse spleens or from yolk sac suspensions appear to be of value.

Heartwater or Veldt Disease.—This is a highly fatal and economically important disease of cattle, sheep and goats, caused by *R. ruminantium* and transmitted by the tick, *Amblyomma hebraeum*. Angora goats are most susceptible. For further details, see Cowdry (*J. Exp. Med.*, 1926, **42,** 231, 253; 1928, **44,** 803).

Chapter XVI

DISEASES OF UNKNOWN, DOUBTFUL OR INDEFINITELY DETERMINED ETIOLOGY

FILTERABLE VIRUSES

THERE IS RATHER a large group of infectious diseases of man and lower animals that are caused by a heterogenous assemblage of different agents which in all probability are microorganisms. The actual causative agent is, however, unknown, not definitely determined or is doubtful, due to the difference of opinions among many of the competent observers. They are known as *viruses*. If a definition is required, we may say for the present that *viruses* are self-reproducing agents, probably in most cases microorganisms, which are much smaller than bacteria and can only multiply within the living cells of a suitable host. They are obligate parasites and also have been designated as *filterable viruses* or *ultramicroscopic viruses* or *invisible microbes*. They are ultramicroscopic in the sense that viruses are not visible with the ordinary microscope, using the commonly employed techniques. The term *filterable virus* is more frequently employed rather than the other designations. A filterable virus is an active transmissible agent capable of producing characteristic pathological conditions. Many workers would also add the following: and the agent is capable of passing through clay, siliceous or porcelain filters. This is not necessary for, as Dr. Rivers has pointed out, "filterability of the etiological agents does not sharply delimit this group of diseases." In fact, it is known that some of the viruses causing certain diseases, especially smallpox, usually placed in the filterable virus group, are either not filterable or filter only with difficulty. On the viruses of other diseases, as chickenpox, no filtration experiments are recorded. Then we also know that certain small bacteria and protozoa share the characteristic of passing through clay filters, while most other known microorganisms do not. Nevertheless, in spite of what has been said against them, filters, if used under proper conditions, are useful when working with diseases of unknown etiology. One is able to determine at least whether we are dealing with agents smaller than the commonly observed bacteria. Furthermore, filtration through specially prepared membranes of modified cellulose serves as a means of determining the relative sizes of any virus. Elford (*Proc. Roy Soc. London*, 1932, Series B, **112,** 384) applied filtration through collodion membranes of graded porosity as a means of estimating particle size. Other indirect methods used for measuring the size consist in either photographing the virus particles by special methods or by the use of high-powered centrifuges, where there is a relation between the rate of sedimentation and the particle size. In expressing the size, the "milli-mu" (mμ) is generally used as the unit. See also pages 16 and 17.

Though the exact nature of the viruses is unknown, it is possible to detect the presence of the latter in a variety of material. They can be separated from one another and from ordinary bacteria.

In most instances, they are known by their activities, by the type of host or hosts attacked, by the clinical and pathological conditions produced and by the immunological responses excited. It is interesting to note that the diseases caused by the different viruses manifest many striking features in common. Many of the diseases induced by them can be produced experimentally in animals and highly protective and neutralizing sera can be obtained. There are also available successful methods of immunization against many virus infections, especially smallpox, rabies, yellow fever, canine distemper, fowl pox and cattle plague.

The limitation of virus growths to living cells makes it necessary to use methods for the cultivation of pathogenic viruses quite different from the usual procedures employed for culturing bacteria. Living cells must be used and we are frequently limited to the use of particular or specific living cells, as some viruses are fastidious in regard to the kind of cells in which they will grow. Indications point to the fact that multiplication occurs within the involved cell. In a number of instances, the only satisfactory method of cultivation is the inoculation of the suitable susceptible living host. The method of cultivation by using a suitable living host is the standard method of virus culturing, though recently the tissue culture method and the cultivation on the chorio-allantoic membrane of the developing chick embryo (nine to eleven days old) have been used. In the tissue culture method, embryonic cells are placed in small glass bottles in a properly balanced salt solution and kept at body temperature. A drop of a virus capable of infecting the cells is added to the cell suspension and growth will occur. In the chick embryo method, the tissues of the unhatched chicken are used as the susceptible cells in which the virus can grow. For a summary of culture methods, see Sanders (*Arch. Path.*, 1939, **28**, 541); for quantitative studies, see Burnet and Faris (*J. Bact.*, 1942, **44**, 241); and for recent advances, see Lennette (*Science*, 1943, **98**, 415). Laboratory methods are frequently required as an aid in the diagnosis of virus diseases. Culture methods and inoculation procedures aided by the usual serological tests, such tests as agglutination, precipitin, complement-fixing and neutralization or protective reactions are employed. It is of interest to note that though pathogenic viruses have not, saprophytic viruses have been successfully cultivated in media free from living cells.

Viruses as a group are unique in that their infectivity is exerted through intracellular activity. Those which show a predilection for the skin are termed *dermatropic*, such as herpes and warts. *Neurotropic* viruses display an affinity for the central nervous system, such as poliomyelitis, encephalitis lethargica, St. Louis encephalitis and rabies. Those affecting the respiratory tract and especially the lungs are known as *pneumotropic* viruses, such as epidemic influenza, psittacosis and the common cold. *Viscerotropic* viruses attack the abdominal or thoracic viscera or produce systemic or a generalized infection, as in the case of yellow fever, dengue fever, smallpox, chickenpox, measles, German measles and the poxes in lower animals. *Pantropic* is a term employed by some to indicate affinities for many tissues.

In their resistance to destructive agents, the viruses tend to behave as the vegetative forms of bacteria. They are readily inactivated by sunlight, heat and oxidizing agents. Extreme cold, freezing, drying, 50 per cent glycerin and 0.5 per cent phenol exert a preservative action. Recovery from most virus diseases is accompanied by a high degree of a lasting immunity. Second attacks are not common. Serum obtained from convalescents reveals the presence of specific antibodies. The viruses themselves, in most cases, possess antigenic properties. Vaccines as prophylactic agents originated with the viruses and many virus vaccines are in use. Upon histological examination of the tissues affected by viruses, certain conspicuous bodies or structures of varying size not found normally are observed in many instances within the affected cell, either in the cytoplasm or in the nucleus or both. These structures, known as *inclusion bodies*, are found in most but not all virus diseases and are not found in bacterial infections. They frequently are of great diagnostic value, though their exact nature and significance are not certain. It has been suggested that the inclusion body is composed of a mass of small virus particles, which are called *elementary bodies*, and that the inclusion body represents the intracellular colonies of the virus. Typical inclusions (typical as to shape, appearance, location in a cell, etc.) may suggest the presence of a virus and, at times, indicate the type of virus possibly present, perhaps in the same way as macroscopical cultural colonies may indicate the species of bacteria. However, it also is well to remember that inclusions may appear without demonstrable viruses. Yellow fever, chickenpox, herpes simplex, herpes zoster and warts are examples of virus infections with nuclear inclusion colonies. Cytoplasmic inclusion colonies are observed in vaccinia, rabies, mumps and psittacosis. Both nuclear and cytoplasmic inclusion colonies are found in smallpox (variola) and epidemic encephalitis (lethargica). Demonstrable inclusion colonies are not apparent in epidemic influenza, common colds, measles, German measles, dengue, lymphogranuloma venereum and foot-and-mouth disease.

Viruses are widespread in nature. Every type of organism appears to be attacked by some kind of a virus. If we accept d'Herelle theory on bacteriophage, the latter, an eater of bacteria, is a virus and bacteria suffer from virus diseases. A large number of viruses attack plants. The solanaceous plants, tobacco, potato and tomato, in particular, are susceptible. The mosaic diseases of tobacco and of sugar cane do a great deal of damage and the result is a considerable economic loss. Most plant viruses are spread by insect vectors. Every species of animal may suffer from some virus infection. Among the bees and silkworms, the only domesticated forms among the invertebrates, we have the "sac-brood" of bees and jaundice or "grasserie" of silkworms. Even fishes and frogs have a virus disease, such as carb pox, lymphocystic disease, and carcinoma in frogs. Parrots suffer from psittacosis and there are other virus diseases among fowl, such as fowl pox, fowl plague, canary and pigeon pox and infective laryngotracheitis. The fowl tumors are of interest in that they are indistinguishable from true sarcomata. Almost every domestic animal is subject to plagues and poxes, caused by viruses; cowpox, horsepox, sheep pox, swine pox, cattle plague, foot-and-mouth disease, swine fever and dog distemper are some of the more commonly observed virus infections among domestic animals. Lymphatic leukemia in mice, salivary disease of rats and epizootic disease of ferrets are virus infections. Man is susceptible to many of the virus infections of animals. Many of the virus diseases in humans were mentioned above and will be considered in more detail. A few virus diseases of man are spread by insect vectors, but most of them appear to be disseminated through contact or by droplet infection.

Only few viruses have been prepared and purified in sufficient quantity to permit detailed study and especially a possible chemical analysis. It happens that we know much about certain viruses and relatively little about other viruses, and it is not possible to draw conclusions of a general character. Furthermore, availability, stability and the existence of a good experimental host make one virus especially suitable as an experimental subject and another virus unsuitable because of the lack of all or even one of these essentials. In 1935, Stanley (*Physiol. Rev.*, 1939, **19,** 524) was able to obtain a crystalline nucleoprotein from the juice of tobacco plants infected with mosaic virus, which possessed all of the characteristics of the incitant of the disease. It has also been demonstrated that other plant viruses are of a similar nature and some of them have been crystallized. Is this the link between the living and the nonliving? Or are we to assume that the virus is not a living agent? Further investigations are being conducted and perhaps we will learn soon whether the crystalline tobacco mosaic virus and other viruses are composed of inanimate material or living molecules, a so-called *organule* or a *molechism*. For the present at least, we adhere to the.animate nature of pathogenic viruses found in humans.

In the following pages mention will be made of the important diseases found in man and animals, mainly in this country, which are caused by filterable viruses, other not definitely determined agents or in which the causative agents are unknown. Only the important facts concerning these diseases will be set forth. A few of the more important ones found in tropical climates will be considered briefly.

Chicken Pox or Varicella.—This is an acute, highly contagious disease caused by a filterable virus occurring only in man characterized by mild constitutional symptoms and by an eruption of papules and vesicles. These develop in crops, dry up in a few days, and leave a granular scab. The etiological agent is present in the nose, throat, blood and more frequently in large amounts in the vesicle fluid in the skin lesions. Age, race, sex, climate and season have no effect on the incidence of this infection. Most cases, however, occur among young children. Transmission is by contact and through the discharges of the nose, throat and from the vesicle fluid. Uncomplicated chicken pox is never fatal as the disease is usually mild. Scars may persist if the pocks become infected or are scratched off before they are completely healed. There is no specific serum or chemotherapeutic agent available. Suitable laboratory animals for experimentation have not been found. The filterable virus occurs in the form of *elementary bodies*, which are specifically agglutinated by convalescent chicken pox serum. Second attacks of chicken pox are extremely rare. Though convalescent serum may be tried for prophylaxis, its value is indifferent. In most instances, on account of the mildness of the disease, protective measures as inoculations play a small role.

Common Colds.—This should not be confused with true influenza. The "common cold" is probably a definite entity which is milder than the so-called "grippe" to which it is related, while the true influenza is probably a more severe infection and caused by a different primary agent. This affection is probably identical with "catarrhal fever," a term applied to upper respiratory infections, originally suggested by Fantus (*J. A. M. A.*, 1920, **75,** 1694) and its use recommended again recently by Jones (*U. S. Nav. M. Bull.*, 1943, **41,** 573). Many bacteria found in the nose and throat have been thought of as the causative agents. Many workers believe that the primary factor is probably in the nature of a filterable virus and it is likely that a number of types of this virus exist. Definite proof, however, is lacking. It may be said with some degree of assurance that the bacteria present at least increase the severity of the infection as important secondary factors. In addition to bacteria, other agents, in lowering infection, may assist in predisposing to infections of the upper respiratory tract of the type of the common cold. They are: poor sanitary conditions, especially associated with inadequate ventilation and insufficient light; food deficiencies as inadequate amounts of vitamin A; certain chronic infections and at times various abnormalities or malformations of the upper part of the respiratory tract; and exposure to drafts, chilling, wetting, etc. The infection is spread especially by close contact. Proper sanitary and hygienic measures will probably lower the incidence of cases of the common cold. The immunity is variable in different individuals. Local factors affect the latter considerably. The use of mass immunization has been disappointing and vaccinotherapy appears to be of value only in those cases wherein the secondary bacterial invaders play an important role. In most instances any immunity, if present, is usually very temporary.

Dengue (*"Seven Days"* or *"Breakbone Fever"*).—This, a general acute mild infection of tropical and subtropical climates marked by a tendency to epidemic outbreaks, is supposed to be caused by a filterable virus, which is known to be transmitted solely by the bite of different species of mosquitoes, but especially by the *Stegomyia fasciata* (*Aedes aegypti*). *Aedes albopictus* and *Armigeres obturbans* are probable carriers. Evidence concerning *Culex fatigans* is conflicting. The acute symptoms are at times followed by indisposition and protracted weakness. Immunity to dengue is inconstant and brief. The disease is rarely fatal. General measures directed toward the elimination of mosquitoes have been found a successful procedure for the prevention of this disease.

Distemper of Dogs.—Distemper is a very common and important disease of young dogs, occurring occasionally among other young carnivorous animals. There has been considerable discussion whether canine distemper is due to *Bacillus* (*Brucella*) *bronchisepticus* or, as is accepted by most investigators, that the primary etiological factor belongs to the group of filterable viruses. Infection occurs through the ingestion of contaminated water and food and probably by way of the respiratory tract.

Encephalitis Lethargica (*Epidemic Encephalitis or Epidemic Coma*).—There are a number of diseases involving the central nervous system and causing an encephalitis or inflammation of the brain. These are caused by different etiological agents and by others which are obscure, but all of the diseases are generally designated by the term *epidemic encephalitis*. A frequently used classification of the encephalitides due to viruses or agents suspicious of being viruses is:

I. Infectious encephalitis:
    (1) Type A—von Economo, or lethargic type, chiefly sporadic;
    (2) Type B—chiefly epidemic:
        (*a*) Japanese form, and
        (*b*) St. Louis form;
    (3) Other forms.
II. Post or para-infectious encephalitis.

Lethargic encephalitis is a disease which, though prevalent throughout the world has only recently received a degree of attention. A diagnosis can be established only after considerable careful study. Though possessing certain resemblances to epidemic poliomyelitis, this disease is etiologically and clinically distinct from the latter. No general agreement has been reached as to the causative agent, the source of infection or the mode of transmission of this febrile affection in which a stuporous or lethargic condition prevails together with asthenia and cranial nerve palsies. The fatality rate is high. The fact that this disease has been observed in former and in the last pandemic of influenza (1918–1919) has led some observers to regard encephalitis as a direct sequel of influenzal infections, but this is questioned by most workers. Strains of herpes virus and herpes-like viruses were isolated from patients suffering from Type A or von Economo infectious encephalitis, but most workers question the significance of such findings in relation to considering this as an etiologic agent. This type of encephalitis occurs sporadically and epidemics are rare. Cases occur generally in the colder months, and children and young adults suffer most heavily. The encephalitides differ from cases of poliomyelitis in that they are characterized by greater lethargy and fatigue and present cerebral symptoms mainly, with spinal cord involvement only occasionally. Convulsions rarely occur in poliomyelitis but are common in encephalitis.

St. Louis Encephalitis is a new clinical entity which has been recognized recently as caused by a virus. (See *U. S. Pub. Health Service, Bull.* **214**, 1935 and *Third Report of the Matheson Commission*, Columbia Univ. Press, New York City, 1939.) Outbreaks of this infection have appeared within the last decade in many parts of the United States. Monkeys and mice are susceptible to infection by intracerebral inoculation of brain tissue. The virus has been grown by tissue culture methods and upon the chorio-allantoic membrane of chick embryos. The infectious agent was neutralized by the serum of recovered patients but not by the sera from recovered cases of von Economo encephalitis, Japanese encephalitis, poliomyelitis, equine encephalomyelitis and other known virus diseases. This infection is naturally transmitted by various species of *Culex* (mosquitoes).

Japanese Encephalitis is another form of Type B encephalitis which also has been recognized as a clinical entity. Though epidemiologically and clinically closely related to the St. Louis encephalitis, it differs immunologically and antigenically. The Japanese type usually produces a severe infection in monkeys and sheep. The latter are innocuous to the St. Louis virus and this virus produces little or no reactions when inoculated into monkeys. For further details, see Mitamura and associates (*Trans. Soc. Path. Jap.*, 1937, **27**, 573; 1938, **28**, 135) and Webster (*J. Exp. Med.*, 1938, **67**, 609). Sabin (*J. A. M. A.*, 1943, **122**, 477) announced recently the production of a vaccine against both the St. Louis and Japanese B types of encephalitis.

Other Types of Infectious Encephalitis.—A form of encephalitis similar to Japanese Type B Encephalitis and known as *Australian X Disease* occurred in Australia and later in New South Wales. The causative agent of this disease is unknown, is believed to be contracted from and is transmissible to sheep, and the lesions produced are similar to those observed in *louping ill.* The latter is a disease primarily of sheep occurring in Scotland and Northern England and is caused by a virus, which is present in the blood stream during the febrile stage. In Nature, louping ill is transmitted by a tick, *Ixodes ricinus*. Laboratory workers engaged in the study of this disease have become infected. *Equine encephalomyelitis*, an epizootic disease caused by a filterable virus and observed in horses, has been reported in humans (*J. A. M. A.*, 1940, **114**, 1725). The disease is confined mainly to North America, where the "Eastern" type is endemic in the marshy country along the seaboard and the "Western" type is found in more extensive regions in the western river valleys. Human infections frequently carry a high mortality rate. It appears in the late summer and early autumn and it is believed that the disease is transmitted by certain species of mosquitoes. Other insects have been implicated as vectors or as reservoirs of the virus. For further details on human cases of this infection, see Howitt (*Am. J. Pub. Health*, 1939, **29**, 1083), Fothergill and associates (*New England J. Med.*, 1938, **219**, 411), Leake (*U. S. Pub. Health Reports*, 1941, **56**, 1902) and Randall and Mills (*Science*, 1944, **99**, 225).

Secondary Encephalitis.—An infrequent though important complication of various viral infections, especially following epidemic influenza, measles, smallpox, mumps and whooping cough, is a secondary encephalitis. The exact nature of the latter is not definitely known. It has been suggested that the infection is an extension to the central nervous system of the primary viral disease or that the apparent secondary encephalitis is caused by a virus separate and distinct from that causing the initial infection.

Epidemic Influenza.—Until the great pandemic of influenza of 1918, the influenza bacillus or Bacillus of Pfeiffer (*H. influenzae*) has been most commonly regarded as the causative agent of this infection. Since the pandemic, much uncertainty has existed as to the precise relationship of this organism to the disease. A specific green-producing streptococcus, a filterable virus and a minute filter-passing anaerobe (*Bacterium* [*Dialister*] *pneumosintes*) have been introduced by different workers as the specific initiating or primary cause of the last great pandemic of influenza. Mills and associates (*J. Exp. Med.*, 1928, **47**, 193) found *Bact. pneumosintes* in individuals throughout the year and assign no causative role to this organism in the etiology of influenza or the common cold.

Smith, Andrewes and Laidlaw (*Lancet*, 1933, **2**, 66) succeeded in establishing the disease in ferrets by the installation of filtrates of human nasopharyngeal washings into their nares. The disease in these experimental animals is similar to human influenza. Ferret virus can be transmitted to mice (*Science*, 1935, **82**, 353) or adapted to the fertile egg (*Med. J. Australia*, 1935, **2**, 651). Transmission of the animal strains back to man has occurred (*Am. J. M. Sc.*, 1937, **194**, 159). Due to recent findings by Francis (*Science*, 1940, **92**, 405), there appears to be at least two antigenically distinct agents, capable of producing indistinguishable clinical influenzal symptoms. The Smith, Andrewes, Laidlaw virus has become known as *Influenza A virus*, the more recently isolated virus as *Influenza B virus*. Magill (*Proc. Soc. Exptl. Biol. Med.*, 1941, **46**, 316) presented evidence which suggests the existence of other immunologically distinct types of the virus. The symptomatology and severity of the disease vary in different epidemics, but in all there usually appears a characteristic symptom complex consisting of sudden onset with fever and marked prostration, severe aching pains throughout the body especially the back and extremities, upper respiratory inflammation and headache. The complications of this disease and notably the pneumonias may be accepted as caused by one or a combination of two or more definitely known organisms, the bacteriology varying in different localities. As a prophylactic measure, general procedures of hygiene and sanitation and strict quarantine are advocated. Immunization with different virus vaccines are being tried and may prove useful.

For data on the epidemiology of influenza, see Francis (*J. A. M. A.*, 1943, **122**, 4). Acute respiratory epidemics with *pneumonitis* are reported from time to time. Lung involvement is apparent and a diagnosis of *pneumonitis* or *virus pneumonia* is generally made. Robertson (*Virginia M. Monthly*, 1942, **69**, 542) reported 79 such cases in an epidemic among students. Peterson and associates (*Science*, 1943, **97**, 167) reported recently that in virus pneumonia and other primary atypical pneumonias of unknown etiology, autohemagglutinins (or cold agglutinins) are found at 0° C. in dilutions (of serum or plasma) ranging from 1:10 to over 1:10,000 and generally in titers of from 1:160 or 1:320 (at 0° C.). They are found but infrequently in pneumococcus pneumonia, so that the presence of these so-called cold agglutinins (designating the cold temperature at which agglutinins occur) may possibly serve as a differential and diagnostic aid. For further details on virus pneumonias, see Reimann (*Bull. New York Acad. Med.*, 1943, **19,** 177) and Bahlke (*New York State J. Med.*, 1943, **43,** 315).

Epidemic Poliomyelitis (*Acute Anterior Poliomyelitis, Epidemic Infantile Paralysis or Heine Medin Disease*).—This, an acute systemic infectious disease, affects chiefly the central nervous system of humans, occurring usually in children (90 per cent of the cases found in children under ten years of age), appearing sporadically and in epidemics in many countries, but mainly in temperate climates. Adults may become infected. The virus causing infantile paralysis is not carried by lower animals but is confined to man. It enters the body chiefly through the membranes of the nose, and passes along the nerves of smell to the brain and spinal cord, where its main attack on the body is made. The nasal and throat secretions carry the virus and may be the means of spreading it to cause new cases of the disease. Other workers have revealed that the intestinal tract and the lymphatics are also involved and have suggested that it may be possible that swallowing the virus (present in contaminated foods) may be the means of disseminating the disease and just as important to consider in epidemics as "droplet" infection. It is known that the virus is present in the feces of those diseased (acute and convalescent cases). Sabin and Ward (*Science*, 1942, **95,** 300) present evidence that flies are carriers of the virus. They regard poliomyelitis as a disease which occurs the year round. The incidence, however, is greater during the summer and autumn as a greater dissemination of the virus is possible due to a number of factors including the presence of insects and especially flies. An editorial review (*J. A. M. A.*, 1943, **122,** 40) points out that observations by Jungeblut and Dalldorf (*Am. J. Pub. Health*, 1943, **33,** 169), in which virus-infected rodents are probably serving as an extrahuman source of human poliomyelitis, are an outstanding contribution to the epidemiology of this disease. Another editorial review on insect vectors was presented recently (*J. A. M. A.*, 1943, **122,** 1250). The possible spread of the virus through infected water or food has been suggested but not proved. Monkeys and the eastern cotton rat have been inoculated experimentally with this virus. Whether or not a natural immunity against this disease exists is not known. Individuals recovering from the disease, who in most instances remain immune for life, possess in their blood antibodies or principles capable of killing the active virus. The early use of such serum from convalescent cases injected intraspinally, intramuscularly and intravenously in the treatment of this disease, especially before the onset of paralysis, may be used, but in all probability little therapeutic benefit results. The uses of an attenuated virus (Kolmer vaccine) and an inactivated virus (Brodie vaccine) were suggested as prophylactic agents. The former agent is too dangerous to use and the latter has not proved effective. Applications of various chemicals to the olfactory area in the nasopharynx have been advocated so as to set up a barrier to infection. No method of chemoprophylaxis has as yet proved of sufficient value for general use. Convalescent serum, if of value at all, is of greatest value as a prophylactic agent. The virus is one of the smallest (8 to 12 mμ). It can be preserved in 50 per cent glycerin. It is susceptible to ultraviolet light, formaldehyde, mercuric chloride and oxidizing agents. The virus resists light, drying, x-rays, moderate degrees of heat, and freezing. It may persist in water and milk for more than a month. The contagiousness of this disease is generally accepted. Flexner and Noguchi claim to have cultivated the filterable virus causing this infection by using special culture media and culturing under anaerobic conditions. This organism, appearing as globoid bodies singly, in chains or masses is regarded by Rosenow the same as the streptococcus which he has isolated. This aerobic streptococcus which has an affinity for the central nervous system, he claims, shows only minute globoid forms when grown anaerobically. It has, therefore, not been definitely established whether the etiological factor is the filterable virus which appears as globoid bodies when cultured anaerobically or whether the streptococci found in the tissues are the primary agents. In a more recent presentation, Rosenow (*Proc. Staff Meet., Mayo Clin.*, 1943, **18,** 5) states that he was able to isolate consistently specific types of streptococci from the stools of patients having epidemic poliomyelitis or encephalitis and again suggests that growth of the streptococci may be an important source of virus in epidemic poliomyelitis. He also presented a cutaneous test which he claims is diagnostic of this disease (*Proc. Staff Meet., Mayo Clin.*, 1943, **18,** 118). Evidence seems to be insufficient to regard any of the factors mentioned as the etiological agents.

The disease and its virus bear a resemblance to rabies and its virus. There are a number of different classifications of types of poliomyelitis, some depending upon anatomical involvement. The following classification is frequently used: abortive type; nonparalytic (meningitic) type (or the preparalytic stage of the paralytic type); and the paralytic type. These have their subdivisions. The fatality rate of epidemic poliomyelitis is not high, though those who recover usually display some permanent injury to portions of the motor areas of the nervous system, resulting in some deformity. The so-called abortive type of the disease is more prevalent than is suspected and such cases probably serve as a means of spreading this dreaded infection (*J. A. M. A.* 1932, **98,** 2262). For further details see *International Bulletin for Economics, Medical Research and Public Hygiene: Infantile Paralysis*, Vol. A-40, National Foundation for Infantile Paralysis, 1939–1940; *Poliomyelitis*, Williams and Wilkins, Baltimore, 1932; and "Round Table on Problems in Poliomyelitis" (*J. Bact.*, 1943, **45,** 85).

Foot-and-mouth Disease (*Aphthous Fever*).—This is a disease of cloven-footed animals in all parts of the world and caused by a filterable virus. The horse is not susceptible. It is one of the most contagious diseases known in veterinary medicine. The disease is transmitted from animal to animal by means of the virus present in the vesicles which characterize the disease. The vesicles present in the mouth, between the hoofs, on the udder, etc., rupture, contaminating various material and objects with the virus, such as food, water, pastures, etc. Man is susceptible, and when he does contract this disease, it is usually by handling infected animals, usually cows, or by drinking the raw milk of infected animals. Outbreaks of foot-and-mouth disease, especially in California during 1924, 1929 and 1932, are recorded. The latter outbreak was confined to hogs and not cattle. No cure is known for this disease, which spreads like wildfire among any kind of hoofed animals. The only remedy employed today is the immediate massacre or mass slaughtering of those animals, known to be infected or who have been exposed to foot-and-mouth disease, and quick burial, using quicklime or other suitable disinfectant to cover the carcasses. The virus is one of the smallest known, being from 8 to 12 mμ in diameter. It can be propagated in tissue culture and three types (A, O and C) have been differentiated by immunological reactions. The guinea pig is the most suitable test laboratory animal. For complete details, see the "Report of the Committee for the Study of Foot and Mouth Disease," U. S. Bur. Animal Industry (U. S. Dept. Agr., *Tech. Bull.* **76**, 1928).

Human infections are infrequent, are mild and seldom fatal. They can be prevented by the suppression of the disease in animals, slaughter, disinfection, and by the pasteurization of milk.

German Measles (*Rubella*).—This is a disease similar to measles but with symptoms not so severe and distinct from it. The causative agent is unknown, but it is believed to be a virus. The disease may be transmitted by direct contact with infected individuals or with articles freshly soiled with the discharges from the nose and throat of the latter. In general, rubella occurs more frequently in epidemics and among older children rather than infants. The catarrh and constitutional manifestations are mild and insignificant. There is little or no fever and the eruption is fine and changeable, neither constant nor uniform throughout. Koplik spots found in measles (small red patches, pinhead in size, with tiny whitish opalescent specks in the center, or inside of cheek) are absent. Convalescence is rapid and complications are rare. Fatalities are unknown. This disease is spread by droplet infection. Injections of immune globulin have been used, apparently with success, for the prevention of the spread of epidemics of rubella.

Granuloma Inguinale.—This is a chronic disease of venereal origin which primarily involves the skin and mucous membrane on the external genitalia, causing the appearance of vivid-hued, shining, verrucous, vegetating nodules of granulation tissue, which bleed readily. The disease spreads by peripheral extension and auto-infection, frequently involving the entire genital area. The first symptoms appear usually from three to six weeks after exposure. Inguinal lymphadenitis may occur as a result of secondary infection of the initial lesion. Scrapings from the latter, or deep tissue scrapings or biopsy of a peripheral area of diseased tissue (comparing it with a section of normal adjacent skin), will reveal the presence of Donovan bodies. The latter, leishmania-like organisms, are diagnostic of this infection and are seen after staining by one of the techniques used for staining blood, such as Wright's or Giemsa's method. Appropriate tests must be carried out to exclude a mixed infection with lymphogranuloma venereum (giving positive Frei test), chancroids (presence of *H. ducreyi*) and syphilis (dark-field examinations for *T. pallidium* and serologic tests). Treatment consists in the administration of antimony compounds. Intravenous injections of *tartar emetic* or administration of *fuadin* (*4,5-dihydroxy-1,3-benzene disulfonic acid*), *anthiomaline* (antimony lithium thiomalate) and other organic antimony compounds are also used. Courses of treatment are to continue for at least four months after all lesions have completely healed to prevent relapses. Local therapy may be limited to daily dressings. X-ray treatment or excision may be necessary. Recently Somskey and associates (*J. Urol.*, 1942, **48**, 401) employed successfully local applications of 20 per cent podophyllin in olive oil combined with intravenous therapy of tartar emetic.

Herpes Febrilis or **Simplex** is manifested in humans in the form of small vesicles on the skin or mucous membrane. They are frequently located on the borders of the lips or nares, are known as *cold sores* or *fever blisters* (*Herpes labialis*), and may be distributed bilaterally or more widespread on the skin of the face, mucous membranes of the mouth and nasopharynx and occasionally on the cornea (*keratitis herpetica*). The mucosa of the genital tract may be attacked (*Herpes genitalis*), but some workers claim that the virus here is similar in all respects to *Herpes labialis*, except that it differs somewhat immunologically.

The virus is apparently widely disseminated, accompanies fevers of various types and is prone to occur more frequently secondary to coryza, pneumonia, meningitis and after exposure to drafts of cold air, local irritation, artificial fever therapy and factors producing systemic disturbances. The virus is filterable, can be propagated in tissue culture and upon the chorio-allantoic membrane of the chick embryo, is inactivated by heat and oxidizing agents, and it is relatively large in size, having a diameter greater than 100 mμ. In infected tissues, characteristic acidophilic inclusion colonies are to be seen in the affected cells. Human herpetic vesicular fluid, when applied to a scarified area of a rabbit's cornea, produces rapidly a keratitis, which is transmissible from rabbit to rabbit. This is a convenient method of demonstrating the presence of herpes virus. Intracerebral inoculation of mice produces an encephalitis. The virus can be maintained indefinitely by passage through mice.

In contrast to the other viruses, an immunity of a long or permanent nature in humans is not conferred by herpes virus. It is, at best, of short duration and usually localized. Little or no general immunity occurs. The presence of the virus in the saliva and spinal fluid of individuals with or without herpes lesions has been demonstrated, but the significance of these findings is uncertain. Much of the immunological data available concerning the distribution of immune substance in the blood of individuals who are apparently immune and others who develop herpes vesicles recurrently are paradoxical. More studies are needed for a better understanding of these findings. The possibility that epidemic encephalitis (lethargica) is caused by a neurotropic strain of the herpes virus has been considered by different workers, who claim to have isolated herpes virus from those cases. The most recent report was presented by Smith and associates (*Am. J. Path.*, 1941, **17,** 55). The neurotropic tendencies of herpes virus in experimental animals have been demonstrated. However, most workers feel that these observations require further investigations before concluding that herpes virus is etiologically related to encephalitis lethargica. Armstrong (*U. S. Pub. Health*, 1943, **58,** 16) presented evidence recently which suggests that herpes simplex virus may in rare instances be the causative agent of aseptic or lymphocytic meningitis, for which the cause is otherwise undetermined and no laboratory confirmation of infection with any other virus is elicited. In contrast to infection in man, herpes in animals or active immunization in the latter produces a general immunity which may last for several months, but at times may be of low grade.

Herpes Zoster, commonly known as *shingles*, is a subacute or chronic inflammation of the sensory nerve roots associated with pain and a vesicular eruption which involves the skin supplied by the affected nerves. The causative agent is regarded as a virus, closely related if not identical with the virus causing varicella (chicken pox), but having no relationship, as far as is known, with herpes simplex virus. Herpes zoster infections differ from those of herpes simplex. The vesicles in the former are larger than in the latter infection and are accompanied by more severe pain. Clinical evidence reveals that one attack of herpes zoster confers a high degree if not a lasting immunity.

Elementary bodies have been found in the vesicular fluid and intranuclear inclusion-colonies were observed by some in the affected cells. The virus has not been filtered and laboratory animals are refractory. Evidence is available to show that varicella may result from association with herpes zoster or when the virus causing the latter is transferred to a person nonimmune to varicella. The serum of individuals recovered from an attack of varicella reacts equally well with antigens prepared from both varicella and herpes zoster lesions in the performance of a complement-fixation test. These two infections have the same incubation period, but in chicken pox the virus attacks mainly children and reaches the blood stream from the nasopharynx; whereas in herpes zoster, the virus has a low infectivity, usually attacks adults, and reaches the skin by the neutral route. In the absence of suitable experimental animals, definite conclusions cannot be drawn regarding the exact relationship of these two diseases.

Hodgkin's Disease.—This, a granulomatous inflammation of the lymphadenoid tissues, is characterized by an insidious onset, the enlargement of the glands on one side of the neck first attracting attention. All of the glands about the neck finally become involved, so that we may have an encircling collar of neck glands. The *Corynebacterium hodgkinii* and other diphtheroid bacilli have been found with considerable frequency in this and other gland affections as to suggest an etiological relationship. Diphtheroids and even avian tubercle bacilli, which have been implicated, are not, however, to be regarded as the causative agents of this and other enlarged gland affections. In 1933, Gordon reported the production of a fatal meningo-encephalitis in rabbits following combined intramuscular and intracerebral injections of enlarged lymph glands from patients with Hodgkin's disease, but with no other closely related affections. He regards this test as specific and of practical diagnostic value. Furthermore, he is of the opinion that the causative agent is a filterable virus. Further study is needed to prove the validity of these claims.

Hog Cholera.—This disease causes severe losses and is the greatest menace to hogs with which the livestock industry in this and European countries has to contend. The causative agent is a filterable virus of unknown identity. Ten Broeck (*J. Exp. Med.*, 1941, Nov.) recently reported the artificial cultivation of the latter. The mode of infection is through the ingestion of contaminated foods and water. The virus is present in the urine of infected animals and this contaminates material. The *Salmonella cholera-suis* (*Bacillus suipestifer*) which was at one time considered the causative agent is now regarded only as a secondary invader. Some workers suggested that *Spirochaeta suis* may be a stage of the specific organism which later becomes or produces the filterable virus. This is not accepted by most observers. An effective method of artificial immunization is available against this contagious and fatal disease. The technique consists in using "serum alone" from a hyperimmunized animal or the "simultaneous method" where immune serum and infected blood are administered simultaneously. Two new vaccines have been recently advocated, the crystal-violet vaccine (Cole and McBride, *Proc. 44th Ann. Meeting U. S. Livestock Sanitary Assoc.*, 1940) and the tissue vaccine (Boynton and associates, *ibid.*, *45th Annual Meeting*, 1941).

Kerato Conjunctivitis, Infectious (*Superficial Punctate Keratitis, Nummular Keratitis*) has only recently been recognized as of sufficient importance to be included in the manual *Control of Communicable Diseases*, sponsored jointly by the U. S. Public

Health Service and the American Public Health Association (*U. S. Pub. Health Repts.*, 1943, **58,** 405). This infection is considered as being caused by a filterable virus (*J. Exp. Med.*, 1943, **77,** 71). It has an acute onset usually with the sensation as if a foreign body were under the upper lid. There is pain, excess lacrimation, marked edema with swelling of the preauricular node and membranes may form which, on removal, leave raw bleeding points. Corneal opacities usually appear. The involvement, though unilateral, may spread to both eyes as noted by Berliner (*Am. J. Ophth.*, 1943, **26,** 50). No age, sex or race is known to be immune. The infection occurs in epidemic form in warm and in temperate climates especially among industrial workers. During the latter part of 1922 and early part of 1943, many cases were found among welders in shipyards on the West Coast and so-called *shipyard disease* received considerable publicity. It is probable that masks and other protective equipment may have been responsible, in part, for the spread of this infection among the welders.

Lymphocytic Choriomeningitis is a mild disease of the central nervous system caused by a virus and characterized by an acute onset, headache, stiffness of the neck and vomiting. Other names by which this infection is known are *acute aseptic meningitis, idiopathic meningitis* and *benign lymphocytic choriomeningitis*. Complications are infrequent and complete recovery usually occurs. The seasonal distribution and respiratory symptoms noted in this disease suggest a respiratory route of infection. The virus is most readily recovered from spinal fluid or blood obtained at or prior to the height of the attack. It has been isolated at times from the urine and nasal discharges. Inoculation of susceptible animals (mice, guinea pigs and monkeys) should be carried out promptly. Mice are suspected as the animal reservoir for the virus from which man becomes infected. Armstrong (*Bull. New York Acad. Med.*, 1941, **17,** 295) divides the proved cases of this infection into grippal or non-nervous system, meningeal and meningo-encephalitic types. Following intracerebral inoculation, mice show the same types of envolement. Recently (*J. Exp. Med.*, 1940, **72,** 331) infection of guinea pigs was reported by the application of the virus to their normal skins. The estimated size of the virus is between 70 and 80 mμ. It is resistant to desiccation, freezing and glycerin and it is distinct from the virus of poliomyelitis, equine encephalomyelitis and St. Louis encephalitis. Virus-neutralizing antibodies are demonstrable in the blood from six to ten weeks following the onset of symptoms and they persist for years. Complement-fixing antibodies, of value as diagnostic aids, appear early in the disease. A specific treatment of proved value is not known. Reducing or eliminating mouse infestation appears to serve as a valuable prophylactic measure.

Lymphogranuloma Venereum.—This, a well-established disease entity, has been and is known by such names as *lymphogranuloma inguinale, lymphopathia venereum, nontuberculous granulomatous lymphadenitis, tropical* or *climatic* or *strumous bubo, esthiomene, Nicolas-Favre disease,* and *inflammatory rectal stricture*. It is a venereal disease caused by a filterable virus, probably of multiple strains. It appears to be increasing in incidence throughout the world and Slaughter (*Collect Rev., Internat. Abstr. Surg.*, 1940, **70,** 43) has suggested that this may be of the same order as the incidence of syphilis and gonorrhea. The disease occurs in all ages, affects men more frequently than women, attacks all races, though the incidence is higher in the Negro race and its prevalence is greatest in tropical and subtropical regions. The infection originates in a trivial and transitory painless lesion of the penis, vagina, vulva or rectum. Within from ten to thirty days later, the lymphatic glands are invaded. Occasionally this may be delayed for months. Inguinal adenitis is unilateral and often bilateral but may subside without suppuration. Constitutional symptoms set in. As the inguinal swelling increases in size, the skin over the affected area reddens and becomes tense. Lymph nodes may fuse to the skin, resulting in multiple areas of softening followed by the appearance of multiple fistulae, discharging a purulent material. Aspirated material from the purulent glands is free of bacteria unless a secondary infection occurred. The chronic inflammation may produce an elephantiasis of those anatomical structures drained by the affected lymphatics. In other instances the anorectal variety of the disease occurs as a result of the direct implantation of the virus on the rectal or anal mucosa. Rectal strictures and other envolvements may occur. For data concerning laboratory findings see Johnson (*Med. J. Australia*, 1943, **30**, 28), and for other details see Bettinger (*ibid.*, **30**, 23).

Rake and associates (*Proc. Soc. Exptl. Biol. Med.*, 1940, **43**, 332) succeeded in growing the infective agent in the yolk sac of the developing chick embryo and claim it is not ultramicroscopic, but that it more closely resembles the agent causing psittacosis than the characteristic viruses, such as those causing vaccinia or poliomyelitis. This disease is unique among the virus infections in that a diagnosis is possible by the aid of a skin test. Frei (*Klin. Wochnschr.*, 1925, **4**, 2148; 1927, **6**, 2042) demonstrated that the intradermal administration of diluted heated material from the unruptured bubo of a person suffering from lymphogranuloma venereum produces a cutaneous reaction in one who has the disease but not in a normal person. The original *Frei antigen*, used in the *Frei Test*, was prepared by aspirating affected inguinal glands before they had broken down, diluting with saline and inactivating by heating at 60° C. on three consecutive days. Later Grace and Suskind prepared an antigen from the brains of mice infected with the virus by intracerebral inoculation This antigen was superior to Frei's human antigen, but, owing to its high foreign protein content, reactions were produced at times. A new antigen prepared by growing the virus on chick embryos (chorio-allantoic membrane) and inactivating by heat is used at present. This material is marketed as *Lygranum S. T.* Howard and Hilly (*J. Infect. Dis.*, 1940, **68**, 73) report also on a similar product. In the *Frei Test*, 0.1 cc. of the diluted antigen is used intradermally. A positive reaction gives rise to an inflammatory papule of at least 0.5 cm. in diameter, which appears within forty-eight hours and lasts for several days. If mouse brain or chick embryo antigens are used, control tests are to be carried out.

It is important to rule out mixed venereal infections and especially the existence of syphilis by the use of dark-field examinations of material from lesions and by frequent serologic tests for at least six months after the disappearance of the lymphatic symptoms. Until recently, no adequate therapy was available. Since the introduction of the sulfonamide compounds, uniform good results have been reported following medication with these chemotherapeutic agents. Felton and associates (*Proc. 8th Amer. Sci. Congress*, 1942, **6**, 449) report on the therapeutic activity of sulfapyridine, methyl sulfathiazole, sulfanilamide, sodium sulfanilate and sodium sulfanilyl sulfanilate. The first three in the order named were most effective. The time required with the use of sodium sulfanilate was much longer, but its toxicity appears to be very low and therefore may prove more useful in many cases. See also U. S. Pub. Health Service, *Ven. Inform. Dis. Supplement*, Nov. 13, 1941, and Coutts (*Urol. & Cutan. Rev.*, 1943, **47**, 1).

Measles (*Rubeola* or *Morbilli*).—This acute, febrile, widely prevalent communicable infection, occurring naturally only in man, is still listed by some among the diseases of unknown etiology. The causative agent is a filterable virus, but an unfiltered virus, various bacilli and cocci and even a delicate spirochete associated with a Gram-negative bacillus have been implicated at one time or another. A measles streptococcus producing a soluble toxin has been isolated by Tunnicliff and associates. None of these, however, yield definite information as to the exact etiological factor, except the filterable virus, and the present available evidence indicates that this is the primary causative agent. It is possible that the finding of other agents is due to the fact that the blood of patients suffering from measles is easily invaded by different organisms.

The disease is transmitted directly from person to person and indirectly through articles soiled with the discharges (eyes, nose, throat) from infected individuals. The period of communicability is from as long as four days before the rash appears and until at least one week afterward. The virus is found in the blood and in the nasopharyngeal secretions during the early stages of the disease. Shaffer, Rake and associates (*J. Immunol.*, 1941, **41,** 241) succeeded in obtaining a clinical picture of measles by inoculating pooled human blood containing the measles virus into children and monkeys. These workers (*J. Infect. Dis.*, 1941, **69,** 65) also propagated by serial passage in tissue culture the agent of measles obtained from nasopharyngeal washings of human cases, and successfully propagated the measles virus on the chorioallantoic membrane of chicken embryo for at least 30 serial passages. Measles is probably the most common of the acute communicable diseases. It is primarily a disease of childhood since 85 per cent of all cases occur by the eighth year. Once the eruption has faded, it apparently is no longer communicable. Though the mortality of measles does not exceed 1 per cent, its grave dangers lie in the severe, dangerous and frequently fatal complications which often follow, such as bronchopneumonia, mastoiditis otitis media, sinusitis, post-measles encephalitis, enteritis and the tendency to activate latent tuberculosis. Measles, unlike scarlet fever, does not appear to be spread by patients suffering with complications.

There is apparently no natural immunity to measles. Infants under four months of age rarely contract measles even if exposed to it, as usually there is a passive placental transfer of antibody from the mother, especially if she has had measles. Acquired immunity is characteristic of the disease. One attack usually protects against subsequent attacks. Methods of active immunization by the use of vaccines or other antigen have not proved successful. Skin testing to determine the presence or absence of immunity is not of practical value. No immune animal serum (other than human) is available for treatment. The only effective means of securing some protection against measles or modifying the course of the disease is to administer passively immunizing agents such as pooled adult serum or human convalescent serum or immune human globulin. The immunity so acquired lasts for about a month and usually suffices to protect only against one contact with the disease. Another preventive dose will have to be given following a subsequent exposure. Prevention solely is to be used for checking an outbreak among children in an institution, and in very young infants and children suffering from some chronic or debilitating disease at the time of exposure. Otherwise, wherever practical, exposed healthy children, especially in private homes, should be treated so as to modify rather than to totally prevent the infection, such a modified attack resulting in a more permanent active immunity as effective as that following the natural disease. In modified measles, the incubation period is prolonged (requiring lengthening of the quarantine period), the symptoms are absent or milder and secondary complications are uncommon or minimized. These agents appear to be efficient as prophylactics and for modification of the disease. There is no conclusive evidence that they are of value in the treatment of measles even when given in larger doses.

Molluscum Contagiosum is a contagious chronic disease, occurring more frequently in children than in adults and is characterized by the development of small pearl-grey or pink pealike nodules possessing a small central depression. They appear on the face, eyelids and mucous membrane of the genitalia. White caseous-like molluscum bodies may be expressed from the central cavity. These bodies are apparently inclusion bodies and make their appearance possibly due to nuclear extrusion. The inclusion-colonies are composed of elementary bodies or granules which average about 250 mμ in diameter. Infection is transmitted by towels and other articles used in common. The virus is filterable, has not been cultivated, does not produce disease in experimental animals, but typical lesions develop when it is transmitted in man.

Mumps (*Epidemic Parotitis*).—This is an acute communicable disease characterized by tenderness, inflammation and enlargement of one or more of the salivary glands, usually the parotid, occurring only in man. Comparatively mild constitutional symptoms prevail. The generative organs, especially in adult males, may become involved. A diplococcus and a spirochete have been implicated as the etiological factor. Wolstein (*J. Exp. Med.*, 1916, **23**, 353; 1918, **28**, 377) claims that the causative agent is a filterable virus. Findlay and Clarke (*Brit. J. Exp. Path.*, 1934, **15**, 309) recently confirmed the isolation of a filterable virus reported by Johnson and Goodpasture (*Am. J. Hyg.*, 1935, **21**, 46; 1936, **23**, 329). One attack of mumps usually confers a lasting immunity. In the vast majority of cases the disease runs a mild course, terminating in complete recovery. Complications are infrequent; and when present in cases after puberty, they are usually meningeal involvements, orchitis, pancreatitis, inflammations of other glands and kidney involvements. The use of convalescent serum as a prophylactic has been tried with favorable results. There are no specific therapeutic agents of value in this treatment.

Pappataci Fever (*Phlebotomus* or *Sand-fly Fever*) is a virus disease closely resembling influenza and dengue and occurs in tropical and subtropical climates. The infection is characterized by chills, a fever of short duration, conjunctivitis, lassitude and pains. A rash may appear occasionally. The virus is present in the blood of the patient one to two days before the onset of the fever and for at least twenty-four hours thereafter. The disease is transmitted by the sand fly, *Phlebotomus papatasii*, which appears to serve as a natural reservoir. Shortt and associates (abstr. in *Trop. Dis. Bull.*, 1940, **37**, 274) cultivated the virus upon the chorioallantoic membrane of fertile eggs. Serum neutralization tests can be carried out with this as the antigen. One attack of this disease is said to confer a lasting immunity, but second and even third attacks have occurred. For details, see Sabin, *et al.* (*J. A. M. A.*, 1944, **125**, 603, 693).

Pellagra.—This is essentially a chronic disease, but may appear as an acute affection terminating rapidly with death. The symptoms are generally neurological and digestive disturbances, followed by the characteristic pellagral rash, which shows a preference for the backs of hands, extending up forearms, ridge of nose and neck, and which appears like sunburn patches. Epidemics are very common among the poorer classes. Available evidence indicates that this affection is caused by nutritional disturbances due to a lack of the so-called P-P (pellagra-preventive) factor in the diet, so that pellagra is regarded as one of the important food deficiency diseases. Goldberger's work seems to prove this conclusively, as well as yielding evidence against the infectious nature of this disease.

There are some workers, especially MacNeil and his colleagues on the Thompson-McFadden Pellagra Commission, who believe that the ingestion of damaged corn or probably an unknown infectious agent may be the etiological factor. A fungus, recovered from stools of pellagrins, has been implicated. It also has been suggested that food deficiency as the primary factor and some infectious agent, operating as a secondary invader, are both concerned in the cause and spread of this disease, but the deficiencies of the P-P factor are in large measure responsible for this affection. It is now known that this P-P factor is one of the constituents of the vitamin B complex, and that nicotinic acid (niacin) and vitamin B_2 (riboflavin (so-called vitamin G)) are the essential elements required in the dietary to cure and to prevent pellagra.

Poxes.—The term pox is applied to acute, febrile infectious diseases affecting cattle, goats, hogs, sheep, man, etc., and characterized by a vesicular or pustular exanthemata. In man the affection is known as smallpox and in the animals named above it is known, respectively, as *cowpox*, *goat pox*, *swine pox* and *sheep pox*. The pox viruses, if they have not originated from a single type, are certainly closely related. In fact, this is observed in the use of cowpox vaccine among humans for immunization against smallpox. Glycerin does not affect pox virus, so that when added to virus lymph, bacteria will eventually die, but the pox virus will not be affected to any great extent.

The virus of *fowl pox* is different from the pox virus considered above. The virus of fowl pox also produces *avian diphtheria*, and the two forms of the disease are, at times, observed in the same bird. In the diphtheritic condition, pseudo-membranes are found on the mucosa of the nose, throat, mouth and conjunctivae. In the pox manifestation, nodular eruptions are observed on parts of the body where feathers are scarce or absent, such as on the comb, wattles, etc. "Chalmydozoa," regarded by some as the carriers of the virus, are found in the affected areas of cases of fowl pox and avian diphtheria. The use of fowl-pox and pigeon-pox vaccines for immunization has proved highly satisfactory. Vaccination is accomplished either by the "stick" or "stab" method or by the "follicle" method. In the latter, 6 to 10 feathers are pulled from the leg and the vaccine is rubbed vigorously into the follicles with a brush. In the stick or stab method, a narrow sharp lancet is dipped into the vaccine and then stabbed into the skin on the outside of the leg near the knee.

Psittacosis.—This disease is due to a filterable virus (*Lancet*, 1930, **1**, 235, 345) and most human infections are contracted by inhalation of infecting particles mainly from parrots, parakeets, lovebirds or canaries. The term ornithosis has been proposed as all-embracing, rather than psittacosis. It is possible that well birds (carriers) transmit the infection. Occasionally the virus is transmitted from a human case. Adequate control measures require abolishing the use as house pets of birds of the parrot family or at least keeping them under strict regulations. Even their importation to zoological gardens for educational purposes requires precautionary measures as: the quarantine of new shipments of psittacine birds for from four to six months, the proper disposal of the excreta of the birds, and the use by attendants of masks, goggles and rubber gloves. Unless psittacosis is suspected in humans because of association with sick psittacine birds, the diagnosis based on clinical symptoms is usually influenza or atypical pneumonia. Laboratory aids consist in the inoculation of rice-birds or canaries and usually mice with the blood (obtained in the first week of the illness) or with sputum, which cause characteristic pathological changes. Elementary bodies are found in the spleen and they also are found in smears made from the meninges or choroid plexuses, readily observed by a special technique using Machiavello stain. It may also be advisable to administer intranasal infiltrations as well as subcutaneous injections. An outbreak of psittacosis among birds with 60 deaths at the National Zoological Park was reported recently by Tomlinson (*U. S. Pub. Health Rept.*, 1941, **56,** 1073); and an interesting account of an outbreak of psittacosis among human beings in Buenos Aires, Argentine, which involved 30 cases with 13 deaths, together with clinical epidemiologic impressions, are presented by Garcia (*Prensa méd. argent.*, 1940, **27,** 2463, 2514). Levinthal and Coles and Lillie, all independently, found small coccoid bodies resembling rickettsiae in infected material. Evidence has been furnished that these bodies are the virus. They are the elementary bodies and at times are known as L. C. L. bodies. Rivers and Berry (*J. Exp. Med.*, 1935, **61,** 205) described a diagnostic method which consists in inoculating mice intraperitoneally with filtered or unfiltered sputum from suspicious cases and finding typical lesions and L. C. L. bodies in the liver and spleen.

The recovery of psittacosis virus from apparently normal pigeons (*Lancet*, 1943, **244,** 292) indicates that pigeons, particularly if ill, may be a menace to humans. The disease is not found in birds kept under sanitary conditions. The possibility of the extension of the host range of psittacosis must be kept in mind and the military use of pigeons makes the problem of concern to humans.

Rabies.— *Rabies* or *hydrophobia*, one of the oldest and most feared of diseases, is an acute, infectious disease of warm-blooded animals and common among the lower animals. Practically all mammals are susceptible, but it is most common in dogs, cats and wild carnivores. The bite of an animal must be considered as potentially suspected of being rabid. It may be transmitted to man as a result of bites inflicted by infected animals. About 90 per cent of human rabies is due to dog bites. The incubation period in man varies from twenty to sixty days but may be less in the case of bites about the head, neck and upper extremities. The first definite symptoms are difficulty in breathing, a feeling of oppression and an inability to swallow. Convulsive contraction of the throat muscles is followed later by generalized convulsive attacks over the whole body. Most of the special reflexes are exaggerated. Paralysis finally sets in and death occurs due to the effects upon the heart or respiratory center. The fatality usually results within one week (and generally on the third or fourth day) after symptoms have appeared. The virus resides in the saliva and nervous tissue. Diagnosis of rabies in suspected rabid animals is best made by examining their brains and finding *Negri bodies* in the large nerve cells of the hippocampus major or in the Purkinje cells of the cerebellum. Negri bodies are the inclusion bodies and are round or oval, oblong, triangular or ameboid, from 1 to 20 μ in diameter, and when properly stained, deep staining granules may be visible.

What are these inclusion bodies or, in this specific case, what are the Negri bodies? Is an inclusion body merely a peculiar type of cell degeneration, characteristic of the specific disease (as Negri bodies specifically mean rabies beyond a doubt), without possessing any etiological significance? Or are inclusion bodies not only diagnostic of the specific disease (Negri bodies diagnostic of rabies), but also actually the specific causative factors or viruses? Such are the two distinct opinions of thought. Whichever may be the case, this we do know: that the virus causing rabies is filterable and that the demonstration of Negri bodies in brain specimens indicates rabies. In fact, rabies is the only virus disease usually diagnosed upon the finding of the inclusion bodies, so-called Negri bodies, in smears or sections from the central nervous system of the infected animal. When brain specimens or sections of the latter do not reveal Negri bodies or the findings are doubtful, it may be best to check all negative or suspicious observations by inoculating an emulsion of some of the suspected tissue or, better still, a Berkefeld filtrate of this emulsion into guinea pigs, rabbits or mice, preferably the latter. The injection is made under the dura mater. These animals usually show symptoms within a week if the tissue is positive (*J. Am. Vet. M. A.*, 1939, **95,** 659).

In the treatment of wounds, caused by suspected rabid animals, the wound should receive immediate surgical attention, including cauterization which should be thorough and should be done as soon as possible after the bite, using pure nitric acid and preferably fuming nitric acid. By placing a piece of a match stick (or pine wood) in a test tube with chemically pure nitric acid and boiling the mixture for a minute, fuming nitric acid is produced. This can be stoppered, cooled and used. The cauterization is imperative, even though the Pasteur treatment (page 498) is given later. This later immunization treatment should also start as soon as a diagnosis of the suspected animal is made. If the animal cannot be caught or if the diagnosis is in doubt or may take too long before being definitely established, the immunization should commence at once.

Systematic destruction of rabid dogs and all animals bitten by them, the imposition of a quarantine on all dogs shipped into the country and the use of canine prophylactic immunization will aid in the control of rabies. As pointed out by Oleson (*U. S. Pub. Health Repts.*, 1935, **50,** 1087), there are many difficulties in attempting a solution of this problem and much more experimental work is yet to be done. The use of antirabic vaccine for humans in the so-called Pasteur treatment is to start as soon as possible after being bitten by rabid or suspicious rabid animals. This is essentially a prophylactic agent and the treatment one of prophylaxis. This and other available therapeutic agents are of no value in the treatment of rabies after clinical symptoms have appeared.

Rheumatism.—Rheumatism is a very vague term under which are grouped several constitutional diseases which present different symptoms. The two main groups are, however, the acute form, preferably called *Juvenile Rheumatism*, including rheumatic fever or acute articular rheumatism, with its frequent association of rheumatic heart (cardiac lesions), manifestations in the joints (arthritis) and chorea or St. Vitus's dance. The other group, chronic rheumatism or chronic arthritis, includes rheumatoid arthritis or arthritis deformans or any form of fibrous or muscular inflammation. The distinction of rheumatism from gout is still unsatisfactory. It is also unfortunate that cases of "neuritis," which is a definite disease condition with definite symptoms, are frequently misdiagnosed as rheumatism or vice versa.

From the standpoint of etiology, rheumatism remains an unsolved problem. Many believe that bacteria, especially members of the cocci group, are fundamentally the causative agents. The green streptococci (*Streptococcus viridans*) have long been held responsible for these conditions. Others claim that the streptococci present in many of these cases (*Streptococcus* [Diplococcus or Micrococcus] *rheumaticus* of Triboulet, Poyton and Paine, Rosenow and others) possess a selective affinity for the tissues of the joints. Small claims to have demonstrated the constant presence of a specific nonviridans, inulin-fermenting streptococcus in the blood of acute rheumatic fever patients, and which he calls *Streptococcus cardioarthritidis*. The study of the immunological response of those affected with rheumatism strongly suggests the presence of an antecedent streptococcal infection, especially belonging to Group A. The possibility of a filterable virus being the real cause and the streptococcus as secondary though constantly associated has been suggested. Others have indicated that the visceral and peripheral lesions are allergic. It is to be observed that the anatomical structure of the joints and synovial membranes favors bacterial growth, and it is probable that in constitutional diseases and blood infections the circulating organisms may find their way into these tissues and cause the various disorders. Yet, on the other hand, it is interesting to note that cultures taken from rheumatic joints are almost always sterile. Of course, this does not preclude the presence of bacteria in the joint tissues, for perhaps there is needed more perfection in the techniques that are used in culturing. There is also the possibility that it is only the bacterial toxins which are present, because they possess a selective affinity for these tissues, just as tetanus toxin does for nerve cells. This would account for negative cultures from the tissues of joints. Whatever may be the exact causative agent, most workers agree that infection in some form, directly or indirectly, plays an important etiological role in producing most cases of rheumatism. It is, of course, just as probable that not all forms of this disease are due to infection. All workers are emphatic on the importance of removing any septic focus. The areas most frequently involved are bad teeth, tonsils, adenoids, sinuses, especially the intestines (large and more frequently the small) and occasionally the focus may be in the prostate gland, gallbladder, etc.

Immunity in rheumatism rarely occurs. In fact, a hypersusceptibility to recurrent attacks is observed frequently. Treatment with vaccine and serum therapy have been tried. More data are needed before these biological products can be advocated as efficient preparations to be used on all cases. The essential in treating juvenile rheumatism is rest. Sanatorium care is preferable. Measures should be employed to improve the individual's resistance in all types of rheumatism. In a discussion on possible methods for the prevention of rheumatic manifestations in the armed forces, Hare (*Can. Med. Assoc. J.*, 1943, **48**, 116) states that this disease is best avoided by preventing streptococcal infections, especially by segregating carriers of hemolytic streptococcus Group A (detected by throat swabs), by preventing cross-infection by wide bed spacing, avoiding double-tiered bunks, and by minimizing dust in sleeping quarters. These precautions are probably more essential for recruit training depots than for units containing trained men. Ultraviolet light, aerosols, propylene glycol vapor and blanket oiling are either too elaborate or not yet sufficiently standardized for service use. For further details see Paul (*Epidemiology of Rheumatic Fever*, Am. Heart Assoc., 1943, New York City) and pamphlet on rheumatic fever (issued by Metropolitan Life Insurance Co.).

Rift Valley Fever is a disease which affects primarily sheep, cattle and goats and is present in East Africa. The etiological agent is a filterable virus, which is found in the blood, liver and spleen of infected animals.   Man appears to be highly susceptible and the symptoms experienced are as encountered in influenza and dengue fever. It is thought that an insect, probably the mosquito, is the vector.   A high degree of immunity results following an attack.

Rinderpest or Cattle Plague.—This, a highly fatal disease of the bovine species in practically all countries but the United States proper, is an acute, febrile affection, characterized by inflammation of the mucous membranes of the alimentary tract. The causative agent is an unknown filterable virus, which is passed from animal to animal, largely through the agency of contaminated food and water.   The use of immunized sera conferring a passive immunity has been used both in the treatment and prevention of this disease.   A vaccine is being used for immunization.

Scarlet Fever.—This is an acute, febrile, highly contagious disease, occurring sporadically and in epidemics.   It is one of the most dreaded diseases of childhood, not only because of its high degree of infectiousness, but especially because of the many and grave complications with which it may be attended.

Epithelial protozoa have been implicated at one time as the causative agents.   A virus was regarded as the cause, but most observers no longer consider scarlet fever a virus disease.   The evidence is in favor of regarding hemolytic streptococci (which see) as the causative agents.   See Dick Test (page 489), Scarlet Fever Toxin and Antitoxin (pages 464 and 489) and Schultz-Charlton Reaction (page 464).

Smallpox (*Variola*); *Varioloid* (*attenuated cases*); *Alastrim* (*mild form*) **and Allied Diseases.**—This is an acute, highly contagious disease, occurring spontaneously in man, although lower animals may be infected.   This disease is related to cowpox, sheep pox, goat pox, swine pox, all of which are also characterized by a vesicular exanthemata.   The relationship between cowpox and smallpox in particular is a close one.   The etiological factor which causes smallpox and the other "poxes" is still unknown.   Many workers have claimed that the prevailing inclusion bodies (which as parasites or parasite-like bodies have been included among the so-called chlamydozoa) and even other protozoan groups are the causative agents.   Smadel and Hoagland (*Bact. Revs.*, 1942, **6**, 79) present a detailed consideration on the identification of and the physical, chemical and antigenic properties of the elementary bodies of vaccinia.

.Whatever the actual causative agent, we do know that the virus is not filterable, and is transmitted with extreme ease.   It is present in the skin of the diseased individual in all stages, in the lesions of the mucous membranes, and in the body secretions including the urine and feces.   Smallpox has been a scourge of mankind attacking all races and all ages, prevailing during all seasons in all countries over the entire globe and occurring throughout all periods of man's·existence.   At one time it was more common than measles, and during the eighteenth century, when the best records are available, almost everyone had the disease before adult age and usually before the seventh year of life was reached.   In days gone by, it is estimated that more than one-half million died annually due to smallpox.   The disease is characterized by sudden fever, pronounced chills, aches, nausea and vomiting and an eruption.   The latter, after passing through various stages of papule, vesicle and pustule, dries up and distinct scars remain.   When the pocks are separated from each other by areas of skin free of eruption, the disease is known as *discrete* or *distinct* smallpox in contrast to a more severe form, *confluent smallpox*, a name employed when the vesicles and pustules run together, usually covering extensive areas of the skin surface.   The virus does not always display the same virulency, so that other types of the disease have been enumerated. There is the mild form, *varioloid*, which is smallpox modified probably by vaccination. Then in unvaccinated individuals we have the true smallpox, *variola vera* (with its milder types known as *variola minor*, *alastrim*, *Kaffir pox*, *milk pox*, etc.). The most fatal type of the disease is *variola haemorrhagica*. Here blood spots appear due to the occurrence of hemorrhages into the skin and mucous membrane.

Though we know little about the etiology and do not have available a specific therapeutic agent for treatment, our knowledge of the means of defense against this dreaded disease is far advanced. Isolation, quarantine, proper sanitation and personal hygiene will aid in the prevention of smallpox, but the safest procedure to prevent getting this disease, and a measure which should be made compulsory the world over, is *vaccination* and *revaccination*. The production of modified smallpox virus and a brief consideration of vaccination are given in another chapter.

Trachoma.—This is a contagious chronic disease of the eye, which commences as a follicular conjunctivitis and, if untreated, leads to scarring of the eyelids with deformity or to an impairment of vision through "pannus" formation or corneal ulceration. Some workers regard the etiological factor as a filterable virus, which they include among the *chlamydozoa*. The latter is a group containing parasite-like bodies, occupying a place midway between the bacteria and protozoa. Others believe that the inclusion bodies in trachoma are nothing more than masses of hemoglobinophilic bacilli or nests of growing bacteria or cell-reaction products stimulated by bacterial infection. Rickettsia and a virus have been implicated as the etiological agent. There seems to be no general agreement as to the etiological factor. The disease is usually controlled by observing the rules of personal hygiene, isolating diseased cases and carrying out the usual sanitary precautions. Recent reports reveal that trachoma, in its early stages, responds to sulfonamide therapy, either sulfanilamide or sulfapyridine, the former being favored as the drug of choice.

Trench Fever.—This, as a clinical entity, was reported among the troops in France in the first World War. It is caused by an unknown virus which is present in the blood. The human louse, *P. humanus* is the vector and the infection is usually derived from the excreta of infected lice scratched or rubbed into skin abrasions. Though not a fatal disease, trench fever is a crippling one. Prophylaxis consists chiefly in measures directed against lice. The sputum and urine must be disinfected, as they contain the virus.

Tumors (Malignant).—As far as is known, malignant tumors occur spontaneously among all races of human beings. There seems to be no adequate immunity produced and no means are as yet available for creating such an immunity. There is no agreement as to a possible etiological factor, mode of transmission, communicability, etc. Though no general agreement on many questions has resulted, considerable valuable information has, nevertheless, been gained within the past decade. Since the discovery of spontaneous malignant tumors in mice, rats and other lower animals, and their transmissibility when emulsions of these growths are injected into normal animals of the same species, considerable knowledge has been made available. It seems probable that the conditions influencing the production of tumors and the methods employed to create an immunity among the lower animals are comparable to those operative among human beings.

The germ theory of cancer is discounted by many. The thought that cancer cells are of some abnormal species foreign to the human body is also discounted today. It has been suggested that these are normal cells which have grown wild because they have been compelled to live in the wrong (too alkaline) environment. The question has been raised whether cancer is a general rather than a local disease (Editorial, *J. A. M. A.*, 1943, **122,** 509). Cancer is not contagious and there is every reason to believe that it is not caused by a specific infectious agent. It appears that cancer is the result of normal cells being transformed into malignant cells, which are permanently altered cells. The latter have an abnormally high rate of multiplication as compared with normal cells and are capable of invading and destroying the latter, thus causing death. It may be that cancer is not a single disease, but a group of diseases in which each type of cancer is derived from a different type of normal cell, and each type possessing its own peculiar characteristics. Diverse factors are probably the cause of cancer and are divided into two broad groups—"external" or "extrinsic" and "internal" or "intrinsic" causative factors. The former act from without and the latter from within the body. External carcinogenic agents are to be found in soot, certain coal tars, various chemicals in the manufacture of aniline dyes, excessive exposure to some physical agents as sunlight, radium or x-rays. Certain hormones, especially the sex hormones, are examples of the intrinsic causative factors which, in part, may cause cancer. A cure is only possible if cancer is localized, so that surgery, x-rays or radium can be applied for the complete destruction of the growth. Recently, Taylor (*Science*, 1943, **97,** 123) reported on the successful production of a mammalian tumor with a virus or virus-like principle free of tumor tissue or cells. The implications of this are obvious, and it is possible that the hypothesis held by some workers that a virus is the primary cause of tumorous growths will again be brought to the forefront.

Vaccines of cancer cells and cells from other tumors have been used by some workers for the treatment of malignant tumors in human beings, both in inoperable cases and in cases where the primary tumors have been removed. The vaccine (preferably autogenous) was and is employed with the hope of preventing any further progress of the disease so that additional growths will be avoided. Actual cures and prevention of further involvement have *not* been recorded. Temporary relief has been achieved in many instances by the use of a variety of injections of cells from tumors, other normal tissues, and even the patient's own blood or blood serum (autoserum therapy). It is probable that the temporary beneficial effects of these substances are due to nonspecific protein reactions. See also Coley's fluid (page 495).

Verrucae or Common Warts are infectious dermal lesions found in various animals and man and are regarded as being caused by filterable viruses. These tumor-like bodies are known as *papillomas* in rabbits, dogs, cattle and other animals and as warts (*verruca vulgaris*) in man. They all contain intranuclear inclusion bodies. More investigation is required to supply needed data and especially information concerning the susceptibility to and the immunity created by this condition.

Yellow Fever.—This is an acute infectious disease occurring spontaneously only in man. Though prevailing endemically in the tropical countries of the Western Hemisphere and along the western coast of Africa, it has been, at times, introduced into the temperate zone, where it is eventually checked by the cold weather. The virus is present in the human blood stream to a maximum in from twenty-four to forty-eight hours after infection and usually is absent in the blood by the fourth day.

Early blood inoculation into susceptible monkeys (*Macacus rhesus*) may establish the diagnosis. Albumin appears in the urine usually on the second or third day; of diagnostic value is the fact that it increases rapidly and the albuminuria reaches a maximum from the fifth to the seventh day. A vast reservoir of yellow fever persists in West Africa, in certain parts of Brazil and other South American areas. Due to increased and more rapid means of travel, the presence of yellow fever in any part of the world becomes the immediate concern of all countries, so that quarantine measures become a necessity. The causative agent is a filterable virus. Based on epidemiological studies, two types are recognized, *urban yellow fever* and *jungle yellow fever*. The infecting agent and the clinical and anatomical features are the same in both types, but the dissemination, incidence and method of control are different.

Urban yellow fever is transmissible in most instances by the bites of female mosquitoes of the species *Aedes aegypti* or *Stegomyia calopus*. In West Africa, many species of *aedes* and species of *anopheles, culex, mansonis* and *eretmopodites* transmit the virus by bite. Jungle yellow fever is transmitted by several species of mosquitoes. The possibility that certain monkeys are carriers has been suggested. Viscerotomy or, specifically, the routine postmortem removal of liver tissue for microscopical observation revealed the existence of "silent" areas especially in Brazil (*Tr. Roy. Soc. Trop. Med. & Hyg.*, 1938, **32**, 297). As a result of viscerotomies and the introduction of the mouse-protection test for determining immunity (*J. Exp. Med.*, 1931, **54**, 533), followed by field surveys (*Am. J. Trop. Med.*, 1937, **17**, 457), there was presented evidence that in jungle yellow fever man is not necessarily an important source of the main entrance of the virus and the *Aedes aegypti* is not the vector.

A period of about nine to twelve days is necessary after a mosquito has fed on a yellow-fever patient before it can affect another individual. A permanent immunity develops in recovered cases. It is possible to give yellow fever to monkeys but not to other animals. If, however, an irritating substance is injected into the brain of a mouse at the same time as the yellow-fever virus is injected, the disease is produced in the mouse. Passage of this mouse virus through many mice will weaken the virus. This weakened virus is being used in experimental investigations.

The most effective method of combating yellow fever is to attack the mosquito host. The most valuable method for the control of both urban and jungle yellow fever is by immunization with attenuated *17-D* yellow fever virus, an effective vaccination procedure (see page 499). For a consideration of yellow fever, see Emmett (*U. S. Nav. M. Bull.*, 1943, **41**, 575) and of yellow fever in the Americas, see Sawyer (*Proc. 8th Amer. Sci. Congress*, 1942, **6**, 297).

PART III

STERILIZATION AND DISINFECTION

Chapter XVII

THE DESTRUCTION OF BACTERIA (STERILIZATION)

No BRANCH of bacteriology is of more practical importance than that which deals with the agencies and methods which bring about the destruction of all kinds of microorganisms.

Sterilization means the destruction of living microorganisms in or their removal from materials. The term is used generally when referring to any method or procedure by which such end results may be accomplished. It is, however, used more specifically or frequently limited to the destruction of bacteria by *heat*. *Disinfection* is synonymous with the term sterilization, but it is employed mainly to designate that process where chemicals are used as the means of ridding environments free of bacteria. In the broad sense, the term may be used when referring to the destruction of insects, or to free from infection, mainly by destroying microorganisms causing disease (especially vegetative forms and not spore forms). The term sterilization under these conditions applies to a more rigid process, for here all organic life is destroyed. As some individuals employ the term disinfection, it is possible to conceive of something being thoroughly disinfected (free of infection) but not completely sterilized (rendered sterile). *Fumigation* is also synonymous with the above terms, but applied only to those procedures in which a gaseous chemical or fumes generated from a chemical or drug are used to obtain the desired end result (destruction of bacteria and insects). The following three agents are most frequently employed in the everyday practical routine in the laboratory for the sterilization of material: (*a*) heat; (*b*) chemicals; and (*c*) filtration.

PHYSICAL AGENTS

Before entering into a consideration of the above-named methods, mention should be made of certain physical agents, which exert a deleterious action upon bacteria, but which are employed only to a limited extent as practical procedures by the bacteriologist.

Light.—Light exerts an action upon bacteria as to attenuate and even totally destroy microorganisms after exposure for a long period. Diffuse light will require a longer period of time to destroy bacteria than will direct sunlight. The rays of the sun act as powerful destructive agents for almost all bacteria except the sulfur bacteria, which utilize sunlight as do the plants containing chlorophyll.   It seems to be not so much the high heat which the rays emit that destroys bacteria, as the fact that they exert a certain action, regarded as a photochemical change within the bacteria themselves, in all probability due to the absorption of the rays by the bacterial protoplasm.

After close observations and experimentations with the various colors of the spectrum, it was observed that each color exerted a different action on bacteria, the intensity of which increases from the red toward the violet, the destructive powers being at their maximum at the ultraviolet rays.   The yellow and red lights possess no bactericidal powers, while the green light is only slightly bactericidal.   The blue, violet and ultraviolet rays are bactericidal.   It was soon discovered that this remarkable property was due to the fact that the latter possess a short wave length.   This brought about the introduction of the ultraviolet rays (which were produced by a Cooper-Hewitt mercury arc).

At present the ultraviolet rays cannot be regarded as a practical means of sterilizing pharmacuetical and chemical mixtures or solutions for bacteriological purposes. This is due to the fact that many of the latter are either decomposed or that they cannot be completely sterilized.   A still greater defect is that the sterile glass containers, in which the solutions must be kept, absorb the rays of shortest wave lengths, which are the ones that possess the most active destructive powers.   Turbidity, organic or inorganic, some proteins, intense colored solutions and other bodies interfere with the action of the rays.   The ultraviolet light has been employed only on a large scale.   It is used by some for the sterilization of milk; and during World War I its use was extended to the sterilization of drinking water, especially in those regions where it was impossible to use any other method of purification.   The sterilization was effected by placing the lamps directly into the water, and allowing the light to act for a few minutes, within which time a potable sample without any marked physical or chemical change was produced.   The rays were only used in clear water, as they were found to be ineffective in turbid samples.   The more recent use of ultraviolet light as a sanitary aid is detailed in a separate chapter, pages 267–269.

Other forms of light as the Roentgen rays, radium rays and rays from the different strong electric lights have been reported by workers from time to time as possessing definite inhibitory or slight destructive powers upon bacteria, but these cannot be used practically.   Electric light exerts an influence similar to the sun's rays.

Air.—"Plenty of sunshine and fresh air" is the old maxim.   The sterilizing quality of sunshine has been touched upon.   The free circulation of pure air is very essential; and though not a direct practical laboratory method in use for ridding material free of bacteria, it is a procedure used every day by the layman in sterilizing his household goods, and by the physician in his treatment of the numerous diseases with which he comes in contact, inasmuch as atmospheric oxygen will dilute the bacterial content, will usually carry along the germicidal action of sunlight, and will favor drying which in turn will hasten the death of many organisms.

Drying (Desiccation).—Many of the pathogens will sooner or later succumb in environments where *complete* desiccation exists.   Organisms like the influenza bacillus, the vibrio of Asiatic cholera, the meningococcus and the gonococcus are especially sensitive and are destroyed by drying within a few hours after the withdrawal of moisture.   It is based on this fact that many hygienists claim that dust does not necessarily contain pathogenic nonspore-forming bacteria, because moisture is absent in most instances. They say that ordinary dust is injurious to human beings because of the irritation produced on the mucous membranes and the subsequent invasion of virulent bacteria, and not due to the fact that the dust itself contains pathogens.

Various investigations reveal that many factors other than the desiccation *per se* have an influence upon the survival of bacteria. Among these are the nature of the medium or environment in which the bacteria are present, the temperature and the concentration of oxygen prevailing, the number of bacteria present, whether the latter are subjected to an alternate moistening and drying or to an alternate temperature change or to an uninterrupted drying and even to the rapidity of the latter. For instance, freezing a suspension of bacteria and drying under vacuo as in the lyophile process preserve the bacteria intact with even such factors as virulence and antigenicity unaltered. The marketing of dried fruits and vegetables, dried eggs and milk and other foodstuffs results in a reduction of the total numbers of bacteria due to the heating as well as the effect of desiccation. Bacteria in the dehydrated products will not multiply or exert their effects, as the moisture content is generally far below that required for bacterial activity.

Electricity.—The use of electricity as a sterilizing agent is at present limited. It is, however, employed in the purification of sewage in small sewage disposal plants, and also for the sterilization of small quantities of water. Its action appears to be due to the fact that it oxidizes organic matter and is not due to the current itself or any heat evolved, as usually the rise in temperature is almost *nil* (see Fabian and Graham (*J. Bact.*, 1933, **25,** 34) and Tracy (*ibid.*, 1932, **24,** 432)). However not all workers agree, as others regard the destruction as due to an elevation of temperature, and in some instances electrolytic changes resulting in the production of chlorine and ozone may be responsible for bacterial changes. The so-called *electropure pasteurizers* have been used for the treatment of milk. The latter is exposed to the electrical current for about ten seconds by flowing through two carbon electrodes which carry the electric current.

Cold.—Cold may be regarded as a preserving agent. As has been mentioned previously, freezing temperatures check bacterial growth and after a prolonged period of time, many of the pathogens finally die. Cold, recognized as a valuable and effective means of checking bacterial growth and as a method of protection against attack by insect pests, is universally used to preserve foodstuffs. In the pharmacy and bacteriological laboratory, biological products and other preparations are directed to be kept at low temperatures for the same reason.

Haines (*Proc. Roy. Soc.*, Ser. B, 1938, **124,** 451) reports on the temperatures at which frozen bacteria are stored as markedly influencing their death rate. It must be remembered that many bacteria survive very low temperatures for long periods of time, not only due to the fact that more time is required for the formation of products of metabolism to affect them, but also due to the lessened effect of these products at low temperatures. Even known bactericidal substances as well as all antibacterial agents become less and less active as the temperature becomes lower. For the use of cold storage in the preservation of food, see page 299.

Vibration.—A so-called "singing" tube (a nickel tube caused to vibrate intensely and at a high rate of speed by being placed in a rapidly alternating magnetic field controlled by a mechanism similar to that used in radio broadcasting) has been used to destroy bacteria in milk. *Sonic and supersonic vibrations* will reduce the bacterial content in materials but will not render the latter sterile. In the author's laboratory, *high frequency sound waves* vibrating at 8900 cycles per second (*Am. J. Pharm.*, 1940, **112**, 373) produced a definite killing action but sterility was never produced. Even with the use of a more powerful oscillator, similar findings were obtained (unpublished results). This vibration treatment is being used in the study of bacterial enzymes, toxins and other products and in the study of antigenic components. Perhaps further perfection may make available a means of sterilizing or at least reducing markedly the bacterial content of products which cannot be treated by chemicals or be heated at all or only at a low temperature.

Other Physical Agents.—*Agitation*, by violent and protracted shaking, will produce disintegration of bacterial cells but will not produce sterility. Curran and Evans (*J. Bact.*, 1942, **43**, 125) found that bacterial spores and vegetative forms were progressively destroyed when their fluid suspensions were agitated vigorously with finely divided abrasives. Vegetative forms of bacteria are more rapidly disintegrated than spores. The mechanical destruction of spores is apparently not correlated with thermal resistance, but is dependent upon the kind, particle size and amount of abrasive and the species and density of the spore suspension. *Pressure* as can be applied in practice has little influence upon the destruction of bacteria, unless it is very high (5000 to 6000 atmospheres) and prolonged. On the other hand, adding a soluble gas, especially CO_2, to the medium under pressure and then suddenly releasing the latter results in bacterial disruption, due probably to mechanical injury. Sudden release of pressure with other gases does not appear to produce the same results.

Chapter XVIII

ULTRAVIOLET LIGHT

INASMUCH AS ultraviolet light is used extensively in practice today, a more extensive consideration is herein presented.

Forms of Radiant Energy.—The visible spectrum was discovered in 1665. This visible spectrum which was thought to be one band of light, colored white, was found to be in reality a combination of many different colors of light. In addition to these bands of visible radiation there are other rays emanating from the sun which are invisible to the human eye. Some known as infra-red rays are invisible, but this radiation is detected by the heat produced. Others, spoken of as ultraviolet rays, also are invisible; this form of radiant energy is not detected by any of our senses, although some of the effects produced subsequently may become apparent. These three forms of radiation, one visible and the other two invisible, all emanating from the sun differ in the lengths of their waves. The ultraviolet rays are the shortest; the visible light rays are longer; and the infra-red waves are the longest.

Wave lengths of light rays are measured in terms of Angstrom units. An Angstrom unit is 1/10,000th of a micron. The visible light is subdivided into colors of the spectrum by the energy of different wave lengths of an approximate range from the red, 8000 Angstrom units, to the violet 4000 Angstrom units. To be exact, the longest visible rays, the red, have a length of 7610 Angstrom units; and the shortest visible rays, the violet, have a length of 3970 Angstrom units or approximately 1/63,000th of an inch. The infra-red rays, which are heat rays, are longer than the red and the ultraviolet rays are shorter than the violet.

Ultraviolet Light.—The ultraviolet portion of the spectrum consists of wave lengths which extend from a range of 3970 Angstrom units to about 1000 Angstrom units. By passing a beam of ultraviolet light through a quartz prism, this can be subdivided approximately into three divisions, the far ultraviolet rays (1000 to 2000 Angstrom units), middle ultraviolet (2000 to 3000 Angstrom units), and near ultraviolet (3000 to 4000 Angstrom units). In another more convenient breakdown, the ultraviolet spectrum is divided into four parts. From 1000 to 2000 Angstrom units are radiations which form a toxic gas, ozone, the so-called ozone-forming ultraviolet radiations. In the range from 2000 to 2950 Angstrom units are to be found radiations which are effective in destroying bacteria. In the range from 2800 to 3300 Angstrom units are to be found the "biologically effective" radiations, those producing sunburn; and because they also are useful in activation of vitamin D, they sometimes are called the antirachitic ultraviolet radiations. In the range from 3300 to 4000 Angstrom units or the region closest to the visible spectrum are to be found radiations useful for their fluorescent display and of value in some types of photography. These divisions are not very sharply defined; they frequently merge and often actually overlap considerably.

Transmission of Ultraviolet Light.—Most ultraviolet rays from the sun fail to reach the earth. Actually the air acts as a differential filtering medium holding back many rays. In most places radiations shorter than 2900 Angstrom units never penetrate to the ground; in fact, the shortest to reach us is usually from 2950 to 3100 Angstrom units in length. Less than 0.1 per cent of the total radiations from the sun is in the form of ultraviolet rays and almost all of the latter are longer than 2900 Angstrom units. Furthermore, only the long ultraviolet rays will pass through ordinary window glass. While the latter is transparent to the visible light rays, it is opaque to light of wave lengths shorter than 3100 Angstrom units. Sunlight reaching us therefore is most frequently devoid of an active germicidal effect and that is especially the case of sunlight that has passed through an ordinary pane of window glass. On the other hand, a special type of commercial glass and in particular quartz allows the passage of ultraviolet light possessing wave lengths shorter than 2900 Angstrom units. Most ultraviolet light is absorbed by thin layers of fluids containing proteins or turbid material, by layers of oil and grease, and also by tissue cells. Tissue is not penetrated more than one millimeter (0.039 of an inch) in depth. Very short wave-length radiations are absorbed by air in the production of ozone. These facts must be considered in the practical use of ultraviolet light as a bactericidal agent.

Generating Ultraviolet Light.—Artificially generated light is just as effective as the corresponding rays of sunlight that possess the same wave lengths or the same intensity. After several years of careful research and extensive experimental work, Dr. Harvey C. Rentschler, engineer and research director, Dr. Robert F. James, bacteriologist, and other workers associated with Westinghouse Lamp Division succeeded in designing equipment for ultraviolet radiation which overcomes most of the objections made against other previously introduced ultraviolet generators. The radiations produced by the latter were found to cover broad rather than selective bands of wave lengths, which were found to be most effective as germicidal agents. The newly introduced equipment or so-called ultraviolet lamps have evolved from a careful segregation of different wave lengths and the elimination of other short-wave radiations that are valueless as bactericidal agents and even undesirable. By a simple and rapid method for measuring ultraviolet radiation, a better understanding of the action of short waves on germs has become possible. In fact, it was found that radiations or short waves generated at the 2537 Angstrom unit region of the spectrum possessed the greatest sterilizing or germicidal power. The introduction of this new equipment with an effective ultraviolet lamp and the practical application of selective bactericidal ultraviolet waves or radiations developed into a process known by many as the Rentschlerizing process or Rentschlerization.

Sanitization.—Ultraviolet radiation, when used, is employed to reduce the total germ content and especially for the destruction of those organisms causing disease or capable of decomposing materials. It is not practical to effect complete sterilization. It is on this account that for want of more suitable terms the words *sanitize* and *sanitization* have been advocated in place of sterilization and disinfection. Sanitization is that process which renders materials free of organisms that produce disease, or are capable of decomposing substances, or which are indicative of insanitary conditions.

Application.—In practical application, ultraviolet sanitization is being employed in operating rooms of hospitals, in nurseries, cubicles, children's wards, and other parts of these institutions, in combination with air-conditioning units to better control the sanitary quality of the air supplied, in pharmaceutical, biological, chemical and bacteriological laboratories to aid in obtaining sterile products or to eliminate contamination when testing material, in the operation of bakeries, in the meat and beverage industries, in other food establishments and bottling plants, in the sanitization of eating and drinking utensils, and it is being adapted for a wide variety of other purposes.   In a detailed and final report, Robertson and associates (*J. A. M. A.*, 1943, **121**, 908) conclude that respiratory infections are controlled by ultraviolet radiation curtains.   See also Editorial Review (*J. A. M. A.*, 1943, **121**, 261).

Irradiated Oils and Ointments.—Oils and different ointment vehicles (petrolatum, lanolin, etc.), after irradiation, have been reported as possessing bactericidal properties.   It has been suggested that a gas or some volatile substance (possibly volatile peroxides) is given off and serves as the antiseptic.   Other workers claim that the destructive effects are due to secondary rays which are given off.   Another hypothesis advanced claims that the bactericidal effect is due to a nonvolatile agent produced as a result of an oxidative process.   Oils and ointment bases are affected differently by irradiation.   Some of these agents appear to be affected only slightly even by long exposures.   Eising (*Am. J. Surg.*, 1933, **19**, 244) reported favorable results with the use of ultraviolet irradiated petrolatum.   For further details, see Sears and Black (*J. Bact.*, 1934, **27**, 453) and Harris and associates (*ibid.*, 1932, **23**, 429).

Ultraviolet Blood Irradiation Therapy.—The Knott technique (*Northwest. Med.*, 1934, **33**, 200) of subjecting blood to irradiation with ultraviolet light and using the irradiated blood in humans as a therapeutic agent is being practiced, especially in acute pyogenic infections, in chronic arthritis, intrinsic bronchial asthma and as a preoperative control.   *Hemo-irradiation* is regarded by some as a valuable nonspecific supportive measure and its widespread use is advocated.   The technique consists in withdrawing and citrating a predetermined quantity of venous blood collected from a patient, immediately passing this citrated venous blood through a special irradiation chamber (so-called hemo-irradiator) and then injecting this properly irradiated blood intravenously into the patient from whom the blood was originally obtained.   For details, see Miley (*J. Bact.*, 1943, **45**, 303), Blundell and associates (*ibid.*, 1943, **45**, 304), and Miley and others (*Am. J. Surg.*, 1942, **57**, 493, 536; *Arch. Phys. Therapy*, 1942, **23**, 536; *Rev. Gastroenterol.*, 1943, **10**, 1; *J. Bact.*, 1944, **47**, 85).

For further details on ultraviolet light, see article by author (*Annual Report Smithsonian Institution*, 1942, pages 209–225) and comments by the Council on the acceptance of ultraviolet lamps for disinfecting purposes (*J. A. M. A.*, 1943, **122**, 503).

Chapter XIX

COMMONLY EMPLOYED PRACTICAL LABORATORY
METHODS OF STERILIZATION

FILTRATION

THIS IS AN IMPORTANT procedure but not used as frequently as the other methods of sterilization. The action is in a large measure mechanical, the filtrate being sterile and unchanged. *Bacteriological filtration*, a term frequently used for this procedure indicates a bacteria-free filtrate in contrast to other methods of filtration in which the resultant product is not necessarily sterile. This method is employed for pharmaceutical or bacteriological purposes and for the sterilizing of those solutions, culture media and biological products which are affected by heat or chemicals. In many instances the latter cannot be employed due to the fact that they would later exert a toxic effect when injected or taken into the human body; and when used in culture media, the chemical would prevent the growth of the organisms. Heat cannot be employed at times, because it may affect the material or destroy the active agent present therein. It is obvious that the active agents must be soluble.

The filters used in the laboratory for sterilizing media or solutions are made of stone, clay, porcelain, asbestos, diatomaceous earth, sintered glass and other materials. They are available in different sizes and in different degrees of porosity. Some types of apparatus are fitted with suitable filtering pads or membranes. The pads or disks, also available in various degrees of porosity, are used only once and then discarded.

The Berkefeld (known also as the infusorial earth bougie) and the unglazed porcelain Pasteur-Chamberland filters are frequently employed for rendering liquids sterile. These filters are the most reliable of the many types found on the market. Filters may be obtained in a variety of sizes and in different degrees of porosity. It is important to be assured that the pores of the filter are small enough, or that no flaw is present, so as to permit the passage of bacteria. For this reason, such filters are frequently tested. An atomizer or syringe bulb is attached to the nozzle and the entire filter up to the nozzle is immersed in water. Air is passed into the filter by squeezing the bulb. If any fissure is present, the air will pass out into the water and become apparent. It is also advisable to test occasionally the sterility of a filtrate, by culturing a portion of the filtrate from a liquid culture containing known organisms (*i. e., Bacillus prodigiosus*) and observing whether or not bacteria are present. Filters with flaws cannot be used. On the other hand, large users of some of these different types of filters regenerate the latter by baking them under suitable conditions in a furnace. Filtration with these filters is accomplished by means of vacuum or pressure. Pressure may be obtained by air under pressure from an installed system or by the use of a hand pump to equalize the pressure. On a small scale, suction supplies the vacuum and is obtained by means of a filter pump attached to a water faucet. An

270

overflow bottle should be interposed between the filter and the tap to prevent any backflow of water from entering the receiving flask. It is also very important that the vacuum flask (usually used on a small scale as the receiving vessel) shall be provided with a stopper, which will give an absolute airtight adjustment, as otherwise the material will be contaminated. The Berkefeld filters, made of siliceous materials of negative electrical charge, are manufactured in three grades, according to their permeability for water: V (viel), coarse, for rapid filtration; N (normal), intermediate or medium grade; W (wenig), fine grade. The Pasteur-Chamberland, of which a laboratory type is marketed in the form of jointless candles in nine grades, is preferred by many workers. The grade porosities are designated as L 1, L 2, L 3, etc. The L 3

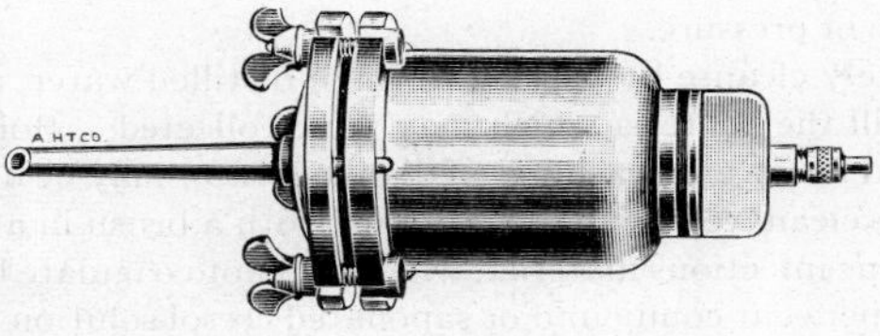

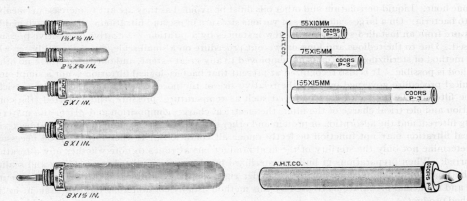

Fig. 14. Seitz filter.

Fig. 15. Filter candles. Fig. 16. Filter candles (Coors, porcelain).

approximates the Berkefeld N in porosity. L 13 is the finest and L 1 the coarsest grade marketed. The Mandler filter, made of kieselguhr, asbestos and plaster of Paris, appears to be an improvement upon the Berkefeld. It is available in three grades: "preliminary," "regular" and "fine," corresponding to Berkefeld V, N and W. The Seitz apparatus has come into use. In the latter, filtration is carried out through an asbestos disk clamped to the bottom of a metal container. The disks supplied in various grades of porosity are discarded after use, and the problem of cleaning, inherent in the other filters (called candles and bougies in smaller sizes), is eliminated. This type of filter can be sterilized by dry heat. The grade EK is used in bacteriological filtration. The Haen filter is a new type in which a membrane is employed. Nitrocellulose (Parlodion) membranes are also in use. An estimate of the rate at which distilled water will filter through under a given pressure is a crude method of comparing filters.

Before using the filter, the following steps must be carried out:

1. Examine the filter for flaws.

2. Sterilize the filter, container for holding the latter, the receiving vessel and all attachments in the autoclave (at 15 pounds' pressure for twenty minutes) by boiling in water for at least one hour or in the hot-air oven (at 170° C. for at least one hour). If there are rubber connections, dry hot air cannot be used.

3. Filter the liquid. The liquid to be filtered should contain little or no suspended matter. If such foreign material is present, filter through a filtering paper first, so as to remove the coarser particles, and then proceed as in these directions. Should it be found that the liquid cannot pass through the pores of the filtering paper, it would be advisable to either let it settle, strain through gauze or cotton, asbestos wool, etc., or centrifugalize the mixture, and use the supernatant fluid. It may be found suitable to filter through a preliminary coarse filter candle and as the final filtration, use a fine filter and vacuum or pressure.

4. After use, immediately cleanse by passing through distilled water, and boil or autoclave (after use) the bougie so as to kill the bacteria which may have collected. Boiling in a 2 per cent sodium carbonate solution followed by several washings of distilled water may be used.

5. If the filter is soiled, clean well by light scrubbing with a brush in a plentiful supply of running water. If the filter contains infectious material, which will not coagulate by heat, sterilize first before cleaning, or soak first in 5 per cent compound or saponated cresol solution or in a disinfectant solution which does not coagulate albumen (if present in the solution which was filtered). Dry and resterilize.

New candles should be cleansed before use by passing through distilled water, followed by boiling for one hour. Liquid petrolatum and other oils must be avoided as they are apt to increase permeability to bacteria. On a large scale, filters of various sizes are in use and filtration is usually hastened by pressure from an installed system and in few instances by aspiration. Negative or positive pressure is used. Due to the tedious and long-drawn-out procedure on a small scale, one can readily see why this method of sterilizing material is not employed to any great extent, and only used where no other method is possible. It is also recognized at present that bacteriological filtration is not a simple mechanical procedure governed only by the relative size of the pores of the filter and of the particles to be filtered. Other factors are involved such as temperature, pressure, time allotted, the composition and electrical charge of the filter, the electrical charge, composition and pH of the material being filtered, and the adsorption of protein and other substances. It is on this account that bacteriological filtration may not function perfectly under all conditions. It therefore may be necessary to determine not only the sterility of the final product but at times to note whether any alteration occurred. When preparations in bulk are sterilized by this process, distribution, filling and sealing in the final container must be conducted under rigid aseptic conditions. Antitoxins, therapeutic sera and medicinal preparations treated by this method usually contain a bacteriostatic agent in the finished product.

Ultrafiltration.—The so-called "ultrafilters" are thin membranes of porous material and in bacteriological work, they are used extensively in the study of ultramicroscopic viruses. The use of a series of such membrane (generally collodion) filters of graded porosity presents an approximate determination of the size of the virus particles. Most of the ultrafilters in use are modifications of Bechhold's series of membranes, introduced by him for the study of colloids (*Ultrafiltration and Electro-ultrafiltration*, Colloid Chemistry, 1926, **1**, 820, N. Y. City). For further details on graded collodion membranes for bacteriological use, see Krueger and Ritter (*J. Gen. Physiol.*, 1929, **13**, 409) and Elford (*J. Path. & Bact.*, 1931, **34**, 505).

STERILIZATION BY HEAT

The most widely used agent for sterilizing material in the laboratory is heat. It is also the most efficient.

Direct Flame or Incineration.—(*a*) *Substances without Value* should be destroyed by burning in a furnace or flame—sputum (collected in cardboard containers or gauze, etc.) and clothing, books and other material used by patients suffering with a transmissible disease. Urine, feces and other refuse are frequently deposited (especially in camps) in trenches made in the ground. At designated intervals, usually once or twice a day, straw and other materials, that can burn, are thrown in, kerosene is poured on the mixture, and the kerosene is ignited, thus effecting sterilization.

(*b*) *Materials That Possess a Definite Value* such as platinum and nichrome needles, iron and nickel spatulas, the metallic orifices of a Berkefeld or similar filters, tweezers and forceps, are quickly sterilized by heating to redness in an alcohol flame or Bunsen burner. Slabs, mortars and one-piece pestles, stoneware and any metallic ware, in emergencies, can be sterilized in the direct flame of a Bunsen burner. In all instances, the application of such direct flame must be for a period of not less than twenty seconds to each part thus treated; and care must be taken to be assured that the articles will not be injured by this technique. They must be cooled before being used. The lips of flasks, tubes or bottles are always sterilized by passing through a flame after the momentary removal of and again before replacing the cotton plug or other stopper.

Some equipment can be readily sterilized by passing through a hot flame (Bunsen burner or alcohol flame). Slides and cover slips are sterilized by this procedure. Pipettes and glass rods for emergency or quick use are sterilized in a like manner. If ampuls are needed as containers for a preparation to be dispensed quickly, such ampuls, if not already sterile, can be conveniently sterilized by passing through the flame, and supporting them (neck downward) in the meshes of a wire basket, until cool and ready for use. After being filled, they are quickly sealed and the filled ampuls are sterilized as described later. However, there is always the possibility of breaking this glassware if heated in a direct flame, and such procedure is not advocated for general use.

Medical and surgical instruments (if not sterile and required for immediate use) may be sterilized by passing through a flame. Such procedure should only be practiced in emergency cases due to the fact that considerable injury is done to instruments by this method. The direct flame can also be used to heat water and solutions containing medicaments to boiling temperatures, providing the temperature in the individual cases does not affect in any way the various ingredients that may be found in the particular solution. Sterile Distilled Water and Isotonic Salt Solution can both be sterilized by this method. Mention will be made of these products later.

The use of so-called *Fire Guns* (Stafseth and Camargo, *J. Am. Vet. M. A.*, 1935, **39**, 162) or attempts to moisten instruments, etc., with or dipping in alcohol or other volatile solvents and igniting the latter are not always effective procedures. In the latter instance, the cooling of the volatile solvent during vaporization, forming a layer of vaporized alcohol between the surface and the flame, may prevent effective sterilization during the very short period of time of the burning. In the use of fire guns, bacteria are not exposed to the heat of the flame for a sufficient length of time to produce effective results.

Hot Air.—Dry heat as a method of sterilization has definite limitations. The rate of penetration of dry heat is very slow. The frequently performed experiment of inoculating dough and chopped meat with bacteria, then baking or roasting them, after which the bacteria are recovered from the center of the material, proves this fact. Dry heat cannot very well be used for the sterilization of media and organic matter in general, as charring would promptly result at the temperature which must be employed. Containers made of heavy or thick glass (as in gallon bottles and carboys) quickly crack and hot air is not satisfactory here. Moist heat is generally employed for the sterilization of such containers. Exposure to hot air is the usual procedure of sterilizing all empty glass, porcelain and metallic containers, *which are to be kept on hand for future use*. The latter can readily be sterilized in an autoclave (as described later), and such procedure is frequently used, if the containers are required for *immediate use*. But empty glass, porcelain and metallic containers for *future use* are to be kept in stock on shelves, and it is desired that they should be dry. It would, therefore, be necessary to dry them if the autoclave or steam heat was employed. To avoid

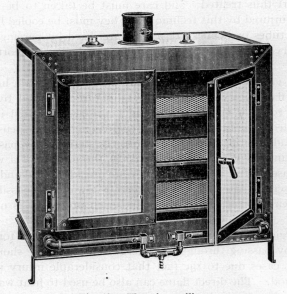

Fig. 17. Hot air sterilizer.

such extra amount of work, containers for future use are sterilized by hot air, for at the end of the operation the apparatus is both sterile and dry.

The dry heat sterilizers, commonly known as *hot-air ovens* or *hot-air chambers*, are simple devices, constructed like the ordinary baking ovens. The apparatus most frequently used is a double-walled, sheet-iron chamber, the joints being closed by rivets and not soldered. The inner compartment of this chamber is entirely closed, except for an opening in the top. A thermometer is placed in this opening, being sure that it reaches into the chamber, so that a correct reading may be recorded from the heated air present. The outer chamber has at least one and usually two small op n-ings in the top and a large one at the bottom. Into one of the openings at the top a thermoregulator is sometimes placed, but this is not necessary. The heat, applied by means of a Bunsen burner or electrical arrangement, is directed against the bottom of the inner chamber, the air circulating between the inner and outer walls becoming quickly heated.

Technique of Sterilization by Hot Air.—The materials must be perfectly clean and free from traces of organic matter. This is very important in this method, more so than in any of the many other procedures. If the cleansing of the glass were not thorough, traces of organic matter would remain. During the heating process the latter will char and black stains will be found on the containers after sterilization. Plug and cap, if necessary, or place in wire baskets or suitable receptacles.

1. Place the materials in the oven at room temperature. Care should be taken to see that no inflammable materials (as paper or cotton) touch the sides or the floor of the chamber, as they will char if they come in contact with the heated metal. Charring usually leaves the containers soiled, and the plugs and wrappings quickly crumble when touched. This necessitates rewashing, plugging, wrapping and resterilization. Do not pack the oven too tight and do not place heavy articles on top of lighter ones.

2. See that the thermometer is in position. Before turning on the gas, *be sure that the door is open*, so as to allow the escape of any gas that may otherwise accumulate between the inner and outer compartments and subsequently cause an explosion when a light is applied.

3. Light the gas and close the door.

4. Regulate the light so that the gas rises slowly, or a thermoregulator may be attached.

5. When a temperature of 160° C. (320° F.) to 170° C. (338° F.) is reached, lower the gas, leaving a flame sufficient to maintain this temperature preferably for two hours, but never for less than one hour. By practice, one can quickly judge by the height of the flame as to the temperature which will be reached. If the material being sterilized requires an appreciable period of time before the entire contents attain the minimum sterilizing temperature, an allowance in the total timing period must be made. Some observers have reported that tetanus spores are not killed at 170° C. for at least one hour. Fortunately, in the average laboratory, the apparatus is rarely if ever contaminated with these spores. However, in big industrial plants and manufacturing laboratories, where stables and horses are numerous, such danger is apparent.

If Tetanus Spores Are Likely to Be Present, 180° C. for at least One Hour Should Be Used or, Better, Still Use the Autoclave.—At 180° C. (dry heat) the paper and cotton become distinctly scorched.

6. At the end of the designated time, turn out the gas. Allow the temperature to fall gradually and wait, preferably until the oven cools to room temperature, before removing the apparatus. Opening the door of the oven will hasten the cooling of the containers.

Equipment, especially glassware, should never be placed in or removed from a heated oven, as the quick change of temperature is apt to crack the glass containers.

Apparatus and Material for Future Use to Be Sterilized in Hot-air Chamber.—Temperature, 160° to 170° C.; time, preferably two but not less than one hour; flasks (plugged and capped), test tubes, centrifuge tubes and fermentation tubes (plugged); bottles (corked or plugged), if glass-stoppered, cotton, gauze or paper is to be inserted between stoppers; Petri dishes and pipettes (wrapped in paper and tied); cotton (in small quantities, wrapped or placed in suitable jars); gauze (in small packages or cut in suitable lengths and placed in wide-mouthed capped containers); bedpans (for the collection of feces, wrapped in paper and tied); funnels, graduates, beakers, watch-glass crystals (wrapped in paper); ampuls (placed in wide-mouth capped containers); powders (as boric acid, kaolin, talc and zinc oxide, placed in Petri dishes or other suitable containers in a stratum not more than $1/4$ inch thick); bonewax placed in small tubes; glass syringes (plunger removed from barrel and both wrapped in paper); hypodermic needles (placed in a cotton-plugged vial or test tube or placed in Petri dishes with points buried in gauze); scalpel and other cutting instruments; collapsible tubes (in wide-mouth, glass-stoppered or capped containers); and ointment jars.

For medicaments as the sulfonamide compounds (powders) and zinc peroxide (powder), which decompose at high temperatures, a lower temperature for a more prolonged period of time is used. For the powdered sulfonamide compounds, 145° to 150° C. and for zinc peroxide (powder), 140° C. for four hours appear to be satisfactory. See page 331.

It frequently happens that a temperature higher than 170° C. can be conveniently used, especially in the sterilization of apparatus not stoppered or wrapped with inflammable material, as: Petri dishes, pipettes and ampuls (placed in copper or other metallic containers); and petrolatum, ointment and similar jars (stoppered with metallic caps, used for the collection of sputum and other fluids for examination). These can be sterilized by heating in the hot-air chamber at a temperature between 200° and 300° C. for at least forty-five minutes.

Petrolatum can be sterilized in the hot-air oven by placing it in a protected container or jar, raising the temperature to 200° C., and allowing it to cool slowly. Many oils and fats, as well as glycerin and sutures in oil, may be sterilized in the same way. This temperature may be obtained through a direct flame or a sand bath, but more conveniently in a hot-air oven, as in the latter, a more uniform temperature can be obtained, as well as one which is gradually reached. Some of the ointment bases, however, are affected by the high heat and are either decomposed or changed in physical appearance.

Electrically heated ovens are preferred by many workers as they offer better facilities for an even temperature rise and a more reliable and accurate temperature control within the desired range. The use of *automatic regulators* is advocated to assure proper temperature adjustment and control. Inasmuch as some hot-air ovens may display an uneven distribution of heat and a wide temperature differential in different parts of the apparatus, care is required in operating these sterilizers to insure thorough heating of the load before timing the exposure. The *entire contents* in each container or batch of material must reach the minimum required sterilizing temperature and then timed at this temperature for the designated period of time. It therefore may be necessary for the operator to determine the *total* time period for every class of article or particular substance being sterilized.

Moist Heat.—(*a*) Inspissator and pasteurization; (*b*) boiling water bath; (*c*) steam; (*d*) steam under pressure (autoclave).

Dry heat kills bacteria due to the fact that the cell protoplasm is decomposed or oxidized (as in incineration). In some instances it may be due to the destruction of the enzymes and as the heat reaches higher temperatures there may occur denaturation of the cell proteins and even coagulation. In the case of moist heat, the effect appears to be a direct action, either physical or chemical (coagulation and alteration) upon the bacterial protein. Proteins, however, coagulate more readily and at a lower temperature when moisture is present than in a dry atmosphere. Bacteria therefore are more quickly destroyed by moist heat than by hot air. Boiling for five to ten minutes may be sufficient to destroy the vegetative forms of most disease-producing bacteria. This method can be used when it is desired to be assured that liquids and foodstuffs intended for human consumption are free of pathogenic microorganisms. Water, milk and similar products can be boiled by direct flame for at least five to ten minutes. Solid foodstuffs are placed in water and boiled for at least twenty minutes and preferably one-half hour, so as to rid them of microorganisms.

Syringes needed for immediate use are wrapped in gauze. Safety pins and needles are stuck in pads and wrapped in gauze. Medical and surgical instruments having cutting edges are protected by wrapping in gauze or cotton. These, as well as catheters, tubing, stoppers and other rubber material, can be sterilized in a water bath, if a steam sterilizer or autoclave is not available. Placing in a boiling water bath for at least twenty minutes is sufficient. However, should the presence of spore-forming organisms be suspected (which are apt to be present when one is doing field work), boiling for one hour is necessary. In sterilizing material as here described, it is customary to add 1 to 2 per cent of sodium carbonate to the water. This chemical aids in destroying the bacteria, saponifies fat, and the corrosion of instruments is greatly inhibited. Other workers increase the efficiency of the water bath by adding a germicidal agent, usually 5 per cent phenol or 2 per cent of a coal-tar disinfectant. Instruments and other equipment are usually removed from a water bath by means of a mechanical conveyance or by using a forceps, which can be sterilized by passing through a flame.

In using the boiling water bath for sterilizing purposes, it is important to be assured that all parts of the equipment or materials being treated are well covered with water and that the heat is regulated to maintain a boiling condition of the water. It is not necessary for the water to boil vigorously, unless portions of the materials are exposed above the water. Inasmuch as the temperature at which water boils depends directly upon the atmospheric pressure, it is apparent that at higher altitudes water will boil at a temperature lower than at sea level (below 100° C. or 212° F.). At Denver, Colorado, water boils at approximately 96.6° C. (206° F.) and the sterilizing effect is proportionately lessened. Under these conditions, it is necessary to prolong the time of exposure.

Steam.—Exposure to direct steam is an efficient method of sterilization if its limitations are recognized. Its action is similar to that of boiling water. As in the case of the latter, the temperature of live or free-flowing steam is less at higher altitudes than at sea level. Live steam not only heats materials and permeates porous substances during the process of condensation, but during this condensation process a considerable amount of latent heat is made available. The procedure of destroying bacteria by steam is frequently practiced on a large scale, where enormous quantities of live steam are available. In all fermentation industries (as in the making of beer, vinegar, yeast, etc.) and in dairies, steam, because of its convenience, is used for the sterilization of all pipings, tanks and containers. Where available, especially in destroying bacteria in refrigerators and large compartments used for the storage of foodstuffs, this treatment is also used. It is dangerous to wash such compartments with chemical solutions, as the latter are usually toxic, and unless they are gotten rid of, they may in turn contaminate the foodstuffs. If free-flowing steam is not available, the only other safe method to adopt for the sterilizing of refrigerators would be the cleansing with soapsuds and boiling water and subsequent washings with boiling water. Weak dilutions of chlorine or hypochlorite solutions followed by washings with boiling water are also used.

Steam free-flowing and not subjected under pressure is used also in the laboratory. The apparatus most frequently employed to utilize moist heat in the form of live or free-flowing steam is the Arnold steam sterilizer. This consists of a copper box constructed with a false bottom through which the steam rises and passes into a compartment wherein the apparatus to be sterilized is placed. A minimum amount of water is heated to produce steam quickly, which, as mentioned, rises through a funnel-like arrangement in the center of the apparatus and passes to the sterilizing chamber. The excess of steam in the latter escapes around the cover and is confined under a hood, forming a steam jacket around the outside of the sterilizing chamber and thus aiding to maintain a uniform maximum temperature within the chamber. As the steam is eventually forced down from above, it comes in contact with the air, and condenses. This collects and is carried back by an outer jacket into the reservoir. (Fig. 18).

A simple steam sterilizer can be made by taking a copper or other metallic boiler or bucket covered with a lid. Arrange a false bottom or place in a tripod, covered with a piece of sheet iron or other metallic plate upon which the material to be sterilized is placed.   Enough water is poured into the container to reach up to about one-quarter the height of the tripod, and heat is applied by means of gas from a burner or a stove. The material can thus be subjected to the influence of steam as long as may be desired.

The steam in any of these sterilizers can be used in two ways—continuously or intermittently.   One prolonged exposure to steam (at 100° C.) can be resorted to. *Apparatus commonly sterilized in the water bath can just as readily be subjected to the influence of steam for an identical period of time.*   In order to sterilize some culture media, steaming for twenty to sixty minutes (preferably over a period of two or three days) can be employed.   If other methods are not available steam sterilization may be used for sterilizing water and isotonic salt solution.   This method of sterilization is not to replace autoclaving or the use of steam under pressure if the latter is available.

Prolonged steaming, however, tends to affect or alter the composition of some material.   This is especially true when sterilizing nutrient media containing sugars, or in attempting to rid gelatin media free of microorganisms.   Sugars are decomposed with

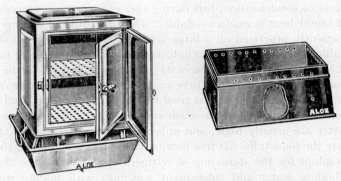

Fig. 18.   Arnold steam sterilizer and base.

the production of acids and gelatin medium is frequently so affected that it cannot congeal on cooling if either is exposed under the influence of steam for a prolonged period.   Many chemicals are similarly affected.   They are decomposed with the production of other substances, which possess entirely different properties.   On this account, the intermittent method is employed.   This method of sterilizing consists in exposing the material under the influence of steam for short periods (from ten to thirty minutes) each day for at least three consecutive days, and is frequently known as *discontinuous, fractional, interrupted or intermittent sterilization or Tyndallization.*

Three exposures for such short periods are used for the sterilization of most of the nutrient media and many pharmaceutical products which are otherwise decomposed. The following facts will explain the principle of this method.   The first exposure of fifteen minutes to steam will cause the destruction of all the vegetative forms of bacteria, but not the spore forms.   During the interval between the first and second heating (twenty-four hours), most of the spores will redevelop into the original bacteria from whence they came and give rise to feeble resistant, vegetating organisms.   The latter will be killed upon exposure to the steam during the heating on the second day.

During the interval of the second and third heatings, the remaining spores are given a chance to germinate. The third heating, which is mainly a safety-first procedure (assuring a greater margin of safety), will kill all bacteria not destroyed by the first two heatings and render the material sterile. This method is, therefore, of value and works best when sterilizing substances which offer a favorable medium for bacterial growth, so that spores might develop into vegetative forms. During intervals between heatings in all fractional methods of moist-heat sterilization, materials should be placed either in the incubator at 37° C. or at temperatures not lower than 20° C. (room temperature).

In exposing material under the influence of steam, note the time after the steam fills the compartment, or after the chamber has reached 100° C. and leave at this temperature for the designated length of time.

By means of a simple steam-sterilizing apparatus, one is able to perform many of the necessary sterilization operations. But on a large scale and even in a laboratory where sterilization is carried out many times a day, steam sterilization is employed only when necessary, as ordinarily too much time is consumed, and at times certain spores will resist the action of live steam even for hours.

Autoclave (Steam under Pressure).—Steam at ordinary atmospheric pressure never exceeds 100° C., but if it is confined within a given area, the temperature will rise with an increase of pressure. It is important to note that pressure *per se* has no destructive effect upon bacteria. Its sole purpose, as previously mentioned, is to obtain higher temperatures than that (100° C.) attained by steam at atmospheric pressure. The moist heat of the steam under pressure is the sterilizing agent. Steam under pressure is the most powerful method of ridding material free of bacteria and their spores and has given rise to the extensive use of an apparatus known as the *autoclave*. This apparatus is made in different shapes and sizes, depending upon the material to be sterilized. Though expensive, it is a necessary adjunct in the hospital, pharmacy, laboratory and in any establishment where sterilization by steam is carried out at frequent intervals. The principle governing the construction of all types of autoclaves is the same. They usually consist of a gun-metal cylinder, supplied with a lid fastened to the body by thumbscrews. In addition, there are always present a thermometer, safety valve and a steam-pressure gauge which records the pressure of the steam, the latter being generated in the cylinder itself; or in the more elaborate autoclaves, the steam from the heating system is utilized.

The following is a more detailed description of the autoclave used in the laboratory on a small scale: It is a vertical or horizontal cylinder, looking like a waterboiler, possessing an airtight lid, which is fastened by means of thumbscrews. This lid can be opened to permit loading and unloading. Attached to the latter is a pressure gauge with an exhaust and safety valve. At the top of the safety valve there is found a screw which regulates the pressure. *By means of the latter, the safety valve is set to blow off at 15 pounds' (attaining a temperature of 121.5° C.) or any desired pressure (and temperature).* The temperature actually attained is more reliable than pounds of pressure recorded. Further manipulation is not necessary at any subsequent time, inasmuch as once regulated, the pressure will always register the same. At the bottom of the autoclave a gas burner is placed to heat the water. The heat is directed against a water jacket several inches deep. The material to be sterilized is placed upon a perforated false bottom which rises above the water. Many of the laboratory autoclaves are fitted with a thermometer at the extreme top of the sterilizing chamber. These temperature readings may be misleading unless one is definitely assured that all air has been discharged from the apparatus. The only dependable method of being assured that the autoclave is performing its function satisfactorily is to measure the temperature in the discharge system, which indicates the true internal temperature. It, therefore, is important to equip all autoclaves with thermometers, located in the exhaust line and at the lowest point in the sterilizer. It is also desirable to place a timer in the exhaust line which will indicate the time of *period of exposure*. The following directions must be closely observed when using the autoclave as its successful use depends upon proper operation.

1. See that sufficient water is present (at least three inches).

2. Wrap material, place in wire baskets or prepare otherwise as previously directed, and place on the false bottom. Do not place heavier articles on top of lighter ones. Do not pack the autoclave too tight. Adequate attention must be given to the proper preparation of all materials to be sterilized and to all details of loading. This is very important to remember at all times in the use of any type of autoclave and, in fact, in the use of all kinds of sterilizers. For effective results, where heavy packs

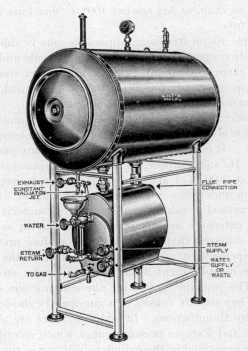

Fig. 19. Autoclave.

are being sterilized, as in hospitals, the autoclave is to be loaded so as to provide a horizontal path for the escape of air in those instances where the factor of penetration for heavy loads is to be considered.

3. The lid is then fastened tight by *hand*. Never use a wrench or hammer.

4. Open the exhaust valve and light the burner.

5. As the water is heated, steam is produced. This rises and replaces the air, which is forced through the exhaust valve. When steam issues through the latter, all air has already been displaced and steam only is present in the cylinder. If this is not done, a poor heat-conducting air column is left around the objects, and the exact temperature is not attained, though the pressure gauge records the desired pressure. Air pockets prevent diffusion of the moist steam so that all objects are not reached by the latter. Steam must have free access to all materials to insure dependable and rapid sterilization. The steam is allowed to pass for a minute and the valve is then closed. For further details concerning the significance of air in the autoclave, see Hoyt and associates (*J. Bact.*, 1938, **36**, 639).

6. The pressure now rises as indicated on the gauge. As soon as 15 pounds (121.5° C.) is reached, note the time. If the flow of gas from the burner is high, it may be advisable to turn it low at this

point, as otherwise a portion of the steam produced is forced through the safety valve. This is merely a waste of gas.

7. Maintain 15 pounds' pressure (121.5° C.) for at least twenty minutes and then turn off the gas.

8. Gradually release the pressure by slowly opening the exhaust valve, for the steam to escape. Never open the exhaust valve too suddenly, as the sudden outrush of steam will force many of the stoppers from the containers. Liquids subjected to steam under pressure are heated to temperatures above their boiling points. The pressure present prevents active boiling, but its sudden release results in a vigorous ebullition of the superheated liquid.

9. When the pressure has fallen to zero, the thumbscrews are unfastened, and the lid loosened. The contents of the autoclave are removed without waiting for the apparatus to completely cool.

If the exhaust valve is left open, the autoclave can be used for fractional or intermittent sterilization at 100° C. Steam subjected to 15 pounds' pressure will give a temperature of 121.5° C. *Sterilization by the use of steam under pressure is to be gauged upon the basis of the temperature attained rather than the pressure recorded.* The following temperatures are attained by different degrees of pressure:

Pounds pressure	Temperature, ° C.
5	109.0
10	115.5
15	121.5
20	126.5
25	130.5
30	134.5
40	141.5

A higher pressure (and temperature) for the same period of time or a lower pressure for a longer exposure than twenty minutes are used by some workers, depending upon the materials being treated and the load in the autoclave. It is good practice, however, to adjust and maintain the same pressure (and temperature) in the autoclave at all times and to vary, if necessary, the periods of exposure depending upon the materials and the load being sterilized. It is best to determine the time requirements for the *period of exposure* for different batches being constantly sterilized and to maintain these time periods of exposure rigidly at all times.

In the autoclave, it is possible to attain any temperature lower than 100° C. or over 100° C. to high temperature (by regulating the pressure and heat). One must distinguish between *steam under pressure* (as in the autoclave) and *superheated steam.* If a Bunsen burner is directed against the outside of the compartment of the Arnold steam sterilizer, in which steam is present, a high heat will be produced. This will cause the steam to expand, the pressure, however, remaining normal. Passing steam over heating surfaces or coils will produce the same effect. Such steam, known as superheated steam, does not have the destructive powers possessed by steam under pressure, which has been raised to the same temperature. Superheated steam possesses but little advantage over hot air, while live steam is a better agent than the latter for sterilizing material due to its penetrating property.

Large autoclaves embodying the same principle as the small autoclaves are used by boards of health, hospitals, quarantine stations and all sanitarians for sterilizing bedding, clothing and all wearing apparel, large quantities of gauze, cotton, sheeting and thickly padded articles, etc. Some increase the efficiency of such steam by introducing gaseous formaldehyde. These large autoclaves and bulk type pressure steam sterilizers usually are fitted with equipment (ejector valves) to produce a *vacuum* so that the steam can be quickly released and hot air introduced to dry the material. On a small scale such material can be dried in an easily made hot-air oven. Inasmuch as the sterilization of material in the large and other autoclaves is entrusted to assistants, various methods have been introduced whereby one can be assured that the proper temperature was used and sterilization has been effected. One procedure consists in introducing small ampuls (containing a mixture of powdered benzoic acid and 0.01 per cent of safranin or brilliant green) into various parts of the apparatus or material to be sterilized. The dye in this ampul is not visible, but if the proper sterilization was conducted and 121° C. was reached, the benzoic acid melts, the dye diffuses through it and upon cooling a colored bead is formed. For temperatures

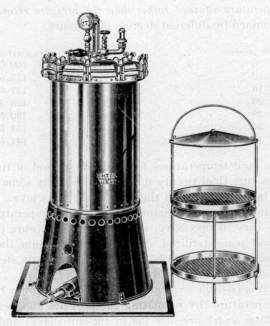

Fig. 20. Autoclave.

lower or higher than attained at 15 pounds' pressure, chemicals of corresponding melting points are employed.

In addition to the above, there are other types of so-called *telltale detectors* or *sterility detectors*. Strips of pasteboard covered at various points with indicators which change in color as the proper temperature reaches the sterilizing range are available. *Diack Controls* depend upon the use of light brown tablets contained in a hermetically sealed glass tube. When subjected to 118° C. for twenty to thirty minutes, the tablet melts, turns to a bright carmine color and upon cooling a colored fused mass is produced. On large autoclaves, the use of recording thermometers is invaluable as a check that the desired temperature was set up and maintained. A very satisfactory type of control is that suggested and designed by Walter (*Surg., Gynec. & Obst.*, 1938, **67,** 526). The control is a foolproof and tamper-proof device of simple design and rugged construction, which automatically impounds the load until it has been properly sterilized. Another device is the wrapping of a steamproof thermoswitch set for the desired temperature. This is placed in the center of the load. The timer meters the duration of the set sterilizing temperature.

Sterilization in Arnold sterilizer (steam at 100° C.) fifteen to thirty minutes for three consecutive days.

Culture media: Gelatin, all media containing *sugars* as glucose, lactose, saccharose, etc., Endo's medium and media containing bile or bile salts.

Medicaments: Adrenalin, arsenic and inorganic and organic arsenical salts, caffeine, calomel and gray oil, mercurial salts, cacodylates, mucilages and gums. Many alkaloids and alkaloidal salts are heated for two or three consecutive days.

Anything that can be sterilized in the autoclave without injury may be sterilized in the "Arnold steam sterilizer" by steaming the material from one-half to one hour each day for three consecutive days.

Sterilization in the autoclave (15 pounds' pressure for twenty minutes (121.5 °C.)):

The following culture media: Plain bouillon, agar, glycerin agar and glycerin bouillon, potato medium; distilled water; isotonic salt solution; Ringer's solution; solution of magnesium citrate; camphorated oil; all fixed oils.

Apparatus: Instruments, needles, rubber tubing, caps, stoppers and other rubber goods; glassware for *immediate use;* cotton, gauze, bandages, clothing, bedding; etc.

Old cultures (before the cleansing of containers); large bottles and carboys (of heavy glass); hair (raw) (for all types of brushes, suspected of containing anthrax and its spores); ligatures and catgut (always suspected in containing tetanus spores) or catgut in ampuls containing liquid petrolatum or alcohol.

Inspissators, etc.—Some substances, especially material rich in albumin, are altered somewhat if heated at a temperature of 100° C. (or to their boiling points). Such material can be treated to attenuate pathogens or destroy other undesirable bacteria (in industrial pursuits) by heating at a lower temperature (55° to 80° C.) for a period of time ranging from one-half to one hour. This process is known as *pasteurization.* It is commonly practiced in rendering milk supplies safe for human consumption, and is accomplished by heating the milk to 60° C. for thirty minutes or 65° C. for fifteen minutes. The milk is immediately cooled and kept at a temperature below 4.4° C. or 40° F. until used.

As was pointed out previously, the vegetative and spore forms differ in their resistance to destruction. The lowest temperature found to be destructive to the further development of the vegetative forms of bacteria is known as the "thermal death point" of the particular microorganism in question. Most all vegetative forms of the commonly observed pathogenic bacteria will be destroyed, if heated in a water bath at 55° to 60° C. for ten minutes, and the latter is the thermal death point for most commonly observed nonspore-forming bacteria. Pasteurization, properly conducted, will therefore kill the vegetative forms of all pathogenic bacteria, and spores that may remain will not develop if the milk is kept at a low temperature.

For the sterilization of pharmaceuticals and preparations other than milk or products required for immediate use, pasteurization in itself is not effective, but must be combined with an intermittent or discontinuous heating for a period of four to seven days. This constitutes a process known as *inspissating*, and when used is conducted by heating the particular material (placed in sterile containers) in a water bath or an inspissator at a temperature from 60° to 80° C. or at the highest temperature below 100° C. which the substance being treated can withstand without decomposing or being altered, for one-half to one hour each day for from four to seven days. Fractional heating methods (at 100° C. or lower) are of value providing the material so treated will support bacterial growth. It is advisable that the containers be placed in an incubator or at a warm temperature during the intervals between the heatings. The finished preparation should be tested for sterility. It is customary to add a bacteriostatic agent to medicinal preparations sterilized by this method. Phenol (0.5 per cent), tricresol (0.1 to 0.4 per cent) or other suitable chemical preservatives are employed for this purpose.

MATERIAL STERILIZED AT 60° TO 70° C.

	Time	Days
All vaccines.	1/2 to 1 hr.	1 to 2
Atropine, cocaine, ergot, hyoscine, quinine and its compounds, physostigmine, scopolamine, strychnine.	1/2 to 1 hr.	4 to 6

In practice, blood (defibrinated), blood serum, ascitic and hydrocele fluids used for fortifying culture media are collected under aseptic conditions and preserved with precautions. Some even add 1 per cent of chloroform, which is usually allowed to evaporate before the material is used. If any of these substances should have become contaminated, filtering through a Berkefeld or similar filter will sterilize them. If this procedure is not convenient, sterilization may be attempted by placing the material in a water bath at 60° C. for one hour each day for five to six days.

Other Baths.—Materials have been placed in various liquids and then sterilized, due to the fact that such liquids have high boiling points. In a pharmacy or small laboratory, containers with material can be sterilized in a *saturated salt solution bath* in place of an autoclave (if not at hand), inasmuch as the temperature of a boiling brine bath is almost equal to the temperature used in the autoclave. Some use a boiling *ammonium chloride bath*. This gives a temperature somewhat lower than obtained in an autoclave at 15 pounds' pressure. It would be necessary, however, to rinse such containers in water after sterilization, as otherwise the crystallized chemical salts will appear on the outside of the container.

Within recent years, the *oil bath* has been used to advantage. Liquid petrolatum or paraffin oil is employed, as this can be heated to a high temperature without decomposition. The oil can be used over and over again. A temperature of 160° C. for at least sixty minutes is employed, and the temperature is recorded either by a thermometer or by using a chemical to which a dye or coloring is added (contained in an ampul), and which will fuse at the desired temperature. This, in reality, is sterilization by dry heat. The quantity of oil should not be excessive, should be limited to the amount required for single applications and the containers should not be filled to more than two-thirds capacity. Medical and surgical instruments will quickly become dull if sterilized in water or steam. The oil bath is being used by many for the sterilization of such instruments, which are wrapped in gauze or cotton and placed in the oil for the designated time. Not only is one more assured that the instruments are sterile, but instead of becoming dull, the oil acts as a lubricant and keeps them sharp. Catgut contained in ampuls filled with liquid petrolatum can be conveniently sterilized in an oil bath.   Ampuls and other sealed vials containing medicaments can also be sterilized in an oil bath at any desired temperature if an autoclave is not at hand.

IMPORTANT NOTE

In noting the time of exposure in any of the sterilizers, it is important to time the process from the moment when the particular temperature had been reached, and not from the time when the flame was lighted.

The desirability of allowing a large "safety margin" in all sterilization, disinfection and fumigation procedures cannot be overemphasized.   In all instances, use the maximum temperature and strongest concentration of disinfectant or fumigant and the maximum period of time compatible with no alteration or premature deterioration of the products being sterilized or any effect on the environment being treated.   Where the time element and cost involved are factors to be considered (economy factor, saving time, conserving power, etc.) the period of time can be varied, but this should never be below the minimum amount required for the temperature or strength of disinfectant or fumigant used.

Chapter XX

PREPARATION AND STERILIZATION OF INSTRUMENTS AND OTHER EQUIPMENT

Bulk Goods.—Bulk material of all kinds, including surgical supplies, linens, towels, dressings, sheets, sponges, jars, cans, basins and utensils, etc., should be packaged in small bundles, folded or wrapped loosely and securely tied. A double thickness of muslin or suitable enclosing muslin bags make the most satisfactory wrappers. Heavy wrapping paper can be used. Do not use canvas, as the latter goods interferes with steam permeation. Large bundles are to be apportioned into smaller packages and heavy materials are to be wrapped individually and separately. In arranging loads in steam sterilizers, the packs are placed on edge without crowding, and all measures are taken to facilitate the free access of steam for penetration. Heavier packs are placed on the lower tier or shelf and the light ones above. Allow at all times a free passageway for the steam in all parts of the sterilizer. The arrangement of the materials in the sterilizer is very important. It is advisable that each autoclave (steam sterilizer) should be tested at periodic intervals as to proper packing, so that at no time will there be required more than thirty minutes for the sterilization period at 15 pounds' pressure (121.5° C.). This will give the assurance that all portions of the sterilizer attained the desired temperature for the minimum period of exposure and, at the same time, an extended time period of sterilization which usually affects or injures most material will not be prolonged unnecessarily.

Bulk goods coming from operating rooms and from quarters of sick patients, as linens, gowns, sheets and other dry goods, are gathered preferably into muslin bags and sent to the laundry. The bag is emptied into a breaker, allowed to soak in cold water for at least fifteen to thirty minutes, soap is added to produce a stiff lather, and as the water is heated to boiling, the breaking is continued. After the boiling temperature is reached, an exposure of the load to the latter for twenty to thirty minutes is generally practiced. Thereafter, the treatment is the same as is practiced for ordinary laundry. On a small scale, soiled contaminated bulk goods as above can be immersed in a suitable disinfectant before laundering. For white goods, a chlorine solution is preferred. Immerse the load in a 2 per cent Labarraque's solution. Colored goods may be bleached and a 2 to 3 per cent saponated cresol solution (or an equivalent strength of a coal-tar disinfectant) can be used. The length of time of exposure to the disinfectant solution will depend upon the material being treated and the amount of the contamination. A safe time period, however, is not less than thirty minutes for the common run of contaminated dry goods. Infected basins and utensils are placed in a pail containing one of the above disinfectants. They are then washed, cleansed, rinsed, wrapped or placed in a muslin bag and sterilized in the autoclave at 15 pounds pressure (121.5° C.) for thirty minutes.

Sterilization of Rubber Goods.—Different kinds of rubber goods are used in hospitals and clinics, which are to be prepared and sterilized before use. The technique varies with the type of rubber or rubberized material whether new, old or used, and depending upon their application. Among the rubber goods are to be found gloves, tubing, catheters and table covers, and each requires special handling and treatment. Some general details should be considered for all rubber goods. Store the latter flat in their natural position, in a cool room (but not at a freezing temperature), protected from dirt, excessive moisture and sunlight. Clean and dry thoroughly before storage. Avoid contact with oils, fats and greasy material; but if the latter are present, remove as soon as possible preferably with a solvent as acetone and then quickly remove the solvent by washing with water. Soiled rubber goods should be washed thoroughly without delay. The careful use of lukewarm water and soap, followed by successive rinsings with water may be sufficient in most instances (for exceptions, see below). All rubber goods prepared for sterilization should be wrapped or packaged loosely, sterilized preferably in the autoclave, and never placed in the latter crowded together with other packs. Never use pins in fastening wrappers of rubber goods, as there always is the danger of puncturing rubber. Avoid puncturing with fingernails, rings, pins or sharp instruments.

Rubber Gloves.—Gloves must be handled and prepared with care, so as to preserve the time period of their usefulness. Haphazard methods and unnecessary rough handling are to be avoided. Everyone should be cautioned to avoid contact of fingernails with the gloves when drawing them on and users of rubber gloves should be advised to rinse them in cold water before removing them. Some workers insist upon a preliminary sterilization of used rubber gloves before the washing process. Most individuals eliminate the preliminary sterilization and employ a thorough washing procedure, followed by a carefully controlled sterilization method. The latter technique has proved successful and has been responsible for the saving of much time, labor and money. If a preliminary sterilization, however, is to be used, boiling in tap water is sufficient. The cleaning or washing process, however, must be done with meticulous care. This can be carried out as mentioned above by one wearing gloves, if infected material is being handled. A carefully controlled and supervised washing, with a consideration for all important details, means that the sterilization procedure to follow will not be as difficult a problem. Gloves should be tested for leaks after washing, using preferably slight tension after the gloves are filled with water. In the sterilization technique, the gloves are to be wrapped in such a manner as to be assured that the steam will come in contact with all the surfaces (inside and outside). A good practice is to insert a pad of cotton, gauze, muslin or paper between the wrist surfaces of the glove, as this is folded back and a similar pad to be inserted in the hand as far as the fingers. This will allow more readily a free entrance of steam. Specially designed glove packs or roomy envelopes (arranged like a billfold) made from two thicknesses of muslin or even of a thick or tough paper serve as suitable containers for each pair. The packs are arranged loosely in a tray and they should never be pressed or crowded together or covered with anything that may interfere with the free passage and thorough permeation of the steam. Sterilization is carried out in the autoclave at 15 pounds pressure (121.5° C.) for not less than fifteen and not more than twenty minutes. When the period of exposure is complete, exhaust the steam, dry as rapidly as possible and remove the glove from the hot chamber as quickly as possible. Heating for periods of time longer than necessary will affect the tensile strength of the rubber and, in turn, the useful life of the gloves.

Small muslin or paper envelopes or bags containing enough talcum for each pair of gloves are placed within the envelope or wrapper but not inside the glove or wrist fold. These powder puffs are sterilized at the same time with the gloves. Where muslin or other folders are not used, the gloves must be wrapped and properly marked left and right or so arranged that the position of the thumb is known. During sterilization, the gloves are arranged on edge with the thumbs up to assure complete clearance of air.

Rubber Tubing.—Pure gum rubber of the highest quality should be used, if at all possible. Ordinary tubing contains sulfur and other impurities, so that if such new tubing is to be used for the parenteral administration of medicaments, it must be cleansed thoroughly before sterilization and use. All used rubber tubing employed for routine parenteral administrations is cleansed immediately after use. The thoroughness of the washing procedure will depend upon the agents used in the therapy, whether blood, serums, dextrose, saline solutions or other medicaments. Improperly washed rubber tubing is frequently responsible for pyrogenic reactions. It is sound practice to keep blood transfusion tubing separate and even segregate the rubber tubing for each individual type of medicament, when large amounts of the latter are used. New tubing and old tubing for thorough cleansing are washed in soap and water and boiled for one hour in a 4 per cent solution of sodium carbonate, being sure to circulate the hot fluid through the tubing several times. Flushing the tubing with a solution, prepared by mixing 12.5 cc. Tergitol "08," 8 cc. diluted sulfuric acid (10 per cent) and water, to make 100 cc., is highly recommended especially if blood, pus and other albuminous material was used. This is similar to the solution suggested by Winer and La Cava (*J. Urol.*, 1940, **43**, 611) for cleansing ureteral catheters. The Tergitol "08" digests pus and albuminous material. Wash tubing in hot water and then attach to a faucet and allow tap water to run thoroughly for at least one or, preferably, two hours. As the last washing, before draining and sterilization, allow one to two quarts of pyrogen-free water to pass through the tubing. In placing the drained rubber tubing in the autoclave, arrange this so that one end is kept elevated throughout its length above the other end. This is conveniently accomplished by carefully enveloping the rubber tubing around a cylinder, made of heavy cardboard, or several large towels, or a muslin pack. Avoid any restriction of the tubing. Cylinder and tubing are placed in a tray and the latter is kept on its side or the cylinder and tubing can be wrapped in heavy paper or muslin and this placed in the sterilizer, so as to allow for the free circulation of steam through the tubing. Sterilization is effected in the autoclave at 15 pounds' pressure (121.5° C.) for twenty minutes.

Rubber Catheters and Stomach and Gastroduodenal Tubes.—When these are to be sterilized, especially for the collection of specimens for bacteriological examinations, use the technique as advised under rubber tubing.

Sterilization of Instruments.—*Preliminary Treatment.*—Instruments should be clean, free of all tissue shreds, dried blood, pus and from scale in crevices and joints. Sterilization by the use of the boiling water bath results in the deposition of scales of insoluble alkali-earth compounds Obviously this does not occur in the use of steam under pressure as the sterilization agent. There, therefore, is less need for oiling jointed and other instruments sterilized in the autoclave. Instruments which are lubricated prior to storage should be oiled sparingly. A thin film of oil will retard effective sterilization by moist-heat techniques, unless the oil or grease is first removed. Instruments routinely boiled remain wet for some time and rusting occurs from contact with air. When properly autoclaved, and removed after exhausting the steam pressure, the instruments dry quickly and rusting rarely occurs by this technique. Tarnish spots should not be mistaken for rust spots.

Instruments contaminated even grossly with infected discharges and materials are cleansed and sterilized rapidly and effectively when exposed to a detergent solution in a specially designed autoclave, as suggested by Walter (*Surg., Gynec. & Obst.*, 1938, **67**, 244). This technique is advocated wherever possible and especially in hospitals and clinics, as it effects many economies. If, however, it is not available, the instruments are unlocked, placed in a stainless steel or porcelain basin covered with a 5 or 10 per cent soap solution or a 1 or 2 per cent trisodium phosphate solution and the container and contents are autoclaved at 15 pounds' pressure (121.5° C.) for twenty to thirty minutes. Otherwise, the contaminated instruments have to be autoclaved or boiled or placed in a suitable disinfectant (soaking for one hour in a 5 per cent saponated cresol solution), then scrubbed and cleansed, and sterilized ready for use.

Clean, unlocked instruments are placed in perforated metal trays. It is preferable to place in the bottom of the latter a layer of muslin (double thickness) or other suitable porous soft fabric. This is advocated especially when delicate and light instruments, scalpels, etc., are being sterilized. Each tray should contain only one layer of instruments and a protective covering consisting of another top layer of soft fabric or towel should be employed. The use of a bottom lining and top covering is a safe protection for the instruments.

Individual scalpel blades can be placed in small glass vials or test tubes which contain a piece of cotton or gauze at the bottom and are wrapped in gauze or cotton-plugged. These glass vials can be placed on top of other covered packs in trays, always resting on their sides. Hypodermic needles can be prepared as mentioned under "individual scalpel blades" or preferably by the use of test tubes drawn out to form restrictions which will hold the needles and stylets, so that the points are suspended within the lower portion of the tube, thus protecting it against injury. The tubes are wrapped in gauze or cotton-plugged. Suture needles and safety pins are sewed into or imbedded in muslin or a muslin pack and wrapped in muslin. In the case of glass syringes, remove the plunger from the barrel and wrap the plunger and barrel separately in muslin or towel or paper. Syringes, scalpel blades, hypodermic and suture needles and safety pins are sterilized with other loads preferably by dry heat.

Sterilization Technique.—There should be no compromise of aseptic technique. Obviously the best method is the safest method. The sterilization of instruments by the use of the autoclave, steam under pressure, is the method of choice in most instances. In routine procedure, the autoclave is used at 15 pounds' pressure (121.5° C.) for fifteen to twenty minutes. Some workers have advocated higher pressures (and temperatures) for shorter periods of time, so as to hasten the procedure of sterilization. A pressure of 20 pounds (132° C.) for three minutes has been advocated. The use of higher pressures and temperatures in autoclaving procedures is not commonly practiced as, in most instances, unless sufficient equipment is available, it would necessitate frequent adjustments of apparatus (autoclaves), so as to obtain the different pressures and temperatures. Autoclaves and all sterilizers should not be packed tight. The use of shelves is advocated, so as to provide the maximum utilization of space without packing too tight, thus preventing the free access and penetration of the steam.

Chapter XXI

DISINFECTION

STERILIZATION by the aid of chemicals is commonly known as *disinfection*, though the latter term still carries with it merely the thought of destroying microorganisms causing disease. (See page 263.) The chemical used in such process is known as the *disinfectant*. The first action of a chemical substance is to inhibit the growth of an organism. If the particular chemical is present in a large enough quantity or is one that is highly poisonous, the bacteria will eventually be killed. There are, however, many substances that are weak as toxic agents and are unable to destroy bacteria, but will retard or prevent their further development. Such substances have been termed *bacteriostatic agents*. The commonly used preservatives as the salicylates, benzoates and the numerous preparations employed as mouthwashes are examples of this class. Those disinfectants that kill bacteria are known as *bactericides*. The term *germicide*, though mainly used synonymously with the latter term, is somewhat broader and may include the destruction of microorganisms other than bacteria. A *bactericide*, however, when sufficiently diluted may act as a bacteriostatic agent. Phenol (1 to 20 dilution) acts as a germicide. Phenol (1 to 100 dilution) acts as a bacteriostatic agent.

The term *antiseptic*, derived from the Greek, literally means rotting, that is, anything which opposes decay, putrefaction and sepsis. In foreign scientific circles, the term is used practically synonomously with the term bacteriostatic agent. Laymen, however, appear to consider that antiseptics actually destroy microbes. It is with this in mind that in this country the term antiseptic has been legalized by definition in the Federal Food, Drug and Cosmetic Act of 1938. Section 201 (O) of the Act states: "the representation of a drug, in its labelling as an antiseptic shall be considered to be a representation that it is a germicide, except in the case of a drug purporting to be, or represented as an antiseptic for inhibitory use as a wet dressing, ointment, dusting powder or such other use as involves prolonged contact with the body." In other words, antiseptics, as the term is legalized in this country, are substances which, when applied to microorganisms, will render them innocuous either by actually killing them or preventing their growth, according to the character of the preparation or the method of application. Preparations such as ointments, salves, and dressings, which remain in contact with the organisms in the affected part of the body for a long period of time, may properly be designated as antiseptics, if their action is merely to inhibit the growth of bacteria. Products as eyewashes, mouthwashes and gargles, all kinds of douches and disinfecting solutions, which are in contact with the affected parts for but a brief period of time, may be called *antiseptics*, only if they will destroy organisms if used as directed.

Unfortunately, laymen and even scientists are confusing these terms. Some workers are using the term *inhibitors*, employed correctly when referring to bacteriostatic agents, the latter causing inhibition of growth or activity as long as there is contact between the chemical agent and microbe. There are some substances called *inhibitors* which unlike the bacteriostatic agents, merely delay growth or activity for varying periods of time. They are best designated as *retarders*. An example of the latter is in the use of propionates (Mycoban) in the baking industry. Their presence in the bread or cake does not completely inhibit mold growth, but the latter is delayed or retarded for varying periods of time depending upon the concentrations of the retarder. A *fungicide* is a substance which kills fungi and a *viricide* destroys viruses.

An *insecticide* is a preparation that kills insects. A *deodorant* is a particular substance that removes or masks obnoxious odors. It may or may not be a disinfectant or insecticide.

The following important and yet simple regulations must be observed when using chemicals or a chemical solution as a disinfectant or insecticide:

Be sure:
1. That the chemical has been proved to be a disinfectant or insecticide.
2. That the chemical will not be changed into an inert substance when coming in contact with the material you are about to disinfect.
3. That a sufficient quantity of the disinfectant or insecticide is used.
4. That the germicidal or insecticidal agent will come in direct and intimate contact with all of the bacteria or insects.
5. That the disinfectant or insecticide will remain in contact for a sufficient length of time to exert its action.

Though the foregoing rules must always be considered when using a disinfectant or insecticide, the following factors are also of value and influence the use of one chemical instead of another:

1. Low cost, availability and ease of application.
2. Ready solubility or miscibility with water or commonly employed solvents. Inflammability or explosive character.
3. Should not be toxic to man and animals and should not bleach, stain, tarnish or otherwise affect the furnishings in a household or material to be disinfected. If the disinfectant is to be used for humans or animals, it should not interfere with the natural defensive mechanism of the body cells.
4. Temperature that can be used. Warm solutions of chemicals are more effective disinfectants than cold solutions.
5. A chemical having a great penetrating property and requiring but a short period of time for disinfection is to be preferred.
6. A stable compound under ordinary conditions and when employed as a disinfectant.
7. Should not possess a disagreeable odor.

Practical Use of Disinfectants.—Many chemicals dissociate when in solution, the amount of dissociation being dependent to a great extent upon the solvent. Ionization (dissociation into ions) is at its height when the solvent is water. Other factors which affect the degree of dissociation are the concentration of the substance in solution and the nature of the particular chemical. Organic compounds do not seem to possess the property of breaking down into ions. Such dissociation is, however, commonly found among the inorganic compounds, especially acids, bases, salts and certain oxidizing agents. It has been shown by many workers that a distinct relationship exists between the disinfecting property of these inorganic compounds and the degree of their dissociation in solutions. The greater the dissociation, the greater the disinfecting powers. Other important factors which influence the efficiency of bactericidal agents are: the temperature used, surface tension, osmotic pressure, amount of organic matter present, pH and chemical structure.

A chemical may display bactericidal properties merely against one group or an individual type of bacteria. Within a given range of concentration, the bactericidal agent may display a destructive effect for one variety or group and only an inhibitory effect toward another variety or group of microorganisms. The nature of the material in which the latter are present, and under which disinfection must be applied, will frequently influence the concentration of the chemical which must be used. The degree of infection or contamination, that is, the numbers of bacteria present in the environment to be treated, must be considered.

The use of chemicals as sterilizing agents is restricted. Their use in the laboratory is limited, because they cannot be removed easily from substances which they have sterilized. Though free of bacteria, the material remains unfit for human consumption or therapeutic administration, due to the toxicity of the particular chemical. If the substance is a culture medium or a container in which the bacteria are to be sown, they are rendered useless, as the germicidal agent, still remaining, will inhibit the multiplication of any bacteria. Disinfection is most generally applicable for clinical, surgical and sanitary purposes.

Chemical germicides may be used dry (as iodoform), in solution (bichloride, 1 to 1000), or in a gaseous state (formaldehyde). The number of chemical agents having destructive action on bacteria is very large. Each possesses its own particular usefulness; and due to such individual characteristics, each is more or less ideal in its own field.

The personal equation frequently dictates the selection of one product instead of another. It is good practice, however, to perfect oneself in the use of the antiseptic selected and to learn the possibilities and limitation of a few of these agents rather than to use many of them indiscriminately and haphazardly. A word of caution is also to be given to laymen, who attempt self-medication with internal antiseptics. This should be discouraged at all times.

Disinfectants Offered for Sale in the United States.—Those offering preparations for sale on the open market as antiseptics, disinfectants, insecticides, fungicides, etc., must familiarize themselves with the various regulations of the individual states where the products are being manufactured or are to be sold. If the products are shipped in interstate commerce, all of these preparations must also comply with the various federal regulations. For instance, insecticides and disinfectants for general use, other than upon humans or animals, must meet the regulations of the Insecticide and Fungicide Act of 1910, administered by the U. S. Dept. of Agriculture. If they are to be used for man or animals, such preparations must comply with the regulations of the Federal Food, Drug and Cosmetic Act of 1938, administered by the Food and Drug Administration of the Federal Security Agency. If the preparations are organic arsenicals for intravenous use, they cannot be manufactured before a license is procured from the National Institute of Health and all regulations promulgated by the latter are to be carried out. In a few instances, the provisions of the Federal Caustic Poison

Act of 1927 are also to be considered. In all instances the regulations of the Federal Trade Commission are to be observed.

INORGANIC DISINFECTANTS

Though an attempt will be made to group the inorganic and organic disinfectants under separate headings, it will be impractical to limit considerations of all active agents to their respective groupings. Obviously, there is much overlapping and frequently it will be found more desirable to consider several compounds together, though one may be an inorganic and the others organic disinfectants.

Acids

The bactericidal and antiseptic properties of many acids are due almost entirely to the hydrogen-ion concentration they produce. The greater their dissociative powers, the more effective are they as bactericidal agents. Generally, inorganic (mineral) acids are highly dissociated and are more powerful than organic acids, which are less dissociated. Most living matter appears to be incapable of surviving in concentrated acid media. Acids precipitate proteins and as such are protoplasm poisons. Strong acids, which dissociate readily, however, have little practical use as disinfectants, inasmuch as they are irritating to the skin and mucous membranes, are caustic and even poisonous and also destroy fabrics, attack wood and corrode metals. Acids in weak concentrations, too low to kill bacteria, are frequently employed to increase the activity of other disinfectants.

There are some acids which exert their bactericidal effects due to the undissociated molecules, and in other instances the anion or negative ion may be responsible for the toxic effect. Such acids will be considered later along with their salts. They include especially acetic, lactic, benzoic, salicylic and mandelic acids.

Mention might be made of the presence of 0.3 per cent free *hydrochloric acid* in the stomach contents of humans, this serving to prevent putrefaction. An acid treatment for the disinfection of hides which are apt to contain anthrax and its spores is used. This consists in soaking the hides for forty hours in a water bath (at 60° to 70° F.) containing from 1 to 2 per cent absolute hydrochloric acid and 10 per cent NaCl. *Acetic acid*, in the form of vinegar, and *lactic acid* are considered later as legitimate food preservatives. A moist dressing of 1 per cent acetic acid in isotonic salt solution has been and is being used especially for *P. aeruginosa* infections. Acid vaginal douches, using acetic or lactic acid, are frequently useful in cases of nonspecific vaginitis (see Karnsky (*South. M. J.*, 1937, **30,** 69)).

Sulfurous acid, $(SO_2 + H_2O)$ treatment of various dried and preserved fruits is employed in different areas. This adds to the keeping qualities of such products. However, there are some states that have regulations limiting the sulfur dioxide content and a few which prohibit its use as a food preservative. Sulfur dioxide as a fumigant is considered under fumigation.

The use of *carbon dioxide* in the carbonation of ice cream and raw milk under ordinary pressure has been attempted with the thought that such products could be kept for longer periods of time. The indications are that this treatment under ordinary pressure results in little or no inhibition or destruction of bacteria. Sterile samples are only obtained under a high pressure and if exposure is for long periods of time.

Alkalies

The bactericidal efficiency of alkalies is mainly in proportion to the concentration of hydroxyl (OH) ions, but this also is influenced somewhat by other physical factors, such as osmotic pressure, buffer index, surface tension and adsorption. In some instances, the metallic ion or cation is toxic in itself. All Gram-negative nonspore-forming bacteria and all filterable viruses are readily destroyed by alkalies, even in dilute solutions. The Gram-positive nonspore-forming bacteria are more resistant, though 1 per cent solutions are usually effective within ten minutes. For spore formers, higher concentrations for more prolonged periods of time (5 per cent for at least one hour) are required. The greatest use of *lye* or free alkali (sodium hydroxide) as a practical disinfectant is around barns, stables and in agricultural pursuits. Sufficient concentrations of the lye should be added to give an adequate free alkali final concentration, and wherever possible this should be not less than from 0.5 to 1 per cent. Due to its solvent action in dissolving protein and in saponifying fats, free alkali is used by itself or, more frequently, as an adjunct with other disinfectants to treat sputum, mucus and body secretions. Concentrated solutions are irritating and corrosive and are rarely used other than as indicated above. Weak concentrations are used for their solvent effects and enhance the bactericidal efficiency of other disinfectants. The use of lime as a disinfectant is considered under the calcium salts.

Sodium carbonate and *sodium bicarbonate*, in concentrations of 1 to 2 per cent, are frequently added to water in which instruments and metallic implements are being heat-sterilized. They prevent corrosion to some extent and increase somewhat the bactericidal efficiency of the boiling water.

Trisodium phosphate (erroneously called *triphosphate*) is slightly alkaline and widely used in bottle washing and in the dairy industry and kitchen as a detergent. Some of the commercial products, under trade or brand names, are fortified with carbonate or bicarbonate of soda. At the high temperatures and time periods usually employed for general washing and cleaning purposes, trisodium phosphate, in concentrations of 1 to 3 per cent, will kill many of the nonspore-forming pathogens.

Peroxides

Solution of Hydrogen Peroxide (Liquor Hydrogenii Peroxidi, U. S. P.).—Peroxide of hydrogen containing not less than 3 per cent by weight of H_2O_2, representing approximately 10 volumes of available oxygen, is an active bleaching and deodorizing agent. In the presence of organic matter, it decomposes readily, with the liberation of oxygen, upon which its disinfecting action depends. Because of such active oxidizing properties, it is not used for general disinfection; and it is rarely employed, other than as a local germicide for small cuts and wounds and (diluted two or three times) as a spray or gargle. It is useful in the treatment of anaerobic infections. Some surgeons are also interested in the use of this preparation in wounds as the mechanical effect of the liberation of the gas loosens and destroys masses of infected material. However, no great dependence can be placed on its disinfecting qualities for large wounds, unless excessive amounts are used; and under these conditions it will be found to be an expensive solution to employ. *Superoxol* contains 30 per cent by weight of H_2O_2 representing approximately 100 volumes of available oxygen and is used for preparing the 3 per cent solution or other concentrations by dilution.

Metallic Peroxides and Other Oxygen-liberating Disinfectants.—There are many compounds available, which are readily decomposed with the liberation of hydrogen peroxide or of oxygen. Most of them are strong oxidizing agents, vary in their solubility and alkalinity, and are affected by the nature of the metal or basic radical which goes into solution.

Sodium peroxide has been advocated for the disinfection of water supplies and next to chlorine is said to be the most effective disinfectant for such purpose. It, however, is used infrequently.

Zinc peroxide is the most widely used of the metallic peroxides. Its use in surgery has been mainly due to the efforts of Meleney (*Ann. Surg.*, 1938, **107,** 32; *ibid.*, 1939, **109,** 881), who demonstrated its antiseptic action on certain aerobic, anaerobic and microaerophilic organisms commonly found in surgical infections. Recently Noel and Lynn (*J. Am. Pharm. Assoc.*, 1942, **31,** 523) reported that this product is probably a combination of zinc oxide and hydrogen peroxide and it should not be called zinc peroxide.

Sodium perborate, U. S. P. contains not less than 9 per cent of available oxygen. Solutions (1 to 3 per cent) of this chemical have been used especially in mouth and throat infections, as a gargle, to eliminate or reduce the bacterial flora. The laity frequently uses such solutions, flavored or unflavored, or even the dry powder or various tooth powders containing the perborate for an antiseptic dentifrice and gum massage. A report of the Council on Dental Therapeutics (*J. Am. Dent. Assoc.*, 1935, **22,** 1761) advises the use of sodium perborate only under professional supervision.

In the author's laboratory, bactericidal efficiency tests conducted on sodium perborate revealed that 3 per cent solutions of the latter killed *Staphylococcus aureus* and bacteria found in saliva within fifteen seconds.

Ozone (O_3) is a powerful oxidizing agent and disinfectant, but it is readily decomposed, is irritating and has little or no penetrative properties. Its only practical use as a disinfectant is in the treatment of small water supplies, swimming pools, and for beverage and bottled waters. It is favored by some manufacturers of the latter and swimming pool owners inasmuch as it destroys all odors in the water in the immediate environment, and exerts a disinfecting action. However, ozone treatment is expensive as compared with chlorination. Elford and Ende (*J. Hyg.*, 1942, **42,** 240) in an investigation of the merits of ozone as an aerial disinfectant (or bactericidal aerosol) conclude that in concentrations (0.04 per cent) which can be breathed over long periods of time without irritation, this gas cannot be expected to provide any effective protection against air-borne bacterial infection.

Permanganate and Dichromate of Sodium and Potassium.—These are both powerful oxidizing agents and are used to a limited extent as bactericidal agents. Neither should be employed for the disinfection of material or environments where large quantities of organic matter are present as they are rapidly reduced and inactivated. Where an astringent is required at the same time, *zinc permanganate* is useful and should receive more attention. Permanganates are used in 1 to 5 per cent solutions for the disinfection of hands and skin. Permanganate baths, 1:4000, are useful in controlling widespread infected and weeping types of dermatoses. In dilutions, 0.1 to 0.3 per cent, they are employed for gargles, mouthwashes, irrigations and douches.

Mercurial Compounds

Compounds of mercury and, in particular, the simple inorganic mercurials have been used for the destruction of bacteria for more than six decades. For many years, a 1:1000 solution of bichloride of mercury enjoyed widespread popularity as a general disinfectant. In this concentration (0.1 per cent), one-half hour exposure will kill all vegetative forms of bacteria. Spores are said to require a 1:500 dilution and an exposure for at least one hour. It is, however, questionary whether bichloride of mercury or any compound of mercury can be relied upon to kill bacterial spores even after long periods of exposure under conditions as commonly found in practice. The use of the simple inorganic mercurials is limited by their irritant and marked toxic action upon the tissues of man and animals. In their tendency to form precipitates with proteinaceous material as would be found in pus, sputum, feces and, in fact, in most body secretions and excretions, the resultant insoluble coagulum of inactive albuminate of mercury prevents the further penetration of any excess of active disinfectant. The corrosive action of bichloride upon metal, its fixation of stain (even blood) in linens and fabrics, its decomposition by sulfur compounds and alkalies producing mercurials inactive as disinfectants, are other reasons for not relying too much upon this compound for its bactericidal properties.

Two other simple or inorganic compounds of mercury have been advocated to replace bichloride. *Mercuric iodide*, in a concentration of 1:1000, dissolved in an excess of a soluble iodide (potassium mercuric iodide), and *oxycyanide of mercury* in a 1:1000 dilution are being used. They do not have the same irritating and marked caustic action nor do they appear to possess the property of displaying the same degree of reactivity with protein material or of attacking metallic substances as that possessed by bichloride of mercury. Solutions of these mercurials are advocated in preference to the latter for skin disinfection, wound irrigation, and for sterilizing instruments. Catheters, filiforms, bougies and other equipment which may be affected after repeated sterilization by heat treatment or by bichloride are being disinfected with these solutions. The latter also have been used for washing and disinfecting floors, tables, etc., especially those that are constructed of cement, tile or enamel. However, the best practice to employ when using solutions of any of these inorganic mercurials as disinfectants if they are to be employed at all is to be assured that the articles or environment treated are mechanically clean before treatment and then use the proper dilution for the minimum period of exposure (which is never less than fifteen minutes and preferably thirty minutes for 1:1000 concentrations).

A so-called Tincture or Compound Solution of Mercuric Chloride (alcohol-acetone-water vehicle) has been highly recommended as a skin antiseptic (*Surg., Gynec. & Obst.*, 1935, **61**, 333). More recently the following solution has been employed as an ideal inexpensive skin disinfectant (*U. S. Nav. M. Bull.*, 1943, **41**, 533): acid fuchsin, 0.08 Gm.; eosin "Y," 0.6 Gm.; mercuric chloride, 0.7 Gm.; tricresol, 5 cc.; acetone, 100 cc.; alcohol, 525 cc.; water, 375 cc.

The addition of inorganic mercurials to soap to produce a so-called *germicidal soap* has been advocated and such soaps are marketed. The opinion held by most workers is the same as that expressed by Norton more than two decades ago, who, in studying the effect of washing the hands with ordinary soap and with "germicidal" soaps (*J. A. M. A.*, 1920, **75**, 302), said when speaking of removing bacteria from the hands:

"This may be done by ordinary toilet soaps as effectively, if not more so, as by the special brands of the so-called 'antiseptic' or 'germicidal' soaps."

Bichloride of Mercury and Other Mercury Salts.—Corrosive sublimate (mercuric chloride or bichloride of mercury) is commonly used in strengths of 1 to 1000 and, in rare instances when spores are to be treated, in a 1 to 500 dilution. Solutions are generally prepared from the small or large poison tablets of mercury bichloride, which can only be sold (U. S. P. requirements), possessing some distinctive color (not white) and of an angular or irregular shape (not discoid). The small tablet contains 0.125 Gm. and the large tablet 0.47 Gm. of $HgCl_2$. The former added to 120 cc. (4 fluid-ounces) of water and the latter to 475 cc. (one pint) of water makes a 1:1000 solution. One-half hour exposure of the latter strength will kill all vegetative forms of bacteria, while for spores, a longer exposure of a 1:500 solution, usually one hour, is desirable. The latter time limit is best to employ in practice. This compound has the disadvantages mentioned previously which must be considered (under such conditions, bichloride cannot be employed).

Solutions of corrosive sublimate are used for the disinfection of hands, wounds, floors, walls, ceilings, furnishings, linens, gas and face masks, etc.

Mercuric Iodide.—Mercuric iodide dissolved in water in the presence of an excess of sodium or potassium iodide has been claimed by some as a highly efficient germicide. It is employed especially for the disinfection of the hands and body; and is also used by some for the sterilization of instruments and vessels, it being claimed that this compound does not attack metals. It is used in 1:1000 dilutions. See above.

Oxycyanide of Mercury.—This is a basic mercuric salt of hydrocyanic acid, containing approximately 54 per cent mercuric cyanide and 46 per cent mercuric oxide. Oxycyanide of mercury in 1:1000 dilutions is used almost exclusively in some localities in place of bichloride of mercury. It apparently possesses no irritating or caustic action, although it is a more powerful germicide than the bichloride. It does not seem to possess the property of reacting with albuminoid material or attacking metallic substances. Smith (*U. S. Nav. M. Bull.*, 1938, **36,** 522) recommends as a venereal prophylactic an ointment containing: base, 67 per cent; colloidal calomel, 33 per cent; and mercuric cyanide, 0.125 per cent. He later (*U. S. Nav. M. Bull.*, 1941, **39,** 80) suggested that *oxyquinoline sulfate* be used to replace the cyanide if the latter causes any burning. The ointment base is *d*-sorbitol, 2 per cent; petrolatum, 98 per cent.

For further details concerning mercurial compounds as bactericidal agents, see page 312.

Silver Compounds

Silver as a disinfectant is available in the form of *finely divided (colloidal) silver,* which is responsible for an *oligodynamic action;* as soluble inorganic salts, such as *silver nitrate;* organic compounds as the lactate and citrate; and a large number of so-called colloidal silver preparations, which may be roughly grouped as *protein silver, strong type; protein silver, mild type; collargol type; electric type;* and *silver halides.* The long-continued use of any silver compound may produce irremediable discoloration of the skin or mucous membranes ("argyria").

Silver nitrate, in concentrations of 0.5 to 1 per cent is used by instillation into the eyes; and in stronger concentrations, up to 10 per cent, it is applied in infections of the mouth and throat. Its astringent, irritating, corrosive and toxic action mitigates against its wide use. *Ammoniacal silver nitrate*, which contains approximately 30 per cent silver as silver diamino nitrate, is used to some extent in dentistry. *Silver lactate* (0.1 to 0.5 per cent) and *silver citrate* (0.01 to 0.03 per cent) have been used in the treatment of wounds and affections of the mucous membranes. The latter compound is nonirritating but the lactate possesses irritating properties. *Silver picrate*, in concentrations of 0.25 to 1 or 2 per cent, is used in vaginal and urethral infections and also in upper respiratory conditions.

The so-called colloidal silver compounds consist of indefinite mixtures of metallic silver, silver oxide and various silver protein compounds. The strong protein silver compounds are represented by *Strong Protein Silver, U. S. P.* and by *Protargol (silver albumose)*. They contain approximately 8 per cent of silver, are strong in their bactericidal action, are distinctly irritating and are employed in concentrations of 0.25 to 10 per cent in genito-urinary, ophthalmological and nose and throat affections. The mild protein silver compounds contain from 19 to 25 per cent silver and are represented by *argyn* (colloidal compound of silver oxide and serum albumin); *argyrol* (*silver vitellin*); *cargentos* (colloidal silver oxide and modified casein); *silvol* (colloidal silver with an alkaline proteid); *solargentum* (colloidal silver and gelatin); and *Mild Protein Silver, U. S. P.* They are used in concentrations of 5 to 50 per cent for antisepsis on mucous membranes.

The collargol type contains a much higher percentage of silver (75 per cent) in colloidal form and as an oxide, and the remainder possibly as a protein compound. In the electric type, metallic silver is brought into colloidal suspension electrically. These solutions are used in dilute concentrations and are not very stable. The silver halides are colloidal insoluble inorganic silver salts, represented by *Lunosol* (10 per cent colloidal silver chloride) and *Neo-Silvol* (20 per cent of colloidal silver iodide with a soluble gelatin base). They are generally used in concentrations of 1 to 30 per cent, are nonirritating and nonastringent, and have the advantage of not discoloring the skin and mucous membranes.

Minute amounts of the ions of different metals, but not their salts, are capable of destroying various types of organisms in water. This is known as the *oligodynamic action of metals*. Water can be disinfected by allowing it to come in contact with or passing it through silver-impregnated sand. Wernicke and Modern (*Biochem. Ztschr.*, 1929, **214**, 187) found that only one part of ionized silver in 20 million parts of water was bactericidal. In order to utilize this principle on a large scale, Krause produced a special form of silver to be used for its oligodynamic action, the basis of the *katadyn* process. Moiseev (*J. Am. Water Works Assoc.*, 1934, **26**, 217) introduced various types of silver-coated sand, which yielded effective results in water disinfection. The use of this process for the treatment of small water supplies and water in swimming pools is being employed to a limited extent. Goetz and associates (*Science*, 1942, **95**, 537) incorporated atomic silver in resins, so as to obtain a *self-sterilizing surface* with lasting activity. The surface material presented by these workers is tasteless, colorless, odorless and resistant to mechanical wear and chemical attack by boiling water, weak acids and alkali solutions. The total quantity of silver varies depending upon the intended use, but never exceeds one gram for 1000 square centimeters of exposed surface. The bactericidal action depends on a continual replenishment of the surface with atomic silver by diffusion from the interior on wetting. *Gold* and *copper* can be used, but silver is more practical, as it is less toxic than copper and cheaper than gold.

Copper Compounds

Next to silver, copper exerts the most effective oligodynamic action. Copper ions, in a concentration of 0.6 mg. per liter of water, will produce complete disinfection. Copper acts on bacteria by coagulating the albumins in the latter, producing an insoluble coagulum, which, however, under suitable conditions may be dissolved.

Copper sulfate (bluestone or blue vitriol) is highly recommended and has been used as a fungicide for the destruction of low forms of algae, weeds and even protozoa, which are not killed or removed by the ordinary methods in the purification of water supplies (used in dilutions of 1:2,000,000 to 1:1,000,000). It is claimed by some that this chemical is not a germicide, but nevertheless many investigators, as well as the author, have found it effective as a bactericidal agent in the disinfection of water in swimming pools, which are not highly contaminated with refuse and similar organic materials. Swimming pools have been disinfected successfully by adding enough copper sulfate to give a 1:1,000,000 concentration. Copper sulfate may be found of value for the destruction of the common earthworm, as it may become a pest and a source of serious economic loss.

Bismuth and Antimony Compounds

The insoluble bismuth compounds, employed as dusting powders or ointments, are primarily used as protective agents and only secondarily as antiseptics. *Bipp paste*, consisting of bismuth subnitrate, iodoform and petrolatum to make a paste, was used extensively during World War I and is being used in the present war in the treatment of wounds. Various compounds of bismuth have been formulated so as to enhance antisepticity. It is doubtful whether the addition of such antiseptic acid radicals as salicylic, tannic and gallic acids to produce bismuth salicylate, tannate and gallate increases the antiseptic action. Even the introduction of iodine and bromine does not enhance the antisepticity. On the other hand, bismuth compounds with phenol or phenolic groups containing iodine or bromine have an increased antiseptic efficiency. *Bismuth tribromphenate (xeroform)* and *bismuth betanaphtholate* are examples of the latter group. Inasmuch as the bismuth and antimony salts most frequently used are mainly organic compounds, they are considered under the latter heading (see page 326).

Chemicals Used as Food Preservatives

Many food products in their natural state undergo various changes on standing. The three main groups of microorganisms causing decomposition in foodstuffs are molds, which thrive everywhere; yeasts, which attack sugar-containing products; and bacteria, which attack meats and substances rich in proteins. Different processes have been introduced to retard such decomposition, so as to increase the salable and usable life of these products. Many of the physical methods practiced which are most efficient and legitimate are different degrees of cold, cold storage, pasteurization, ultraviolet light, drying, smoking, pickling, sterilization by heat or a combination of heat sterilization and air displacement as used in the canneries. Experiments by chemists of the U. S. Department of Agriculture reveal that while the majority of bacteria capable of producing decomposition in foods are killed by freezing temperatures, a small portion of survivors remain. There are some which were found to resist temperatures as low as $-422°$ F. for as long as ten hours. The keeping qualities of oil-bearing foods (mayonnaise, salad oils, potato chips, butter, etc.) may be enhanced greatly by the use of properly covered wrappers, colored containers, etc., capable of screening out active light wave lengths, which produce rancidity. Care in handling whole skinned oranges and other fruits will aid in their keeping qualities, as the latter suffer heavy spoilage from molds and other fungi due to breaks in the skin made by clipper cuts, box splinters, nails, fingernails of workers, etc.

The following chemicals and drugs have been used as food preservatives: salt, vinegar, lactic acid, high concentrations of sugar and the spices like cinnamon, cloves, mustard, allspice, etc. A minimum 6 per cent salt, 3 per cent acetic acid or 1 to 2 per cent lactic acid content has been found satisfactory in preventing the decomposition of many products. Such substances as these are foods in themselves and are, of course, permissible as preservatives. But apart from the use of these old and well-known methods of food preservation, a modern practice has been attempted at the preservation of foods by the use of one or more inorganic and organic antiseptics which are not to be used in marketed food products unless allowed by law. Benzoic acid is the only permissible chemical preservative allowed for marketable food preparations, and the declaration of its use must be made on the label. It is favored for food products which are either concentrated to be later diluted or consumed in small amounts. Examples of the latter are in the marketing of ketchup and concentrated fruit flavors for fountain use.

There is a general prejudice against the employment of any of these chemicals which may be truly classified as drugs. The objections raised are:

1. That these drugs even in small quantities, due to their accumulative effect (especially if present in all food products), will exercise a toxic effect on the system of the consumer. Individual idiosyncrasies have been reported.

2. They may also assist in retarding the proper functioning of the digestive processes and burden the waste eliminating organs.

3. Some foods may have already undergone decomposition before the addition of the antiseptic. Such decomposition will thus not be apparent, while the food product itself when consumed will be unwholesome, even though the antiseptic is present.

Boric Acid and Borax.—Boric acid and borax have been found by many workers to possess no germicidal and but weak bacteriostatic activity. Either one or both, and at times combined with other chemicals, make up the bulk of many of the preserving formulas or proprietary mixtures recommended to the laity to be used for the preservation of products in the home, as meats, jellies, syrups, butter, fish, etc. They cannot be used as preservatives for foods which are to be sold on the open market.

Boric acid, either as an ointment, in solution or as the well-known "Boroglycerin," is used for inflamed and infected mucous membranes, and as a wash for various forms of mouth irritation. It is used most frequently in ophthalmic surgery, as being less irritating than more efficient antiseptics. A permissible and useful application can be made in preparing pastes of all kinds. By employing an aqueous solution of borax instead of water in making starch and other pastes, there will be no decomposition and practically little formation of molds. Boric acid is a permissible urinary preservative. Decomposition in urine will be delayed by adding 5 grains of boric acid to each 4 fluidounces of urine.

Sulfurous Acid and Sulfites.—Sulfur when ignited yields SO_2. This in the presence of moisture is an efficient gaseous disinfectant. When in solution, sulfurous acid is formed. In the form of its salts, as sulfites, especially sodium and calcium acid sulfites, SO_2 is employed illegitimately, as a food preservative. Neutral ammonium, potassium and sodium sulfites are also used at times. These sulfites are employed mainly in fruit juices, preserving whole fruit (cherries, peaches, etc.), fruit and vege- table pulp, as ketchup and tomato products, etc. They may or may not be admixed with other antiseptics. Sulfur dioxide or sulfurous acid and sulfites are employed legitimately but under restrictions as preservatives in some areas for dried fruits. They are said to improve the appearance of the latter, keep them fresh longer and aid in the preservation of vitamins A and C. They are unsatisfactory preservatives to employ, and it is best to regulate against their use in foods.

Lime.—Calcium oxide or lime in the dry state is rarely used as a disinfectant. It had been reported as being employed for the disinfection of cadavers, dead of infectious diseases. Lime when slaked (by adding 1 part of water to 2 parts of lime) forms cal- cium hydroxide. From this, "milk of lime" is made, by adding from 4 to 10 parts of water. Milk of lime, *when fresh*, is an active germicidal agent, but it loses its disinfect- ing properties if exposed to the air for any length of time, due to the absorption of CO_2 which forms calcium carbonate. The latter (known as air-slaked lime) does not possess germicidal activity. In the absence of other disinfectants, milk of lime can be used around stables and privies, for the disinfection of manure, feces, carcasses before burial, etc. In the form of whitewash it is used to preserve and disinfect brick work, fences, sheds, etc. Though highly efficient, its use is limited because of its instability, its insolubility, and the residue left wherever it is applied.

The Halogens

This is a name given to the compounds of fluorine, bromine, iodine and chlorine. It may be safely said that no two chemicals have as wide a reputation as active germi- cidal agents, as that possessed by chlorine and iodine in their various combinations.

Fluorine, hydrofluoric acid and the fluorides are rarely employed as antiseptics due to their irritating and poisonous properties. For the use of sodium fluoride and silicofluorides, see pages 403 and 416.

Bromine is rarely employed in any of its forms due to its irritating property. *Di- bromin* (*Dibromobarbituric acid* or *Dibromomalonylureide*) is a bromine compound used as an antiseptic and proposed for use in solution (0.01 per cent or stronger) either as an irrigating fluid or as a saturated gauze packing.

Iodine and Iodine Compounds.—Iodine has had a large reputation as an efficient germicide in the form of: *Mild Tincture of Iodine*, containing 2 per cent iodine and 2.4 per cent sodium iodide in diluted alcohol; *Solution of Iodine*, containing 2 per cent iodine and 2.4 per cent sodium iodide in distilled water; *Strong Solution of Iodine* or *Lugol's Solution*, containing 5 per cent iodine and 10 per cent potassium iodide in dis- tilled water; *Tincture of Iodine*, containing 7 per cent of iodine and 5 per cent potas- sium iodide in 90 per cent alcohol; and a 3 per cent iodine (in water or in 50 per cent alcohol containing various soluble iodides). Iodine is employed successfully by many surgeons as the only agent to disinfect any part before an operation, by merely swab- bing over the particular area after previously cleansing and drying. These iodine solu- tions and even iodine as a vapor are used for ringworm and other skin infections, in surgery, etc. Iodine is poisonous, stains and attacks metals and material containing starches. The Tincture or Lugol's Solution (diluted, one teaspoonful of Lugol's or the Tincture or two teaspoonfuls of the Mild Tincture to a pint of lukewarm water or isotonic salt solution) is employed by many workers in place of bichloride of mercury solutions as an efficient antiseptic wash, in irrigations and in douches. Extensive experimentation in the author's laboratory has revealed (*J. Am. Pharm. Assoc.*, 1932, **21,** 894) that a 3 per cent iodine solution in water containing soluble iodides is more satisfactory as an antiseptic than most all of the other commonly employed marketable antiseptic preparations. We examined a number of different iodine solutions and compared them with most of the proprietary and trade-marked antiseptics available then on the market. *In vitro* tests have been repeated under varying conditions and in researches, to be published soon, we found even 2 per cent aqueous iodine solutions were superior to many of the other commonly used bactericidal agents in the dilutions most frequently employed. Using the plasma clot and perfusion techniques (*Am. J. Pharm.*, 1941, **113,** 203, 353), tests in the author's laboratory also revealed that iodine was less toxic than the mercurials, phenols, silver salts, hypochlorites and the other commonly employed antiseptics in the effective concentrations used in practice. However, iodine allergy is known and reactions due to the local use of iodine and iodine compounds may occur in those who are sensitive. Pelnor (*J. Lab. & Clin. Med.*, 1942, **27,** 1150) reports several cases of cutaneous reactions to iodine and iodoform.

Iodine is used for the purification of small quantities of water. This is of value especially for campers, hikers or during periods of floods when the water supply is usually contaminated, or for anyone who knows nothing about or doubts the fitness of a particular water for human consumption. Adding one to two drops of Tincture of Iodine to one quart of the most polluted sample of water will disinfect the latter within ten minutes, so that it may be fit for human consumption. There is no perceptible taste or harm from the small amount of iodine added.

Compounds of iodine, combined organically in various combinations, are employed as dusting powders, due to the antiseptic action of free iodine which is slowly liberated. In most instances, however, the efficiency of such powders in retarding the growth of septic organisms is due to the fact that they diminish the secretion from the wounded surface, thus affording a less suitable medium for the growth of bacteria, or by forming a crust over the wound bacteria are prevented mechanically from penetrating into it, and in some instances phagocytosis may be enhanced. *Thymol iodide* (*Aristol*) is one of the widely used organic iodine dusting powders. It is generally employed as the active ingredient in an ointment or powder.

Iodoform (CHI_3) is, however, most frequently used as the standard bearer of such compounds. It is generally employed in the dry state or as a 5 to 10 per cent ointment. Iodoform is weakly antiseptic in itself, but in the presence of discharges in wounds, etc., iodine is liberated slowly. A lasting disagreeable odor of iodoform is an objection which has hindered a still wider employment of this chemical. Many combinations are available which attempt to disguise the odor, but with limited success. Other organic iodine compounds have been marketed to replace iodoform. Though they avoid the disagreeable odor and to some extent the occasional irritating and toxic symptoms displayed by iodoform, they do not possess the same decided antiseptic activity. Perhaps their action is due to the fact that they diminish the secretion of the wound so that microorganisms cannot flourish. Iodoform is the active ingredient in *Bipp Paste* (bismuth subnitrate, iodoform and enough petrolatum to make a paste), which is used as an antiseptic packing in wounds. *Zipp Paste* (zinc oxide replaces bismuth subnitrate) is also used and is said to be less toxic.

Vioform (Iodochlorhydroxyquinoline) was originally introduced to be used as a dusting powder for application to wounds, ulcers and skin affections and later was employed against *trichomonas* infections, but its greatest use today is for its action against *Entamoeba histolytica*, when it is administered internally.

The use of iodine and iodides in syphilis and actinomycotic infections has created the impression that these compounds are specifics for the destruction of *Treponema pallidum* and the fungus of sporotrichosis. The specific effects of the iodides are not exerted on the etiological agents but upon the tissues in which they are found and which have reacted to them by the formation of gummata or tumors. The latter are destroyed by the iodides, so that the microorganisms are more readily accessible to specific drugs which kill or inactivate them.

Yatren (also *Loretin*), chemically iodohydroxyquinolinesulfonic acid, is used in the treatment of amebiasis. A mixture of this acid, its sodium salt and sodium bicarbonate, containing approximately 28 per cent iodine is sold under the name of *chiniofon*. The latter, originally introduced as a wound antiseptic, is employed widely in the treatment of amebic dysentery. It is used orally and at times rectally.

Chlorine and Chlorine Compounds.—Chlorine gas just as it is being liberated is known as *nascent* chlorine. This when collected in solution and in cylinders will yield *free* chlorine. Chlorine combined chemically as binary compounds, in the form of chlorides, is spoken of as *combined* chlorine. Chlorine which can be made easily available is known as *available* chlorine. The latter is usually made available by the interaction of weak acids or organic compounds with *hypochlorites*. When considering the disinfecting value of the numerous chlorine combinations, the *chlorides* are the least important, inasmuch as they possess little if any bactericidal properties.

Free Chlorine is irritating, attacks metallic substances, bleaches, is easily decomposed by organic matter, and loses its strength quickly. As so-called *liquid chlorine* (chlorine gas under pressure, marketed in cylinders), it is, however, extensively used in the purification of water supplies in the proportion of 1 part of free chlorine to one million parts of water (or 8 pounds of chlorine to 1,000,000 gallons of water). In many of the water filtration and sewage disposal plants, the chlorine is passed directly into the water coming from the sand filters and the effluent from the treated sewage. It is used extensively for the disinfection of water in swimming pools and of bottles in the dairy and bottling industries. For public swimming pools, many states require a residual chlorine content of 0.3 part per million. The chlorine is best controlled automatically by a chlorinator direct feed.

Hypochlorites were employed for years as active germicidal agents.

Chlorinated Lime, $CaOCl_2$, known as bleach, chloride of lime and bleaching powder, contains not less than 30 per cent of available chlorine. Like all hypochlorites, it has distinct bleaching powers, attacks metals, is destructive to fabrics, and is somewhat unstable unless kept in airtight receptacles. It is, however, an excellent germicide and deodorant. It may be employed dry, by sprinkling around stables, privies and anywhere where dejecta may be found, or in a 4 per cent solution for sputum, urine, excreta and other refuse, and for the washing of wooden tanks and vats (as in washing the sedimentation tanks in water purification plants). Where liquid chlorine is not available or found impractical to use, chlorinated lime can be employed to disinfect water supplies, by adding a solution containing 1 pound of the powder to each 40,000 gallons of water to be treated (this gives approximately 1 part of chlorine per 1,000,000 parts of water).

Various compounds have been added to the powder and liquid hypochlorites, so as to stabilize the latter and increase their usefulness. In most instances, some alkali or alkaline salt is added. In few instances, careful refinement has yielded a relatively stable compound. *Perchloron* is an example of the latter stabilized hypochlorites and this product yields from 50 to 70 per cent of available chlorine. Some commonly used soluble stabilized solutions of hypochlorites are: *Labarraque's solution* (*Liquor Sodii Hypochloritis, U. S. P.*) (containing from 4 to 6 per cent NaOCl and an excess of sodium carbonate); *Javelle water* (solution of chlorinated potash and potassium carbonate in excess) (containing approximately 3 per cent potassium hypochlorite); *Bacilli Kil* (*B-K*); *Hychlorite* (solution of sodium hypochlorite, a low alkalinity, and containing 3.8 per cent available chlorine); *Antiformin*, a strongly alkaline solution of sodium hypochlorite, containing over 5 per cent available chlorine; and *Chlorox*, an alkaline solution of sodium hypochlorite used for household purposes.

These soluble hypochlorites are employed as general disinfectants. Due to the presence of an excess of alkali, they are fairly permanent solutions, and on account of the presence of the latter, they possess an added advantage as solvents and germicidal agents. They exert a strong oxidizing action and are active antiseptics and deodorants. Like all other chlorine compounds, they bleach, attack fabrics and metal, are decomposed by organic matter and are irritating. For these reasons, they are not employed as extensively as their germicidal activity warrants their use. As general disinfectants especially around bakeries, dairies and establishments manufacturing foodstuffs, they are used in from 1 to 10 per cent dilutions. A 1 per cent dilution is efficient for disinfecting iceboxes, refrigerators, vats, etc. The chlorine can then be liberated by using hot water, steam or a dilute vinegar solution. *The solutions have a solvent action on almost all bacteria and cellular matter except the tubercle bacillus.* As a spray or antiseptic mouthwash, they are used in 0.25 to 0.5 per cent dilutions.

Chlorine disinfection is used on the dairy farm for pails, coolers, cans, bottles and other equipment where heat sterilization cannot be employed. In restaurants, taverns, luncheonettes and fountains, glassware, dishes and other utensils can be sanitized quickly with chlorine. Hypochlorite or chloramine-T solutions are used, so as to yield not less than 100 and preferably between 200 and 300 parts of available chlorine. The higher concentrations are employed if the solution is changed only once daily. The containers and utensils should be immersed in such solutions for at least three minutes.

Due to the presence of the excess of alkali, the above-mentioned solutions of hypochlorites are generally unsatisfactory for medicinal and surgical use, the alkalinity accounting for the irritating properties. It remained for Dakin, Carrel and their associates to correct these reprehensible qualities and adapt them to the role as surgical antiseptics.

Carrel-Dakin or Dakin's Solution.—The formula, technique and mode of preparation of this solution have been published and are available in the National Formulary and the leading scientific journals. In preparing this solution, the important facts essential to note are that the end product is to be free of alkali, and the solution should not be used if the *hypochlorite content* is below 0.45 per cent or above 0.5 per cent (equivalent to not less than 0.43 and not more than 0.48 per cent available chlorine). This particular strength can be maintained with little variation for about one month, a fact which in itself ought to discourage the use of modified formulas for extemporaneous preparation.

Hypochlorite, previously mentioned, which contains not less than 3.85 per cent available chlorine and only mere traces of free alkali, and that only calcium hydrate (0.14%), when diluted with seven volumes of water yields a solution similar to Carrel-Dakin Solution.

Eupad, Solution of Eusol and Hypochlorous Acid.—Free hypochlorous acid is a more active antiseptic than its salts. Its bactericidal value is high, and it also possesses the advantage of not coagulating albuminous matter. To effect a complete liberation of the hypochlorous acid, a powder is prepared by intimately mixing equal parts of finely ground chlorinated lime and boric acid. This is named *Eupad*. *Solution of Eusol* is made by mixing 25 Gm. of eupad with 1 liter of water, allowing the mixture to stand for three to four hours, then siphoning off the supernatant liquid and filtering the remainder to rid it of the insoluble calcium borate. The filtrate, solution of eusol, contains some calcium chloride and about 0.27 per cent of free hypochlorous acid.

Chloramine-T, sodium tolueneparasulfonchloramide (containing from 11.5 to 13 per cent active chlorine), is nonirritating, nontoxic, a valuable deodorant, and considerably more stable than the Carrel-Dakin Solution. Chloramine-T (official in the U. S. P. as *Chloramina*) is soluble in water and thus a concentrated aqueous solution can be made. It is used in from 0.1 to 3 per cent solutions. *A solution of chloramine-T in water is not identical with Carrel-Dakin (or frequently merely known as Dakin's) Solution and should not be sold as such.*

Dichloramine-T.—Paratoluenesulfondichloramide-Dichloramine-T, containing from 28 to 30 per cent active chlorine, is to be preferred to chloramine-T, due to the fact that the latter lacks the solvent action possessed by the former and by all alkaline hypochlorites. Dichloramine-T (official in the N. F. as *Dichloramina-T*) is but sparingly soluble in water, and such aqueous solution is quickly decomposed. Concentrations as high as 20 per cent of dichloramine-T in chlorinated eucalyptol or chlorinated paraffin oil are prepared.

Chlorcosane (official in the N. F. as *Paraffinum Chlorinatum*), employed now as a vehicle for dichloramine-T, is a liquid obtained by chlorinating paraffin. Solutions up to 7 or 8 per cent may be prepared. It is important to note that all containers for solutions of dichloramine-T should be absolutely dry. The presence of any trace of water, alcohol or any substance for which chlorine has an affinity will hasten the decomposition of the dichloramine-T.

Chlorazene is a brand name of chloramine-T. In some hospitals and clinics, the two closely related antiseptics have been used jointly, first spraying and thoroughly cleansing the wound with an aqueous solution of chlorazene, and then applying an oily solution or a paste of dichloramine-T. From 0.25 to 1 per cent dilutions are being employed by some in nose and throat affections.

Halazone.—This synthetic, chemically known as para-toluolsulfodichloraminobenzoic acid, is the most stable of the Dakin chlorine products. Each tablet, which is the marketable form, contains $1/_{16}$ grain of the chemical and is sufficient to disinfect and render potable one quart of the most polluted sample of water in from five to thirty minutes, without leaving the resultant sterilized product unpleasant to the taste.

Azochloramid (N-N-dichloroazodicarbonamidine), official in the U. S. P. as *Chloroazodinum*, is used as an antiseptic in surgical and medicinal pursuits in saline solution, triacetin (glyceryl triacetate) or olive oil in concentrations varying from 1:3000 to 1:500. *Liquor chloroazodini*, U. S. P. contains 0.26% chloroazodin in glyceryl triacetate. This chlorine compound possesses a relatively low toxicity and is less reactive with organic matter and especially blood serum than any of the chlorine antiseptics, though free hemoglobin (laked blood) decreases its bactericidal efficiency. It is said to release chlorine very slowly and to keep it in solution, maintaining a chlorine concentration of such low potential that it is not used up in side reactions with extraneous organic matter, but its action is largely restricted to that of the invading organisms. This chemical has been used extensively in the prophylactic and therapeutic management of all kinds of wound infections with favorable results (*West J. Surg.*, 1940, **48,** 415). *Azochloramide Sodium Tetradecyl Sulfate Dextrose Compound,* devised by Petroff and Schain (*Quart. Bull., Sea View Hosp.*, July, 1940), is available as a disinfectant, the antiseptic properties of which are enhanced by the addition of the wetting agent, sodium tetradecyl sulfate. Kintz (*Mil. Surg.*, 1941, **89,** 60) in a preliminary report on this compound claims it to be superior to any other agent for use as an antiseptic in surgery.

Iodine and Chlorine Compounds.—Trichloride of iodine in 0.5 per cent (or from 0.1 to 1 per cent) solutions is an extremely powerful germicidal agent.

ORGANIC DISINFECTANTS

In addition to the compounds already mentioned that are of organic origin, there are infinite numbers of possibilities for obtaining organic combinations that will be found to possess disinfecting properties. It will, however, be advisable to mention only those that are extensively employed and that have been found of practical value.

Alcohol.—Ethyl alcohol, either absolute or in 95 per cent strength, is but an indifferent disinfectant, unless the material and organisms to be sterilized contain sufficient quantities of moisture to dilute the alcohol. The greatest disinfecting power is obtained in a strength of 70 per cent by weight (76.9 per cent by volume at 15.56° C.). Only the weak-resistant bacteria are killed. The author (*Am. J. M. Sc.*, 1938, **195,** 358) revealed that bacterial spores could survive in 95 per cent ethyl alcohol for as long a period as nine months. The addition of alkali, even in weak concentrations (from 1:5000 to 1:1000) increases the bactericidal efficiency of alcohol. Acetone may be added as a fat solvent, and frequently 1 per cent phenol and, still better, one of the coal-tar emulsifiable disinfectants is mixed with both chemicals so as to increase the bactericidal efficiency of the mixture. In strengths of 15 per cent or over, alcohol is used in medicinal preparations to prevent decomposition, as this strength will inhibit the growth of bacteria.

Isopropyl Alcohol.—This chemical is employed in many of the bathing alcohols to replace ethyl alcohol. In full strength, it is more bactericidal than ethyl alcohol, even when the latter is present in its maximum bactericidal concentration of 70 per cent by weight. *Methyl alcohol* (wood alcohol) is weaker in its bactericidal effect than is ethyl alcohol.

Acetone is bactericidal in strengths of 50 per cent or higher (unpublished findings).

Formaldehyde.—Formaldehyde is known principally as a gaseous disinfectant. A

37 per cent (by weight) solution of the gas in water is official in the pharmacopoeia as *Liquor Formaldehydi*. *Formalin* is a trade-marked name that has also been applied to the latter. Due to its irritant and coagulant effects, formaldehyde solution is not suitable as an antiseptic wash on the body. Many products are available on the market which are recommended as internal antiseptics, and depend upon a slow and gradual liberation of formaldehyde. Hexamethylenetetramine, known also as methenamine or urotropine, and also marketed under other trade names, is the most effective and the most frequently used of these preparations. Its effects are confined to acid fluids.

Formalin is an efficient deodorizer. Due to its irritating qualities, it may be replaced by many of the other available compounds, as the coal-tar emulsifiable disinfectants, when a disinfectant for general use is desired. Sputum, feces, urine and other body secretions and excretions are at times disinfected with an equal quantity of 10 per cent solution of Formalin, if it is not convenient to burn them or if no other disinfectant is available. Clothing, napkins, towels, handerchiefs, gloves, bedding, face and gas masks, albuminous material, etc., are at times soaked in a 5 or 10 per cent solution of Formalin for one-half to one hour. Furniture, instruments and other equipment which may be attacked by mercury bichloride and where coal-tar emulsifiable disinfectants cannot be used may be disinfected with a 5 or 10 per cent solution of Formalin.

The other commonly found *aldehydes* have little or no disinfecting properties.

Embalming Fluids.—Formalin is probably the most frequently used disinfectant which is the active ingredient of most embalming fluids. In a few commercial embalming fluids, phenol or other coal-tar disinfectants are the active ingredients. Formaldehyde as the basic disinfectant is more popular among embalmers, as it also reacts with the tissues, producing a hardening effect or stiffness of the body. Under no conditions should embalming fluids be made with bichloride of mercury, arsenic or any similar disinfectant, which may be used intentionally and unknowingly to the victim for the destruction of human life. In such a medico-legal case, it would be very easy for the murderer to claim that the inorganic or other poison used was an ingredient of the fluid employed by the undertaker in embalming. Embalming or chemical disinfection should be made compulsory as it is in many communities if occasion demands a public funeral. Icebox refrigeration, as still practiced by some, does not kill the bacteria during the period intervening between death and burial. There is always present the danger of disseminating pathogenic organisms under such conditions, especially if death was due to a contagious disease. Embalming, if conducted properly, actually kills, so there is no danger of disseminating pathogenic organisms.

Chloroform, Ether, Toluol.—Chloroform, ether, toluol and other volatile substances are used as preservatives for retarding decomposition, especially due to the fact that, if found advisable, they may be driven off afterward by evaporation. It is for this reason that toluol is most frequently used as a urinary preservative. It is not necessary to even boil the urine to rid it of the toluol, as this does not interfere with the examination. It is, however, important to remove the chloroform if this is used as a urinary preservative, as it reduces Fehling's solution, and also interferes with the microscopic observations.

Chloroform, ether and other volatile substances have been used for years in the apothecary for the preservation of pharmaceutical preparations which may decompose, due to the invasion of bacteria. They also are used by placing vials containing the chemical in compartments holding various drugs, inasmuch as they have been found to be detrimental to the life of parasites and especially insect pests that these drugs may harbor. Chloroform and ether are used in the bacteriological laboratory for the preservation of serum, and other ingredients to be used for culture media that are to be prepared, by what is known as aseptic manipulation. Saturated aqueous solutions of chloroform will not support bacterial life.

Glycerol.—Rosenau has made an extensive and interesting investigation as to the value of glycerin as a disinfectant. He found that a preparation containing 50 per cent glycerin would restrain all bacterial growth. Dilutions weaker than this would not have such effect. This suggestion is used practically in the preparation of *modified smallpox virus*, known as *glycerinated virus*. This contains 50 per cent glycerin. Other products, especially serum preparations used as reagents, in the biological laboratory are preserved in the same way.

Salicylic Acid and Salicylates.—Pure salicylic acid and its more soluble salt, sodium salicylate, are frequently used in pharmaceutical preparations as mild antiseptics, as a mouthwash, as internal and external antiseptics, and as ingredients in other antiseptic mixtures. Salicylic acid is only about one-tenth as efficient as phenol as an antiseptic, and its efficiency is markedly reduced in the presence of proteins. The salicylates are used almost exclusively for their therapeutic effects in acute rheumatism. They are devoid of marked antiseptic properties, but in the presence of acids, free salicylic acid is liberated. The benzoates are to be preferred to the salicylates when chemical antiseptics are to be added to food preparations.

Benzoic Acid and Benzoates.—Benzoic acid (as such) or its soluble salt, sodium benzoate (which is converted into the former when placed in acid fruit preparations), is used in strengths from 0.1 to 0.2 per cent as a preservative in ketchup and other tomato products, canned goods, jellies and jams, and concentrated fountain syrups. The lower the pH, the more effective are these chemicals as antiseptics. They also enter into the composition of many of the antiseptic mouthwashes. The latter may contain in addition to these mild antiseptics any of the following: borates or boric acid, salicylates or salicylic acid, thymol, phenol, menthol, chlorothymol, eucalyptol, etc. In a study of the preservative properties of benzoic acid and its salts, especially when added to apple juice, O'Connor and associates (*J. Bact.*, 1943, **45,** 37) found that the bactericidal properties of benzoic acid are somewhat greater than several of its salts.

The author has found *hydroxybenzoic acid* and its compounds efficient as preservatives for medicinal preparations. These compounds are also being used for the destruction of pathogenic fungi. Methyl parahydroxybenzoate (one of the active ingredients in *Korium*) and butyl parahydroxybenzoate (one of the active ingredients in *Cerosal*) are used for fungus infections of the skin and other dermatomycoses. The esters of parahydroxybenzoic acid are available under various trade-marked names, as *Nipagin M*, *Nipasol M* and *Nipabenzyl*. *Tegosept M* is a trade-marked name for the methyl ester and *Tegosept P* for the propyl ester of parahydroxybenozic acid. They are also oil-soluble and are used as preservatives in lotions, creams, infusions, etc.

Propionic Acid and Propionates.—Propionic acid is present naturally in various dairy products but usually in amounts which do not serve as bacteriostatic agents. Swiss cheese, however, contains almost 1 per cent of propionates, which accounts for the fact that this product rarely becomes moldy.

Attempts have been made in the baking industry to employ various inhibitors or retarders, which would be harmless but at the same time reduce rope and mold contamination. *Calcium acid phosphate* and *sodium diacetate* will serve as retarders of rope but not of mold in bread, and usually comparatively large amounts are required. Recently the propionates have been introduced, which with the simultaneous observance of strictly sanitary measures are serving as useful aids in preserving the salable life of many products in the baking and dairy industries. These are being sold under the trade name of "Mycoban." Three propionates are now being used: "Mycoban" propionic acid, "Mycoban" sodium propionate, and "Mycoban" calcium propionate. The propionates are used in an acid environment, this resulting in the production of propionic acid. The concentrations employed vary from 0.1 to 0.4 per cent depending upon the product treated, the pH of the product, the conditions (temperature, humidity, etc.) under which it is to be kept, the minimum length of time it is desired that it be stored, etc. Highest concentrations are employed for extreme conditions. In the case of bread, various types of cake, pies, rolls and specialty baked goods, the propionate is added along with the baking powder, leaving out an amount of salt equal to the weight of propionate added, or it may be added at the remix or dough stage. In the case of dairy products, the propionate is incorporated directly in cream and cottage cheeses. Hard curd cheeses are immersed in propionic acid or propionate solutions for varying periods of time and usually packaged in wraps treated with these solutions. Macy and Olson (*J. Dairy Sci.*, 1939, **22,** 527) noted a marked increase in the keeping qualities of butter and especially salted butter stored in propionate impregnated parchment-paper wraps. The calcium propionate is preferred by some when incorporated in products for the slight increase in the calcium content resulting in the marketed product.

Recently these compounds marketed as "Sopronal Solution, Ointment and Sopronol Powder" have been introduced as medicinal agents for use in athlete's foot (see page 212). Keeney (*Bull. Hopkins Hosp.*, 1943, **73,** 379) recommends sodium propionate as a fungicide in the treatment of mycotic infections.

Thymol is an ingredient of many antiseptic sprays and mouthwashes, having been found efficient in destroying bacteria, especially when employed in strengths of 1:1500 or stronger. Possessing a phenol coefficient of 27 to 28, it is found to be a more efficient bactericidal agent than menthol or the essential oils. It is also employed as an intestinal antiseptic, and it has proved to be a specific in the treatment of hookworm and other parasitic diseases. Thymol is being employed as the active agent in aerosol mists (see page 515), and it is used by some as a preservative of urine, but is not to be recommended for this purpose as its presence may at times interfere with the chemical examination of the latter.

Chlorothymol is being employed as the active antiseptic in various mouthwashes, soaps, liquid soaps, baby oils, and it also is added to different coal-tar disinfectants to increase the efficiency of the latter. In contrast to most bactericidal agents, its phenol coefficient is several times higher against *Staphylococcus aureus* (152 without organic matter and 55 with organic matter) than against *E. typhosa* (60 without organic matter and 20 with organic matter). Its efficiency is reduced more markedly in the presence of organic matter than is that of thymol, phenol and closely related bactericidal agents.

Essential Oils.—Menthol, camphor, eucalyptol, oil of cinnamon, eugenol, prunol, oil of thyme, oil of peppermint, oil of camphor and a number of closely related products, which act mainly as antiseptics, have little value as destructive agents in the strengths commonly employed. Saturated aqueous solutions of most of these substances (except thymol) are ineffective for the destruction of bacteria. They may possess some stimulating properties which may benefit the respiratory tract and other areas, but as ordinarily employed, they play a very little part in retarding bacterial growth. Cloves, cinnamon and other spices containing essential oils have been used and do possess value as preservative agents for foods which can be aromatized; this, however, depending upon the amount of essential oil present in the spices and the quantity of the latter employed. The phenol coefficients of the efficient substances in this class as reported by the author and associates (*Am. J. Pharm.*, 1931, **103,** 324) are: eugenol, 9.7; oil of cassia, 5.7; cinnamic aldehyde, 6.1; eucalyptol, 1.44; methyl salicylate, 1.76; menthol, 5.1; betanaphthol, 11.4; oil of lavender, 2.5; oil of sassafras, 2; and anethol, 1.5. The age of the essential oil will influence its bactericidal efficiency, a decrease in such efficiency being noted as time elapses. It also has been noted that a mixture of two or more essential oils or their active ingredients usually results in an end product having a greater bactericidal efficiency than is obtainable when each active principle is used separately and in larger amounts.

In the author's laboratory (*Am. J. Pharm.*, 1933, **105,** 489), solutions of 1 per cent menthol, 1 per cent camphor and a mixture of 1 per cent menthol and 1 per cent camphor in liquid petrolatum did not display bactericidal action in any of the tests performed. Saturated aqueous solutions displayed varying results.

Employing a special solvent, a phenol coefficient (F. D. A. technique) was calculated for menthol as 0.9 against *Staph. aureus* at 37° C. and 0.4 at 20° C. and against *E. typhosa*, it was 5.3 at 37° C. and 5.6 at 20°C.

Resorcinol.—Resorcinol, alone or in combination with salicylic acid, is used as an efficient antiseptic externally in various skin affections. It is the antiseptic employed in differen*t* antiseptic oils, and the addition of 1 per cent resorcinol is recommended for use in cutting compounds. *Euresol* (resorcinol monoacetate) is also employed for infections of the skin and scalp.

Urinary, Intestinal and Other Localized Internal Antiseptics.—A host of compounds are available and recommended as intestinal and urinary antiseptics. The actual efficiency of these preparations as antiseptics is in doubt. A wide difference of opinion exists as to the efficiency of all intestinal and urinary antiseptics, with few exceptions as in the case of the sulfonamide compounds. Some authorities are of the opinion that the amounts required over a period of time to show a decided antiseptic action would at the same time irritate the digestive tract, and, on this account, caution should be exercised in using them.

The question of disinfecting a strictly localized infection covering a fairly large area by the administration of drugs or chemicals is one of the greatest problems in chemotherapy today. The problem involves primarily the penetration of the infected area by the chemicals which should destroy or at least retard the activities of the infective agent and produce no harmful effects upon the body cells. The ideal way to treat such infections is to employ destructive agents, which, in themselves or bactericidal substances produced by them during metabolism, are mainly eliminated in the tracts or areas that are to be treated. Hexamethylenamine or urotropin, for instance, owes part of its beneficial effects in the treatment of genito-urinary infections to the fact that it liberates formaldehyde in the acid urine. Caprokol or hexylresorcinol, if administered properly, is also eliminated in the urine in amounts sufficient to render it bactericidal. Pyridium, Mallophene, Niazo and Serenium are dyes and trade-marked preparations also employed as antiseptics or bacteriostatic agents in infections of the genito-urinary tract. It may be that creosote, guaiacol and other drugs give beneficial results in bronchial infections, because of some action *in vivo*, as the production of bactericidal agents which are not demonstrated *in vitro*, though the average phenol coefficient of creosote, as determined in the author's laboratory, was 3, and that of guaiacol was 1.65. Certainly, one must be on guard against the use of antiseptics, either locally (topically) or internally, which will destroy the tissue. As important, and at times even more important, is the method used in applying or administering an antiseptic rather than the importance of the particular agent employed. For an evaluation of urinary antiseptics, see Burns (*South. M. J.*, 1944, **37**, 320).

Mandelic Acid and Mandelates.—Mandelic acid, hydroxyphenyl acetic acid or phenyl glycollic acid, is used in infections of the urinary tract. It exerts a definite bactericidal effect on the urine when given in sufficient dosage provided the urine is highly acid (*p*H 5.5 or less). The acidity must be controlled by determining the *p*H at frequent intervals and, if necessary, administering concurrently other suitable acidifying agents. When administered by mouth this drug is eliminated in the urine unchanged. Mandelic acid will eliminate bacillary infection in a high percentage of uncomplicated cases. Bacteria which have responded to the treatment include *Escherichia coli*, *Aerobacter aerogenes*, *Streptococcus faecalis* and members of the genera *proteus*, *pseudomonas*, *alcaligenes*, *salmonella* and *shigella*. The sulfonamides have replaced mandelic acid to a large extent as a urinary antiseptic. For further details, see Council on Pharmacy and Chemistry Report (*J. A. M. A.*, 1937, **108**, 1033).

Hexylresorcinol.—Hexylresorcinol, also known as *Caprokol*, is a chemically stable, nontoxic, nonirritating bactericidal chemical employed internally in the treatment of infections of the urinary tract, and as a safe and apparently satisfactory treatment for hookworm, ascariasis, tapeworms and pinworms. It seems probable that the bactericidal power possessed by hexylresorcinol is due to its ability to reduce surface tension, wherein its penetration into the tissues and its rate of diffusion into the bacterial cell are increased. The use of resorcinol and hexylresorcinol as germicidal aerosols is considered on page 515.

Solution S.T. 37 is a solution of hexylresorcinol (1:1000), the S.T. designating the very low surface tension of 37 dynes per centimeter shown by this solution. It has been recommended as a general antiseptic for application to open wounds and mucous membranes. It is odorless, colorless, stainless, noncorrosive, nontoxic, and said to be safe and active under most all conditions. The solution should not be injected into the tissues.

Propamidine (4:4′-diamidinodiphenoxy-propane dihydrochloride) possesses a bacteriostatic activity against *Staph. aureus* of the same order as sulfathiazole. It is also bactericidal, does not cause hemolysis, or inhibit phagocytosis, and its efficiency is not reduced by the presence of pus. It is used in wounds in concentrations of 0.1 per cent in a jelly base. A recent editorial (*Lancet*, 1943, **1**, 145) discusses the promising reports as presented in four different papers in the same issue (*ibid.*, 133–141).

Soap.—Soap, used with a reasonable degree of care, may be found of some value for the destruction of certain pathogenic organisms but, generally speaking, soaps are not highly germicidal. A salt-water soap prepared exclusively from cocoanut oil with a slight excess of alkali is of special value, but unfortunately it may be found to irritate some skins. In a recent presentation (*Lancet*, 1942, **243,** 461), mention is made that adequate treatment of cut hands and minor wounds by soap soaks (for five minutes) will aid considerably in preventing infection.

For a considerable length of time, various "antiseptic" and "germicidal" soaps have been extensively advertised and recommended as ideal cleansing and disinfecting agents. These are prepared by adding different chemicals to the soap. The soap serves not only as a cleanser, but it is used as a vehicle for the bactericidal agent. In the author's laboratory, hard soaps of different composition were tested during the past quarter of a century. In many instances various disinfectants were present in the soaps tested. The author agrees with the opinion expressed by other workers that the cleansing property of soap is more important than the antiseptic or germicidal value of any chemical that may be added. Large numbers of microorganisms are removed, but the hands are not sterile at the end of the process of washing as ordinarily practiced. More bacteria are frequently removed by the ordinary soaps than by the special brands of antiseptic soaps, as the added chemical may interfere with the production of a good lather. For further details concerning the value of soap, see Klarmann (*Soap*, 1933, **9,** 23) and Klarmann and Shternov (*Soap and Sanitary Chemicals*, p. 23, Jan., 1941). See also Jordan and associates (*J. A. M. A.*, 1940, **115,** 1001) who discuss the role of soaps in the etiology of dermatitis and methods for its prevention, and Lane and Blank (*J. A. M. A.*, 1942, **118,** 804), who discuss soaps and all of their characteristics and the various types of detergents. For a report on germicidal soaps, see release by Council on Pharmacy and Chemistry (*J. A. M. A.*, 1944, **124,** 1195).

OTHER ORGANIC COMPOUNDS

Organic Mercurial Compounds.—Since 1920, many organic mercury compounds have been synthesized with the thought of retaining the bactericidal property of mercury and at the same time increasing penetrability and reducing the toxicity, corrosive action, and the tendency to form precipitates with protein and other substances. In general, these compounds are more bacteriostatic than bactericidal, and are less toxic and produce less irritation than the inorganic mercurials.

The following caution in a report on "Organic Mercurial Compounds as Bactericidal Agents," presented by the Council on Pharmacy and Chemistry (*J. A. M. A.*, 1940, **115,** 2083) is given after reviewing the entire subject: "The organic mercurials can be used for certain bacteriostatic purposes and in some instances for bactericidal effects. However, they cannot be expected to destroy pathogenic spores, and even their action on nonsporulating bacteria is limited." See editorial on the use of mercurials as preservatives (*J. A. M. A.*, 1943, **122,** 1253). None of the mercurials, mercurochrome, metaphen, merthiolate or mercuric chloride, are to be recommended as intravenous bactericides (*J. Bact.*, 1936, **31,** 7).

It is with the above limitations in mind, that a brief review of the antiseptic value of the following organic mercurials is presented.

Mercurochrome.—This is the disodium salt of dibromoxymercurifluorescein, official in N. F. VII as *Merbromin*. It contains approximately 25 per cent Hg, and approximately 20 per cent Br. Solutions of this compound have been recommended for almost every conceivable use for which a disinfectant of its general characteristics might be adapted. Reports of its bactericidal efficiency vary widely, and many appear contradictory. Prolonged contact with 5 per cent solutions is injurious to cells; 2 per cent solutions cause only slight and brief smarting of sensitive mucous membranes.

Mercurochrome is ineffective against *Saccharomyces*, *Epidermophyton*, *Trichophyton* and *Monilia* (*Arch. Dermat. & Syph.*, 1935, **32**, 49). Critical tests have shown that mercurochrome cannot be relied upon to sterilize mucous membranes (*J. A. M. A.*, 1928, **91**, 708; *Dental Cosmos*, 1931, **73**, 74). It does not penetrate normal living tissues, but only when the latter are dying or dead (*J. A. M. A.*, 1932, **99**, 127). Injected intravenously in doses of 5 mg. per kilo of body weight, it has been found an ineffective bactericidal agent. In an editorial, the *Journal of the American Medical Association* (1935, **105**, 123) states that: "The consensus appears to be that mercurochrome is a moderately active antiseptic; it is relatively nonirritant, and has a certain definite but quite limited usefulness in the prevention and treatment of certain infections."

Metaphen.—This compound, the anhydride of 4, nitro-5-hydroxymercuri-orthocresol, contains from 56 to 57 per cent Hg, and is used in the form of the sodium salt. For application to the skin, the Tincture is used or is diluted to give a concentration of from 1:1000 to 1:5000. Aqueous solutions are employed by ophthalmologists and by urologists for urethral irrigation in dilutions of 1:5000 to 1:10,000. For the disinfection of instruments, strengths of 1:5000 to 1:1000 are recommended.

Merthiolate.—Various preparations of merthiolate (sodium ethyl mercuri thiosalicylate) are marketed for use as bactericidal agents. This compound contains approximately 45 per cent Hg. A 1:1000 aqueous solution containing 0.1 per cent monoethanolamine buffered with 1.4 per cent of sodium borate and enough sodium chloride to make the solution approximately isotonic is available for the disinfection of instruments, for application in wounds and to denuded surfaces, and for dilution to give weaker concentrations. For use in nose and throat affections, 1:5000 to 1:2000; for ophthalmological use, 1:10,000 to 1:5000; and for urethral irrigations, 1:30,000 to 1:5000 concentrations. For application to the unbroken skin as a surface disinfectant, the Tincture of Merthiolate is advocated. This contains 0.1 per cent merthiolate and 0.1 per cent monoethanolamine dissolved in alcohol 50 cc., acetone 10 cc. and water sufficient to make 100 cc. with or without added dye. A jelly containing merthiolate 1:1000 in a water-soluble base, an ophthalmic ointment 1:5000 and a 1:2000 ointment (both in fatty bases) and suppositories containing 1:1000 merthiolate in a glycerin-gelatin base are available as marketed preparations.

Merthiolate possesses a low toxicity and a relatively low hemolytic activity for a mercury compound, is free from any tendency to coagulate or precipitate proteins, is so slightly ionized that there is no immediate precipitation with either alkaline hydroxides or ammonium sulfide, but it is precipitated by acids and the salts of the heavier metals. Its efficiency as a preservative for biological products (*Am. J. Hyg.*, 1931, **14**, 218 and *Proc. Indiana Acad. Med.*, 1938, **47**, 65), as a skin disinfectant (*J. Lab. & Clin. Med.*, 1932, **17**, 443; *Surg. Clin. North Am.*, 1940, **20**, 931; and *Mod. Hosp.*, 1936, **47**, 67), and as a fungicide (*Arch. Dermat. & Syph.*, 1933, **27**, 12) has been reported.

Phenylmercuric Nitrate.—Birkhaug (*J. Infect. Dis.*, 1931, **49**, 440; 1933, **53**, 250). in comparing this compound with other mercurials as metaphen, merthiolate, mercurochrome and mercuric chloride, revealed that it is a more effective bactericidal and bacteriostatic agent. It yields a phenol coefficient ranging from 640 againt *E. coli* to 2259 for *Staph. aureus* and for the same organisms bacteriostatic actions are displayed in 1:4,000,000 and 1:120,000,000 concentrations, repectively. *Phe-Ni-Mer* and other trade names are used as special brand names for phenylmercuric nitrate. Weed and Ecker also found it to be effective in high dilutions (*J. Infect. Dis.*, 1933, **52,** 354). These workers tested the toxicities of the phenylmercuric compounds and found they were relatively nontoxic whether given orally or subcutaneously. The nitrate has been recommended as a skin disinfectant and urinary antiseptic (*Pharm. J.*, 1934, **133,** 269). Additional research and clinical findings are needed to make possible a fair evaluation of the bactericidal efficiency of these compounds. As with other organic mercurials, it is not to be depended upon to kill bacterial spores.

Merphenyl Nitrate.—Reports on this compound (*J. Bact.*, 1935, **29,** 6) revealed that it is effective in low concentrations (1:15,000 to 1:25,000) and of value especially as a bacteriostatic agent. It is the double salt of phenylmercuric hydroxide and the normal phenylmercuric nitrate. As the basic phenylmercuric nitrate, it is identical with the above which also are usually the basic compound. The Hg ion is the cation. Inasmuch as bacteria usually carry a negative charge, the high bacteriostatic action displayed by this compound is attributed to the positive charge of the Hg ions.

Orthohydroxyphenylmercuric chloride is recommended for use in all conditions where an external antiseptic and fungicide may be required. As *Mercarbolide*, it is available in a 0.1 per cent isotonic saline solution containing 10 per cent glycerin and as a 0.1 per cent tincture containing 50 per cent alcohol and 10 per cent acetone and with or without dye. *Mercresin* marketed as a tincture is similar to Tincture of Mercarbolide but in addition contains 0.1 per cent of secondary amyltricresols. These two tinctures are employed, diluted or undiluted, for skin disinfection, preoperative preparation of the skin, and for surgical antisepsis. Aqueous solutions (1:1000 Mercarbolide) in dilutions of 1:10 to 1:2 are recommended for use in the ear, eye, nose and throat. For irrigations, massive wet dressing, and in urology, the aqueous solution or tincture, diluted 1:40 to 1:20 is used.

The following mercurials were found efficient by the author (*Am. J. Pharm.*, 1939, **111,** 385) as preservatives in ophthalmic solutions: merthiolate (0.01 per cent); phenylmercuric acetate (0.002 per cent); phenylmercuric nitrate (0.002 per cent); phenylhydroxymercuric chloride (sat. sol.), and mercurophen (0.01 per cent). The first three mentioned were found also to be effective as preservatives for nasal jellies made with tragacanth as the base. Other mercurials were found efficient under special conditions. *Merfen* (mercury phenyl borate) is said to be highly bactericidal, and Thomann (*Pharm. Acta Helv.*, 1942, **17,** 57) claims that a 2 per cent merfen gauze proved more effective than a 10 per cent sulfathiazole gauze and a 5 per cent vioform gauze.

Phenylmercuric borate is marketed as a Tincture (1:500) and in this strength is used as a prophylactic preoperative preparation of the skin and in dilutions 1:15,000 to 1:25,000 for infected wounds and application to mucous membranes.

Phenylmercuric Picrate, a (1:200) Tincture with 1.2 per cent picric acid, is a so marketed and its uses and application are similar to the borate.

Meroxyl.—This compound (a mixture of the sodium salts of 2,4-dihydroxy-3,5-dihydroxymercuri benzophenone-2'-sulfonic acid) is soluble in water and produces colored (brownish tint) solutions which gel upon standing if the drug is present in concentrations of 2.5 per cent or stronger. As a local antiseptic, it has been recommended for superficial infections (*Surg. Gynec. & Obst.*, 1923, **36**, 508). It is used in 1:1000 concentrations as a wet dressing for and in the irrigation of wounds. Concentrations as high as 0.5 per cent have been advocated as a prophylactic in the treatment of carbuncles and abscesses, postoperative cystitis and urinary infections.

Mertoxol (acetoxymercuri-2-ethyl-hexyl-phenol sulfonic acid), containing approximately 40 per cent Hg, is available on the market and used in concentrations of 1:1000 to 1:5000 for general surgical antisepsis and various infections. A closely related compound, diacetoxymercuri-heptyl-phenol, is present in an amount of 0.5 per cent in *Profex*, a marketed venereal prophylactic, in which there also is present $33^1/_3$ per cent colloidal calomel in a special ointment base. *Furmerane* (2-hydroxy-mercuri furan) is recommended as efficient for skin and surgical antisepsis.

Merodicein (the sodium salt of monohydroxymercuriiodoresorcin-sulfonphthalein) is the compound present in *Thantis Lozenges* which is responsible for the red color production and antiseptic properties of the latter. Drake and associates (*J. Infect. Dis.*, 1931, **48**, April; *M. J. & Rec.*, 1931, **2**, Sept.) report that in the concentrations used, this compound is nontoxic, nonirritating and that a marked reduction in the bacterial flora of mouth and throat occurred and persisted after the use of this preparation.

Ethylmercury Compounds.—These compounds are efficient bactericides and fungicides and though used to some extent in medicine, their greatest field of application is in agricultural pursuits as a soil disinfectant, in the control of plant diseases and in the preservation of lumber as a dip for pine and sap-gum boards (*Ind. Eng. Chem.*, 1933, **25**, 72). They are especially toxic to plant pathogens (Ohio Expt. Sta. Tech. Ser., *Bull.* **10**, 1932) (*Ind. Eng. Chem.*, 1932, **24**, 745). Phenol coefficients approximating 100 to 200 against different animal pathogens and from 150 to 3000 against plant pathogens have been reported.

Ethylmercury chloride which is most frequently used is noncorrosive, less toxic than bichloride of mercury, a more active fungicide and disinfectant than the latter and when properly diluted it is not unduly dangerous. Powders containing 1 or 2 per cent of this chemical dusted on barley, oats, wheat and sorghum (2 or 3 ounces per bushel) control effectively various types of smuts. It is being employed as a soil disinfectant, plant spray, and as a dip for pine and sap-gum boards.

Mercurophen (sodium-oxymercury-orthonitro-phenolate, containing approximately 43 per cent Hg) first employed in 1919 (*J. Urol.*, 1919, **24**, 547) (Tr. Coll. Phys. Phila., 1919, **39**, 33) is being replaced by other more recently synthesized mercurials. It has been employed for the sterilization of catheters, gloves and medical and surgical equipment in a 1:5000 aqueous solution. Concentrations from 1:1000 to 1:2000 have been and are used for the disinfection of feces, urine, exudates and body fluids; and strengths from 1:15,000 to 1:5000 are applied to mucous membranes. Saleeby and Harkins (*Ann. Surg.*, 1932, **95**, 249) reported favorable results with mercurophen in comparison with other antiseptics. This compound tarnishes aluminum and solutions form a sediment upon the absorption of carbon dioxide.

Avenyl, an organic mercurial (2-myristoxymercuri-3-hydroxy benzaldehyde) (*J. Chem. Soc.*, 1922, **121**, 1055), dissolved in hydnocarpus oil has been employed in the treatment of syphilitic infections in lepers.

Propyl-mercuric chloride and *Pyridyl-mercuric-chloride* (in concentrations of 0.068

and 0.1 per cent in 70 per cent alcohol) are other mercury compounds recommended as skin sterilizing agents (*J. Pharmacol. & Exper. Therap.*, 1939, **66,** 279).

Insoluble Mercury Compounds.—The action of mercury and its compounds as disinfectants depends upon the concentration of mercuric ions in solution, their precipitant action on proteins and their affinity for the protein under the conditions of exposure. Aqueous solutions produce maximum dissociation and the greatest yield of Hg ions. The water-soluble mercuric chloride loses its disinfectant power when alcohol (95 per cent) is employed as the vehicle. The former is not dissociated in the latter and free ionic mercury, necessary for the disinfectant property, is not available. Weak alcoholic solutions of mercuric chloride, however, are active as disinfectants, the bactericidal action here being favored by the fact that the diluted alcohol may penetrate the cell more readily than water with the resultant penetration of the mercurial compound toxic to the organism.

Water-insoluble mercurials become active only by their conversion into soluble mercuric compounds. The actual ionization of the very soluble mercurials is not high, but inasmuch as ion replacement is continuous, the action practically is as if high ionization occurred. Solutions of weakly ionizable mercurials do not precipitate proteins. Absence of protein precipitation favors the penetration of the mercury, a saving in the loss of mercury ions, inasmuch as precipitates are not present to adsorb them, and there is a diminished local irritation.

The important water-insoluble mercurials are *ammoniated mercury* employed in skin affections in an ointment in 2 to 10 per cent concentrations; *yellow mercuric oxide*, employed in an ointment in concentrations of 0.1 to 1 per cent; *calomel* employed as a dusting powder or in an ointment in varying concentrations and as a venereal prophylactic in 30 to 33 per cent concentrations in various ointment bases; *mercury salicylate* injected intramuscularly (1-cc. doses of a 10 per cent suspension in a vegetable oil); *metallic mercury,* employed in an ointment in 30 per cent or 50 per cent concentrations; *colloidal mercury sulfide* and *colloidal mercury (Hyrgol).* During the local applications of these compounds, complex changes take place in the course of absorption, resulting in the production of soluble mercurials, the activity of which varies depending upon the ionization which occurs.

Antisyphilitic Action.—Since 1495 when syphilis first appeared epidemically, mercury and its compounds have been used by different methods of administration to combat this scourge. Until the introduction of arsphenamine in 1905, mercury was the only remedy effective at least in producing a lessening in active clinical symptoms. Today arsphenamine and bismuth are the antisyphilitic drugs of choice. As with most all chemotherapeutic agents, it is difficult to definitely determine the exact mechanism of the antisyphilitic action of mercury *in vivo*. Mercury and its compounds will display a spirocheticidal effect *in vitro*. Theories of the mechanism of its action in the living body, however, include a direct action on the spirochetes, an increase in the production of opsonins and other immune substances, an increase in the susceptibility of the spirochetes to the protective mechanisms and combinations of these factors. Even *in vivo* observations, where mercurials producing high concentrations or prolonged action of ionic mercury come in direct contact with the spirochetes, the latter are destroyed as is evidenced in local applications. It is probable, however, that systemically the concentration of mercury in the blood and in all body fluids and tissues is too low to obtain the same effect and that higher concentrations internally would be toxic to the human system.

Mercury Allergy.—Various local and systemic reactions following the local use of mercury compounds have been reported and, though infrequent, must be kept in mind. Of special interest is a report by Ellis and Robinson (*Arch. Dermat. & Syphil.*, 1942, **46**, 425) who investigated 5 patients and found from patch tests that they were sensitive to some and not to all mercurial antiseptics, indicating that a patient who is sensitive to one of the mercurials is not necessarily sensitive to all compounds containing mercury.

PHENOL AND THE COAL-TAR PRODUCTS

Lister, the father of aseptic surgery, was the first to use phenol. In 5 per cent dilutions, it is highly efficient, and loses but little of its antiseptic property under the most adverse conditions. It does not coagulate albuminous material as actively as other disinfectants. It is not injurious to metals and fabrics in strengths from 1 to 5 per cent as commonly employed. On this account it was at one time the most widely used of general disinfectants, only to be replaced within recent years by other coal-tar products, which are more effective and cheaper in price. In 0.5 to 1 per cent concentrations, it is bacteriostatic, and a 5 per cent solution is bactericidal. Anthrax spores, however, are not destroyed even after twenty-four hours' exposure by the latter strengths.

Carbolated petrolatum has been in use for various skin affections and some workers have spoken at times of the antisepticity of such an ointment. Husa and Radin reported bactericidal action of a 2 per cent phenol ointment in a base of 24.5 per cent wool fat and 73.5 per cent petrolatum and recommended the adoption and inclusion of such an ointment in the U. S. P. Appointed as a referee to investigate such an ointment, critical tests conducted in the author's laboratory revealed that ointments of the above composition did not display bactericidal or inhibitory action in accordance with available techniques (*Am. J. Pharm.*, 1933, **105**, 189). We, however, found that 2 per cent phenol incorporated in water-miscible bases yields products which display *in vitro* bactericidal efficiency (*Am. J. Pharm.*, 1933, **105**, 194).

Coal-tar Disinfectants.—The portion of coal-tar oil remaining after phenol is removed, when subjected to fractional distillation, will yield products, chemically closely related to phenol, but which possess a disinfectant value far superior to the latter and to most all other general disinfectants. These so-called phenols (general term) differ in many respects from carbolic acid or phenol proper. With few exceptions they are all liquid, and are but slightly soluble in water. On this account, they usually require a solvent or other carrier to bring them into a condition so as to exert their activity. In the dilutions commonly employed, they are nontoxic, nonirritating, noncorrosive, and do not cause coagulation of protein. Their efficiency is lowered but little by organic matter. They are active germicidal agents and deodorants for general use, and cost less than do most of the other disinfectants. Soap (both hard and soft) is mainly employed as the vehicle for the so-called coal-tar oils or acids. It is of value due to the fact that it acts as an efficient emulsifier of such products, forming combinations which are readily soluble in or miscible with water. In such preparations, there is also present the cleansing as well as the additional germicidal property of the soaps used.

Cresol, or so-called *cresylic acid*, is one of the most important constituents of the coal-tar liquor or distillate.   Cresol, U. S. P. consists of a mixture of three isomers, and the latter are present approximately in the proportion of 40 per cent *metacresol*, 35 per cent *orthocresol* and 25 per cent *paracresol*.   The phenol coefficient (see below) of these three isomers varies between 2 and 2.5.   The so-called *tar acids* are higher boiling fractions and are used commercially to prepare coal-tar disinfectants possessing relatively high phenol coefficients, varying from 10 to 25.   The coefficients of coal-tar disinfectants on the market depend therefore on the type of distillation, the kind of bituminous coal used, the kind and amount of soap employed in preparing the product, and the amount of free alkali present.

Saponated Solution of Cresol (Compound Solution of Cresol U. S. P.) is representative of the so-called soluble coal-tar disinfectants, made with soap as a base.   The U. S. P. preparation usually is found to possess a phenol coefficient of slightly over 2. It is similar to lysol in many respects, but the phenol coefficient of the latter is 5. Creolin, yielding a coefficient of 10, is a type of the emulsifiable coal-tar preparations which form a milky suspension when mixed with water, inasmuch as a rosin soap is used.   There are many of these coal-tar emulsifiable disinfectants on the market, which give phenol coefficients ranging from 6 to 25.

Sulfonated Oil–Coal-Tar Disinfectant Mixtures.—During an experimental investigation in the author's laboratory with sulfonated castor oil, it was found that cresol and water-immiscible coal-tar disinfectants were soluble in this oil (pH 8.3 to 8.5), and the resultant mixture was miscible with water (*Am. J. Pharm.*, 1939, **111**, 314). The bactericidal efficiency of these mixtures is governed by the amount of the active bactericide and is directly proportional to such concentration.   In a later study, we (*Am. J. Pharm.*, 1940, **112**, 45) found that the phenol coefficient of water-immiscible coal-tar disinfectants made miscible by mixing with 50 per cent Sulfonated Castor Oil (adjusted to pH 8.3 to 8.5) is unaltered upon standing for two years.   The phenol coefficient of cresol made water-miscible by the use of Sulfonated Castor Oil is the same as that of *Liquor Cresolis Saponatus*, when containing the same amount of active ingredients (500 parts, U. S. P. Cresol per 1000 parts of finished product).   The toxicity of cresol sulfonated castor oil mixtures is such as not to mitigate against their use externally on the body or for general household use.

Use of Coal-tar Disinfectants.—The coal-tar products are employed as general disinfectants.   In from 1 to 3 per cent dilutions, they are used in washing the hands and wounds, for the sterilization of instruments, floors, walls, closets, drains, cellars, laundry, wash basins, toilet bowls, garbage pails, dog kennels, clothing, sputum, feces and all secretions and excretions.   The dilution used in practice for general application is twenty times the phenol coefficient (coefficient is 5; dilution used is 1:100). In the concentrations employed, they are usually nontoxic, noncorrosive, do not attack fabrics and metal and are stable.   In weak dilutions, they are also employed as antiseptics especially for the preservation of medicinal products, which are to be injected hypodermically.   Trikresol or cresol in strengths of 0.2 per cent to 0.4 per cent is most frequently employed.

Other Phenolic Compounds as Disinfectants

Many industries are confronted with various manufacturing problems in which bacteria and especially fungi are found to be responsible for destructive and disfiguring activities. Textiles, hemp and jute products, casein paints, glue and other adhesives, paper products, lumber and millwork, leather and many other industrial products are frequently attacked. During recent years a group of phenol derivatives have been developed and used as highly effective industrial germicides and fungicides. The Dow Chemical Company markets a group of 17 such compounds, which include: *orthophenylphenol* and its sodium salt; *trichlorophenol* and its sodium salt; various *chloro phenylphenols* and their sodium salts; *bromophenylphenol* and its sodium salt; *tetrachlorophenol* and its sodium salt; and *pentachlorophenol* and its sodium salt. The bromo and chloro phenylphenol compounds have phenol coefficients of over 100. The trichlorophenol and its sodium salt is only slightly more efficient than phenol. The substitution of halogen atoms increases the fungicidal efficiencies and this increases from chlorine through bromine to iodine.

Some of the above compounds are also used as disinfectants and deodorants in general sanitation, in medical and surgical routine and in agricultural pursuits. *Orthophenylphenol*, with a phenol coefficient of 24 (against *E. typhosa*) and 14 (against *Staph. aureus*) and its sodium salt, with a phenol coefficient of 17 (against *E. typhosa*) and 10 (against *Staph. aureus*), are highly efficient and odorless and are used in household disinfectants, on livestock premises, for athlete's foot and other skin diseases and in washing compounds. Other concerns manufacture closely related products which are similar in action to the above and all of them are also insecticidal. For details concerning the halogen derivatives of phenol and resorcinol, see Klarmann and associates (*J. Bact.*, 1929, **17,** 423).

Permasan is a trade name given to a preparation in which the most important active ingredient is *pentachlorophenol* (present in strengths of 5 per cent). It is used for the preservation of wood against termites and other wood-attacking insects and bacteria. "*Santophen 20*" is a trade name for the powder and "*Santobrite*" to its sodium salt *Ortho-* and *para-benzyl phenol* and *para tertiary amyl phenol* are used to enhance the bactericidal efficiency of other coal-tar disinfectants due to the high activity of the former compounds.

Chloro-Hexol (2-chloro-4-*n*-hexylphenol) supplied as a tincture and aqueous solution is used in medical and surgical treatments as a powerful antiseptic. It is said to possess a phenol coefficient of over 400 against *Staphylococcus aureus*.

Pentacresol, a brand of secondary amyltricresols (1:500), in alcohol-acetone-water mixture is recommended for the cold disinfection of instruments.

A mixture of isomeric chlorphenolates was recommended by Seltzer (*J. Dent. Research* 1942, **21,** 269) for the sterilization of dental cavities and Zondak (*Nature*, 1942, **149,** 334) presents an extensive report on halogenized phenols, especially *chloroxylenols* and recommends them as valuable antiseptics for external use.

Phenolor contains approximately 13 per cent ortho-hydroxy-diphenol, 5 per cent alcohol, soap and other inert ingredients. It possesses a phenol coefficient of approximately 5, is relatively nontoxic in (2 to 5 per cent) dilutions commonly used and is recommended for general disinfecting purposes in the hospital, clinic and home.

Creosote (consisting of phenols, cresol and guaiacol) and *Cresatin* (meta-cresylacetate) are antiseptics and analgesics and are efficient as pulp and root canal germicides. In the author's laboratory (*J. Am. Pharm. Assoc.*, 1933, **22,** 198), samples of natural and synthetic guaiacol, of natural and synthetic creosote and of different fractions of creosote were tested for their bactericidal efficiencies. The natural products were more efficient than the synthetic products and all of them were more effective against *E. typhosa* and *Staph. aureus* than was phenol. Creosote as found on the market revealed a phenol coefficient against *E. typhosa* of 3.9 and against *Staph. aureus* of 3.8 in one instance and another sample displayed a coefficient of 2.45 against both of these organisms, thus revealing the variability of creosote.

Betanaphthol is used externally as an antiseptic and parasiticide and occasionally internally as an intestinal antispetic. In dentistry, a 3 per cent solution in a mixture of equal parts of alcohol, glycerin and water is used as an antiseptic and a 10 per cent solution in ether (with 18 per cent gum copal) is employed as an antiseptic cavity varnish. Weak hydro-alcoholic solutions are used by some as an antiseptic on the hair.

Alkyl Phenolic and Quaternary Ammonium Compounds

Klarmann and associates (*J. Lab. & Clin. Med.*, 1934, **19**, 835; **20**, 40) presented a detailed and critical study of the relationship between the chemical structure and the bactericidal action of aliphatic and aromatic substitution derivatives of ortho- and para-chlorophenol derivatives and the halogen-free para-alklyphenol compounds. They made many interesting and significant observations and their original paper should be consulted. The products of this group, which are available on the market, are not only bactericidal, but they are effective wetting agents or detergents, and accordingly are efficient penetrating agents.

Phemerol (para-tertiary-octyl-phenyl-diethoxy-dimethyl-benzyl ammonium chloride), a quaternary ammonium compound, is marketed as *Phemerol, Topical*, a 3 per cent aqueous solution; as a Tincture (1:500 in alcohol-acetone-water) and as an aqueous solution (1:1000). It is used as a bactericidal agent for topical application to the skin and mucous membranes and for irrigation of body cavities. Joslyn and associates (*J. Am. Pharm. Assoc.*, 1943, **32**, 49) found this compound effective as a fungicide and bactericide. See also Iland (*Lancet*, 1944, **246**, 49) and Brown and associates (*J. Surg., Gynec. and Obstet.*, 1944, **78**, 173).

Ceepryn (cetylpyridinium chloride), a quaternary ammonium salt, is available especially as an aqueous (isotonic) solution (1:1000) and is recommended for general medicinal and surgical use. Clarke (*Urol. & Cutan. Rev.*, 1942, **46**, 245) in a study on skin sterilization found cetylpyridinium chloride superior to other compounds. See also Warren, *et al.* (*J. Pharmacol. & Exper. Therap.*, 1942, **74**, 401) and Kramer and Sedwitz (*Am. J. Surg.*, 1944, **63**, 240).

Zephiran chloride (a mixture of high molecular alkyl-dimethyl-benzyl-ammonium chlorides) is marketed as a Tincture (1:1000) and as an aqueous solution (1:1000). These three products are used in surgical and medical pursuits in all conditions where a bactericide is indicated and used. They can also be employed for the cold disinfection of medical and dental instruments. For further details, see Council on Pharmacy and Chemistry Report (*J. A. M. A.*, 1942, **120**, 289). See also page 530.

Capacol contains cetyl pyridinium chloride (1:4000) and sodium phosphate (0.5 per cent) in a pleasant tasting vehicle and is used in nose and throat affections.

CTAB, cetyl trimethyl ammonium bromide, is used in Great Britain. For further details, see Barnes (*Lancet*, 1942, **242**, 531), Berry (*ibid.*, 1942, **242**, 632) and Williams *et al.* (*ibid.*, 1943, **244**, 522). *Dosogen*, a mixture of quaternary trimethyl ammonium metasulfates, has recently been recommended by Grumbach (*Schweiz. med. Wchnschr.*, 1941, **71,** 1520).

Roccal, a 10 per cent solution of alkyl-dimethyl-benzyl-ammonium chlorides, is diluted 1 to 250 or 1:500 (giving a 1:2500 to 1:5000 of original chemical) as a general sanitizing agent in the food and dairy industries, for eating and drinking utensils, refrigerators, tile floors, bathtubs and also as an algacide for swimming pool water.

All of the above quaternary ammonium compounds lose their bactericidal activity in the presence of soap, protein and with some of the newer detergents. The latter and soap, even traces, must be removed before these chemicals are applied. They usually bleach colored suture material; bougies made of anode rubber compounds become lighter in color; and shellacked silk catheters are attacked.

Fuller (*Biochem. J.*, 1942, **36,** 548) discusses the antibacterial action of the long-chain amines, guanidines, diisothioureas and mono- and diquaternary ammonium compounds which display trypanocidal properties. He suggests their usefulness for local applications.

COLD STERILIZATION

The ease and convenience of disinfecting surgical instruments by immersion in a chemical solution are responsible for the use of this method by physicians, dentists, and in hospitals, barber shops and beauty parlors. In a survey made in 1937, Ecker and Smith (*Mod. Hosp.*, 1937, **48,** 92) reported that 36 per cent of the hospitals were using this procedure. The usefulness of this method has not been definitely established. Generally speaking, as commonly practiced, this procedure of disinfecting surgical and dental instruments cannot be relied upon as a safe technique. Spores, especially if in a dry state, are not killed, unless a prolonged exposure is used. Blood, pus, other organic matter, oil and grease interfere with the action of the chemical. Steam heat under pressure (autoclave) and, if this is not available, hot water are to be used as the methods of choice in the order named for the sterilization of instruments. Chemical disinfection is to be employed only when heat would affect the articles to be sterilized.

Alkyl phenolic (quaternary ammonium compounds) are highly recommended for the cold disinfection of medical and dental instruments. When the latter are stored in these solutions for long periods of time, 0.5 per cent sodium nitrite is added to minimize corrosion.

Phenolic compounds are not employed extensively in these techniques. The odor, irritating properties and frequently the presence of soap (used to dissolve the active phenolic substance) mitigate against the wide use of these agents. *Pentacresol* (see page 319), which is free of soap, is recommended for this purpose. *Phemerol* and *Ceepryn*, quaternary ammonium compounds (see page 320) are also employed for such disinfection. The Bard-Parker formaldehyde formula is widely used, inasmuch as this also is a stabilized corrosion inhibitive solution. The following formula is satisfactory: formaldehyde, 3 per cent; alchohol, 77 per cent; acetone, 10 per cent; inert ingredients, 10 per cent.

A formaldehyde solution used in many institutions for disinfecting bulky goods, especially bulky rubber goods, consists of: solution of formaldehyde, 135 cc.; sodium hydroxide, 10 Gm.; distilled water to make one liter. Immersion in this alkaline formaldehyde solution is for at least two hours. Tainter, *et al.* (*J. A. Dent. Assoc.*, 1944, **31**, 479) present a detailed consideration on the chemical sterilization of instruments and recommend the following as an acceptable formula, the ingredients being mixed in the order given: isopropyl alcohol, 1000 cc.; oil of rose geranium, 2 cc.; oil of cinnamon (cassia), 4 cc.; distilled water, 780 cc.; sodium nitrite, 4 Gm.; monoethanolamine, 60 cc.; and solution of formaldehyde U. S. P., 160 cc.

As a final caution, when using cold sterilization procedures, it is a safer practice to see that all articles to be treated are made mechanically clean and freed of blood, pus, other organic matter, oil and grease. Inasmuch as the chemical remaining on instruments after treatment may produce irritation, especially on mucous membranes and wounds, the rinsing or the evaporation of these agents is practiced.

Chapter XXII

CHEMOTHERAPY

CHEMOTHERAPY has been defined as: "the prevention and treatment of disease by chemical disinfection or inhibition of the parasitic causes without marked or serious toxic effects." The main thought behind this new and most interesting therapy is the use of chemical agents possessing a high selective parasiticidal action in the body with a minimum of effect upon the body cells, or interference with the function of the latter. There are therefore two primary properties possessed by chemical agents: the one, which is the special and selective affinity for, or in reality a toxicity for, the parasite, and designated as the *parasitotropism*, and the other, which is the effects or toxicity of the agent for the body cells and tissues of the host, and known as the *organotropism*. A suitable chemotherapeutic agent is one which possesses a maximum toxicity for the parasite, and a minimum toxicity for the host. This is frequently expressed in terms of the chemotherapeutic index, a figure which designates the relationship between these two factors (parasitotropism and organotropism), and obtained as follows:

$$\frac{\text{Maximum tolerated dose per kilo}}{\text{Maximum curative dose per kilo}} = \text{Chemotherapeutic Index}$$

Ehrlich, who is the father of this new science, was of the hope that it might be possible to produce drugs which would destroy all parasites in the tissues in a *single* dose, and, of course, leave no effect upon the body cells of the host. This ideal has not as yet been reached, with the possible exception of the following: in the treatment of Vincent's angina and yaws, where in some cases a single intravenous injection of arsphenamine or neoarsphenamine may completely eliminate the parasites.

The greatest value of chemotherapeutic research has been in the treatment of syphilis, relapsing fever, yaws and other spirochetic infections, where the different organic arsenicals have been used successfully as specifics. In malaria, leishmaniasis, amoebic and other protozoan infections, these studies have also proved of value. In bacterial diseases, chemotherapy has made advances in the treatment of localized infections, and rapid strides have been made since the introduction of the sulfonamide compounds and penicillin. In bacteremias, considerable experimentation is in progress. The dyes have been used extensively for a long period of time in bacterial diseases. These include acid and basic fuchsin, gentian violet, brilliant green, acriflavin, proflavin, rivanol, mercurochrome, mercurophen, etc. Ethylhydrocuprein, quinine and cinchona alkaloids, compounds of mercury, copper, arsenic, iodine and other substances are being used experimentally and to some extent in practice in the chemotherapeutic treatment of bacterial infections. It has been found that intravenous injections of most of the previously mentioned chemotherapeutic agents stimulate the blood-making organs to throw forth into the blood stream an excess quantity of leukocytes. This and other observations bear a close resemblance to the "nonspecific protein" reactions previously described. Though there is no distinct evidence that there is an increase generally in the antibody content, the opinion prevails that some chemotherapeutic agents may actually aid by one or several of the changes described under "nonspecific protein therapy." For further details, see under sulfonamides and penicillin.

Chemoserotherapy, the combination of chemotherapy with serum therapy, and the use of chemotherapy in combination with vaccines, nonspecific protein substances and even with blood in blood transfusions are at times more successful in the treatment of diseases than is the use of either agent alone. The entire field of chemotherapy is still in its infancy, and the encouraging results obtained thus far offer much hope for greater success in the future.

ORGANIC ARSENIC COMPOUNDS

From the standpoint of their value as disinfectants, inorganic arsenic is just as valuable as organic combinations of arsenic. The dose of the former required to kill the protozoa will also act as a toxic agent for the host. The organic compounds, on the other hand, are less toxic to mammals and more toxic to protozoa. Comparatively large doses of arsenic can thus be given, inasmuch as the effects are obtained through a slow liberation of arsenic, which remains for a longer time in contact with the parasites than inorganic arsenic compounds. Of the many available organic arsenic compounds in some the arsenic is pentavalent, while in others it is trivalent. It appears that the trivalent arsenic (corresponding to the arsenites) is the one most active pharmacologically and that even the pentavalent compounds (corresponding to the arsenates) must be reduced to the trivalent form in the body before the desirable therapeutic effects are produced. Arsenic and especially organic arsenic compounds are of value and used as chemotherapeutic agents for combating spirillosis, treponematosis, trypanosomiasis and other protozoan infections. They are only weakly bactericidal. Arsphenamine and analogous preparations of arsenic used intravenously must be prepared in an establishment licensed for the purpose by the federal government upon the recommendation of the Surgeon General of the U. S. Public Health Service. Each lot of the product offered for sale must comply with all requirements of the National Institute of Health. See Miscellaneous Publication, No. 31, U. S. P. H. S., 1939.

One of the most important organic compounds of arsenic is a product known for years under the name of *Salvarsan* or *606* and official in the United States Pharmacopoeia as *Arsphenamina*. It is also known under any of the following trade-marked or brand names: "Arsenobenzol," "Arsaminol" (used by Japanese and Americans), "Diarsenol" (used by Canadians and Americans), "Kharsivan" (English), "Arsenobillon" (English), "diamino dihydroxyarsenobenzene dihydrochloride" and "arsenophenolamine hydrochloride." This compound, containing from 30 to 32 per cent of arsenic, possesses a markedly destructive affinity for spirochetes and some of the trypanosomes, and but a comparatively low toxicity for the human being. Though extensively employed as a specific in the treatment of syphilis (inasmuch as the *Spirochaeta* or *Treponema pallidum* is the causative agent), it is nevertheless employed in other conditions where the causative agent is a spirochete, one of the trypanosomes or members of a closely related genus of protozoa.

Arsphenamine is marketed as a light yellow or lemon-yellow powder (in doses ranging from 0.1 Gm. to 0.6 Gm.; ampuls containing 1, 2 and 3 Gm. are also available). It is sealed in ampuls containing a vacuum or an inert gas, which will prevent decomposition. The drug, in a slightly alkaline solution, is administered usually intravenously by the gravity method, and rarely intramuscularly. A solution of arsphenamine cannot be kept for any length of time, but must be used immediately. The active ingredient is decomposed by a high temperature. It is therefore impossible to sterilize the solution of arsphenamine. To be assured of a sterile preparation, which is necessary for an intravenous injection, the product is prepared by aseptic manipulation.

Neoarsphenamine, a soluble compound of arsphenamine containing not less than 19 per cent arsenic is now used more frequently. It consists chiefly of sodium 3,3'-diamino-4,4'-dihydroxyarsenobenzene-N-methanal sulfoxylate. This is official in the United States Pharmacopoeia as *Neoarsphenamina* and is also marketed under any of the following names: "Neoarsaminol"; "Neokharsivan"; "Novarsenobillon"; "Neodiarsenol"; "Neosalvarsan"; "914"; etc. Its action and use are the same as arsphenamine. Though its action is not so powerful, it is, however, less toxic, so that more frequent dosage may be administered. It is usually injected intravenously after dissolving the drug in from 10 to 20 cc. of sterile distilled water. Neoarsphenamine solutions must not be warmed and must be injected immediately after preparation. The powdered drug must be of a normal color and freely soluble.

Various elements have been introduced into the structure of arsphenamine and neoarsphenamine with the thought of increasing the chemotherapeutic activity or reducing the toxicity of the former. The result has been the appearance of many different preparations which are recommended for the same conditions for which arsphenamine and neoarsphenamine are used with claims for a greater efficiency for such products. Among the latter are the following:

Sulfarsphenamine, a formaldehyde-bisulfite derivative of arsphenamine, containing approximately 20 per cent arsenic; *Silver arsphenamine (Argentum arsphenamina)*, sodium silver arsphenamine, which contains approximately 13 per cent of silver and 20 per cent of arsenic and the drug of choice for the intramuscular route, when intravenous administration cannot be employed; *Bismarsen (sulfarsphenamine bismuth)*, the sodium salt of a bismuth derivative of arsphenamine methylene sulfonic acid, containing approximately 24 per cent of bismuth and 13 per cent of arsenic; *Stabilarsan*, a compound of arsphenamine with glucose; and *mapharsen*, the hemialcoholate of 3-amino-4-hydroxyphenylarsine oxide hydrochloride containing approximately 29 per cent of trivalent arsenic.

Pentavalent Arsenical Compounds.—The pentavalent arsenical compounds are more powerful trypanocidal agents and only slightly spirocheticidal. Among these compounds are to be found: *Tryparsamidum U. S. P.*, tryparsamide or sodium N-phenylglycinamide-p-arsonate containing approximately 25 per cent arsenic; and *Acetarsone, Acetarsol* or *Stovarsol* (hydroxyacetylaminophenol arsenic acid), containing approximately 27 per cent arsenic. The latter compound has been reported to produce favorable effects in amebiasis and for infections by *Trichomonas vaginalis*. Tryparsamide is used in the treatment of trypanosomiasis due to *T. gambiense* and in resistant cases of syphilis of the central nervous system. See U. S. Public Health Service, Suppl. No. **18**, *Venereal Disease Information*, concerning acetarsone in the treatment of congenital syphilis and other periodicals on arsenic compounds distributed by the same bureau.

Sodium arsanilate (*atoxyl*), containing approximately 27 per cent of arsenic is not used as widely as it was at one time. It acts with especial intensity on the optic nerve and cases of optic atrophy, frequently resulting in permanent blindness, have been reported. *Carbasone* (*p*-carbamido-phenylarsonic acid) containing approximately 28 per cent arsenic is employed orally for the treatment of intestinal amebiasis. Favorable results have been reported with its use.

Sandground (*Science*, 1943, **97,** 73) recently presented valuable experimental evidence that *p*-aminobenzoic acid possesses a high detoxicating action against massive doses of the different pentavalent arsenicals without interfering with their specific chemotherapeutic effects.

Bismuth compounds are used extensively and are preferred in the treatment of syphilis, unless there is an allergy existing to bismuth. They are only of value when given parenterally, and at present the intramuscular route is the safest and most reliable for bismuth therapy. It should never be given intravenously. Bismuth appears to be less toxic and more rapid in action than mercury and is displacing the latter as an antisyphilitic and in the treatment of yaws as an adjuvant to arsenicals. A variety of bismuth compounds and preparations are in use, aqueous solutions of water-soluble compounds, aqueous suspensions of insoluble compounds, and solutions and suspensions in oils. Bismuth and potassium tartrate, bismuth and sodium tartrate, sodium bismuth thioglycollate (*thio-bismol*), sodium bismuth iodide (*iodobismital* or sodium iodobismuthite), sodium potassium bismuthyl tartrate (*bismosol*) and *sobisminol* (complex organic bismuth compound) are the water-soluble compounds in use. As suspensions either in water or oil, the following bismuth compounds are being employed: finely divided metallic bismuth in suspension, bismuth salicylate, bismuth oxychloride, bismuth oleate, quinine bismuth iodide and sodium potassium bismuthyl tartrate (*tartro-quiniobine*), and *bismo-cymol* (a basic bismuth salt of camphocarboxylic acid). Insoluble bismuth is slowly excreted and the patient is kept under its influence for a long time. Where injections of bismuth are not tolerated, oral bismuth (*sobisminol*) is being used to some extent.

Antimony Compounds.—Antimony compounds have been used successfully as a chemotherapeutic agent in various protozoal and other parasitic diseases. Antimony was first used in trypanosomiasis and good results with it have been obtained in filariasis. It is employed effectively in the treatment of kala azar and in other forms of leishmaniasis and also in granuloma inguinale. It is the standard remedy for bilharziasis. Administration is by the parenteral route. Tartar emetic (antimony and potassium tartrate) is used most frequently, but other antimony compounds which are claimed to be more effective and less toxic are being advocated. Among the latter are to be found: antimony sodium thioglycollate, a compound formed by dissolving antimony trioxide in a solution of a mixture of sodium thioglycollate and thioglycollic acid, containing 37 per cent of antimony; antimony thioglycollamide, the triamide of antimony thioglycollic acid, containing 30 per cent of antimony; *fuadin* (*fouadin, neoantimosan, stibophen*), a trivalent antimony compound of pyro-catechin sodium disulfonate, containing 13.6 per cent of trivalent antimony; *anthio-maline* (lithium antimony thiomalate); urea stibamine, stibamine glucoside (*neo-*

stram); and *neostibosan*. The last two compounds are derivatives of amino-phenyl-stibinic acid.

Drug-fastness.—Drug-fast strains of microorganisms are produced following the continued use of chemotherapeutic agents. This acquired resistance of microorganisms to different antiseptics appears to be due to some change in the infectious organism and not to an altered reaction of the host. Strains resistant to one arsenic compound or one sulfonamide compound are usually resistant to all arsenicals or all sulfonamides. Workers have been able to develop strains resistant to a large variety of chemicals. However, it is well to remember that drug-fastness is not necessarily permanent and may be lost at any time. Acquired resistance to the bacteriostatic or bactericidal action of various chemicals is, however, of practical importance in chemotherapy and where this exists, agents of different chemical composition or structure are necessary for effective treatment. Among the chemotherapeutic agents displaying this characteristic to a pronounced degree are the arsenicals, bismuth and antimony compounds, the sulfonamide drugs, orthoquinoid dyes (oxazine, pyronine and acridine groups) and other dyes, the complex urea derivative *Germanin* (*Bayer 205*) and *Fourneau 309*, the latter two being probably identical and well known as trypanocidal compounds.

SULFONAMIDE COMPOUNDS

A voluminous amount of literature has accumulated on the sulfonamide compounds. The number of papers which have appeared during the last five years and are continuing to appear annually in the literature is far greater than that on any other chemotherapeutic agent or on any subject. It is impossible to even list some of the valuable contributions, but those interested should familiarize themselves with such texts as *Clinical Use of Sulfanilamide, etc.*, by Long and Bliss; *Sulfanilamide Therapy of Bacterial Infections*, by Mellon, Gross and Cooper; and *Sulfanilamide and Related Compounds in General Practice*, by Spink. Fosbinder (*J. Am. Pharm. Assoc.*, 1944, **33**, 1) recently presented a study on the present status of the sulfonamides.

Choice of Sulfonamide Compound.—The factors which influence the selection of one compound instead of another are: specificity in their antibacterial action against various species of bacteria; toxicity; rapidity of absorption, distribution and concentration in fluids and tissues throughout the body, and excretion; amount of acetylation; and ease of administration. The possibility of a sensitization to these compounds must not be excluded. Caution in the administration of the sulfonamides is to be observed when these drugs are given to those who previously suffered toxic reactions in the course of therapy with sulfonamides. For a consideration of the selection and use of the sulfonamides, see Merritt (*Clin. Med.*, 1943, **50**, 316).

Mode of Action.—The effect of sulfonamide compounds is primarily one of bacteriostasis. Different explanations have been given to show how these drugs produce their effects, but at present the exact means by which this is accomplished is still a subject of much discussion. The following are some of the ideas which have been postulated. The effect is not due to the compounds themselves but to some oxidation product. The drugs interfere with capsule formation and neutralize various toxins elaborated by bacteria. Sulfonamide compounds interfere with the ability of bacteria to utilize serum proteins for food or alter the morphology of the infecting organisms or prevent the action of catalase. This anticatalase effect results in the accumulation of H_2O_2, which reaches such concentrations to eventually kill the bacteria. Finally there is the explanation presented by Woods (*Brit. J. Exp. Med.*, 1940, **21**, 74). Para-aminobenzoic acid (PAB), which is probably synthesized by the bacterial cells, is an essential growth substance of these cells. In the enzyme reaction necessary for the utilization of para-aminobenzoic acid, para-aminobenzenesulfonamide (sulfanilamide), if present in excess, displaces the latter, thereby inhibiting growth of the bacterial cell. Evidence has been introduced by different workers in support of Woods' suggestion.

Sulfonamide Resistant Bacteria.—As in the case of other chemotherapeutic agents, organic arsenic compounds in particular, bacteria may develop a resistance to the sulfonamide compounds especially after prolonged contact. Once developed, a well-established resistance appears to be indefinitely retained and once acquired against one of the sulfonamide compounds, the resistance continues for most of the others. In infections caused by these sulfonamide resistant organisms, gramicidin and penicillin have proved of greatest value. See Kirby and Rantz (*California & West. Med.*, 1942, **57**, 174) and Sesler and Schmidt (*J. Pharmacol. & Exper. Therap.*, 1942, **75**, 356).

Sulfanilamide (*p*-aminobenzenesulfonamide; *p*-aminophenyl sulfamide; prontylin; prontosil album; colsulanyde; diseptyl; stramid; streptocide; sulfonamide-P; 1162 F).—When administered by the oral route, this compound is readily absorbed, well distributed throughout the body, and if kidney function is normal, it is promptly excreted. It is the drug of choice in all types of hemolytic streptococcal infections, in meningococcal infections, in chancroid, in the treatment of gas gangrene, and in trachoma. It is equally as effective as sulfapyridine in infections due to *Streptococcus viridans*, species of *Brucella*, gonococci, and in the treatment of lymphogranuloma venereum.

Sulfapyridine (2-sulfanilyl-aminopyridine; 2-(*p*-aminobenzenesulfonamido)pyridine; Degenan; M and B 693).—This compound is irregularly absorbed, but passes quite readily from the blood to the body tissues and fluids. Corresponding doses of this drug as compared with sulfanilamide produce lower blood concentration levels. This compound is the drug of choice in the therapy of all pneumococcal infections. It is also preferred by some workers to the other compounds in gonococcal infections, in lymphogranuloma venereum, in diseases caused by the Friedländer bacillus, in staphylococcal meningitis, in brucellosis and in trachoma. Some workers prefer its use to other compounds in infections by *H. influenzae*. Due to the frequency of nausea, vomiting and dizziness caused by its use, the other sulfonamide compounds are employed more frequently.

Sulfapyridine Sodium Monohydrate, dissolved in sterile pyrogen-free water in concentrations to make a 5 per cent solution and prepared aseptically, is used in emergencies for parenteral (intravenous) therapy to obtain quickly an adequate and usually a high blood concentration level. Intravenous injections should be discontinued upon the establishment of the latter and therapy continued by the oral administration of sulfapyridine. See Marshall and Long (*J. A. M. A.*, 1939, **112**, 1671).

Sulfathiazole (2-(*p*-aminobenzenesulfonamido)-thiazole).—This compound is readily absorbed and in most instances is rapidly excreted. It is distributed in the tissues and body fluids in the same manner as is sulfanilamide and sulfapyridine, but the amount present in specific fluids is inconstant. It does not pass as readily into the spinal fluid as do the other two previously mentioned sulfonamides and much of that which does penetrate exists in the acetylated form. Sulfathiazole is, therefore, not recommended in meningeal infections. Sulfathiazole appears to be the drug of choice in all staphylococcal infections. If the latter are accompanied by a bacteremia, blood level concentrations of 10 mg. per cent are maintained. It is preferred to sulfa-pyridine in the treatment of gonococcus infections because of its lower toxicity, better tolerance and fewer renal complications. In urinary tract infections, caused especially by *S. aureus, E. coli, A. aerogenes, P. aeruginosa, Proteus ammoniae* and species of *Salmonella*, Helmholz (*Proc. Staff Meet., Mayo Clin.*, 1942, **17,** 529) reported that sulfathiazole was more effective than the other sulfonamide compounds. This drug is as effective as sulfanilamide and sulfapyridine in the treatment of pneumococcal pneumonia. Sulfathiazole was reported by Loveless and Denton (*J. A. M. A.,* 1943, **121,** 827) as being effective as a prophylactic agent in the control of gonorrhea and chancroid. It has recently been recommended for use locally in the larynx and nasopharynx (*J. A. M. A.,* 1943, **122,** 180).

Sulfadiazine (2-sulfanilamidopyrimidine; 2-(*p*-aminobenzenesulfamido)-pyrimi-dine).—This compound (see Feinstone and associates, *Bull. Johns Hopkins Hosp.,* 1940, **67,** 427) displays a greater solubility in body fluids than in distilled water. Sulfadiazine is rapidly absorbed into the blood and is excreted slowly. Its absorption, excretion and distribution resemble sulfapyridine more closely than the other sul-fonamide compounds. The lower toxicity of this drug and the high therapeutic activ-ity are responsible for its wide use in pneumococcal, streptococcal, staphylococcal and meningococcal infections. See also Lowell (*Med. Clin. N. A.,* 1943, **27,** 1247).

Sulfamerazine (2-sulfanilamido-4-methylpyrimidine or monoethylethylsulfadia-zine) is more rapidly and completely absorbed from the gastro-intestinal tract and more slowly eliminated from the kidneys. Its toxicity is somewhat less but does not exceed that of sulfadiazine, and it is more efficient therapeutically on a dosage basis. Due to its more rapid absorption orally, resulting also in higher blood levels and the prolongation of time interval between doses, sulfamerazine is preferred by many in place of the other sulfonamide compounds. For further details, see Welch, *et al.* (*J. Pharmacol. & Exper. Therap.,* 1943, **77,** 357) and Murphy, Flippin, *et al.* (*Am. J. M. Sc.,* 1943, **205,** 717, 846; **206,** 211, 216).

Sulfaguanidine (sulfanilyl guanidine monohydrate).—This compound (*Bull. Johns Hopkins Hosp.,* 1940, **67,** 163; 1941, **68,** 94) is the guanidine analogue of sulfa-pyridine. It is poorly absorbed and is therefore used for the effect exerted by it al-most entirely within the intestinal tract. Sulfaguanidine is never used to attain high blood levels and is not to be employed as a substitute for the above-mentioned sul-fonamides. Until the introduction of this compound, an intestinal antiseptic ap-peared to be more efficient if it was but sparingly soluble in water or the intestinal juices. A low water solubility tends to reduce or eliminate absorption. In the use of sulfaguanidine, there is made available a water-soluble therapeutically active drug, which is poorly absorbed from the intestines. This compound is effective in restrain-ing the growth of Gram-negative bacilli in the intestinal tract, and is useful in the treatment of acute bacillary dysentery, and appears to be of value as a preoperative and postoperative prophylactic agent in surgery of the colon. For further details, see Firor and Jonas (*Ann. Surg.*, 1941, **114,** 19) and Hartnett (*Medical Times*, 1942, **70,** 240).

Succinylsulfathiazole (2-(N⁴-succinylsulfanilamido)-thiazole; sulfasuxidine).— This compound (*Arch. of Surg.*, 1942, **44,** 187) appears to be more satisfactory than sulfaguanidine in the treatment of bacillary dysentery infection and the carrier state and also as a preoperative and postoperative prophylactic in abdominal and intestinal surgery. Succinylsulfathiazole has practically no bacteriostatic activity *in vitro,* but *in vivo* it is strongly antibacterial due probably to the liberation of active nascent sulfathiazole in the intestines by hydrolysis. A high concentration of the drug can be maintained in the intestinal tract, and due to the low degree of absorption only low concentrations appear in the blood. Reactions, therefore, do not occur, as have been reported, at times, with the use of sulfanilylguanidine. Furthermore, the latter is ineffective in the presence of ulcerating lesions of the intestinal mucosa, but these lesions appear not to abolish the activity of succinylsulfathiazole. For further details, see Firor (*Ann. Surg.*, 1942, **115,** 829), Kirby and Rantz (*J. A. M. A.*, 1942, **119,** 615) Archer and Lehman (*Ann. Surg.*, 1944, **119,** 518) and editorial review (*J. A. M. A.*, 1943, **121,** 1353).

Other Considerations of Sulfonamide Compounds.—Sulfonamide compounds are employed by some workers as preservatives in stored blood, to be used in transfusions. Sulfanilamide has been employed most frequently, and it is added to the blood in a sterile, concentrated solution to yield a final concentration of from 1:5000 to 1:1000. Sodium sulfathiazole, added to give a final concentration of 0.2 per cent, is also used.

In pneumococcic infections, the sputum or other body fluid should be typed before the administration of the sulfonamide compound, even though serum therapy is not to be used initially. It may be found advisable to employ serum later, but an accurate typing may not be possible if the patient is being treated with sulfonamide drugs.

Bixby (*J. Lab. & Clin. Med.*, 1940, **25,** 476), Kreenin (*ibid.,* 1940, **25,** 690) and other workers have raised the question whether the presence of sulfonamide drugs in the blood in appreciable concentrations is not apt to cause some errors or difficulty in cross matching and in compatibility tests. Though this must be kept in mind and though theoretically there may be a possibility that sulfonamide therapy could produce changes directly or indirectly which might interfere with compatibility reactions, practically there appears to be very little or no relation, when we consider the widespread use of this therapy. The phenomena recorded in the few instances reported are more than likely due to other causes and not to the sulfonamide therapy.

In testing sulfonamide compounds for sterility and in the bacteriological examinations of urine, blood and other body fluids for the identification of specific bacteria while the patient is under sulfonamide therapy, it is necessary to add para-aminobenzoic acid to the culture media so as to inactivate (or neutralize) the bacteriostatic properties of the sulfonamide compounds present in the material under examination. It is important to note that an excess of the para-aminobenzoic acid is to be avoided, as the latter also is bacteriostatic. Different culture media used contain varying amounts of para-aminobenzoic acid. The amount of the inactivating agent required varies for the different sulfonamide compounds being least in amount for sulfanilamide and the largest quantity is required for sulfathiazole and sulfadiazine. In para-aculture studies, it is common practice to add from 2 to 10 (average 5) mg. of blood minobenzoic acid to each 100 cc. of the culture medium.

Microcrystalline sulfonamide compounds, prepared by high-frequency sound vibrations and used in concentrated suspensions in water (20 per cent), are being employed. Such suspensions have proved successful in the treatment of impetigo and other skin affections.

Sterilization of Sulfonamides.—Solutions of sulfanilamide, sulfapyridine and sulfathiazole are sterilized by autoclaving at 15 pounds' pressure (121.5° C.) for twenty minutes. Solutions of sulfapyridine sodium are prepared by aseptic manipulation just before use.

Sulfonamide powders (as above, preferably not too fine—and capable of passing through 40 to 80-mesh sieve—inasmuch as fine powders tend to cake) are prepared and sterilized as follows:

Dry heating is used most frequently. The powder is placed in portions, not exceeding 4 or 5 Gm., in suitable sterilized double envelope containers, in sterilized screwed-top aluminum capped containers, in cotton-plugged sterile test tubes individually wrapped, in sterile ampuls, or in other suitable sterile containers. The containers are then placed in the hot-air oven at a temperature of from 145° to 150° C., which is maintained for four hours. There should be a check and a careful control on the actual temperature of the powder itself. Thermocouples should be used in large-scale sterilization. If convenient, a liquid petrolatum bath can be used instead of the hot-air oven. The sterile container in which the powder is present is immersed in the paraffin oil bath maintained at 145° to 150° C. This temperature affords a margin of safety as far as thermostability is concerned, as the melting points of the sulfonamide powders most frequently used are higher. The melting point of sulfanilamide is approximately 165° C.; sulfapyridine is approximately 192° C. and sulfathiazole is approximately 202° C. McCartney and Cruikshank (*Lancet*, 1942, **243,** 454) advocate the use of the autoclave at 10 pounds' pressure for thirty to sixty minutes. The addition of 2 to 5 per cent bismuth subcarbonate, charcoal, fuller's earth, calcium carbonate, talcum or zinc oxide will give a free-flowing powder, which prevents aggregation and delays absorption of the drug from the site of application. The bismuth compound or zinc compound is suggested as these chemicals are also used for wound packs and dressings.

It is also possible to dissolve the powder in a suitable solvent, filter the solution through a bacteria-proof filter, and to allow the solvent from the filtrate to volatilize under aseptic conditions. Sulfanilamide powder which is soluble in acetone in concentrations as high as 20 per cent was so prepared by the author. Furthermore, acetone, after an adequate period of exposure, is bactericidal and suspensions of bacteria including spore bearers are killed by (undiluted) acetone after several days' exposure. Bacteriological filtration can be eliminated if acetone sulfanilamide solution is kept at least for several days and preferably a week before the acetone is allowed to volatilize, so as to obtain the sterile sulfanilamide powder. Sulfanilamide inoculated with *B. subitilis* spores was dissolved in acetone. After four days, this solution did not reveal the presence of growth upon transplanting. A control with talcum, treated in an identical manner with spores and acetone, did not yield growth, while a similar control treated with saline did yield growth. See also McClintock and Goodale (U. S. Nav. M. Bull., 1943, **41,** 1360).

SPECIFICITY OF DISINFECTANTS

The evolution of knowledge concerning the treatment of disease has been advanced by many workers with the thought as expressed in the words of Chick and Martin: "Some disinfectants are more efficient against a particular organism than against any other." This practically recognizes the specificity of a disinfectant for certain microorganisms (animal or vegetable). The addition of various dyes to different media to favor the growth of some species of bacteria and inhibit that of others is commonly practiced. This specificity is frequently correlated with the behavior toward Gram's method of staining. At times the selectivity is so marked, as in the cases of the three species of *Brucella*, causing undulant fever in man, that these species of bacteria can be differentiated by their behavior toward different dyes (see page 150). Cooper and Mason (*J. Hyg.*, 1927, **26,** 118) present an interesting detailed correlation of chemical and physicochemical properties with specificity.

Quinine has been used for years as a specific for malarial parasites. This alkaloid, its salts and derivatives have been found to act as a specific for the destruction of the pneumococcus and is being used by some for this purpose. *Ethylhydrocuprein (Optochin)* has also been found of distinct value in pneumococcus infections. *Thymol* was introduced in 1880 as a remedy for intestinal worms, especially hookworm. This has been replaced within the last few years by more specific drugs. The sensitiveness to destruction of the gonococcus and other cocci in the presence of silver salts and the specificity of arsphenamine and arsenicals, bismuth, antimony and mercury compounds have been mentioned. *Emetine* (the active principle from ipecac) has been found to be a specific for dysentery (caused by amoeba) and has been employed in pyorrhea (especially where amoeba, a subgroup of protozoa, are found). The miraculous results obtained with the use of the sulfonamide compounds and their specificities displayed in particular bacterial infections are detailed elsewhere in this volume. The use of dyes and of microbiotic agents as specifics is considered below.

Chaulmoogra Oil and its derivatives and the fatty acids of the chaulmoogric series, chaulmoogric and hydnocarpic acids and possibly some isomers possess some activity against acid-fast bacteria. *Avenyl,* an organic mercury compound, employed with hydnocarpus oil as a vehicle has been presented as a safe and effective remedy in the treatment of leprosy complicated by the presence of a positive Wassermann reaction. The heavy metals have commanded much attention as specifics in the treatment of tuberculosis. Gold and copper salts have long held a place of interest. *Sanocrysin,* a gold compound is being used. *Cyanocuprol,* a copper preparation, has been used extensively in Japan. Their exact value cannot be determined as yet. The opinion seems to prevail that where apparently good results are obtained, the effects of some of these agents are not due to any specific action upon the organism but due to a reaction which is produced as in nonspecific therapy (see page 450).

DYES AS DISINFECTANTS

Churchman (*J. Exp. Med.*, 1912, **16,** 221, 822) showed definitely the selective action of gentian violet for certain organisms. Many of the other dyes have been found of practical value as antiseptics, because of their specificity and due to their low toxicity and nonirritating property.   Browning and Gilmour (1912) showed the specific affinity for certain bacteria of fuchsin, brilliant green, malachite green, methyl green, hexamethyl and gentian violet, methylene blue, congo red and other closely related dyes. The claim of the specificity of disinfectants, especially the dyes, was proved by numerous experiments of different workers, which showed that the bactericidal action of a disinfectant on one organism is not necessarily a measure of its action on any other bacterium.   *Brilliant green*, in a 1 to 1000 dilution, was used as a wash or as an antiseptic dressing for practically all kinds of wounds during the first World War.   It was found to be potent, nontoxic and nonirritating.   *Malachite green* in conjunction with bichloride of mercury was also used as "green spray."   This was made of equal parts of 2 per cent malachite green in 80 per cent alcohol and 2 per cent bichloride dissolved in 80 per cent alcohol.   The solutions are mixed before use and form a chemical compound known as *mickelthwait*.   The "green spray" was used with success as an antiseptic spray or dressing before operation, replacing iodine.   When used, it stains the applied area green.   The peculiar property of many of the dyes in use is not necessarily distinctly bactericidal (destructive), but, as many workers have demonstrated, it is a bacteriostatic behavior.

Medicinal Dyes.—While we know that mere staining of bacteria by or in contact with dyes does not necessarily mean their destruction, dyes have been used with considerable interest as medicinal agents.   The natural dyes like carmine, cochineal and cudbear have little or no parasiticidal properties and are never employed for this effect.   Only the synthetic dyes prepared from coal tar have been used for their bactericidal and bacteriostatic properties.   A large number of these coal-tar dyes, the chemistry of which is exceedingly complex, are used.   It may be mentioned that the available dyes vary individually as to their exact composition, so that in turn the toxicity, bactericidal value, etc., may vary.   It is therefore frequently advisable to specify certain manufacturers' products to be sure of the exact composition, or where dyes are official in the U. S. P. or are certified, these dyes of more definitely known composition should be employed.   The toxicity of dyes is markedly affected by the pH; growth is most readily inhibited with the acidic dyes in acid media and with the so-called basic dyes, the inhibition is greatest with an alkalinity.   All medicinal dyes are to some extent toxic to tissues, are less effective in the presence of blood serum and appear to be more effective against the aerobes than the anaerobes.   The different classes of synthetic dyes that have been used belong to the acridine, azo, diphenylamine, nitroso, pyronine and triphenylmethane groups.

The azo dyes, when used, have been employed under the name of *Scarlet R.*   Their exact chemical compositions vary, but they are mainly azo compounds combined with betanaphthol.   Medicinal scarlet red in a 4 to 8 per cent ointment has been used for years as a stimulating and bacteriostatic agent.   *Dimazon*, the closely related diacetylaminoazotoluene is used for the same purpose in the form of a 2 per cent ointment, as a dusting powder or in an oily solution.   The triphenylmethane (rosanaline) dyes are used with apparent success in the treatment of disease among humans.   These especially display selective activity.   Gentian violet and related triphenylmethanes possess a selective action for Gram-positive bacteria (except tubercle bacillus). Acid fuchsin restrains and may even kill most of the Gram-negative bacteria.   Brilliant green, a member of this group, has been mentioned.   Of the acridine group, acriflavine and rivanol are being used.

Acriflavine and Proflavine.—The flavines, acridine derivatives, were first shown to possess therapeutic properties when Professor Ehrlich in 1912 found that they acted as a specific against some of the trypanosomes. Due to this fact, he called this product *trypaflavine* to differentiate it from an existing commercial vegetable dye known as *flavine.* During the first World War, two closely related substances were produced in England. One was named *proflavine* and the other, said to be more active, was called *acriflavine. Neutral acriflavine* is also available. In the treatment of wounds, the flavines are generally employed in 0.1 per cent concentrations. As an ointment, 1 per cent of proflavine oleate in an ointment base composed of equal parts of calcium carbonate and petrolatum is used. Solutions of acriflavine and proflavine can be autoclaved, but they are sensitive to light. Solutions should be kept in amber bottles, away from the light and should not be used if they are older than one week. The flavine dyes, especially acriflavine, are used as urinary antiseptics. Alkalies, such as bicarbonate of sodium, are given to increase their efficiency. In a recent editorial (*Lancet*, 1942, **242,** 429; *J. A. M. A.*, 1943, **122,** 117), comments are given concerning the flavines and especially the recommendation of Mitchell and Buttle (*Lancet,* 1942, **242,** 416), who report good results with and recommend the use of the dry powder proflavine (0.2 to 0.5 Gm.) directly into wounds. Proflavine (2:8-diaminoacridine sulfate) is less toxic than the other flavines and is not precipitated by saline as are other compounds of this series. Proflavine bisulfate, which is used in practice, may produce a *p*H of 2 at various points of contact, which may account for the transient burning sensations reported by some patients. Berry (*Quart. J. Pharm. & Pharmacol.,* 1941, **14,** 363) presents a study on the bacteriostatic values of several different series of acridine derivatives for several bacteria. All the compounds investigated were inactive against *Pseudomonas aeruginosa.*

Other Dyes.—Acriviolet represents an effort in another direction. Attempts were made to combine gentian violet and acid fuchsin so as to obtain their respective selective powers. This was not successful. Acriflavine and gentian violet, two dyes of somewhat different selective powers (the former selective for Gram-negative and the latter for Gram-positive bacteria), do mix, and the resulting product *acriviolet* is now available.

The fluorescein pyronine dyes are very feeble bacteriostatic or bactericidal agents, but possess marked penetrating powers. An attempt to attach or combine a strong non- or weakly penetrating antiseptic to a penetrating dye has been tried by many workers. Many combinations of mercury, and more recently copper and silver, have been brought into use. They represent the addition to one portion of the molecule the virtues of the other part. *Mercurochrome (220-soluble)* is characteristic of such a combination, a union of mercury and a fluorescent dye. For complete details, see page 312.

Oxyquinoline and its salts have been used as antiseptics and preservatives. Oxyquinoline (base) in a concentration of 0.1 per cent is added as a preservative in creams and in oils. Antiseptic Baby Oil frequently contains this base. *Oxyquinoline sulfate,* known under the trade name of *Chinosol,* has been employed in eyewashes, nasal sprays, vaginal douches (0.03 per cent), as a gargle (0.1 to 0.3 per cent) and as a preservative for urine (0.05 to 0.1 per cent) and lubricating jellies. Smith (*U. S. Nav. M. Bull.,* 1941, **39,** 80) recommends *oxyquinoline benzoate* as the nonspecific antiseptic in a venereal prophylactic ointment (see page 297).

Use of Dyes in Infection.—In diseases of humans, the dyes (in solutions of 1 to 50 to 1 to 1000) have lent themselves readily for the disinfection of wounds, localized infections of mucous membranes and in the general treatment of surface infections. Water and, better still, 50 per cent glycerin or 25 per cent propyl alcohol can be used as diluents. Best results are more frequently obtained by thorough preliminary cleansing usually with weak alkaline solutions, and wherever possible or convenient, the dye solutions should be comfortably hot so as to secure enhanced bactericidal effects. Most of these dyes are nontoxic, nonirritating, have no effect on blood and body cells in the dilutions employed, and are penetrative, persisting for long periods of time. Though not very strongly bactericidal, they are highly bacteriostatic even in weak dilutions. A solution containing 0.5 per cent crystal violet and 0.5 per cent brilliant green has been and is being used as a preoperative skin antiseptic. A solution containing 0.5 per cent crystal violet and 0.5 per cent neutral acriflavine is recommended in cases of Vincent's angina.

Gentian (crystal) violet is used effectively for strongyloidiasis, oxyuriasis (pinworm infection) and for certain species of biliary flukes.

The acriflavines, gentian violet or crystal violet, brilliant green, methylene blue and other simple and commonly used medicinal dyes, and trade dye products such as *Pyridium* (the monohydrochloride of phenylazo-2,6-diamino pyridine), *Mallophene* (beta-phenyl-azo-alpha-alpha-diamino pyridine hydrochloride), *Niazo* (2-butyloxy-2, 6'-diamino-5,5'-azopyridine) and *Serenium* (an organic azo dye, the hydrochloride of 2',4-diamino-4'-ethoxy-azobenzene) have been and are being used by mouth as antiseptics or bacteriostatic agents in infections of the genito-urinary tract. The dyes have been used frequently as therapeutic agents to be injected into the blood stream for the treatment of bacterial infections spread by the blood or diseases due to the presence of bacteria in the latter. They are generally injected slowly into the veins in 1 per cent solutions, using 30 cc. or more depending upon the body weight of the patient and the particular dye. The evidence so far available from clinical sources tends to show that some benefits may be derived by the use of some of these dyes in septicemias. The observations do not reveal the actual destruction of the bacteria in the blood stream. The reason for the improvement of the condition after intravenous injection of these dyes is not known. The mechanism is believed by some to be similar to the nonspecific protein reaction (which see).

Aqueous solutions of dyes such as brilliant green and gentian violet are used effectively in the treatment of impetigo and other pyodermias, certain types of ringworm, and subacute cases of athlete's foot are benefited by 2 per cent crystal violet solutions. In the "triple dye therapy" of burns, a jelly is used containing 2 per cent of a powder, which is composed of approximately 46 per cent crystal violet, 31 per cent brilliant green and 23 per cent neutral acriflavine.

Chapter XXIII

ANTIBIOSIS, BACTERIOTHERAPY, MICROBIOTIC AGENTS AND PHAGOTHERAPY

ON PAGE 21, the terms *symbiosis* and *association* were briefly defined as mutually beneficial relations in contrast to *antibiosis* and *antagonism* which designate an opposite relationship wherein a reduction in growth and activities occurs as a result of two or more organisms living together. Varying degrees of compatibility and antagonism are found and some workers recognize such differentiation as *in vitro* antagonism and antagonism *in vivo,* and limit the term *antibiosis* to the latter. Then there exist the direct, indirect and true antagonisms; repressive bactericidal and lytic forms of antagonism; and an antagonism of growth or of function. The antagonism may be one-sided or two-sided. The antagonism may exist between strains of the same species and among different species, the so-called iso- and hetero-antagonism. The antagonistic bacteria may dissolve living or only dead bacteria. *Lysobacteria* is the term applied when both living and dead bacteria are lysed or dissolved. The mechanism of the action of the antagonist varies. *E. coli* may lose the property of attacking carbohydrates when grown together with paratyphoid bacilli. Fermentative and proteolytic bacteria generally do not flourish equally well in mixed culture. Acid production inhibits the tryptic action of the bacterial proteases which is the basis for *Lactobacillus acidophilus* therapy in intestinal disorders. A stagnant pool will be apt to contain few or no pathogenic bacteria in contrast to a clear chemically untreated water from a pond or lake. The well-known antagonistic action of staphylococci on *C. diphtheriae* is not merely the result of an overgrowth, but the latter undergoes marked changes in morphology. The therapeutic use of filtrates of *Klebsiella pneumoniae* was suggested when it was found that such filtrates inhibit the toxin production of *C. diphtheriae.* There are many available records which reveal a reduction in pathogenicity of one organism by the presence of others. Among the theories presented to attempt and explain the mechanism of antagonism are some of the following: the competition for certain essential food requirements; the accumulation of metabolic products or the exhaustion of growth-stimulating substances; changes in pH, surface tension, osmotic pressure and oxidation-reduction potential; production of enzymes and other substances which directly or indirectly affect cellular structure or development.

BACTERIOTHERAPY WITH MICROBIOTIC AGENTS

As one looks back in retrospect, we find that many old-time remedies and practices when effective owed their virtue to the possible creation of conditions favorable to the development of antagonistic microorganisms. The application of urine to localized wounds and the method of cast surgery without the application of antiseptics used in the Spanish Civil War are illustrations. Chance may introduce favorable antagonists. Pasteur (*Compt. rend. Soc. biol.*, 1877, **85**, 101) and Emmerich (*Arch. Hyg.*, 1887, **6**, 442) found that anthrax in animals can be controlled by the simultaneous inoculation of different bacteria, and Pawlowsky (*Arch. path. Anat.*, 1887, **108**, 494) and Bouchard (*Compt. rend. Soc. biol.*, 1889, **108**, 713) obtained some resistance against anthrax infection by inoculation with various organisms.

Lorenz and Ravenel (*J. A. M. A.*, 1912, **59**, 690) suggested the use of cultures of *Staphylococcus aureus* in the clearing of the throats of diphtheria carriers. Nicholson and Hogan (*J. A. M. A.*, 1914, **62**, 510) used cultures of lactic acid bacilli in the treatment of diphtheria. The use of the latter organisms in intestinal affections was mentioned and it was also recommended as a treatment for gonococcal vaginitis.

Baer in 1929 introduced the use of surgical maggots as a viable antiseptic in wounds. He found the display of a definite bactericidal action in addition to the removal of necrotic debris (see page 380). Simmons (*J. Bact.*, 1935, **30**, 253) found a bactericidal principle in the excretions which was bactericidal against *Staphylococcus aureus*, hemolytic streptococci, and *Clostridium welchii*. Sherman and Hodge (*J. Bact.*, 1936, **31**, 96) found that the freshly extracted juices of certain plants possess bactericidal action.

PENICILLIN

Many of the early data were overlooked and little practical use of these observations was made until recently. In 1929 (*Brit. J. Exp. Path.*, 1929, **10**, 226) and later, in 1932 (*J. Path. & Bact.*, 1932, **35**, 831), Fleming reported on "Penicillin" which he isolated from the broth cultures of *Penicillium notatum*. For cultural characteristics of the latter, see Kocholaty (*J. Bact.*, 1942, **44**, 469). Penicillin was found to possess a powerful inhibitory activity against Gram-positive cocci, but had little or no effect against Gram-negative bacteria, except the gonococcus. Penicillin was found to be separate from the pigment produced by the mold, was relatively thermostable, resisted 100° C. for five minutes, was destroyed by ultraviolet light and oxygen, did not dialyze through collodion membranes, and was used in isolation and for the recovery of feebly growing organisms in pure culture. Penicillin possesses a very low toxicity and Fleming suggested its use as a dressing for septic wounds. It completely inhibits staphylococci in a 1:800 concentration. Adjusted to pH 6.8, it retains its potency for three months. Due to the fact that penicillin does not maintain its potency for very long periods of time and that until recently yields were extremely small and therefore its production was expensive, its use as a therapeutic agent has been limited mainly for the armed forces and for special cases among civilians. It is believed that general release of this product will occur shortly.

Production of Penicillin.—Culture media seeded with a spore suspension of the mold are incubated at 24° C. for approximately seven days. The culture medium is acidified and the penicillin is extracted by an organic solvent, such as ether, amyl acetate or chloroform. The first extraction must be carried out rapidly at low temperatures. For other methods of preparation, see Meyer and associates (*Science*, 1942, **96**, 21). Penicillin is relatively stable in the organic solvent and further purification is carried out from this solution. The purified material is assayed for its antibacterial potency against *Staphylococcus aureus*. The oxford (Florey) standard (*Lancet*, 1941, **241**, 177) had an activity of 42 units per mg., but Meyer and associates

(*Science*, 1942, **96**, 20) described an ammonium salt of penicillin which gives a much higher value, and McKee and Rake (*J. Bact.*, 1942, **43**, 645) used a sodium salt with a potency of 240 units per mg. Other salts of penicillin have been recently introduced. For biological properties of penicillin, see Florey and Jennings and for physical and chemical properties, see Abraham and associates (*Brit. J. Exp. Path.*, 1942, **23**, 103 120). See also statement released by and report presented by the National Council Committee on Medical Research (*J. A. M. A.*, 1943, **122**, 235, 1217) and the tentative methods for assay presented by the Food and Drug Administration.

Use and Action.—Toxic effects were not observed when penicillin was added to a tissue culture, to the chorio-allantoic membrane of the developing chick, when applied directly to the human eye and no toxic responses were observed in human beings who had received 170 mg. of penicillin intravenously, daily, for a period of six days (*Proc. Soc. Exptl. Biol. Med.*, 1942, **50**, 285). Experimentally, penicillin has been found capable of protecting animals from infections of beta hemolytic streptococci or pneumococci (*Chem. & Industry*, 1941, **60**, 828). Clinically, it has been used intravenously effectively in the treatment of systemic staphylococcal and streptococcal infections, which have been resistant to the sulfonamides. Penicillin does not display antibacterial action against *E. coli*. Abraham and Chain (*Nature*, 1940, **146**, 837) isolated an enzyme, "Penicillinase," from *E. coli* which was able to destroy the activity of penicillin. It has been used with success for the topical treatment of infections of the eye. The bacteriostatic action of penicillin is not affected by pus, the products of tissue autolysis and by protein catabolism—substances which are known to inhibit the activity of the sulfonamides and other chemotherapeutic agents. Penicillin has proved to be a valuable therapeutic agent in the treatment of infections which do not respond to sulfonamide therapy. It exerts its antibacterial action regardless of the initial concentration of the organisms. Penicillin is regarded as a bactericidal substance. When it is added to a culture of rapidly growing cocci, there is a geometric reduction in the number of viable organisms along an arithmetic scale (*Proc. Soc. Exptl. Biol. Med.*, 1942, **50**, 281), which is in contrast to the action of the sulfonamide drugs that are primarily bacteriostatic agents. Lyons (*J. A. M. A.*, 1943, **123**, 1007) presents an interesting report on penicillin therapy of 209 surgical infections (various types) in the U. S. Army. For further and more complete details, see papers read at a symposium on antibiotic agents (*J. A. M. A.*, 1944, **124**, 633, 798), Florey and Cairns (*Brit. Med. J.*, 1943, **11**, 755), British Council's penicillin compilation (*Mfg. Chem.*, 1944, **15**, 97), British Penicillin Clinical Trials Comm. Medical Research Council's War Memoranda (1944), U. S. National Research Council Chemotherapy Committee's release on penicillin with indications, methods of administration and dosage, and compilations issued by most manufacturers and distributors of penicillin (available on request).

Other Considerations.—The cup-plate method or ring test, the serial dilution method and the turbidimetric methods are being used as assay methods for determining the potency of Penicillin and its compounds. For details, see Foster and Woodruff (*J. Bact.*, 1944, **47**, 43), Schmidt and Moyer (*J. Bact.*, 1944, **47**, 199) and the special committee reports of the United States Pharmacopoeia.

In testing for the sterility of Penicillin and its compounds, the antibacterial effects of these substances are first neutralized or inactivated. Taka-diastase and especially Clarase, a more active diastatic enzyme are used for this purpose. For details concerning these anti-penicillin agents, see Lawrence (*Science*, 1943, **98**, 413; 1944, **99**, 15) and "Tentative Methods" for assay suggested by the Food and Drug Administration.

Buxbaum and Fiegoli (*J. Bact.*, 1943, **46**, 543) suggested the use of penicillin in media for the isolation especially of Gram-negative bacteria and they used it successfully for the isolation of *H. influenzae* in blood-agar plates.

Meyer and associates (*Science*, 1943, **97**, 205) recently described the use of *methyl* and *ethyl esters of penicillin* as derivatives which possess greater stability than the original penicillin, and that partial protection may be possible by the oral administration of these compounds.

Penatin is an antibacterial substance, different from penicillin, produced by certain strains of *Penicillium notatum*. The particular strain is designated as *P. notatum* (PEN 2). Kocholaty discusses its properties and the cultural requirements for production (*J. Bact.*, 1942, **44**, 143, 469). More recently, this same worker (*Science*, 1943, **97**, 186) reported that penatin is a more powerful antibacterial agent than penicillin and that it was also effective against bacteria, notably Gram-negative organisms, which are not susceptible to any appreciable degree to the action of penicillin. Of 50 pathogenic and nonpathogenic bacteria studied, none of them was capable of growing in media in which penatin was present in concentrations of not less than 1:10 million. To a lesser degree, this agent is also bactericidal. In contrast to penicillin, penatin cannot be extracted by organic solvents. It can be precipitated as an insoluble penatin-phosphotungstate or adsorbed on kaolin. Methods of concentrating and purifying the latter are used. The antibacterial action is not reduced in the presence of even 90 per cent serum, and it apparently is nontoxic. Roberts and associates (*J. Biol. Chem.*, 1943, **147**, 47) produced *Penicillin B*, an antibacterial substance also obtained from *P. notatum*.

GRAMICIDIN

In 1939, Dubos and associates at the Rockefeller Foundation (*J. Exp. Med.*, 1939, **70**, 1, 249; *Proc. Soc. Exptl. Biol. Med.*, 1939, **40**, 311) isolated a metabolic product from the soil bacillus, *B. brevis*, which possessed a high degree of bactericidal efficiency against the Gram-positive bacteria, but had no effect against Gram-negative organisms. Hoogerheide (*J. Bact.*, 1940, **40**, 415) and later other workers reported on a similar inhibitory agent obtained from spore-bearing soil bacilli. Due to the high specificity for Gram-positive bacteria, the name gramicidin was applied to this antagonistic substance. A simple, rapid method for isolating antagonistic bacteria from soil is described by Stokes and Woodward (*J. Bact.*, 1942, **43**, 253).

Preparation and Use.—Gramicidin is extracted from cultures of an aerobic sporulating bacillus belonging to the group typified by the *B. mesentericus*. The organism is grown under an obligate aerobic environment in a special peptone medium and is obtained by extraction of an acid precipitate (*p*H 4.7) of the culture with alcohol, acetone or dioxone (*J. Exp. Med.*, 1939, **70**, 1, 11, 249). Differential fractionation in alcohol-ether mixtures yields *tyrocidin* and *gramicidin*, a crystalline neutral substance. The latter is insoluble in water and aqueous media and soluble in the above-mentioned volatile solvents. Dispersing agents as sulfonated and sulfated oils and also oxbile permit the substance to remain in solutions in water even in the presence of electrolytes. Gramicidin does not appear to belong to the class of enzymes (*Ann. Int. Med.*, 1940, **13,** 11) and its bacteriostatic and bactericidal effect upon Gram-positive bacteria appears to be due to a probable interference with some essential metabolic function of the susceptible microorganisms. Gramicidin exhibits its effectiveness *in vitro* and *in vivo*. A single dose of 0.001 to 0.002 mg. of gramicidin injected into the abdominal cavity is sufficient to protect mice against 10,000 fatal doses of pneumo-cocci or streptococci (*The Harvey Lectures*, 1939–1940, **35,** 223) and larger amounts will cure them of a well-established infection. Gramicidin has proved ineffective when administered by the subcutaneous, intramuscular or intravenous route. All successful investigations to date have involved intraperitoneal administration or injection into cavities. Reports of its effectiveness in bovine mastitis have been presented (*Proc. Soc. Exptl. Biol. Med.*, 1940, **44,** 444; **45,** 462). Bryan and associates (*Vet. Med.*, 1942, **37,** 364) infused each quarter of 157 cows with streptococcic mastitis with 150 mg. of tyrothricin and 142 (90 per cent) were freed of the infection. Workers from the Mayo Clinic and Massachusetts Memorial Hospital and from the Franklin Institute reported recently on the use of gramacidin in humans. Empyemia from pneumonia, sinusitis, bladder infections and infected wounds were treated successfully. They also reported that gramacidin is a hemolytic agent but heating will inactivate this property, though at the same time there will result a reduction in the efficiency of this chemical. However, heat-treated gramicidin is recommended (*Science News Letter* of May 10, 1941). Rammelkamp (*War Med.*, 1942, **2,** 830) used *tyrothricin* in 58 localized infections in man with encouraging results. Wright (*J. Franklin Inst.*, 1942, **233,** 188) reports good results for Gram-positive bacteria in the use of a product similar to gramicidin used by irrigation in infected wounds in 90 cases. See also Herrell (*Surg. Clin. North Am.*, 1943, **23,** 1163) who reports good results in the use of gramicidin and penicillin.

"Tyrocidin," present in the water-soluble, acetone-insoluble fraction, is not as potent as gramicidin, but appears to be effective against Gram-negative as well as Gram-positive bacteria. The separation of these two substances, gramicidin and tyrocidin, is beset with many technical difficulties. In practice, the fraction named "tyrothricin," which contains both active principles, is more frequently used as the therapeutic agent. Stokes and Woodward (*J. Bact.*, 1943, **45,** 29) report on the production of tyrothricin in submerged cultures of *B. brevis.*

OTHER MICROBIOTIC AGENTS

The above-mentioned microbiotic agents were considered somewhat in detail as these active substances are being used and investigated experimentally and clinically on a larger scale than those which follow and have not as yet received wide acclaim. Active microbiotic substances have been isolated from representative types of non-spore forming bacteria, spore-forming bacteria, actinomyces and fungi.

Species of *Actinomycetes* were found to yield three kinds of antibiotic substances. *Actinomycetin* is a water-soluble, thermolabile substance, which acts mainly on dead bacteria although living organisms may be affected. Waksman and Woodruff (*J. Bact.*, 1941, **42,** 231) described a chromogenic species of *Actinomyces* under the name of *A. antibioticus*, from which they isolated two substances, *Actinomycin A* and *B*, the former possessing extremely high bacteriostatic properties and only slowly bactericidal, and the B fraction being actively bactericidal and possessing little bacteriostatic action. These two substances exerted a highly selective action upon different micro-organisms. An actinomyces lysozyme isolated from *Actinomyces violaceus* and other species of Actinomyces was found to be a thermostabile substance of protein origin, lysozyme- (or egg-white) like in nature and possessing antibiotic action. *Strepto-thricin* was isolated from *Actinomyces lavendulae* and reported by Waksman and Woodruff (*Proc. Soc. Exper. Biol. Med.*, 1942, **49,** 207) as being particularly effective against Gram-negative bacteria. See also Woodruff and Foster (*J. Bact.*, 1943, **45,** 30); *Arch. Biochem.*, 1943, **3,** 241), and Robinson, *et al.* (*Science*, 1944, **99,** 539) who report on "the marked effect of streptothricin *in vitro* against Gram-negative and Gram-positive organsms." Jones, *et al.* (*Science*, 1944, **100,** 103), discuss the efficiency of *streptomycin*, which they claim behaves like streptothricin, but is effective against a greater number of different bacteria.

Aspergillin, isolated from species of *Aspergillus*, was found effective as a bacterio-static agent *in vitro*. Its effectiveness *in vivo* and its toxicity have not been reported as yet. *Fumigacin* and *clavacin* are names given by Waksman and associates (*Science*, 1942, **96,** 202) to antibacterial substances produced by *Aspergillus fumigatus* and *Aspergillus clavatus*, respectively. Fumigacin is formed in the culture medium during the early stages of growth (five to nine days) of the fungus and is destroyed upon further incubation. It is active against Gram-positive bacteria and possesses only limited activity against Gram-negative organisms or fungi. Clavacin is particularly active against Gram-negative bacteria but also possesses high bacteriostatic and high bactericidal properties against Gram-positive bacteria, especially staphylococci and spore-forming bacteria. Wiesner (*Nature*, 1942, **149,** 356) details the properties of the antibacterial substance obtained from *Aspergillus clavatus*. He found it effective on many organisms not affected by penicillin, sulfonamide drugs and other chemo-therapeutic agents and used it on human subjects without adverse effects. For fur-ther details on fumigacin and clavacin, see Waksman and associates (*J. Bact.*, 1943, **45,** 233); (*Science*, 1944, **99,** 220). Hooper and associates (*Science*, 1944, **99,** 16) claim that *clavacin* produced by *Aspergillus clavatus* and *patulin* produced by *Peni-cillium patulum* are identical. *Chlorellin*, an antibacterial substance obtained from *Chlorella vulgaris* and *Chlorella pyrenoidosa* was recently presented by Pratt and associates (*Science*, 1944, **99,** 351).

Gliotoxin, a sulfur-containing substance possessing antibiotic action and produced by certain fungi belonging to the genera *Trichoderma* and *Gliocladium*, was isolated by Weindling and Emerson (*Phytopathology*, 1936, **26,** 1068; 1937, **27,** 1175). It is bactericidal and fungicidal but is highly toxic. Studies have been recently presented on *gliotoxin*, the antibiotic principle of *Gliocladium fimbriatum* and also from a species of *penicillium* and *aspergillus* (*J. Am. Chem. Soc.*, 1944, **66,** 501) and on *flavacidin*, obtained from a white strain of *Aspergillus flavus* (*J. Bact.*, 1944, **47,** 187).

Pyocyanase and *pyocyanin* are the antibiotic agents obtained from nonspore-forming bacteria which have received most attention. Pyocyanase is a crude product obtained from *Pseudomonas aeruginosa* by extraction with ether and concentration. It appears to consist of a phosphatide, a neutral fat and a free fatty acid, and possesses lytic ac-tion against many bacteria. Pyocyanin is a chloroform-soluble blue pigment, ob-tained from *P. aeruginosa*, but it is also produced synthetically. Its bactericidal action is limited. For further details of these products, see Ehrismann (*Zentr. Bakt. Para-sitenk.*, 1934, **112,** 285) and Kramer (*Z. Immunitäts.*, 1935, **84,** 505).

To briefly summarize the value of the above newly introduced microbiotic agents, the following comment by Waksman and Woodruff (*J. Bact.*, 1942, **44**, 373) gives in general the present accepted differences and significance: "Striking differences were found to exist in the selective action of these substances upon various bacteria. Gramicidin was most specific, acting primarily upon Gram-positive micrococci. Actinomycin, tyrothricin, tyrocidine, purified penicillin, gliotoxin and the chemical detergent (lauryl sulfate) acted in low concentrations upon Gram-positive bacteria and only to a limited extent upon Gram-negative organisms. Pyocyanase, pyocyanin and crude penicillin were similar in their action over the whole range of the test organisms used. Streptothricin was unique in its action, being highly active against certain Gram-negative bacteria and having no action against certain Gram-positive organisms. Upon a weight basis, the substances of microbial origin were found to be much stronger bacteriostatic agents than the chemical antiseptics tested. Marked differences were also obtained in the selective bactericidal action of the different preparations. Certain substances possessing high bacteriostatic properties were not necessarily also highly bactericidal."

Recently, Timonin (*Science*, 1942, **96**, 494) found that a culture of *Aspergillus*, sp. of the *Candidus* group, gave a positive reaction for the presence of *citrinin*, which he isolated. Oxford (*Chem. & Industry*, 1942, **61**, 48) published data on the value of citrinin as a bacteriostatic agent, originally isolated by Raistrick and Smith (*Chem. & Industry*, 1941, **60**, 828). Bailey and Cavallito (*J. Bact.*, 1943, **45**, 30) obtain a rapid production of citrinin in a glucose medium with diammonium tartrate as the source of nitrogen. See also Timonin and Rouatt (*Can. J. Pub. Health*, 1944, **35**, 80).

For references, in addition to those given above, see also: Waksman and Woodruff (*J. Bact.*, 1940, **40**, 581), Waksman (*Bact. Revs.*, 1941, **5**, 231), Program issue (*J. Bact.*, 1942, **43**, 9–12), and Wilkins and Harris (*Brit. J. Exp. Path.*, 1942, **23**, 166). The last-named workers present a preliminary report on 100 fungal substances during an investigation into the production of bacteriostatic agents by fungi. Their results of subjecting a large number of fungi to tests to determine whether they produce substances which inhibit the growth of *E. coli*, *Staphylococcus aureus* and *Pseudomonas aeruginosa* revealed that the Aspergilli gave approximately 40 per cent positive results, the Penicillia gave about 25 per cent positive results and the *Fungi Imperfecti* are mostly negative. The composition of the medium appears to be of importance in the production of inhibitory substances, and some of the fungi which have given negative results might reasonably be expected to give positive results if suitable cultural conditions could be established. See Chain (*Brit. M. Bull.*, 1944, **2**, 8).

It is well to point out that many of the compounds considered here are being used experimentally and are not as yet available for general use. It is possible that a few of them will find a place in the therapeutic armamentarium.

PHAGOTHERAPY

The significance of bacteriophage and a consideration of its properties and method of production are detailed on page 24.

Therapeutic Use of Bacteriophage.—Bacillary dysentery, bubonic plague, cholera, streptococcic and staphylococcic infections have been treated with bacteriophage preparations. Phagotherapy has been employed for the destruction of staphylococcus in the treatment of boils, carbuncles and other localized infections by local and even hypodermic injections. Results thus far reported reveal that the bacteriophage in these cases is far less effective in the living tissues (*in vivo*) than in the test tube (*in vitro*).

The bacteriophage preparations in use are either in liquid form and dispensed in ampuls, or these sterile lysates are incorporated in water-soluble jelly bases to which a suitable bacteriostatic agent is added. They are administered topically, orally, subcutaneously, intramuscularly, intravenously, and by rectum in enemata. The doses are generally large and are given as frequently as clinical experience in inividual cases determines. They are nontoxic, apparently harmless and stimulate phagocytosis. Eaton and Bayne-Jones (*J. A. M. A.*, 1934, **103**, 1769, 1847, 1934) conclude that "the evidence for the value of lytic filtrates is for the most part contradictory. Only in the treatment of staphylococcus infections and perhaps cystitis (due to *B. coli* and staphylococci) has evidence at all convincing been presented." The marketable bacteriophage preparations have been found to vary greatly in potency (Straub and Applebaum, *J. A. M. A.*, 1933, **100**, 110). Recently several favorable reports in the bacteriophage treatment of bacillary dysentery in the war areas and especially in Egypt have appeared in the literature through British sources (*Science News Letter*, August 1, 1942), (*Brit. Med. J.*, 1944, **1**, 407). The only recent German reference (*Deutsche med. Wchnschr.*, 1941, **57**, 375) also reports good results in the use of a dysentery phage.

Chapter XXIV

STERILE MEDICAMENTS

THE USE OF sterilization is applied in the practical dispensing of medicinal products intended for administration:

1. Parenterally.
2. Upon accessible mucous membranes for direct absorption (eyes, nasal passages, tongue, throat, bronchi) or by irrigations, given rectally, through the urethra, by gastric lavage, etc.
3. By inunction through the skin or where applied to inflamed surfaces in wounds or by "common ion transfer" (in which penetration of the medicament is aided by the use of the galvanic current).
4. Infrequently by inhalation.
5. At times, medicinal preparations are sterilized merely to preserve them, as they would otherwise decompose rapidly.

ASEPTIC MANIPULATION

There are many substances which cannot be heated or otherwise disinfected without injury to the preparation. Certain culture media (as blood agar), if sterilized by heat, will be decomposed, and if chemical disinfection is resorted to, the product will be unsuitable for the cultivation of bacteria. The occasion frequently arises to prepare extemporaneously sterile mixtures, which must be dispensed quickly, and which would probably be decomposed or otherwise affected by the commonly practiced methods of sterilization. Such preparations are prepared by "aseptic manipulation." All containers used are sterile. The ingredients employed are sterilized beforehand and the end product is prepared under aseptic conditions. Aseptic manipulation, as employed when making certain culture media, was mentioned. The finished product required for quick use, even though prepared by aseptic manipulation, may be further sterilized in an autoclave, a water bath (pasteurization or high temperatures if possible) or a steam sterilizer for one heating (fifteen to thirty minutes), *provided they are not rendered inactive, or have their composition otherwise affected.* Solutions which cannot be heated at high temperatures, or time does not permit intermittent sterilization, as in extemporaneous work, or even those sterilized by bacteriological filtration and by aseptic manipulation may have added to them an antiseptic as phenol (0.5 per cent), tricresol (0.1 to 0.4 per cent), chlorocresol (0.1 to 0.2 per cent), chlorobutanol (0.5 per cent), phenylmercuric nitrate (0.002 per cent), thymol (0.1 per cent) or other suitable bacteriostatic agent to insure sterility, providing there is no danger of these chemicals producing irritation or being incompatible with the other ingredients. A suitable bacteriostatic agent is one which should possess an efficiency equivalent to at least a 0.5 per cent aqueous solution of phenol.

Wherever bacteriological filtration (use of Berkefeld type filter) *is possible, this technique, if properly conducted, is to be preferred and can replace heat sterilization.* It is important to determine whether the medicinal solution being filtered is not altered or that one or more ingredients are partially or completely adsorbed by the filter.

If the preparations are not required for immediate use, they can then be sterilized for the designated length of time over a period of days at the desired temperature.

PREPARATIONS FOR PARENTERAL ADMINISTRATION

The trend of modern medicine seems to be that therapeutic agents should be administered wherever possible by a method which is direct, and which will yield rapid results. It is for this main reason that intravenous and intramuscular injections are given, especially in acute conditions. Then we have the hypodermic injection. By this method, one is assured that a definite dose of the drug gets into the tissues which will reach the circulation in a short time.

The value and frequent use of the parenteral administration of medicaments is so well known today as not to require here an extended consideration. It is, however, best to understand what is meant by the term *parenteral*. Some workers employ this as an all-inclusive term to designate the use of any route of administration other than when given orally or rectally. However, the definition as suggested by the author and given on page 219, U. S. P. XII, appears more suitable or at least leaves no doubt as to its exact meaning: "The terms 'parenteral' and 'for injection' as used here refer to the administration of a drug under one or more layers of the skin or mucous membranes." It is this therapy which is called by some workers "needle administration," as it is apparent that a needle of some kind is needed in administering the medicament. Parenteral administration is given *intracutaneously* or *intradermally* (between the layers or within the substance of the skin); *subcutaneously* or *hypodermically* (in the lymph spaces under the skin); *intramuscularly* (into the muscular tissues and lymph spaces); *intravenously* and infrequently *intra-arterially* (into the blood by way of the veins or arteries); into the serous sacs, *intrapleurally, intraperitoneally, intrapericardially, etc.;* into the spinal canal (*intraspinally* or *intrathecal* administration); into the tissues of organs (*intraparenchymally*); and in emergencies into the heart muscle or cavities (*intracardially*).

Regulations for Parenteral Solutions.—Not only is a knowledge of the therapeutic use of drugs necessary, but it is equally as important to have available a detailed knowledge of the source and method of preparation of the product to be administered parenterally. The important requirement of the necessity of having a sterile solution for parenteral administration is obvious, yet about ten years ago when the author directed this to the attention of the profession, some astounding findings were reported in a subsequent survey by the Council on Pharmacy and Chemistry of the A. M. A. (*J. A. M. A.*, 1934, **103**, 678), resulting from this editorial (*Am. J. Pharm.*, 1933, **105**, 155). The need for proper legal supervision over the manufacture and distribution of such preparations became more apparent from these findings. Furthermore, wherever possible, standardization of formulas and uniformity in packaging as far as sizes are concerned are needed in these preparations, even though there is a definite assurance of sterility. Certain methods of sterilization may change or modify the medicaments so treated. The introduction of a variety of different chemicals as stabilizers or as bacteriostatic agents or for other purposes may serve their usefulness in producing a more lasting marketable preparation, but in the final analysis, this may be objectionable, as the added ingredients may yield untoward reactions, or otherwise interfere with the therapeutic efficiency of the preparation upon injection. Such added ingredients may also interfere with the proper performance of suitable assays or identification and other tests for the active medicament. It is obvious that the above should be recognized, and steps taken through some legal avenue to guard against these possible pitfalls. The result has been the regulations as found at present in U. S. P. XII and N. F. VII.

Containers for Parenteral Solutions.—These containers are usually made of glass. The most satisfactory glassware is that which possesses a high resistance to heat and mechanical shock and also has a stable annealed surface capable of resisting hydrolysis by the contents. For detailed requirements which such containers should meet, see U. S. P. XII, page 567. Glassware before being used must be chemically clean. Various cleansing methods are employed preparatory to sterilization. The last rinsing, however, should be with freshly distilled and, preferably, pyrogen-free water and the containers sterilized, if possible, or dried. If sterilization is not practicable, the cleansing and draining or drying should be performed just prior to the preparation of the parenteral solution. The containers until used should be placed in suitable positions to protect the inside from dust, then filled, and the contents sterilized at once. Glassware, not sterilized or not properly cleansed and finally washed with pyrogen-free water and drained, is apt to contain on the inner surfaces dried pyrogenic substances, and also any moisture remaining may be utilized by the bacteria for further growth. If the individual containers are not hermetically sealed, care must be observed in the use of the type of stopper which must always be of good quality and sterile. Cotton-stoppered plugs are not to be advocated. In all instances, containers should not be filled to capacity, but sufficient air space should be left above the liquid to prevent the wetting of stoppers during sterilization. The quality and sterility of the contents must not be impaired by improper packaging.

The proper washing of ampuls and vials requires careful attention, if the U. S. P. and N. F. requirements of solutions being free from foreign suspended matter are to be met. In many instances, the suspended particles are fine specks of glass, adherent on the inside of the containers and not washed out during the preliminary washing procedure, but which usually become loosened when the heat during the sterilization technique is applied. It might well be that these official compendia consider a requirement that glassware for parenteral use should not contain glass specks after the containers are filled with water, autoclaved and the water examined for such particles. The use of steam for washing empty glassware as an additional step is most helpful in removing particles adherent on the inside of containers. However, it is well to remember that wash-water and steam should be filtered unless it is definitely known that they are free from suspended matter at all times. Care must also be exercised in the use of suitable caps or stoppers for multiple-dose vials, as synthetic rubber and various composition materials frequently deposit specks of these materials after sterilization or even merely upon agitation of the contents.

Preparing the Solutions.—These should be prepared only with high-grade fresh chemicals and pyrogen-free water. The use of stabilizers and other substances to aid in preserving the preparation is permissible with certain limitations (see below). Solutions are adjusted to as nearly neutral reactions as conditions of stability will permit. Solutions of soluble medicaments for parenteral use are to be prepared with care and all foreign and insoluble materials are to be removed. Filtration until perfectly clear (to get rid of insoluble material) is practiced, but care must be observed that the filter or filtration method used does not adsorb active or potent material from the solution. Filtration is not warranted, however, where the active ingredients are themselves insoluble, as mercury salicylate, bismuth salicylate or other insoluble chemicals suspended in oil. Oil solvents should be free of acidity and capable of absorption from the tissues. The possibility of tumor production by oils must be kept in mind (see report by Conrad and associates ($J. A. M. A.$, 1943, **121**, 240)). Scrupulous cleanliness and all sanitary precautions should be observed throughout the entire process of preparation. In fact, aseptic conditions might well be carried out even though the finished preparations in suitable containers are to be sterilized by an adequate process. The use of ultraviolet light and propylene glycol, wherever possible, as a sanitary aid are advocated.

Pyrogens.—The use of preparations presumably properly prepared and administered directly into the blood stream (and usually by the intravenous route) results at times in untoward reactions of a nature different from those reactions displayed by an individual idiosyncrasy to a drug or to the presence of known substances which are known or found to be antigenic. In modern therapy and practice, these reactions should be and can be avoided. These reactions appear either only as a slight elevation in temperature (up to 100° F.) which returns to normal quickly, or as a febrile reaction (100° F. or higher) associated with a feeling of cold and pain in the back or legs but no actual rigor, and the most severe kind in which a marked fall in blood pressure and an actual rigor also are present. All of the symptoms are suggestive of protein shock. Inasmuch as the substances causing the latter also produce fever or pyrexial reactions, they are frequently spoken of as *pyrogens*. There has been much conjecture concerning the latter, but at present pyrogens are regarded most commonly as dead bacteria (disintegrated or intact), viable but nonpathogenic bacteria, and more frequently as products produced by bacteria (liberated endotoxins or exotoxins). Few workers ($J. Am. Pharm. Assoc.$, 1943, **32**, 65) state that the antigenic and thermogenic components are apparently not interrelated and claim that the antigenic substances (at least in some instances) can be removed and the thermogenic components be left remaining in the solution. The pyrogenic substances appear to be of foreign protein origin. The human body, on the other hand, can tolerate only a limited and a very small amount of foreign protein, when introduced into the circulation. It is apparent that a high incidence of pyrexial reactions from products given by intravenous therapy reflects markedly either on the efficiency of the medicinal preparation Susedor upon the equipment employed when giving the injection. In either instance, the hazard is avoidable. The use of the greatest care in preparing a safe parenteral product, and scrupulous cleanliness and a careful technique throughout will reduce and even eliminate these reactions.

Water for Injection.—Improperly prepared or "stale" distilled water is most frequently responsible for the production of febrile reactions. In 1911, Wechselmann (*München med. Wchnschr.*, 1911, **58**, 1510) observed this fact, regarded bacterial contamination responsible, and insisted upon the use of freshly distilled water, after showing that such water does not produce reactions when injected intravenously. Hort and Penfold (*Brit. Med. J.*, 1911, **2**, 1589) confirmed these findings. The latter workers and Muller (*München med. Wchnschr.*, 1911, **58**, 2739) described the bacterial flora of different samples of distilled water, and mentioned those specifically responsible for producing pyrexial reactions. When the first arsenicals were being used, McIntosh and associates (*Lancet*, 1912, **1**, 637) traced the so-called *saline fever* to the distilled water employed. In our own country, Seibert and associates, who named the fever-producing substance *pyrogen*, presented many contributions on fever-producing substances in distilled water (*Am. J. Physiol.*, 1923, **67**, 90); temperature variations in the rabbit (*Am. J. Physiol.*, 1923, **67**, 83); other protein fevers (*ibid.*, 1923, **67**, 105); substances causing febrile reactions following intravenous injection (*Arch. f. exper. Path. u. Pharmakol.*, 1927, **121**, 247); and other works along similar lines (*Am. J. Physiol.*, 1925, **71**, 621, 652; *Arch. Int. Med.*, 1925, **36**, 747). Recently Co Tui and Schrift (*J. Lab. & Clin. Med.*, 1942, **27**, 569) presented additional data on the production of pyrogens by bacteria.

The above workers demonstrated that bacteria grow in distilled water; old or "stale" distilled water was usually contaminated; freshly distilled water (pyrogen-free), if sterilized immediately, will remain pyrogen-free if kept sterile, but pyrogenic properties are imparted if it is not sterilized, as contamination results from air-borne bacteria; and that the pyrogens were most frequently filterable, soluble bacterial products, removable by distillation, if the latter is properly carried out. Later we find that Banks (*Am. J. Clin. Path.*, 1934, **4**, 260) revealed that pyrogens could be rendered innocuous if the solutions containing them are heated to 140° C. for thirty minutes, and Co Tui and associates (*J. A. M. A.*, 1937, **109**, 250) found that adsorption filtration was effective in removing pyrogens.

With the wider use of intravenous therapy especially in blood transfusions, a more extensive experience resulted, and, as noted by Lewisohn and Rosenthal (*J. A. M. A.*, 1933, **100**, 466), reactions were reduced from 12 per cent to 1.2 per cent merely by following a scrupulous cleansing technique and using freshly distilled water. The application of these basic principles has definitely proved that reliable intravenous solutions can always be made available. (See: Eggleston, *et al.* (*J. A. M. A.*, 1927, **88**, 1798); Titus and Dodds (*Am. J. Obst. and Gynec.*, 1927, **14**, 181); Rademaker (*Surg., Gynec. & Obst.*, 1933, **56**, 956); Nelson (*J. A. M. A.*, 1939, **112**, 1303); Meade (*Hospitals* (Nov., 1939)); Walter (*Ann. Surg.*, 1940, **112**, 603); and Whitby (*Lancet*, 1942, **1**, 581).)

Preparation of Water for Injection.—The technique used to prepare a pyrogen-free water is of greatest importance. We must be assured that the type of apparatus used will provide a pyrogen-free distillate, assuming that all other possible contaminating factors have been eliminated. The still must be fitted with proper baffle arrangements to prevent the carrying over of foreign materials. One of the most frequent causes of contamination is the entrainment by the steam (which becomes the distillate) of droplets of raw water thrown forth as a spray or foam by the ebullition. Careful control of heat and water-flow and especially properly placed well-designed baffles will prevent contamination of the condensers with a spray of raw water, splashed from the surface of the boiling water and thus the subsequent pollution of the distillate. Intelligent operation at all times even of a satisfactory still is essential.

The apparatus and especially the storage vessel for the distilled water must be scrupulously clean and properly protected to prevent contamination. The storage tank should be large enough to hold a working supply for not more than a day. Always drain dry the storage vessel, so as to prevent the growth of bacteria in the residual water, as this contaminated water will pollute subsequent collections of distillate. If the storage vessel is not sterilized, flush with live steam or wash out with several rinsings of pyrogen-free water before using it.

Pyrogen-free water should be distributed in suitable containers and properly sealed and sterilized in their final containers immediately after distillation. Where the pyrogen-free water is to be used for preparing solutions for parenteral use, it is not necessary to sterilize it, but it must be used immediately after distillation for preparing the parenteral solution. This in turn should be prepared, distributed into suitable containers, the latter preferably sealed or protected against the entrance of organisms, and the completed unit preferably sterilized within one working day. If this is not practicable and a bacteriostatic agent is not present, the parenteral solution is compounded with pyrogen-free water as the vehicle, placed in containers holding not more than the amount necessary for a working day, and these working-day batches are stored under refrigeration at a temperature below that at which bacterial growth or deterioration will occur.

Chemicals in Parenteral Solutions.—Chemicals only of the highest grade should be used as ingredients in parenteral solutions and especially in the preparation of those for intravenous medication. Particulate matter is present in most containers holding especially bulk chemicals. Dust, dirt, debris and insect parts have been found, though but infrequently in those containers holding high-grade materials. Dirty chemicals signify carelessness in handling and present the possibility of contamination with foreign proteins. They should not be used. Transfer of chemicals should be carried out with the use of suitable implements. The use of hands, dirty implements and scale pans (for weighing) should be avoided. Portions of chemicals which drop on the table and on the balance should be discarded and not returned to the bulk container. Where known quality grades have proved to yield constantly satisfactory finished preparations, it may be desirable to buy only such grades of chemicals of known purity. For instance, it is known that some dextrose samples change during sterilization or storage to a yellow color, mistaken for caramelization. The coloring is due to an aging of levulinic acid. The latter and hydroxymethyl furfural are acid dehydration products, which may form in some dextrose samples during the manufacturing process. In other instances, certain samples of dextrose are found to impart pyrogenic properties to pyrogen-free water. Walter (*Ann. Surgery*, 1940, **112**, 603) states that "dextrose may contain protein split products, and/or various acid dehydration products of dextrose formed by side reactions during the manufacture of dextrose." Sodium citrate and other bulk chemicals are known to contain pyrogenic substances.

Other Equipment.—Care must be exercised in the use of all equipment for parenteral solutions that the latter do not become laden with pyrogens because of contaminated equipment. The author has found on frequent occasions the presence of pyrogens on filters used for obtaining bacteria-free filtrates. These filters and all equipment should be cleansed immediately after use; an ample supply of pyrogen-free water passed through them; and they should be sterilized immediately if such procedure is possible. Bacteria-proof filters and other equipment, but especially the former, should be tested periodically for the absence of pyrogens by passing through them pyrogen-free water and testing the filtrates. For other practical aspects of pyrogen problems, see also Co Tui (*J. Am. Pharm. Assoc., Practical Pharm. Ed.*, 1944, **5**, 60).

Sealing Containers.—*All ampuls should be sealed immediately and parenteral solutions in other containers closed with suitable stoppers after they have been filled, and sterilized the same day as prepared, unless the solution is self-sterilizing.*

Sterility Tests.—Testing of finished preparations for sterility is one of the last operations and a most important step in determining the marketability of products for parenteral use. For details, see page 534.

Tests for Pyrogens.—It is important to have available a test so as to determine the presence or absence of pyrogenic substances in parenteral solutions and especially in the water used for preparing the latter. Bacteriological examinations are inadequate unless the sample is heavily polluted. It is known that samples of water revealing sterility by the routine techniques may contain pyrogenic substances. Albuminoid ammonia may be present in waters containing the latter, and Knott and Leibel (*Ann. Surg.*, 1940, **112**, 603) state that an albuminoid ammonia content of 0.005 to 0.025 part per 1000 will always give rise to pyrexial reactions. The Ampul Water of N. F. VII must correspond to all tests for Redistilled Water (National Formulary VII, page 54). One of the tests for the latter is the permanganate test for oxidizable substances. Walter (*Ann. Surg.*, 1940, **112**, 603) suggests frequent examinations to note the purity of water by determining its conductivity. Until a definite and clear-cut relationship can be established between the above-mentioned chemical, physicochemical and similar tests and the absence or presence of pyrogenic substances, no final or conclusive reliance can be placed on negative findings by these tests as indicating the absence of pyrogens.

In the final analysis, however, biological methods must be employed to reveal the actual pyrogen content. For the present, the Pyrogen Test given in U. S. P. XII (page 606) appears adequate. Ten cubic centimeters of the parenteral solutions are injected into the ear vein of each of five healthy rabbits (10 cc. per Kg. of body weight). Rectal temperatures are made hourly for three or four hours. Some workers advise extending the latter period to at least five hours. The test is considered positive if three or more of the five animals show an individual rise in temperature of 0.6° C. or more above the normal established for each of the animals injected. Co Tui and Schrift (*Proc. Soc. Exptl. Biol. Med.*, 1942, **49**, 320) presented a tentative method for testing for pyrogens in distilled water, which involves the use both of the rabbit and dog as test animals. They state that the rabbit is the better animal to test for the absence of pyrogen and the dog is the better animal to establish the presence of pyrogen. At present, a subcommittee of the United States Pharmacopoeia is conducting a study of tests for pyrogenic substances (*J. Am. Pharm. Assoc.*, 1943, **32**, 69). Recently Chapman (*Quart. J. Pharm. & Pharmacol.*, 1942, **15**, 362) employed a modification of the Co Tui technique and recommended performing leukocyte counts at intervals after administering the intravenous solution being tested. A marked leukopenia (decrease in white cell count), usually a drop of 4000 or more per cu. mm., appears within forty-five minutes of the entry of a pyrogen-containing solution into the circulation and this persists for at least 90 minutes. Young and Rice (*J. Lab. Clin. Med.*, 1944, **29**, 735) report on the production of a leukocytosis within three to six hours after an initial leukopenia.

Sterilization of Medicaments.—With the few exceptions where some preparations for immediate use are prepared by aseptic manipulation, sterilization processes are and must be employed, especially on a small scale, even though bacteriostatic agents are added. Various methods are suggested for the sterilization of parenteral solutions and other medicaments. Heat sterilization and the use of the autoclave are to be used whenever they can be employed.

Bacteriological filtration, using the Berkefeld or similar type bacteria-proof filters,

Material	*Procedure*
Antimony and Potassium Tartrate	Autoclave
Atropine Sulfate	Steam at 100° C. (Fractional Method)
Bismuth Subsalicylate	Autoclave
Caffeine and Sodium Benzoate	Autoclave
Calcium Chloride	Autoclave
Calcium Gluconate	Autoclave
Camphor in Oil	Hot Air at 150° C. (for one hour)
Cocaine Hydrochloride	Steam at 100° C. (Fractional Method)
Dextrose	Autoclave or Fractional Method
Dextrose and Sodium Chloride	Autoclave or Fractional Method
Digitalis (constituents of)	Filtration
Emetine Hydrochloride	Steam at 100° C. (Fractional Method)
Ephedrine Sulfate	Steam at 100° C. (Fractional Method)
Epinephrine Hydrochloride	Steam at 100° C. (Fractional Method)
Indigocarmin	Autoclave
Iron and Ammonium Citrate	Water Bath at 65° C. (Fractional Method)
Isotonic Salt Solution	Autoclave
Histamine Phosphate	Autoclave at 65° C. (Fractional Method)
Insulin	Filtration
Liver Extracts	Filtration
Magnesium Sulfate	Autoclave
Mercuric Salicylate	Water Bath at 65° C. (Fractional Method)
Mercurophylline	Steam at 100° C. (Fractional Method)
Methenamine	Steam at 100° C. (Fractional Method)
Morphine (all salts)	Steam at 100° C. (Fractional Method)
Neostigmine Methylsulfate	Autoclave
Ouabain	Steam at 100° C. (Fractional Method)
Parathyroid	Filtration
Picrotoxin	Filtration
Pituitary	Filtration
Procaine Hydrochloride	Steam at 100° C. (Fractional Method)
Quinine Dihydrochloride	Steam at 100° C. (Fractional Method)
Quinine Hydrochloride and Ethyl Carbamate	Water Bath at 65° C. (Fractional Method)
Quinine and Urea Hydrochloride	Water Bath at 65° C. (Fractional Method)
Ringer's Solution	Autoclave
Sodium Cacodylate	Autoclave
Sodium Citrate	Autoclave
Sodium Iodide	Autoclave
Sodium Salicylate	Steam at 100° C. (Fractional Method)
Sodium Thiosulfate	Steam at 100° C. (Fractional Method)
Strophanthin	Filtration
Strychnine Hydrochloride	Steam at 100° C. (Fractional Method)
Sulfobromophthalein Sodium	Filtration
Theophylline Ethylenediamine	Autoclave
Thiamine Hydrochloride	Water Bath at 65° C. (Fractional Method)
Water	Autoclave

especially with vacuum, can be employed for the sterilization of all aqueous solutions containing soluble ingredients to replace the use of all other methods of sterilization. But on a small scale this method is practiced infrequently. The user on a large scale is better prepared to recognize the shortcomings of this method and guard and equip himself accordingly. Copper and other metallic fittings are to be avoided when filtering various medicinal solutions, such as sodium thiosulfate or calcium gluconate or ascorbic acid. Stainless steel fittings or glass rather-than metal are to be used. Endocrine products usually have a low pH and must be filtered through filters fitted with glass, not metal. Some solutions or suspensions are self-sterilizing after an adequate period of exposure. Camphor in oil, the many mercurials and other preparations will sterilize themselves in periods of time ranging from ten to twenty days. The manufacturer on a large scale may prefer to age such self-sterilizing preparations, after having determined the minimum period of time required before the product will respond satisfactorily to sterility tests and only after such adequate periods of storage to release the product for sale. Where fractional steam sterilization is used, some workers add a bacteriostatic agent and heat the solution containing the latter at the designated temperature for one heating. The presence of the added chemical increases the efficiency of the sterilization technique so that only one instead of three heatings is required.

Preservatives and other substances used as stabilizers, etc., may be added as mentioned above. In single-dose containers, preservatives (see page 347) are preferably added in all preparations prepared by aseptic manipulation or by bacteriological filtration. Special attention is to be observed concerning the toxicity of a preservative when present in solutions to be administered in volumes exceeding 5 cc. by any route, or when given in any volume intravenously, intrathecally, intracisternally or intracardially. Multiple-dose packages must contain a bacteriostatic agent. For further details, see article on "Sterile Medicaments" by author (*Am. J. Pharm.*, 1943, **115,** 5).

On page 351 are suggested sterilization procedures for solutions or suspensions of some of the commonly employed drugs used for parenteral administration.

PART IV

ANIMAL PARASITOLOGY

Chapter XXV

CLASSIFICATION OF ANIMAL PARASITES—PROTOZOA

THE ANIMAL kingdom is divided into the two great subgroups, *metazoa* and *protozoa*. The former includes everything from worms, jellyfish, the vast number of insects, etc., to the vertebrate animals, including man himself. They are generally pluricellular, with each cell, making up the whole, performing some special function, which it quickly loses when it is separated from the other allied cells.

The protozoa, on the other hand, are unicellular, microscopic primitive animals, and regarded as the simplest forms of animal life. In size, they range from organisms scarcely larger than bacteria to organisms several centimeters in length. They occur singly or may be encountered as groups or colonies of cells. A protozoon is morphologically a single-cell or perhaps a noncelled microorganism, functioning complete, and composed of protoplasm. The latter, known as cytoplasm, is differentiated into an outer portion, the ectoplasm, and an inner portion, the endoplasm, together with a nuclear substance. These may show variations throughout a complicated life-cycle that each individual undergoes. It is higher in the evolutionary scale than the individual unicellular forms of the vegetable kingdom (bacterium) because its structure and life-cycle show a greater complexity. Inasmuch as many species of protozoa are identified and classified upon the structure of the nucleus, it is most important that those who make an attempt at diagnosis should familiarize themselves with all details concerning the morphology and structure of this body as it occurs among the different genera and species of protozoa. The latter are primitive, and are placed in the lowest group of the animal kingdom, in the sense that their structure is relatively simple, and especially distinguishable from the higher animals, or metazoa, which are complex individuals, differentiated into many cells and even tissues. It is, however, to be remembered that this group is very extensive and includes some organisms of great simplicity and some whose structure is elaborate. For further details, see Calkins and Summers (*Protozoa in Biological Research*, Columbia Univ. Press, New York, 1941) and Wright (*Science*, 1944, **99**, 207).

The following is a brief classification:

Protozoa (*Unicellular*).—Due to the characteristics and difference in locomotion, the following four groups or classes form the usual classification:

    (*a*)   *Sarcodina* or *rhizopoda*, motion obtained by means of simple ("streaming") outflowings (changeable processes) from the cell protoplasm (called *pseudopodia*). They reproduce by simple division (fission), or by spore formation.

(*b*) *Mastigophora* or *flagellata*, motion obtained by means of one or more long lash-like or whiplike protrusions or filaments called flagella, which originate from a deep-seated staining material.

(*c*) *Ciliata* or *infusoria*. The organs of locomotion here are numerous, short hair-like projections (known as *cilia*) arising from granules situated in the cell. They reproduce by transverse fission and by budding.

(*d*) *Sporozoa* consist of a heterogeneous group, many of which do not possess organs of locomotion, and they usually reproduce by spore formation. All species are para-sitic, living in tissues of other animals and obtaining food by osmosis.

SARCODINA OR RHIZOPODA

This group includes the forms occurring mainly in the ocean and in fresh water, the majority of which belong to the Order *amoeba*. There are many distinct genera and species of the Order *amoeba* living as parasites in the bodies of animals. The following, usually getting into the system from foodstuffs, are most harmful or more frequently observed. They are all members of the genus *endamoeba*.

Endamoeba (*Entamoeba*) *histolytica* occurs in the intestines, causing amoebic dysentery and liver abscess. These diseases occur more frequently in tropical than in temperate zones. *Endamoeba coli* is a very common but apparently harmless parasite. *Endamoeba buccalis* (*gingivalis*) is found in the mouth and thought by some workers to be associated with pyorrhea.

Transmission and Drugs Used.—Individuals who are diseased by or carriers of *endamoeba* are perhaps the chief offenders in the spread of these organisms. Infected water and foodstuffs act as intermediary agents. Flies may be other agents in the transmission of dysentery amoeba.

Infection of man with amoeba (and especially *E. histolytica*) is known as amoebiasis. A diagnosis of amoebiasis is best made upon the microscopic study of unstained and stained preparations of the stools and the finding therein of *E. histolytica*, a uninucle-ated actively motile amoeba. In order to accurately diagnose this infection one must be thoroughly familiar with the morphology of not only this parasite but also of other amoeba which may be found in the intestinal tract (as *E. coli*, *Endolimax nana*, *Ioda-moeba butschlii* and *Dientamoeba fragilis*) and of other cellular structures found in bowel discharges, which may resemble the intestinal protozoa. In warm and undecomposed feces, *E. histolytica* is found to be actively motile and frequently containing ingested red blood cells. The nonpathogenic *Entamoeba coli* is not as actively motile and never contains red blood cells. The excretion of *E. histolytica* is frequently intermittent, so that several examinations of the stools are frequently necessary to detect their pres-ence. Amoebiasis differs in an important and fundamental respect from other in-fectious diseases in that the more acute the condition is, the less is the hazard to others. In the presence of active acute symptoms, such as diarrhea and dysentery, only the nonresistant and noninfective motile forms are passed. The encysted forms, found in symptomless cases and in carriers, are the resistant and infective forms. Unusual manifestations of amoebiasis have been reported, many of which are envolvements of the liver. So-called tropical liver abscess is an amoebic hepatitis.

Ipecac and, better still, injections (or other methods of administration) of emetine hydrochloride have been found as a specific for amoeba in the vegetative stage. There are some cases in which emetine cannot be used in the treatment of amoebic dysentery. Oxyquinoline derivatives administered by mouth as well as by enema have been employed and found to be less toxic and to possess more therapeutic value in the treatment of amoebic dysentery. *Yatren* or *chiniofon*, $C_9H_6O_4SNI$, *Nioform*, *Anayodin*, *Diodoquin* and *Quinoxyl* have been employed. Organic arsenicals as *acetarsone* (*Stovarsol*) have been used in amoebiasis, but with only slight effect. The alkyl resorcinols and the kurchi alkaloids have been employed. Claims have been made that *carbarsone* (4-carbamino-phenyl arsonic acid, containing 28.8 per cent of arsenic) meets the requirement of an ideal antiamoebic agent. It is conveniently administered orally, 0.25 Gm. twice daily for ten days. Knotts and Thompson (*M. Ann. District of Columbia*, 1942, **2,** 375) recently reported the successful use of succinylsulfathiazole in the treatment of amoebiasis. Liu reported that *Kosam*, an old oriental remedy for diarrhea, was a specific for amoebic dysentery, but Kuzell and associates (*Am. J. Trop. Med.*, 1941, **21,** 731) were unable to confirm this observation. There is evidence of the prophylactic value of the oral use of *Diodoquin* (5,7-diiodo-8-hydroxyquinoline) for the prevention of amoebic dysentery. Liu and associates (*Chinese M. J.*, 1941, **60,** 229) recently reported favorable results with a new amoebicide, *Yatanine*, the active ingredient of kernels of Ya-tan-tzu. Elliott (*Trans. Roy. Soc. Trop. Med. Hyg.*, 1943, **37,** 163) reported favorable results on the oral use of phenothiazine in *Entamoeba histolytica* and intestinal helminthic infestations in adults. For some modern conceptions of amoebiasis, see Faust (*Science*, 1944, **99,** 45, 69).

Prophylaxis of Intestinal Parasites.—So as to prevent intestinal infestation with all species of animal parasites, attention must be given to the simple basic principles of personal hygiene and sanitation. Water used for drinking and bathing purposes and all food must be beyond suspicion. Proper sanitary disposal of sewage must be practiced. Adequate screening of houses and the introduction of measures to prevent flies and other pest vectors from contaminating food and drink should be carried out. Of the various personal hygienic measures, the simple precaution of the frequent washing of the hands, especially after defecating and always before mealtime or when eating, is most important.

Routine studies of human feces have not been made in the same degree of frequency as is done in the examination of body fluids for bacteria. As this is bound to occur following the return of the Armed Forces to our shores, we will undoubtedly learn more of the frequency of occurrence of different parasites in the intestinal tract of man. Hopp (*Am. J. Hyg.*, 1944, **39,** 138) reported finding the stools of over 75 per cent of the patients in a state hospital infected with parasites. Their occurrence was *Endamoeba coli* in 61.9 per cent, *Endolimax nana* in 31 per cent, *Chilomastix mesnili* in 8.8 per cent, *Iodamoeba butschlii* in 3.8 per cent, *E. histolytica* in 3.1 per cent, *Giardia lamblia* in 1.9 per cent, *Trichomonas hominis*, *Trichuria trichiura*, *Strongyloides stercoralis*, *Enterobium vermicularis*, *Hymenolepis nana* and *Heterodera radicicola*.

FLAGELLATA OR MASTIGOPHORA

This class contains some of the very lowest as well as some highly developed types of animals. There is a question whether or not to include many members of this class in the plant kingdom. Some free-living forms possess chlorophyll and are included by biologists in the plant kingdom. However, the parasitic species are all typical animals in almost all respects. With the flagellates were to be found at one time the spirochetes. The tendency by most workers is to place the latter with the bacteria (so listed in this volume). As mentioned previously, this group is regarded as transitional from bacteria to protozoa and placed by some in a separate group known as *proflagellata*.

There are many distinct subgroups here, but the following important pathogenic flagellates only will be considered. The most important flagellates of interest to us form a large group of blood parasites of vertebrate hosts, known as the hemoflagellates. The two important genera are *leishmania* and *trypanosoma*.

Leishmania are parasites (referred to as "Leishman or Leishman-Donovan bodies") that are capable of living in the blood and special tissues of warm-blooded animals. Four species are recognized:

Leishmania americana (*brasiliensis*) is believed to be identical with or perhaps a variety of *Leishmania tropica*, causing sores and ulcers on mucous membranes and skin (especially the nose and mouth cavity). The disease, prevalent mainly in Mexico, Panama and South American countries, is known as *American leishmaniasis*, also as *espundia*. It is not known how the disease is transmitted, though species of sand flies are believed to be the vectors. The use of protective clothing and odorous insect repellents is helpful as preventive measures.

Leishmania donovani causes kala-azar, dum-dum fever, tropical splenomegaly or leishmaniasis, a systemic disease which is found in Asiatic and African countries and which has caused many deaths. How this disease is transmitted is not known, though it is thought that the parasite is transmitted by some insect, and in particular by the sand fly (genus *Phlebotomus*).

Leishmania infantum causes infantile kala-azar or infantile leishmaniasis which is rampant in the Mediterranean countries, and is a fatal disease which in many ways resembles true kala-azar. The dog harbors these parasites and it is thought that the dog flea may act as a transmitting agent.

Leishmania tropica is a generalized leishmaniasis of the reticulo-endothelial system, which causes (especially in the countries of southwestern Europe and southwestern Asia) ulcerating cutaneous sores (known also as Oriental sore, cutaneous and dermal leishmaniasis) usually in children. The parasite is probably transmitted by some biting insect, probably the sand fly, *Phlebotomus papatasii*.

The diagnosis of infection with: (1) *L. donovani* is made upon the finding of this parasite in peripheral blood or in material obtained by puncture of the spleen, sternum, lymphatic glands or, rarely, the liver; (2) with *L. tropica*, upon the demonstration of the latter in material obtained from the tissue at the base of the ulcer or by puncture with a hypodermic needle and aspirating gently to obtain the material; (3) with *L. brasiliensis*, upon finding this parasite in preparations obtained from the skin or mucous membrane lesions.

A Brazilian investigator in 1912 discovered that antimony (used in the form of tartar emetic) was a specific for Leishman bodies. It is used for all leishmanian infections, usually injecting small quantities of a 1 per cent solution intravenously, increasing the dose gradually, depending upon the tolerance of the patient. *Neostibosan*, *stibamine glucoside* (*neostan*) and *urea stibamine* have also been found of value. Recent reports reveal very favorable results given by the use of *diamidene stilbene* (*Indian M. Gaz.*, 1942, **77**, 71).

Leishmania chagasi is a newly discovered species held responsible for American visceral leishmaniasis. It is primarily a jungle infection and human beings and domestic animals are infected. Dogs and cats can act as carriers of the parasite. *Phlebotomi* are suspected as the transmitting agents. For further details, see Chagas (*Proc. 8th Am. Sci. Congress*, 1942, **6**, 393).

Trypanosoma.—Trypanosomes are closely related to the Leishman bodies and next to the malarial parasites they are man's most deadly enemies among the protozoa. There are many different species of trypanosomes inhabiting many different animals. There are more than seventy known species. Many of them can only be distinguished by pathogenicity tests on different animals or by biological (serological) tests. Of the different species, there are only three, which are known to affect human beings, causing a disease known as *trypanosomiasis* or *African sleeping sickness*, transmitted usually by certain species of tsetse or biting flies. A large number of mammals, including antelopes, oxen, goats and sheep, act as reservoir hosts. This so-called *African sleeping sickness* is different from the sleeping sickness found in this country, the causative agent of which is believed to be a virus (see page 243).

Trypanosoma gambiense causes the commonly observed and widespread form of sleeping sickness in Western Africa (transmitted by the bite of *Glossina palpalis* and *G. tachinoides*). Untreated cases are usually fatal.

Trypanosoma rhodesiense causes the recently established East African form of sleeping sickness (transmitted by the bite of *Glossina morsitans* and *G. swynnertoni*. This variety of trypanosomiasis is more serious.

Trypanosoma nigeriense causes a milder form of sleeping sickness in South American countries (transmitted by the bite of *Glossina tachinoides*). This trypanosome is considered by some as identical with *Trypanosoma gambiense*.

The diagnosis of trypanosomiasis in man is made upon the examination of blood, gland juice and of spinal fluid (in advanced cases). Stained preparations are required. If these are negative, susceptible laboratory animals (monkey, dog or guinea pig) are inoculated with the blood of the suspected individual. The trypanosomes, though not found in the blood and spinal fluid, may nevertheless be present in the brain.

Intravenous injections of *tartar emetic*, *antimony trioxide* or intramuscular administration of arsphenamine or, better still, *atoxyl*, other arsenic compounds and especially *tryparsamide* and *Bayer 205* (Germanin), (British, *Suramin*) have been found effective in destroying the trypanosomes. More recently, *stilbamidine* (4:4'-diamidino stilbene), *pentamidine* (4:4'-diamidino diphenoxy pentane), and *propamidine* (4:4'-diamidino diphenoxy propane) have been recommended in addition to *antrypol* and tryparsamide in the treatment not only of *trypanosomiasis*, but also in cases of *leishmaniasis* and *babesiasis* (see Lourie, *Ann. Trop. Med.*, 1942, **36**, 113). Lawson (*Lancet*, 1942, **243**, 480) regards pentamidine as the best drug for early African sleeping sickness. *Guanidine compounds*, especially *synthalin*, are used in the treatment of arsenic-resistant cases.

Trypanosoma cruzi transmitted by a bug, *Triatoma megista* (*Panstrongylus magistus*), produces *Chagas' disease*, the Brazilian form of trypanosomiasis, prevalent almost entirely among children. No drug has been found efficient for this parasite, though Bayer 7602 is said to possess some therapeutic activity. Control measures consist in the use of modern sanitary procedures, general cleanliness, the destruction of animal burrows, the elimination of insect pests and rodents, and proper screening facilities. Gasic (*Proc. 8th Amer. Sci. Congress*, 1942, **6**, 239) recently reported on Chagas' disease in

Chile, where it is quite widespread. He found dogs and cats as carriers of this disease.

Trypanosomes occurring in animals other than humans are: *Trypanosoma lewisi*, found in wild rats; *Trypanosoma evansi*, causing a disease among horses, cattle and camels in Asia and Africa known as *surra; Trypanosoma equinum*, causing a disease among horses in South America known as *mal de Caderas; Trypanosoma brucei*, causing a disease among horses, mules and oxen in Africa known as tsetse-fly disease or *nagana;* and *Trypanosoma equiperdum*, causing *dourine* or *maldu coit*, found among horses in Europe, and even in Western Canada and United States. Peculiarly this disease is spread exclusively by sexual intercourse. The vampires in Panama are vectors of trypanosomiasis among horses.

INTESTINAL FLAGELLATES

The human intestinal tract furnishes a habitat for a considerable number of animal parasites belonging to this and the other classes of protozoa. Sanitary disposal of feces is the most important means of preventing infection by intestinal parasites. Many of them get into our systems through the use of infected water and through other drinks and foodstuffs. Some of these are probably only accidentally parasitic and opinions differ concerning their pathogenic properties. Their importance lies in the fact that their presence is an indication that the host has been exposed to potentially objectionable or even dangerous sanitary conditions. Most of the intestinal protozoa show a resemblance to each other in some respects. Transparent cysts are produced by nearly all of them to serve as a means of protection. In the encysted state, they may exist for long periods of time, even under unfavorable conditions. Analogous to the resistant eggs of intestinal worms, these cysts of intestinal protozoa gain access to a host and produce infection. The unencysted protozoa usually die quickly. None of the human intestinal protozoa require a second host to transmit them as do the parasites inhabiting the blood (trypanosomes, plasmodium, etc.).

The intestinal flagellates are separated according to the number of their flagella. One Order of this class consists of those possessing less than three flagella (usually two and known as bi-flagellate protozoa). The several genera of the latter found in the human intestines are *cercomonas, bodo* and *prowazekia*. Members of the first genus are of no importance. The parasites in this genus are even regarded by some workers as deformed trichomonas. As regards *bodo*, the several species are nonpathogenic and this genus is grouped by some with the *prowazekia*. Several poorly defined species in the latter genus have been recorded as human parasites, but their pathogenicity has not been definitely established. The following flagellata belong to an Order in which the members of the several genera possess from 3 to 8 flagella.

Trichomonas.—Several species have been found in the intestines, in vaginal discharges and in the urinary tract, especially among the natives in tropical countries.

Trichomonas buccalis, found in the mouth, and *Trichomonas vaginalis*, found in acid vaginal secretions, are apparently identical in morphology with *T. hominis* (*T. intestinalis*) found in the intestines.

Though generally regarded as harmless parasites, some are inclined to believe that various species may be the cause of diarrhea. Infection takes place probably by contact. Food and inanimate objects may become contaminated by flies or by being handled by infected individuals or perhaps carriers who are careless about their personal hygiene.

Though the *T. vaginalis* is found in cases of vaginitis, there is no general acceptance to the belief that this parasite is responsible for the infection. On the other hand, some workers claim that the infestation is of venereal origin and others express the opinion that both local and systemic factors combine to alter the vaginal tract and prepare the latter for infestation. It is known that vaginal inflammation is accompanied by a change in pH from approximately 4.5 toward neutrality and even a slight alkalinity. In the examination of secretions from the vaginal tract, prostatic fluid and freshly collected urine samples, both the dry and wet techniques are used. Dry smears are stained and examined. Wet specimens and, in particular, the sediment from centrifuged wet specimens are examined on a sterile slide with a sterile cover slip, kept at a temperature of 90° F. Identification is based on gross appearance, motility, manner of locomotion and size of the flagellate. *T. vaginalis* varies in size from 8 to 30 μ to 3 to 18 μ. It is narrow, elongate to spherical and usually pyriform. There are 4 free flagella, a sausage-shaped parabasal apparatus and an undulating membrane, which varies in length from one-third to two-thirds of the body. The flagellum on the outer edge does not trail. Allison (*Southern M. J.*, 1943, **36**, 821) and other workers report that a high percentage of cases, both males and females, when examined routinely by smear for gonococci, revealed the presence of trichomonade and consider the infection as a possible venereal disease. No specific drug has been found of value, though methylene blue (by mouth or by means of an enema) and at times weak iodine solutions (by enema) have been found effective. Among the various agents used for vaginal trichomoniasis are to be found the following: douches of lactic acid (one teaspoonful to a quart of water) followed by vaginal insertion of tablets containing 3.5 Gm. of lactose and enough citric acid and bicarbonate to yield 300 cc. of CO_2; floraquin (containing diodoquin (5,7-diiodo-8-hydroxyquinoline) with lactose and dextrose adjusted with boric acid to establish and maintain a pH of about 4.0); tampons containing acetarsone; the insufflation of trycogen (containing sodium thiosulfate, thymol, oxyquinoline sulfate in a base of boric acid, starch and magnesium carbonate); silver picrate solutions, and negaton (a water-soluble colloidal organic product which contains sulfonated meta-cresol groups joined to one another by methylene (CH_2) groups through condensation with formaldehyde).

Lamblia or Giardia.—Flagellates placed in this group are found in the small intestines of human beings and animals. Though considered harmless by most workers, some regard them as capable of causing diarrhea and even dysentery. The presence of large numbers of *Giardia* may hide the presence of *E. histolytica*. Infection follows the ingestion of the cysts with contaminated food or drink. Betanaphthol in combination with bismuth salts, together with varying doses of castor oil or repeated doses of calomel, have been found successful in causing the disappearance of these parasites. More recently, atabrine (quinacrine or mepacrine hydrochloride, U. S. P.) in doses of 1.5 grains three times daily for five days has proved to be very effective.

CILIATA OR INFUSORIA

The ciliata or infusoria are the most highly developed and the most complex class of the protozoa. According to the arrangement of the cilia, four Orders are placed in this class. The Order *heterotricha*, containing the genus *balantidium*, is of some interest to us. Otherwise this group is the least important of the classes of protozoa. There is only one species commonly found which is pathogenic to man. This parasite is known as *Balantidium coli*. Next to *Entamoeba histolytica* it is the most commonly found protozoon causing dysentery or an affection similar to this (balantidiasis) which may terminate fatally. No specific treatment for balantidial dysentery has been found. This organism is normally a hog parasite and it is this animal that passes these parasites to man through eating food and drinking water contaminated by fecal material containing the parasite. Those working in slaughtering houses and butchers may become infected directly by handling the intestines of infected hogs. This parasite is best observed in feces in unstained preparations. No specific treatment for balantidiasis is available, but favorable results have been reported from the use of enemata of various arsenicals and methylene blue (1:3000).

SPOROZOA

This class, so named because reproduction in nearly all species is by spore formation, is divided into two subclasses. Among the latter are to be found several Orders, genera and species. Many of the species, all of which are parasitic, cause fatal diseases in vertebrate as well as invertebrate animals, but few of them other than the malarial parasites are parasitic in man and of importance in the causation of human disease. Malarial parasites, belonging to the genus *plasmodium*, are the most important parasites not only of the class sporozoa but of all the classes of the protozoa. There is some disagreement as to the different malarial parasites that affect man. At least three well-defined species of *plasmodium* have been long established as the cause of human malaria, and a fourth species has been recently accepted. So far as is known, the lower animals do not act as natural reservoirs of human malaria. The most widely distributed species are:

Plasmodium vivax, causing benign tertian malaria (chill and fever every forty-eight hours or third day);

Plasmodium falciparum, causing the aestivo-autumnal or malignant tertian type (a fatal form) of malaria, found mainly as the cause of most cases in tropical and sub-tropical countries (an irregular fever like typhoid);

Plasmodium malariae, causing quartan malaria, is not observed as frequently as the other species, though, when found, countries in temperate zones are more apt to be suffering than other localities (chill and fever every third day);

Plasmodium ovale, causing a fever with tertian paroxysms. This species closely resembles *P. vivax* in morphology and is now accepted as a distinct species.

Other species of malarial plasmodia causing disease in man have been described: *P. falciparum quotidiamum; P. falciparum* var. *aethiopicum; P. perniciosum; P. tenue; P. vivax* var. *minuta;* and *P. wilsoni.* These are not accepted as yet as true separate species.

Malarial Fevers.—*Malarial Parasites.*—Malaria is a recurrent fever, caused by one of the malarial parasites (plasmodium), which is carried by an infected mosquito (anopheles) and enters the human body when the latter is bitten by the infected insect. The disease is not transmissible except through the bite of a mosquito, which has bitten diseased individuals or has otherwise become infected with the malarial parasites. The males of all mosquito species do not possess the mechanism for drawing blood and therefore do not have a direct role in the transmission of malaria. The disease itself is extremely variable. The early stages of all types of malaria are similar except that the quartan type produces the intermittent fever on every third instead of every second day. The symptoms are related to the time of segmentation of the *plasmodium* concerned and the attack in each case may be divided into three stages: (*a*) cold, or chills; (*b*) hot, or fever; and (*c*) sweating stages.

The malarial parasites live in the blood stream at the expense of the red blood cells. They develop within the red cells, filling the corpuscles, and finally become segmented into smaller bodies that develop into parasites. The development is complete within forty-eight to seventy-two hours, depending upon the type of parasite. The red blood corpuscles are then ruptured, liberating the developed segments which, getting into the circulating blood, cause the chill, fever and sweating so characteristic of malaria. The destruction of so many red blood cells will explain the anemia which is found so frequently. The diagnosis is assured by finding the parasites in the blood. This can be accomplished by pricking the finger or lobe of the ear, making blood films, which can be examined or stained and then examined in a systematic manner. Concentration methods are also useful. The segments form rounded bodies known as merozoites and the latter, on being liberated, fasten themselves to new red cells and begin again the cycle of development. It is necessary to become familiar with the various stages of the different species (each of which differs from the other species), so as to be able to identify the latter and then institute proper treatment. The stages as observed in the red blood cells of man as well as those forms found in the mosquito must be known if proper measures, of prevention are to be instituted. Malarial parasites have two cycles of development, one within man, which is asexual in type, and the process of development is spoken of as schizogony. The other cycle which is within certain species of the *Anopheline* mosquito is sexual in type and the process of development is spoken of as sporogony.

Quinine and other cinchona alkaloids, cinchona and totaquine are used in the treatment of malaria. Plasmochin (panaquine or aminoquine naphthoate, U. S. P.), an aminoquinoline derivative, and atebrin (quinacrine or mepacrine hydrochloride, U. S. P.), an alkylamino-acridine derivative, are synthetics recently introduced in malarial treatment. The *plasmodium* is introduced into human beings as the sporozoite, and there is no drug known which is effective against this stage of the parasite. It is generally held that for routine mass prophylaxis, atebrin is superior to quinine, though the latter is safer to use where medical supervision is not available. Quinine and atebrin do not but plasmochin does destroy falciparum gametocytes. Atebrin in daily doses of 0.3 Gm. or quinine in daily doses of 1 to 1.3 Gm. is given for treatment usually for a period of five to seven days. As prophylactic agents, atebrin is given daily in doses from 0.05 to 0.1 Gm. and quinine in daily doses from 0.3 to 0.6 Gm. Plasmochin is given in doses of 0.01 Gm. three times daily for five to seven days. A combination of quinine and plasmochin appears safe to use, but other combinations are not advised as various toxic reactions may occur. Plasmochin and atebrin should be given only under proper medical supervision. For an evaluation of these three antimalarial drugs, as well as *Certune, Malarin,* and other compounds, see *J. Trop. Med. & Hyg.,* 1942, **45,** 1, 3, 5, and Barlow (*J. Clin. Investigation,* 1942, **21,** 647). The spread of malaria is controlled by all measures that aim at the extermination of the mosquito. It is also advisable to see that individuals sleeping in the open air in malarial regions should sleep under mosquito nets, as the malarial mosquito bites preferably at dusk or at night. For further details, see Manson-Bahr (*Brit. M. J.*, 1942, **24**, 461, 489), Dove (*Am. J. Trop. Med.*, 1942, **22**, 227), "Malaria Commission of League of Nations Health Organization Conclusions" (*Am. J. Hyg.*, 1938, **27**, 390), "Malaria," one of the A. A. A. S. symposia publications and present-day problems of malaria infections (*J. A. M. A.*, 1944, **124**, 1179).

Other Sporozoa.—The other members in this group that are of interest are the following:

The Order *coccidiidea* is divided into two genera, the *isospora* and *coccidium* (or *eimeria*). There are several species of *coccidia* found almost exclusively in the intestines and allied organs of many lower animals and causing disease. These parasites are rarely found in man, the only species of any concern being the *Isospora hominis*. It rarely produces marked clinical symptoms and it is important to remember that other parasites (members of *Eimeria*) may be mistaken for it. The latter are not parasites of man but may be found in the feces of those who ate fish, mackerel, herring and sprats which were infected with these species.

The *piroplasmata* includes a group of parasites, related to the malarial parasites, which are the cause of some of the most fatal diseases of domestic animals, known as piroplasmosis, babesiasis or "red water fever," and includes "Texas fever" caused by a species of the genus babesia (*piroplasma*); East coast cattle fever in Africa (caused by a species of the genus theileria); yellow jaundice of dogs and a disease of sheep found in the Balkan regions, known as *carceag* (the latter two caused by different species of babesia). These diseases are invariably transmitted by the bite of specific species of ticks.

Sarcosporidia includes many parasites found in the striped muscle of various birds and mammals. Infections by these parasites have been reported in sheep, cattle, pigs, horses, in birds and reptiles, and rarely in man.

A species of *rhinosporidium* belonging to the *sporozoa* was reported in several cases in India and found in the nasal mucous membrane causing pendunculated tumors, known as nasal polypus.

Chapter XXVI

METAZOA—WORMS

THE METAZOA, or pluricellular organisms, that cause or assist in the dissemination of disease can be classified as follows:

WORMS.

(a) *Flatworms (platyhelminthes)*—flukes; tapeworms.

(b) *Roundworms (nemathelminthes)*—ascaris; filaria; hookworm; trichinella.

(c) *Segmented worms (annelida)*—not important as parasites of man, though the leeches (classified in this group) may be the cause of certain infestations, especially in foreign countries.

ARTHROPODS.

(a) *Onychophora*—(only genus in this class is peripatus) very primitive, of no importance.

(b) *Crustacea*—water fleas, etc.—parasites of aquatic animals, not of man. Certain species of cyclops and crabs serve as the intermediate hosts of human parasites, the former as a host for the guineaworm and the latter as hosts of the lung fluke.

(c) *Arachnida*—spiders, scorpions, etc.
   Parasitic species—mites; ticks.

(d) *Myriapoda*—(centipedes, millipedes)—(nonparasitic)—do not carry disease.

(e) *Insecta*—bedbugs and other bugs; fleas; flies; lice; mosquitoes; roaches; ruinous pests.

HIGHER ANIMALS.

Rodents as rats, mice, ground squirrels, prairie dogs, rabbits, etc.; cattle; cats; dogs; fish; hogs; horses.

WORMS

The term *worm* is indefinite and there is hardly a class in the different groups, as classified, which does not contain a so-called worm as one of its members. These worms (called such on account of their *worm-like* character) differ widely as to structure. All possess different peculiarities. In a more restricted sense, the term worm is applied to members of the three great groups mentioned above. The term *vermin* is widely misused. At one time and even today, it is restricted by some to small creeping animals, especially those classified under *insecta*. The constant use of this term has so developed that it has been broadened to include almost any animal that is harmful or even useless. It may be that after a better understanding of the relationship of the numerous pests and animals will be known, the term *vermin* may be restricted to designate particular classes or species of animal parasites. The term *helminths* (or *worms*) refers to the species of the platyhelminthes (or flatworms) and the nemathel-

363

minthes (or roundworms). For complete details of the scope of helminthology and of helminthic infections, see *Human Helminthology*, Faust, Philadelphia, 1939.

The insects and higher animals rarely cause disease in man directly (*i. e.*, they themselves acting as the causative agents) but act mainly as intermediaries (go-betweens) in the transportation of protozoa, the other classes of the metazoa, and bacteria which may act as parasites in humans. The insects, which act as intermediaries, causing microorganisms to become human parasites, may act either mechanically or biologically. The mechanical method which is practiced by the vast majority of insects, consists in carrying organisms from infected material to man, or, more frequently, to foodstuffs and drinks, which are to be consumed by humans. Transmission by the biological method is practiced by some insects, the most important of which are the tsetse fly and various species of ticks and mosquitoes. Hydrophobia is transmitted in like manner from infected dogs or cats. In most cases, as has been found thus far, the microorganisms transmitted biologically are protozoan in nature. These protozoa or animal parasites pass a part of their cycle of life in the insects or animals, which act as the transmitters of the parasite to man. This part of its life is known as the sexual cycle and consists in a propagative reproduction or a development into sexually mature organisms. They become parasitic on the insect or animal first before they become pathogenic parasites of man. Some time must elapse before the sexual cycle has developed in insects, etc., so that disease can be transmitted by mosquitoes biologically (malaria is transmitted by mosquitoes biologically). If a mosquito (special species) bites a man infected with malarial parasites, about two weeks must elapse before it can transmit the disease to another man. The period of time in which the sexual stage develops in the insect or animal is known as the extrinsic period of incubation. The sexually developed parasite finds its way to the salivary glands of its host (insect and animal) and when the latter bites man, the deposited saliva (containing the parasites) finds its way into the blood stream or tissues of the infected human being. Within the body of its new host (man), the sexually developed parasite begins under favorable conditions its other stage of development, known as the asexual stage or multiplicative reproduction, as a result of which there may be an enormous increase in the number of the same species of parasites.

Insects pass through many stages before becoming an adult. These stages explained as briefly as possible are: (1) egg, or embryo; (2) larva; (3) pupa; (4) imago or adult. If an insect undergoes all of these stages, such insect is said to undergo a complete metamorphosis. If all stages are not reached, an incomplete metamorphosis is the result, *i. e.*, complete—mosquitoes, maggots, midges, flies, ticks, roaches; incomplete —bedbugs, lice, etc.

FLATWORMS

Flukes or Trematoda.—The flukes are very primitive animals, and are true parasites during the major portion of their existence. They are nonsegmented, flat and often leaflike, ovoid and but infrequently cylindrical, and vary in size from the smallest which is $1/12$ inch to the largest which is almost 3 inches. They possess a special armature of hooks and at least one developed sucker, by means of which they attach themselves to the tissues of their hosts. All species of human trematodes except the blood flukes are hermaphroditic. Those that are found in man may be divided for convenience as follows:

(a) *Human Blood Flukes or Schistosomes.*—These are the most important flukes parasitic in man. They are about $1/2$ inch in length, and are found mainly in the abdominal blood vessels of their host (especially the portal vein). They penetrate the bladder and are voided in the urine. Several species of snails feeding on human excreta and recognized as the transmitting agents infect water. See also Iturbe (*Proc. 8th Amer. Sci. Congress,* 1942, **6,** 371). Infection may take place by drinking or bathing in contaminated water, the disease developing in about three months after infection. The disease, known as *schistosomiasis* (for the four parasitic species belong to the genus *schistosoma* (*S. haematobium* (*Bilharzia haematobia*), *S. mansoni,* *S. bovis, S. japonicum*)), is common in African and Asiatic countries and in parts of central and northern South America, where the snail intermediate host is indigenous. *Schistosomiasis haematobia* which is the more accurate designation for infections by *S. haematobia* has been referred to as vesical schistosomiasis, urinary schistosomiasis, bilharzia infection, bilharziasis, bilharziosis and endemic hematuria. The diagnosis is made by finding eggs of *S. haematobia* in the urine, especially in the last portion voided and less often in the stools. Infection with *S. japonicum* and *S. mansoni* is best diagnosed by finding the ova in the stools, examining especially adherent mucus.

(b) *Intestinal Flukes.*—Little is known about the numerous species classified under this subgroup, the important species belonging to the genus *Heterophyes, Matagonimus, Echinostoma* and *Gastrodiscus.* Human infection results from the consumption of fish eaten either raw or inadequately cooked, containing the viable cysts of these species of flukes. Disease caused by these resembles light dysenteric symptoms. They seem to be affected by the same treatment, as used for tapeworms or roundworms.

(c) *Liver Flukes.*—Several species are observed. *Fasciola hepatica, Fasciola gigantica, Fasciolopsis buski* and members of the genus *Dicrocoelium, Eurytrema, Clonorchis* and *Opisthorcis* have been recovered from man. They are common in Oriental and some European and American countries, infecting man and lower animals. These flukes live chiefly in the bile ducts and gallbladder and produce mechanical obstruction. Fish may act as intermediate hosts, but in endemic areas there is the possibility that infection may take place by eating infected raw vegetation and drinking infected water. Raw infected livers of sheep and goats also may be responsible for fascioliasis. Preventive measures consist in avoiding the use of uncooked meats and fish, and the proper treatment of vegetables and water supplies.

(d) *Lung Flukes.*—Disease caused by these flukes is common in Oriental and in some South American countries. Infection usually takes place by eating infected crabs (not adequately cooked) or by drinking water harboring infected crabs. *Paragonimus westermani* is the most important species which concerns medical zoologists. Besides man, dogs, cats and hogs may become infected. For a consideration of paragonimiasis, see Iturbe (*Proc. 8th Amer. Sci. Congress,* 1942, **6,** 371).

Cercaria dermatitis, or "swimmer's itch," found around the Great Lakes resort regions, is caused by *Cercaria elvae* or *stagnicolae,* a nonhuman schistosome larva developing in the snail. The only general method of control is to eliminate the snail population in infested places. Copper compounds in the proportion of 3 pounds per 1000 square feet of water surface (2 pounds of the sulfate and 1 pound of the carbonate) have proved effective. Thorough rubbing of the skin with a dry, rough towel immediately upon leaving the water will aid in crushing the *cercariae* and prevent their penetration into the skin.

Tapeworms or Cestoda.—Peculiar in their structure, tapeworms seem to have no need for a digestive system, inasmuch as they are constantly bathing in the digestive fluids of the intestinal tract of the host. The food passes through the entire surface of the body and is transformed immediately into parasite tissue or storage products. The term tapeworm describes the tapelike (girdle- or ribbon-like) character of these organisms. A mature tapeworm is not one worm, but actually hundreds and even thousands of individual ones linked together like a chain. They may be regarded as a ribbon-like colony of individual flukes united together, consisting at the anterior end of a relatively minute "head," the mother segment, which is provided with structures for attachment to the tissues of the host. This entire region of attachment including the head is referred to as the *scolex*. Behind the latter, the region is spoken of as the "neck." A series of daughter segments (or *proglottids*) arise from the posterior portion of the neck, by a continuous process of cell proliferation. The number and size of these proglottids determine the length and size of the tapeworm. It is important to remember that permanent evacuation of a tapeworm depends not only upon expelling the segments but especially the head, as the presence of the latter will result in the reformation of a scolex and the entire chain of proglottids. They usually get into the human body, when eaten by a suitable intermediate host. Injury caused by them is more serious than is the common belief. Anemia is of frequent occurrence.

Taenia saginata (*beef tapeworm*) is the commonest human tapeworm, affecting man by eating raw inadequately cooked contaminated beef.

Taenia solium (*pork tapeworm*) is a more dangerous parasite than *Taenia saginata*, and is not found so frequently in America. Man is affected by eating raw or inadequately cooked contaminated pork.

Echinococcus granulosus (*Taenia echinococcus*) is a parasite of the dog and other carnivorous animals. Humans who have swallowed eggs eliminated by an infested dog may become diseased and the encysted larvae (hydatid) are found in the body. The hydatid cyst is more complicated than the cysts of other tapeworms. It may attain a considerable size and may be the cause of serious damage and even death. Dogs should not be permitted to lick human beings especially about the face, and food and drink likely to be contaminated by infested dogs should be avoided. For further details, see Senekji (*Tr. Roy. Soc. Trop. Med. Hyg.*, 1940, **33,** 461; 1941, **34,** 401) and Culbertson and Rose (*J. Clin. Investigation*, 1941, **20,** 249).

Hymenolepis (*Taenia*) *nana*, generally known as the *dwarf tapeworm* (for it is the smallest of the human tapeworms, rarely longer than one inch), is a very common parasite throughout the warm areas of most all countries. It often occurs in great numbers, especially in children, causing considerable intestinal irritation and even severe nervous and generalized toxic symptoms. The common presence of this parasite or an allied variety in mice and rats has led to the belief that infection in man is caused by eating food soiled with feces coming from these animals and infected with ova of this parasite. It may be that other animals and even insects act as intermediate hosts, but in most instances, man is the source of his own dwarf tapeworm infection especially by hand to mouth contamination.

A diagnosis of dwarf tapeworm is based on finding the characteristic ova in the stool. In the case of beef and pork tapeworm, it is impossible to differentiate the eggs of these two species. The recovery of proglottids and the demonstration of from 7 to 13 main lateral branches of the uterus make possible a diagnosis whether the worm is *T. saginata* or *T. solium.*

Oil of chenopodium, preceded and followed by a purgative, has been found efficient in ridding the intestinal tract of these parasites. Oleoresin of aspidium and kamala together are still preferred by some practitioners, providing the former drug is not contraindicated due to other complications. Hexylresorcinol (1 to 6 Gm.) and carbon tetrachloride (4 cc.) are being recommended very highly. Other anthelmintics have been tried with success, when the previously mentioned were found to be ineffective or could not be used. Among the latter are: preparations of pomegranate bark, including pelletierine tannate; infusion of pumpkin seed or of quassia; decoction of areca (betal nut); and tetrachlorethylene (4 cc.). It has been suggested that defecation (during the passing of the parasite) should be over a chamber or vessel of warm water, as sudden contact with cold may cause a sudden contraction of the tapeworm, resulting frequently in the breaking of the latter before it has been completely expelled.

Other Tapeworms.—Sheep, dogs, rats, cats, fish, flies, etc., may occasionally act as hosts of other tapeworms, and man becomes infested by eating either raw or inadequately cooked contaminated food. Human beings may become directly or indirectly infected from these animals. The common fish tapeworm of man (*Dibothriocephalus latus* or *Diphyllobothrium latum*), known also as the broad Russian tapeworm, is an important species found in countries where infected fresh-water fish are extensively eaten. The fish tapeworm, common in various parts of Europe, has also become established in this country in the Western Great Lake region. In some cases, the affection caused by it among humans does relatively little harm. At times it may, however, induce a marked anemia, which terminates in death.

ROUNDWORMS OR NEMATODA

Ascaris or Eelworm (Ascaridae).—These commonly observed parasites are found among humans of all ages but especially in children in all countries, and more frequently in the warm rather than in the colder zones. They are large and robust, the eggs getting into the intestinal tract by eating contaminated foodstuffs or by drinks, or by children soiling their fingers with infected soil. In the main, man is the source of his own *ascaris* infection. Prevention consists in using sanitary methods of excreta disposal, observing general principles of personal cleanliness, and avoiding the use of infested food and drink. The most important species is the *Ascaris lumbricoides.* The original intermediary host is probably the hog. Eggs of this genus may develop in soil, water, etc. Symptoms observed by infestations with these worms are varied. In some cases, no ill effects are apparent. Oil of chenopodium has been found almost 100 per cent effective. Santonin, however, which, though not as efficient as oil of chenopodium, is used more frequently especially for children due to its relative safety. More recently, hexylresorcinol (1 Gm.) has been found to be highly efficient and practically nontoxic.

Trichostrongylus orientalis is a strongylate nematode found in herbivorous animals and in man, especially in the intestinal tract. Carbon tetrachloride as employed in hookworm infection is a semispecific.

Filaria.—This genus contains only one species, which is now known to affect man. *Wuchereria bancrofti*, originally placed in this genus, is now placed in another genus, but the term filariasis is still used conveniently to designate infections with nematodes of the order *filariodea*. The latter, containing one of the most interesting and puzzling groups of human parasites, is common in all tropical and semitropical countries. The most important and widespread species is *Wuchereria bancrofti* (also known as *Filaria bancrofti* and as *Filaria sanguinis hominis*). Many species of mosquitoes (culicines, anophelines and aedines) act as the intermediate hosts. The parasites enter the human system, usually by the larvae gaining entrance, when an infected mosquito bites into the flesh of warm-blooded animals. In the case of the loa worm (*Loa loa* or *Filaria loa*), the transmitting agent is several species of biting flies, genus *chrysops*, family *Tabanidae*, which feed during the daytime. The vectors are probably mango flies of the genus *chripops*, family *Tabanidae* (horseflies). In some cases the transmitting agent is not known. The larvae in filariasis and loaiasis gain entrance into the blood stream through the lymphatics, where they will live for a considerable length of time. Symptoms of filaria infection can usually be traced to interference with the lymphatic system, as the parasite lives in the lymphatics of the trunk and extremities. During different stages of this disease (a common manifestation being known by some as elephantiasis), the contents of the lymph vessels may escape into the bladder and kidneys, resulting in a condition known as *chyluria*, wherein the urine is very milky. In many cases, filariasis is often asymptomatic, and no marked ill effects of the infection may be felt for years, or perhaps ever. There are many other species of filaria, found in animals as well as human beings. Diagnosis usually depends upon demonstrating the presence of larvae in the blood, from chylous exudate of lymph varices, and occasionally from chylous urine or ascitic fluid. A cutaneous skin test also has been devised (*Tr. Roy. Soc. Trop. Med. & Hyg.*, 1931, **24**, 635). Antimosquito and in some instances antifly campaigns, as far as known, are the best means of preventing filarial diseases. No standard or widely accepted treatment or a drug which is specific for filariasis is known.

Closely Related Parasites.—There are several parasites closely related to the filaria (belonging to the same family but different genera) which affect mainly the subcutaneous connective tissue. The *Onchocerca volvulus* is a commonly found parasite of Mexico, Central America and Africa, producing small superficial tumors or nodules (a nonabscessing fibrous tumor). Excision of the latter for gross section or biopsy of small pieces of skin will reveal the presence of these microfilariae. The intermediate host is certain species of *Simulium*, blood-sucking black flies (gnats). It is believed that wild animals such as the antelope, may serve as reservoir hosts. Other species of *Onchocerca* may be responsible for onchocerciasis. In Central America lesions in the eyes sometimes result in disturbances of vision and blindness and the disease is referred to as the blinding filarial disease. For a detailed study on etiology, prevention and treatment of onchocerciasis, see Strong (*Proc. 8th Amer. Sci. Congress*, 1942, **6**, 383).

Dracunculus medinensis (the *guinea* or *medina worm*), commonly known also as the *serpent worm* or *dragon worm*, is a parasite found frequently in many parts of tropical Asia and Africa, and more recently in Central and northern South America. These parasites creep into the deeper layers of the subcutaneous tissue, where they are felt rather than seen, causing a disease known as *dracontiasis*. Various species of *cyclops*, small fresh-water crustaceans, act as intermediate hosts. Man becomes infected by drinking unfiltered water, contaminated with infected *cyclops*. An intradermal test used as an aid in diagnosis is said to yield positive results in over 80 per cent of cases.

Hookworms.—Two species of human hookworms, similar in structure, are known. They are members of the group of Nematodes, and belong to the family *Strongyloidea*. The species are: *Necator americanus* (the American or new world hookworm) and the old world hookworm or *Ancylostoma duodenale* (more prevalent in European countries). The adults of both are found in the intestinal tracts of their hosts, attached to the mucous membrane by means of their buccal armature, and produce the same symptoms. They are almost similar in structure and agree in all important details of life history. Prevention and treatment are the same in both cases. Cases of human infection with *A. braziliense* have been reported, especially in India.

Ancylostomiasis (Hookworm or Uncinariasis) (caused by Necator Americanus or Ancylostoma Duodenale).—The disease caused by hookworms (rarely found except in warm regions and where insanitary conditions prevail) varies in different individuals. Infection generally takes place through the skin, through which the parasites gain entrance from the feces of infected persons. The larval forms pierce the skin of the feet and pass through the lymphatics into the circulation reaching the heart, lungs, pierce the capillaries, and pass into the alveoli, bronchi and trachea to the throat. They are then swallowed and pass on through to the small intestines. The mouth may be the direct source of infection, by drinking water or soiled food containing the larvae. The adult worms may remain alive in the intestine, in diminishing numbers, for many (as long as six) years. Hookworm is almost always preceded by a case of ground itch, due to the irritation or ulceration of the skin from wounds made by the boring of the parasite, into which bacteria may also gain entrance and cause a secondary infection. The commonest symptom is anemia, due to the loss of blood devoured by the parasites, and accompanied by some fever or dyspeptic trouble and general retardation. The disease is diagnosed with certainty by a careful microscopic examination of bowel discharges, and the finding of the eggs of these parasites in the latter.

Thymol and oil of chenopodium (or its active principle, ascaridol) have been used as specifics in treatment, though today they are superseded by other anthelmintics. Chloroform (dose dissolved in castor oil given once every three weeks) and betanaphthol are also used. Carbon tetrachloride has proved very efficient, but its use is not free from danger. Tetrachloroethylene has been recommended and is said to possess a lower toxicity. More recently, hexylresorcinol was introduced as a safe and apparently a satisfactory remedy for hookworm treatment. Though only moderately efficient in evacuating hookworms, it is the drug of choice in combined hookworm and ascaris infections. General measures for eradication of this and other intestinal parasites consist in the installation of sanitary disposal systems for human discharges; wearing of shoes; elimination of flies and insect pests; general personal cleanliness; pure food supplies; thorough heating of cooked foods; washing of fruits and vegetables eaten raw, etc.

Strongyloides.—*Strongyloides stercoralis* is usually found in the feces as the so-called "rhabditiform" larvae, the eggs being recovered only in severe cases of diarrhea or after strong purgation. The infective stage ("filariform") of larvae of *S. stercoralis* closely resembles the same stage of hookworm larvae. Man is the most frequent host and the common source of infection is by contaminated soil. The usual portal of entry is the human skin. Strongyloidiasis found in tropical and semi-tropical regions is coextensive with human hookworm infection. Gentian violet has been found as a specific for this infection.

Trichinella.—The most important species is *Trichinella spiralis*, which possesses peculiarities different from the other intestinal parasites. The hog, by eating contaminated garbage or other hogs or rats usually infected with *trichinella*, is the intermediate host. Infestation in man will take place by eating contaminated, raw or improperly cooked pork, sausage or so-called "wurst" containing embryos. The adult worm develops from the encysted embryos. The adults themselves disappear from the intestines but the embryos find their way through the lymph spaces in the blood stream and then in various parts of the body, especially the muscles, where they may survive for many years. Other than hogs—cats, dogs and rats may also act as intermediate hosts, as they do especially in European countries. The disease in its early stages in man is frequently diagnosed as cholera and dysentery and later as typhoid fever. The duration and outcome of the disease known as trichiniasis or trichinosis are variable, though the fatality sometimes is as high as 25 per cent of the total number of cases. For a specific diagnosis, biopsied muscle strips are examined for encysted larvae. Intracutaneous tests are proving to be of value (*U. S. Pub. Health Repts.*, 1937, **52,** 539), though Abesman and associates (*J. Allergy*, 1942, **13,** 583) regard the greatest value of intradermal tests with trichinia antigens in their negative significance as ruling out trichinosis. The important preventive measures consist in refusing to eat pork, sausage, etc., unless well cooked (boiling for at least one-half hour). A specific remedy for treatment has not been found as yet. According to recent reports, bears kept in captivity as well as those found in their native habitat are heavily infected with trichinelliasis, and human trichinosis following ingestion of bear meat has been reported (*J. A. M. A.*, 1943, **122,** 227).

Other Nematodes.—Other nematodes or roundworms of importance causing disease in humans are:

Pinworm or Seatworm (*Enterobius* (*Oxyuris*) *Vermicularis*).—This is a widely distributed intestinal parasite occuring almost always in children living in tropical and temperate climates. Man is the only known natural host. Marked inconvenience by pinworms is infrequent, the most disagreeable effect is usually an intense itching in the vicinity of the anus. The eggs are seldom found in the feces (not over 5 per cent of infected cases). Since the female worms usually migrate out of the anus, during the early hours of sleep, the perianal region of suspected children should be examined at such time for these worms. The use of the cellophane anal swab (*NIH swab*), consisting of a glass rod tipped with cellophane held in place with a rubber band, as recommended by Hall (*Am. J. Trop. Med.*, 1937, **17,** 445) has been found most suitable for swabbing the perianal area of the patient (*U. S. Pub. Health Repts.*, 1939, **54,** 1148). High soap-saline or "Yatren" enemata in conjunction with calomel and any of the following: santonin, thymol, betanaphthol, aspidium, oil of chenopodium, carbon tetrachloride or tetrachlorethylene, are effective remedies in treatment. Wright, *et al.* (*Proc. Helminthol. Soc. Wash.*, 1938, **5,** 5), have advocated gentian violet therapy and Faust, *et al.* (*J. Pediat.*, 1937, **10,** 542), recommend highly both oral and enema treatment with hexylresorcinol. Evans and Moore (*J. Pediat.*, 1942, **20,** 627) report that gentian violet is more effective than hexylresorcinol and is tolerated better by children.

Whipworm (*Trichocephalus Trichiurus* or *Dispar; Trichuris Trichiura*).—Whipworm is one of the most common intestinal worms parasitic in man and found in both temperate and tropical climates. As a rule serious symptons are not produced.

The usual methods employed for expelling intestinal parasites require frequent repetition to eradicate these parasites. Prevention consists in using sanitary methods of sewage disposal, avoiding the use of infested food or drink, and practicing the usual methods of personal hygiene.

Gnathostoma spinigerum reported from stomach nodules of domestic and wild animals has also been found in humans, especially those living in Burma, Siam and eastern Bengal where the infection is very common in rats.

Heterodera radicicola or *Oxyuris incognita* is a true parasite of plant tissue. The presence of this nematode may thus be found in the feces of man if the latter ingests parasitized vegetable material. The eggs if present in human feces may be inaccurately diagnosed as *Ascaris* or even hookworm eggs, resulting in the unnecessary administration of anthelmintics.

Macroanthorhynchus hirudinaceus is a giant thorn-headed worm cosmopolitan among animals other than man. Infections in human have been reported in Southern Russia.

SEGMENTED WORMS OR ANNELIDA

The annelids are not important parasites as are the two other groups of "worms." In fact, there are only a few members of the hirudinea, or leeches, which are parasitic on the higher animals. Leeches serve as intermediate hosts for many species of trypanosomes of fish and other aquatic animals.

Chapter XXVII

ARTHROPODS

HERE ARE included probably several times as many species as found in all other groups combined. Valuable species, such as the bee and the silkworm, others that are parasitic or merely annoying to man and animal, many that are disease carriers, some that destroy our possessions, those that are admired for their beauty or arouse disgust for their loathsomeness, are to be found listed. The different classes of arthropoda are the most highly organized of invertebrate animals. They resemble the annelids or segmented worms in having a segmented type of body, and like the latter, they are protected by an external skeleton (appearing as a series of horny rings encircling the body). The main distinguishing characteristic is the possession of jointed appendages in the form of the pairs of limbs, mouth parts and, in some species, antennae. Internally, the body cavity is easily distinguished from that of other invertebrates.

The arthropods are divided into five classes (as observed on page 363). The first two orders named are of little importance. The *arachnida* are highly developed terrestrial arthropods. The members of this class have four pairs of legs as adults, two pairs of mouth parts and no antennae. Eyes when present are never compound, usually simple. They breathe by means of invaginations of the body, which contain gills, arranged like the leaves of a book. Some of the higher arachnids have also a system of branched air tubes or tracheae, as found in the insects.

There are two orders of *arachnida* which contain parasitic species, the *acarina* (ticks and mites) and *linguatulina* or tongue worms. Species of the latter have been observed in man and animals, found especially in the liver and lungs (cases usually only discovered at postmortem, as the parasites are but infrequently found in the feces or sputum). Of the acarines, we are chiefly interested in the mites and ticks. The majority of species of the latter are round or oval, frequently highly colored, with head and thorax fused together or coalesced all in one piece, distinctly marked off from the abdomen. They usually have two pairs of mouth parts and four pairs of legs. The life histories of mites and ticks are variable, but usually there are four stages in their development—the egg, larva, nymph and the adult. The nymphs are creatures which closely resemble the parent but differ from the adult in not having sexual organs. They are usually terrestrial, but may be aquatic, free or parasitic and may be poisonous or carriers of disease.

Mites.—Popular knowledge of mites is limited to but a few species. They are usually found in water, decaying vegetation, stored grain, foodstuffs or on the skin of different animals. Many of them are nonparasitic, but it is thought that all may assist in the dissemination of pathogenic bacteria. They are extremely annoying pests. The adults are free-living, and the larva is the parasitic stage. The classification in literature is very confusing.

Harvest mites, known also as red bugs or chiggers, may at times attack human beings, producing a severe irritation and an intense itch together with a rash, commonly known as red-bug rash. One species has been proved to be the carrier of a dangerous disease in Japan (known as flood fever). Sprinkling sulfur on the body may serve as a preventive for those who are easily affected and who may have occasion to walk through places where these pests may be found. Weak alkaline washes (as ammonia, bicarbonate, etc.) will assist in allaying itching after infestation. Louse mites, which are parasitic, may occasionally infest man. These mites live in grain, straw, beans, etc., and human beings may become affected by handling the latter (especially corn, barley and straw (or mattresses containing straw) contaminated by these pests. Then there are the various species of cheese and grain mites. The latter are found in almost all kinds of grain and many foods, and the chicken mites which may infest man, causing an eczema-like rash. This, like in other mite-infestations, will be attended by severe itching, due probably to a poisonous principle excreted by these pests. The tropical rat mite also may attack man. For a consideration of the mite responsible for grain itch, see Rogers (*J. A. M. A.*, 1943, **123,** 887).

The most important kinds of mites is those which are commonly known as *itch mites* and which are the cause of "itch" in human beings and *scabies* or *mange* in all kinds of domestic and wild animals. Each animal seems to have its own specific species of itch mites, of which the impregnated females burrow beneath the skin (especially where it is delicate and thin) and deposit from 15 to 50 eggs, which hatch into 6-legged larvae within four or five days and these in turn undergo a metamorphosis, transforming them into forms similar to their parents. The total life-cycle takes from nine to fifteen days. The human itch mite is *Sarcoptes scabiei*. This can be seen on a white skin in a good light by the aid of a magnifying lens. Where the adult female mites burrow into the skin, an intense itching is produced, which when scratched will result in a secondary infection, giving rise to larger sores. Bedding, blankets, towels, soiled clothing and contact occasionally with toilet seats and usually with infested individuals (especially at night from one bedfellow to another) will assist in the spread of this infestation. Treatment of affected parts consists in the application of sulfur ointment, as described under insecticides. Sulfur preparations do not affect the eggs. It therefore becomes necessary to repeat any sulfur treatment to kill young mites developing from the eggs. Mellanby and associates (*Brit. M. J.*, July 4, 1942), in an evaluation of preparation of sulfur, rotenone, benzyl benzoate and dimethyl-diphenylene disulfide, found that sulfur ointment and emulsions containing 20 per cent benzyl benzoate were to be preferred. Epstein (*Arch. Dermat. & Syph.*, 1942, **45,** 950) suggests the use of rotenone if a mild dermatitis due to sulfur or benzyl benzoate occurs and in those rare instances when the affection is refractory to these two parasiticides. Tetraethyl-thiuram monosulfide (T.E.T.-M.S.) has been highly recommended (*Brit. M. J.*, 1943, **1,** 443).

The rat mite, *Liponyssus bacoti*, primarily a parasite on rats, has been shown capable of transmitting endemic typhus. The destruction of rats results in their control as they cannot subsist on humans alone.

Hair follicle or face mite (*Demodex folliculorum*) is world-wide and found in the hair follicles, sebaceous glands of the nose and forehead and occasionally in the ears of infested individuals. They apparently cause no inconvenience, for in most instances their presence is not known. If present in large numbers they may assist in the production of so-called *blackheads*, due to the deposition of fatty material. In dogs a related species may cause a severe form of mange. (For treatment in man and animals, see Insecticides.)

Ticks.—Ticks are a group of pests which are annoying to domestic animals and human beings, inasmuch as they themselves may infest man, or they may assist in the dissemination of diseases of human beings and domestic animals, as *Rocky Mountain spotted fever, tularemia, tick paralysis, Colorado tick fever, Texas fever*, and *African relapsing* or *tick fever*. The last named is transmitted by a species of tick (*Ornithodorus moubata*, the tampan), while the first-mentioned disease is disseminated by *Dermacentor andersoni* (*Dermacentor venustus*). The latter species also transmits tularemia and is the cause of tick paralysis. *D. andersoni* is responsible for the spread of Q fever in the United States, while in Australia this disease is spread by the hard-shelled tick, *Ixodes humerosa*. In the eastern part of the United States, *Dermacentor variabilis* is the natural vector of *Rocky Mountain spotted fever*. *D. variabilis*, found on the dog and other hosts, may cause tick paralysis (*J. A. M. A.*, 1943, **122**, 86). All ticks are parasitic during some part of their lives. A particular host preference is shown by some species, while others attack any warm-blooded animal. In some species the immature forms and adults select different hosts or different parts of the same host's body. In the two species of ticks, known to be active transmitters of Rocky Mountain spotted fever in man, the pathogenic *Dermacentroxenus ricketsii* passes from the female to the eggs, to larvae, to nymphs and finally to adults. The reservoir is especially in rabbits and ground squirrels. But in addition, the rabbit tick (*Haemaphysalis leporis-palustris*) and other species of ticks transmit the disease in Nature from rabbit to rabbit, thus increasing the natural reservoir. The tick-rodent-tick cycle plays an important role in the transmission of the infection. Means of ridding animals of ticks will in turn reduce infestation in man. Animals are generally treated with dips or sprays. Crude petroleum is the best and most convenient of the materials to employ. Nicotine, arsenicals, lime-sulfur, and creosote dips have also proved effective for ticks, as well as for lice and mange and scab mites. On dogs, the use of derris powder (containing at least 2 per cent rotenone) is effective, if thoroughly worked into the hair and applied at intervals of two or three days throughout the tick season. Humans present in tick-infested areas should examine their bodies frequently during the day (at least twice). If ticks are present, pour some chloroform over them and remove by gently working loose with a forceps, or apply kerosene and remove the dead ticks. A physician should be consulted at once. Sleeping on the ground favors contact. A mosquito net is useful. Strict cleanliness will lessen the chances of tick infestation.

MYRIAPODES AND INSECTS

The myriapodes are arthropods which are generally nonparasitic (though some have been mentioned as pseudoparasites), terrestrial, occurring in dark, damp places and of little interest in medical bacteriology.

The class *insecta* (insects) represents the highest development in the evolutionary scale of invertebrate life. The individual members possess a body in which the head, thorax and abdomen are distinct. The head bears one pair of antennae, eyes (two compound, usually large and frequently several simple eyes) and mouth parts. The thorax possesses the following appendages: three pairs of jointed legs (one pair on the ventral surface of each of the three separate thoracic segments) and on the dorsal surfaces of the two posterior segments are found two pairs of wings. The latter may be reduced to one pair of functional wings and a rudimentary pair (appearing as knoblike projections), or both wings may be rudimentary or absent altogether. The mouth parts of all insects are the same or usually modifications of a single fundamental type. Their digestive tracts are frequently highly developed and differentiated. The abdomen never bears true jointed legs, but may occasionally bear other appendages (though infrequently). The breathing system, represented by the tracheae, is a ventilation system consisting of air tubes spreading all through the body, even to the tips of the wings and antennae. They open by a series of pores (known as spiracles) found along the sides of the insect and are comparable to the nostrils in higher animals. The structures which concern those interested in insect extermination are the organs of locomotion (whether legs, wings, etc.), the nature of the body covering, the mouth parts and the breathing apparatus.

As regards the life history of members of this class, the two common types of development are by incomplete and complete metamorphosis (see page 364). The length of life of insects in the larval and adult stages varies with almost every species and with environmental conditions. Male insects are shorter-lived than females. The latter usually die when all the eggs have been laid. Members of this class are fundamentally terrestrial (including aerial). Many species (especially as larvae and pupae) may be aquatic. They may be free or parasitic.

The classification of the group insecta into orders, families, genera and species is based mainly on the type of development, the modification of the mouth parts and the number, texture and arrangement of the wings. Many complete keys to the various groups of insects are available in the several interesting volumes on entomology and insects, to which students interested in a detailed classification are referred, especially Comstock's "*An Introduction to Entomology.*" Brues and Melander, "*Classification of Insects*" (*Bull. Museum Comparat. Zoology*, Harvard College, 1932, **73**), and Symposium Vol. No. 20 (A. A. A. S., "*Laboratory Procedures in Studies of the Chemical Control of Insects*," 1943).

Many insects eject poisons, or various parts of their bodies may be poisonous, the result being that their contact with human beings or food eaten by them may cause the production of different ailments. Other insects are annoying in that they bite or sting, frequently producing irritation, inflammation, etc., which may become infected. Some insects are true parasites of man. In several instances they display a preference for different parts of the body (internal or external). Other insects are true parasites of lower animals, and occasionally they become human parasites. Others are only accidentally and temporarily parasitic (pseudoparasites) on or in man. There are insects that play a necessary biological role (as intermediate hosts) in the life-cycle of various animal parasites that are disease-producing. These insects (mosquito, tsetse fly, etc.) play an important role in the transmission of disease.

All insects (unless proof to the contrary is offered) must be looked upon as potential carriers of disease. They may carry organisms and filth with which, on account of their migratory habits, they come in direct contact. The organisms when present may be swallowed by these insects, get into their tissues and may later pass out through the excreta or (by regurgitation) through the saliva. In many instances the organisms simply cling to the outside of the insect's body. They may transmit pathogenic organisms through their eggs so that the young become effective transmitters of disease. These insects then act as mechanical transmitters of disease or (in the few instances definitely known and which will be mentioned) they transmit disease by the biological method. There are many insects (especially the so-called *household insect pests*) that are perhaps not so annoying because they may carry disease as due to the fact that they cause considerable damage. They may be destructive to foods, clothes, carpets, furnishings, books, drugs, records, etc. Homes, laboratories and most environments are at times visited by these pests, which may or may not be an indication of negligence or uncleanliness. Space does not permit mentioning, let alone the giving of a consideration of the losses caused by insects which infest our crops, fruits, trees, stored grains, etc. While the scourge to human life from the transmission of disease by insects has been greatly reduced and ameliorated since the beginning of this century, blood-sucking insects are still one of the most important sources of human disease, particularly to nonimmune populations. We still have with us at one place or another on this earth malignant malaria, yellow fever, dengue, the trypanosomiases, leishmania infections, the rickettsial diseases, the filariases, and other scourges to civilization, just as definitely as they existed two thousand years ago. Insects are still one of the most important sources from which man contracts disease.

In the following pages, only those insects will be considered which are frequently parasitic or very annoying as pests.

Bedbugs.—Bedbugs belong to the Order *hemiptera*, which includes the true bugs. The two important species are *Cimex lectularius* and *C. hemiptera* (*votundatus*). The latter is found in the tropics and the former in northern areas. Their habits and life histories are almost identical. Here the metamorphosis is incomplete. The mouth parts are usually fitted for piercing and sucking. The temperate zone insect (*Cimex lectularius* or *Acenthia lectularia*) is a small, oval, flattened insect, about $1/4$ inch long, possessing a dark reddish-brown to black color. It is entirely wingless and possesses six legs and at the end of each leg there is a pair of hooks. Bedbugs, both male and female, suck blood, and are most apt to be found in human habitation. The proboscis is constructed for feeding so as to puncture and suck. Accordingly bedbugs cannot obtain nutriment from decaying material as they move about. Bedbugs emit a very offensive odor. All seem to be night plunderers, while during the daytime they go to cracks and crevices, especially under boards, wallpaper, in mattresses, furniture of all type, etc., for concealment, where the females usually lay their eggs (about 50) which hatch in from six to ten days. The rate of multiplication varies, but under normal conditions there may be about four successive broods a year. The annoyance of these pests is mainly due to their piercing and sucking mouth parts, with which they attack the head, neck, arms and exposed parts of the body, though they themselves will but rarely produce any severe symptoms in man. Blood, mainly human blood, is the normal food of the common bedbug. While getting its supply of blood, the bedbug remains on the clothing and but seldom adheres to the skin. Convincing evidence is lacking as proof that the bedbug plays an important role in the dissemination of disease-producing organisms, though experimentally they have been found to transmit tularemia (in their feces), bubonic plague and relapsing fevers. The insect, however, may be responsible for ill health from lack of sleep caused by annoyance due to skin irritation.

Bedbugs are capable of traveling considerable distances in search of food and migrate from dwelling to dwelling along walls, pipes and gutters, thus causing further infestation. Cleanliness is the best safeguard accompanied by the elimination of all bedbug harborages. All crevices and cracks in walls should be filled in. Picture frames, loose woodwork, broken ceilings and torn wallpaper should be removed or repaired. These and other preventive measures along similar lines must be constantly applied and maintained.

For the destruction of the bedbugs, after infestation occurs, the methods practiced consist in the use of fumigation, contact insecticides, and heat. Hydrogen cyanide (hydrocyanic acid) gas fumigation is the most efficient fumigant for the destruction of bedbugs. Sulfur dioxide gas fumigation is used, but it is not so effective as hydrocyanide acid gas. Fumigation with sulfur dioxide gas should be repeated within fifteen to twenty days so as to destroy any eggs which have hatched since the first treatment. Heavy naphtha treatment is recommended, as is the use of fumigation with ethylene oxide. Spraying or mopping methods, using kerosene or crude oil with or without cresol, are of some value in small areas; but they should be sprayed (or mopping is carried out) directly upon the pests and their eggs, and treatment is to be repeated at frequent intervals. Steam and boiling temperatures can be used for infested bedding. A temperature of 160° F. for ten hours will kill the bedbug and its eggs; but these heating methods have only a limited application.

Other Bugs.—There are many species of the other true bugs. Important members are *cone-nosed, blood-sucking bugs,* most of them found in South and Central America. Their bites are very painful and so annoying as to even cause death in some instances. Some of the species are regarded as carriers of diseases in these countries. Many of the so-called *kissing bugs* found in various parts of the world belong to this family. Several species produce exceedingly painful bites.

Fleas.—These insects are more or less distantly related to flies, but differ from them especially on account of their mode of living. There are many species which are annoying because of their bites, leading to scratching which may result in secondary infections. The *Indian rat flea* (*Xenopsylla cheopsis*), the *European rat flea* (*Nosophyllus* (*Ceratophyllus*), *fasciatus*), fleas harboring on rats infected with plague and the human flea (*Pulex irritans*) assist in the dissemination of bubonic plague by biting individuals and infecting these wounds with their excrement or regurgitated blood, which are contaminated with the *Pasteurella pestis* (causative agent of plague). They may also infect ground squirrels. The latter in turn will spread the disease over the larger areas. A number of other species of fleas are held responsible in preserving and extending the reservoir of plague among rodents. An important species in this regard is *Diamanus montanus* (*Ceratophyllus acutus*).

Fleas (especially dog (*Ctenocephalus canis*) and human fleas (*Pulex irritans*)) are looked upon with suspicion as the probable disseminators of infantile kala-azar. Fleas (dog fleas) are rarely instrumental in infecting children with tapeworms Fleas may transmit typhus fever from individual to individual. This has been proved experimentally by research workers of the U. S. Public Health Service in the employment of the Indian rat flea (*Xenopsylla cheopis*) and the European rat flea (*N.* (*Ceratophyllus*) *fasciatus*). The latter is the common rat flea of Europe and the U. S.

Fleas, though wingless, possess a marked jumping power, so that migration becomes easy. They pass through a complete metamorphosis, laying their eggs usually singly and over a long period of time. The eggs are dropped at random in dust, in cracks in floors, in the fur of animals, etc. Ordinarily, the life-cycle is passed through within a minimum of three weeks, and the adult under favorable conditions may live from a month to a year. In the adult state, fleas are all parasitic on warm-blooded animals. Both male and female fleas obtain their food by sucking the blood of their host and feed at least once daily. The eyeless, legless maggots feed on the wastes found in the surroundings of their hosts. The capacity of the stomachs of most species is not great. They are very easily disturbed and seldom complete a meal at one bite. The human species visit their hosts mainly at night while other species remain constantly in the fur of their hosts.

The presence of fleas in the home indicates frequently the absence of strict cleanliness. Dust in cracks, crevices, rugs, carpets, greasy pantries, the presence of dirt and filth supply opportunities for breeding. Infested dogs, cats, rats and mice serve as hosts. Dust and dirt should not be allowed to accumulate. Control of the animal hosts (dogs, cats, chickens) and disinfestation of domestic animals and their hide-outs are to be practiced. Rats and mice should be eliminated and rat holes disinfested. Wherever possible hard materials are to be used for floors; textile and similar coverings are to be avoided.

For infested areas, fumigation properly carried out is effective. Hydrocyanic acid or sulfur dioxide gases can be used. Naphthalene powder is effective (see page 417). This can be replaced by sodium fluoride, pyrethrum or derris. The spraying of kerosene containing 2 to 3 per cent cresol, or pyrethrum extract or lethane is effective, if applied thoroughly and frequently. Exposure of infested clothing, bedding and other materials to the efficient effect of the direct rays of the sun is a valuable aid or one hour's exposure at 125° F. will kill all fleas. For the control and treatment of rats and rat burrows, see page 394. Repellents (see page 412) and powders such as iodoform, etc., are used with varying results. Attendants and others in the flea-infested areas should wear rubber or leather gloves, overalls and puttees or gum boots.

Flies.—The several species of flies belong to the Order *diptera*, which also contains members of great importance medically (in particular the mosquitoes, gnats and midges). These pests may be parasitic or they may act as biological or as mechanical carriers of bacteria, protozoa or worms. Marked irritation is frequently caused by those species which bite. The important characteristic of members of this order is that, as a rule, these insects have only one pair of membranous wings, the second pair being rudimentary. They are also characterized by mouth parts which are modified in accordance with the habits of the several species of the different insects. In most instances the mouth parts are formed for puncturing, sucking or licking. All of the *diptera* have a complete metamorphosis, otherwise the life histories of the different members vary within very wide limits. The larvae may be simple maggots with or without a differentiated head and appendages. There are marked variations in the antennae. The latter two features are employed to some extent in classification. The order is divided into two great suborders, and each of these is further subdivided into families, genera, etc. The term *fly* covers a host of parasites other than the simple *house fly*, to which the former term is most frequently applied.

The numerous species possess characteristics peculiar to their own groupings. The diseases usually transmitted by flies are produced mechanically (*i. e.*, by infecting foodstuffs, drinks, etc.), with the exception of the tsetse fly, which transmits African sleeping sickness biologically. The parasites undergo a series of changes in the tsetse fly and finally gain entrance in the salivary glands and are passed into the blood of human beings when the latter are bitten. The species considered here are of interest, due to the fact that they assist in the dissemination of disease. They themselves rarely are the direct cause of a diseased condition.

Fly Maggots.—The invasion by the larval stages (or so-called maggots) of several different species of flies (especially those closely related to the house fly) may result in an infestation in man and other animals known as *myiasis*. If the larvae are present in the intestines causing a disturbance (the symptoms of which frequently resemble dysentery) the condition is known as intestinal myiasis. If the larvae develop under the skin or are deposited in neglected wounds or in the natural cavities of the body (nose, vagina, etc.) the infestation is specifically called cutaneous myiasis. When the larvae are deposited in the auditory canals, causing myiasis, the condition is known as aural myiases.

Some workers recognize three groups of myiasis-producing flies, the specific, semi-specific and accidental. In the first group are found those species in which the larvae can develop only in living tissue and include the *tumbu fly* of Africa, *warble flies* (see page 383) and *Carysomyia bezziana* found in India and Africa, which causes myiasis. Species in the semispecific group breed normally in decomposing material, but if attracted by blood and foul discharges, they may attack living tissue. Among such flies are species of *Sarcophaga*, the common Indian bazaar fly, and the American screw-worm fly (*Cochliomyia americana*). The latter attacks both man and animals in tropical and subtropical America. The accidental group includes those species whose eggs or larvae are swallowed usually in infested food or drink and develop in the intestines. This is an accidental occurrence. Preventive measures consist mainly in personal cleanliness. Septic wounds or sores should be effectively protected against flies, especially in the case of helpless invalids, infants and children. Those with offensive discharges from the ears or nasal passages should keep the orifices protected with cotton moistened with an antiseptic or suitable repellent. In the case of intestinal myiasis, thoroughly cooking all meats and washing well or peeling all raw fruits and vegetables should be practiced.

House Fly (*Musca Domestica.*)—The true house fly differs in one important characteristic from the other members in that it does not bite. It will breed in horse or any other animal manure, human excrement and a great variety of animal and vegetable matter, providing moisture and warmth are present. Favorite breeding places are garbage waste, ensilage, in septic tanks and manure. In favorable warm weather, the female house fly lays from 100 to 900 eggs and a new generation may be expected every two weeks. The adult life may extend from a month to over two months. The body of especially this (as well as other) species is covered with hair and bristles, so they readily become contaminated with organisms when crawling over various material. Causative agents of disease may be ingested by these pests and live for long periods of time in their alimentary canal. Their visits to human food result in the contamination of the latter from the hair, bristles and body excrement, as well as in regurgitated matter. Except in the instances where the maggots of the house fly may cause *intestinal* and *cutaneous myiasis*, there are practically no other direct causes of diseased conditions that may be produced by this species. It is, however, the greatest offender in the spread of pathogenic microorganisms (animal and vegetable). The following diseases may be spread by the house fly: anthrax, Asiatic cholera, diarrhea, dysentery, typhoid, tuberculosis and many other respiratory infections. It is also believed that the ova of tapeworms, hookworms and other human parasites may be disseminated by this species.

The control measures practiced consist of the following: eliminating the breeding places by suitable sanitary measures. The eggs and larvae are destroyed in those breeding grounds which cannot be eliminated. For instance, manure piles or the like are treated with various larvacides. A suspension of hellebore is sprayed on manure with a hand pump, using 10 gallons (containing $1/2$ pound of hellebore) to treat 10 cubic feet or 8 bushels of manure. Borax sprinkled in the proportion of 1 pound to 16 cubic feet of manure and this wet down with water is effective. In this proportion, the hellebore or borax has no injurious effect on the manure. Coal-tar creosote, containing from 14 to 18 per cent tar acids, is used as a spray on carcasses, putrefying material, etc. On manure piles, 100 cc. for each horse per day are sprinkled on the heap after fresh manure is added. Where these methods cannot be used, the following methods are used to reduce the numbers of flies: the use of flytraps, larval traps, flypapers, "swatting," poison baits, sprays and the proper use of screens on doors, windows and all openings and for foodstuffs.

Surgical Maggots.—The use of maggots to hasten the healing of wounds after operation has been advocated by some surgeons and was originally introduced by Dr. William S. Baer of Baltimore. In the technique sterile maggots are obtained by a carefully controlled breeding process. The latter are applied directly to the wound and this is kept covered with a piece of wire gauze, the whole arrangement looking somewhat like a cage. Though it is believed by some that the action of the maggots is due to scavenging, other workers have suggested that a specific reaction between the serum of the body and the maggot itself may account for the probable cause of the healing of the wound. More recently, however, it has been claimed that the effective action by the maggots is due to the production of *allantoin* (the derivative of glyoxylic acid). The use of surgical maggots has been superseded by allantoin which is applied as a 0.4 per cent aqueous solution and in a jelly or ointment base combined with 2 per cent urea. It is believed by many workers that allantoin produces urea. The latter may supersede both allantoin and maggot therapy. For further details, see report of the Council (*J. A. M. A.*, 1938, **110,** 813).

Horse Flies (known also as Gadflies or Tabanids).—The *gadflies* (of which over 2500 species have been reported over the world) are of large size and heavy build, often beautifully colored in orange, brown or black tone, with huge eyes, colored black, brown or green. They breed in water or damp places, are usually solitary in their habits and are capable of migrating great distances away from their breeding places. They are primarily important as bloodthirsty pests of domestic animals and man. The females alone are vicious blood-suckers, the males feeding on plant juices, etc. Most of the species are deliberate and persistent in their feeding and are not easily disturbed in the process of sucking blood. The bites caused by them are painful and may cause considerable annoyance. They are the greatest offenders in the dissemination of anthrax, transmitting the disease directly by their bites. They may also act as the intermediate hosts for different protozoa and worms in the tropical countries, and are accused of causing several diseases in man and animals in tropical regions. *Chrysops discalis* is the species which mechanically transmits tularemia among rabbits and jack rabbits.

Stable Flies (Stomoxys).—The most important species, *Stomoxys calcitrans*, closely resembles the house fly in appearance and is often mistaken for it. The stable fly is usually more robust, is browner in color and possesses a black, piercing stout proboscis and mouth parts, which differ from the house fly and from those of many other species of biting flies. The house fly is unable to pierce the skin. It is commonly believed that the stable fly breeds in manure. The presence of these pests about stables is more likely due to the fact that the animals on which they feed are present here, for the breeding place which they prefer is moist straw, rotting vegetable matter or soggy fermented material. Like the horse flies, stable flies are intermittent feeders. If interrupted they leave one animal in the course of a meal to resume their feeding on another animal, so that they are regarded as mechanical transmitters of blood diseases. They disseminate anthrax (and probably other diseases in man and animals). In 1912 many American workers claimed that this species and probably the house fly were the direct disseminators of infantile (epidemic) paralysis (anterior poliomyelitis). The belief at present is that these species are not the important factors in the spread of this disease. Several species are also incriminated as possible transmitters of glanders, surra and probably other tropical infections. Stable flies rarely invade our homes, and are vicious blood-suckers, attacking mainly large, domestic animals, but when opportunity is presented man is also attacked.

Tsetse Flies (Glossina).—Excluding the mosquitoes, this genus (consisting of many (about 20) species) is the most important of the biting flies. Though only a few species are the greatest offenders, they, as intermediate hosts, are all regarded as the usual transmitters of many of the trypanosomes causing infection in man and animals. This is especially true of the so-called *African sleeping sickness*, caused by a trypanosome, one of the most deadly diseases, and common in African countries. The many species of tsetse flies show characteristics which can be identified by one who is familiar with its identity, but to the average worker these characteristics are not so marked or distinctive as to make identification easy. Tsetse flies, fortunately, are distributed for the most part in central African countries. The different species vary in the choice of their breeding places and habitat. They differ from all other members of their family in their peculiar and remarkable manner of reproduction. They do not lay eggs. An individual developing larva is retained and nourished within the body, and when full grown it is thrown forth and as soon as born another larva begins its development. The length of life of most species of these flies is less than a year. Both male and female bite (always in the daytime) and transmit the disease. Their bites are usually less painful than those of other biting flies. They have a quick darting flight, arriving silently and suddenly, seemingly "coming out of nowhere." *Glossina palpalis* is the principal vector of *T. gambiense*, and *G. tachinoides* is a major vector in western Africa. *G. morsitans* is the principal vector of *T. rhodesiense* and *T. brucei*.

Among the prophylactic measures practiced are treating or eliminating breeding places, the use of traps, the use of veils and gauntlets and providing everyone, man and domestic animals, with suitable netting.

Sand Flies (known also as Phlebotomous Flies or Owl Midges).—Sand flies are present in almost all warm and tropical countries, breeding in dark and damp places. Most species are small, mothlike in appearance and are rock breeders. The eggs are frequently deposited in damp cellars, tree trunks, latrines, etc. Too much moisture drowns the larvae. The harmless male and the blood-sucking female pass through the interstices of ordinary mosquito netting. Their bites cause severe irritation. The insect becomes infective ten days after biting an infected human. They have been thought to be the transmitters of a number of human diseases, but the exact role which they play as general disease transmitters is still in doubt. They are, however, concerned in the transmission of the following: *three-day fever, sandfly fever, pappataci fever* or *phlebotomus fever*, a disease, the causative agent of which is unknown (but regarded as a filterable virus) and resembling a mild form of dengue or yellow fever, occurs in India, Palestine, Egypt, Mediterranean countries, etc.; oroya fever, common in Peru and some South American countries. More recently, *oroya fever* and *verruga peruana*, were found to be general and local manifestations of infection by *Bartonella bacilliformis*. It is difficult to control bartonellosis. The vector is *Phlebotomus verrucarum*. Patino-Camargo (*Proc. 8th Amer. Sci. Congress*, 1942, **6,** 217) reported more than 5000 cases of bartonellosis in an epidemic which occurred in 1939 in Colombia and states that "bartonellosis presents a new and serious problem in Pan American health." See also Weinman (*J. Trop. Med.*, 1941, **44,** 62). Some species of sand flies are suspected of complicity in the spread of the parasites of Oriental sore (leishmaniasis). Control measures include the filling in of crevices and cracks, destroying vegetable debris and rotting logs, fumigation of cellars and latrines, observing rigid cleanliness, wearing of protective clothing and the use of repellents, the employment of electric fans to blow away adult sand flies, antifly measures, and the use as a protective of fine mesh muslin or the sand fly bar. The latter is designed to be used in the field and can be attached to the inside of the shelter tent. It can be also used over the steel cot in barracks, hospitals, etc. The netting is cotton and its construction is much finer in quality than the mosquito netting. It has been determined that the size of the opening of the mesh shall not be greater than 0.0325 inch. A netting is being used for this purpose which has a construction of approximately 675 holes per square inch. Another important requirement for this netting is maximum porosity. Inasmuch as the sandfly bar is used in the tropics, the netting must give as little resistance to the passage of air as possible.

Black Flies.—Black flies or *buffalo gnats* (genus *simulium*) are among the most important of insect pests that are exceedingly annoying to man and animals. In a general way their shape and size are comparable to miniature house flies, $1/25$ to $1/6$ inch in length. Their mouth parts are like those of the mosquito, but are dagger-like instead of needle-like. Unlike the mosquitoes and midges they breed in running water, so that the methods to be employed in their extermination are quite difficult and different than ordinarily used in mosquito and fly campaigns. Repellents may be useful. They are not known to be carriers of any organisms, though several diseases have been thought to be disseminated by these pests. They are, however, very annoying, being viscious blood-feeders and the females cause very painful bites. In Mexico, Central America and Africa certain species of black flies transmit the roundworm *Onchocerca volvulus* (see page 368).

Other Species of Flies.—There are other species of flies belonging to different genera, which are of medical and sanitary interest.

The so-called *bluebottles* and *greenbottles* contain many species which are responsible for cases of external *myiasis* (wound infection). They also probably convey other microorganisms to foodstuffs. Some species of *Sarcophaga* ("flesh flies") attack living tissue, cause cutaneous, aural and even intestinal myiasis and produce considerable damage. Bluebottles, greenbottles and *Sarcophaga* are at times known as *carcass flies*, as the females deposit their eggs on decomposing material. In some species of *Sarcophaga* the female gives birth to living larvae and does not lay eggs. The *oestridae*, warble or hot flies, contain species capable of producing cutaneous myiases. The *Congo floor maggot fly* (*Auchmeromyia luteola*) is responsible for maggots, the only dipterous larva known to suck human blood. They are not known to convey any disease, but if present in large numbers, much blood can be extracted from the sleeping victim. The enforcement of sanitary measures, general cleanliness and the use of high beds are effective preventive measures.

Lice (*Pediculidae*).—Lice are among the most important and most disgusting of external human parasites. They are small wingless insects, with well-developed legs which terminate in powerful claws. Most genera and even species of lice are usually closely limited to a single host. There is an incomplete metamorphosis. They feed on blood of mammals and birds and most species (especially those that infest man) resort to two daily feedings. Of interest are recent experimental evidence that lice prefer living on animals having a vitamin B_2 deficiency. The acorn-shaped eggs (so-called nits) are deposited on the host, (hair, clothing, etc.), near the skin, so as to secure a suitable temperature for incubation. The entire life-cycle of the louse is in association with its host.

Lice (even the young as soon as they are hatched) usually feed at night when the host is at rest. They feed when hungry and usually gorge themselves to excess. Warmth renders lice (except crab louse) exceedingly active and they are very active on patients suffering from fever. They tend to congregate in large numbers, breed rapidly, and in temperate climates are more numerous in winter than in summer. Much of the excreta is eliminated, which is of concern when pathogenic organisms are present. Head and body lice are disseminated by direct contact especially in overcrowded places, from combs, brushes, infested blankets, beds and clothing, caps and hats, from seats in public conveyances and in public gathering places and from infested straw and similar material used for bedding. The crab louse is disseminated as above and by the use of public toilet seats and from common towels in gymnasiums and dormitories.

There are only three varieties that infest man (the condition being known as pediculosis), each selecting different parts of his body. The head louse and body louse are now regarded as varieties or biological races of the same species, as they are able to interbreed.

Head Louse (*Pediculus humanus* var. *humanus or Pediculus capitis*).—The head louse differs from the body louse in but few distinct characteristics (as a hairy instead of a naked abdomen, 7 instead of 8 abdominal segments and other minor differences). Reproduction here is about the same as in the case of the body louse, and the egg production is usually 60 in number. This species prefers the fine hair of the head as a habitat, though it may be found in other parts of the body as well, and on human beings all over the world. Its eggs or "nits" are generally attached to the hair. The head louse is more active and feeds oftener and more sparingly than the body louse.

Body Louse (*Pediculus humanus* var. *corporis* or *P.vestimenti; Clothes or Tailor's Louse*).—This, the "cootie" or "gray-back," is the most common and most important louse infesting man. It is larger in appearance than the head louse. This species inhabits the trunk and neck, not the head, is lighter in color, and possesses more slender antennae and less pronounced indentations in the body and seems to live, lay its eggs and constantly adhere to clothing.

It makes its way to the body only to feed. An examination of the underwear next to the body would disclose whether an individual is infested, rather than trying to find them present on the body, as but few specimens will be found. It is rarely found on the head. Under favorable conditions (especially proper temperature and humidity), an adult female lives about a month and lays 5 to 10 eggs daily. The eggs are usually laid on woolen material, in the folds and seams of clothing and on the hairs of the chest. The eggs hatch in from seven to ten days and become mature in about two weeks.

Crab Louse (*Phthirius pubis*).—This species, the so-called crab louse, differs in many respects and is quite distinct from the other species. It has an almost square body (at times very broad and short) with long clawed legs, presenting the appearance of a small crab. Strange to say, the Caucasian race seems to be the only race infested with this pest, while the other species of lice are found on the different human races. This species seems to prefer coarse hair, and is found in the hair around the genitals, anus, beards, armpits, eyebrows, etc. It differs from the head and body louse in that it remains in one area for long periods of time and does not move about in search of food. The female, which is somewhat larger than the male, lays about a dozen eggs, which hatch out in about a week, and the young become sexually mature in about two weeks. It requires careful search to discover crab lice for, being grayish white, they are almost transparent. They are usually attached to the hair, head downward, and close to the skin. This species is not known to be a vector of any disease in man.

Typhus fever (epidemic and probably murine) is transmitted by lice (head and body lice). The same species are the transmitters of the spirochetes, causing *relapsing fever*. It was found that *trench fever*, raging during World War I, was disseminated by lice. These diseases are transmitted through the feces of lice or by crushing infected lice on mucous membranes or injured skin. The bites of lice produce a dermatitis, itching, and frequently secondary infection sets in. It may be that lice serve as mechanical transmitters of other diseases, but no definite proof has as yet been established, though plague has been transmitted experimentally by lice.

In examining human beings, look for skin bites on the skin. These appear as very small punctures with encircling areas of inflammation. In examining the clothing, give special attention to the undergarments and search carefully all seams and folds. The axillary hair should be examined for ova. If the examination is conducted in the open, stand to windward of the person being examined as young lice can be blown from one to another when in close proximity. The problem of control requires measures to prevent infestation, the cleansing of infested persons, and the treatment of infested bedding, clothing and other materials. Strict personal cleanliness efficiently carried out and general sanitary measures under proper control are the most important preventive measures. Overcrowding should be avoided. Among the military personnel, especially on field service, it is important to have a delousing unit consisting of a permanent group, specially instructed and trustworthy. If infestation occurs, vigorous treatment should be employed. Body lice are easily eradicated, as here the problem consists in the proper treatment of infested clothing, by efficient laundering and hot ironing or, still better, by exposure for ten minutes in a hot-air chamber at 160° F. or in a steam bath, by fumigation or by immersing for one hour in kerosene containing preferably 2 or 3 per cent cresol or other coal-tar disinfectant. In severe head-louse infestation, the hair should be clipped. Care should be taken that the hair which is removed is burned or disinfested. For other measures, see page 410.

Some of the following have been employed more recently as louse control remedies: A lotion used on heads consists of phenyl cellosolve (2-phenoxy-ethanol), 1 part in 4 parts of 50 per cent ethanol and aromatized as desired. MYL of the U. S. Department of Agriculture is used in the field by the Army, as are powders No. 153, containing 0.5 per cent of a 20 per cent concentrate of pyrethrins, 0.5 per cent *N*-isobutyl undecylenamide, 0.6 per cent dinitro-6-cyclohexylphenol and 98.4 per cent Pyrax ABB and powder No. 452, containing 0.2 per cent 2,4-dinitrobutyl phenol, 1 per cent light mineral oil and 98.8 per cent Pyrax ABB. Approximately 30 Gm. of these powders are spread over the entire underwear, armpits, etc., and they are effective for about a week. Another widely used and effective antilouse powder is "DDT," dichloro-diphenyl-trichloro-ethane, which dusted into the clothing provides in a single application protection for about a month.

Mosquitoes (Culicidae).—The *Culicidae* have been subjected to a very intensive study. Recent classifications have been varied and detailed. The *Culicidae* are divided into two subfamlies, *Culicinae* and *Corethrinae*. Species in the latter do not bite and are of no medical interest. The *Culicinae* contains four tribes, only two of which, *Anophelini* and *Culicini*, include most of the known vectors of disease. Mosquitoes are enemies of mankind. Other than their importance from a sanitary viewpoint, they cause considerable annoyance by their painful bites when attacking individuals.

In a general way the life histories of all species of mosquitoes are alike. They pass through a complete metamorphosis. There may be special characteristics in physiology or in habits, which are more or less present, so as to meet the existing conditions of environment, etc. The number of eggs which are generally oval in shape with various markings will vary anywhere from 25 to several hundred. Some lay their eggs singly, while others lay them in groups at one time. Some species, as found especially in temperate climates, will lay their eggs on the open surface of standing or stagnant water, while other species found in the cold and tropical areas may deposit their eggs in dry places, which are soon covered with water, In the temperate climates the eggs generally are hatched within twenty-four hours, while in the far North or in the dry, hot countries the eggs probably do not hatch for many weeks or months, having been more or less acclimated to or fortified by unfavorable climatic conditions. The eggs of mosquitoes only hatch in the presence of water, and it must be standing water. At first, they are very minute, but rapidly obtain a length visible to the naked eye. The larvae, developing from the eggs, are always aquatic. Most of the species possess a trumpet-shaped breathing tube, which pierces the surface film of the water, drawing in air, for, though aquatic, the mosquito larvae or *wrigglers* or *darters*, as they are known, are air breathers. Unless the water is well aerated, the larvae make frequent trips to the surface, hang head downward and, breathing through their tails, obtain their air supply. In a water containing no dissolved air, and from which the air from above the surface is excluded, mosquito larvae will die within a few hours. The length of time required for the mosquito to complete the larval existence depends entirely upon the temperature. It will require anywhere from five days to two weeks before the resting or pupa stage is reached. The pupae never eat, but are almost always found, head upright, at the surface of the water quietly breathing. The transformation into the adult stage may in some instances be a matter of a few hours, but in most species, from two days to a week, depending on the condition of the weather, are required before a full-grown mosquito is produced, though some species of anopheles may take from two to four weeks. The female usually dies after laying its eggs.

An important fact is that most mosquitoes seldom stray from their breeding grounds. It is a false impression which has led individuals to believe that mosquitoes are carried long distances by strong winds. This is true of only a few species. The common salt marsh mosquito (frequently found in New Jersey) is, perhaps, the only commonly observed species of mosquito, which, though breeding in enormous numbers along marshy coasts of New Jersey, has been found to migrate inland. The male mosquito is generally a vegetarian and does not bite. It is the female mosquito that does the biting and damage to the human being. The male is differentiated from the female not only in the fact that there is a difference in the construction of the proboscis (i. e., name given to the elongated projecting nose and trunk), so that the male mosquito cannot pierce flesh, but one will generally find that the male has very bushy antennae (jointed feelers upon their heads), while the female's antennae are very sparsely plumed. Over 500 species have been found to exist, most of them in the tropics. The *Anophelini* comprises only one genus, *Anopheles*, which include all known carriers of malaria. In the *Culicini* are included species responsible for the transmission of other diseases mentioned below. The following are the only ones which are important from a sanitary standpoint:

1. The *anopheles* (many species) transmit malaria (a specific species seeming responsible for the transmission of malaria in different countries). Not all anopheline species are capable of carrying malaria. Furthermore the habits of even the same species capable of carrying malaria may vary in different regions so that in one area it may and in another it may not be of importance in epidemics of malaria. For instance, *Anopheles aquasalis* (*tarsimaculatus*) bites man and is a vector of malaria in Trinidad, but appears to be harmless in Panama. Development of malarial parasites has been found to take place in about 50 different species. It is advisable for workers to become familiar with the anopheline species in given localities, study their habits and life histories and determine the degree of responsibility of each in spreading malaria.

2. *Stegomyia fasciata* (known as *Aedes calopus*, *Stegomyia calopus* and *Aedes aegypti*) is responsible for the transmission of most cases of yellow fever. Recently other species of this genus have been found capable of transmitting that variety of the disease known as *jungle yellow fever*. In West Africa, 9 species of *Aedes* and even species of *Culex*, *Anopheles*, *Eretmopodites* and *Mansonia* have been found transmitting the virus by bite.

3. *Culex fatigans* (*quinquefasciatus*) and *Stegomyia faciata* transmits dengue.

Evidence concerning *Culex fatigans* (*quinquefasciatus*) is conflicting, but *Aedes albopictus* and *Armigeres obturbans* are probable carriers.

4. A number of species of mosquitoes of different genera including *Anopheles*, *Stegomyia* (*Aedes*) and *Culex* may serve as intermediate hosts for filariasis. The most widespread transmitting agent is the *common house mosquito of the tropics*, the *Culex fatigans* (a species which also transmits dengue). Species of *Culex* have been implicated recently as being vectors of the virus causing St. Louis encephalitis and western equine encephalomyelitis.

The mosquitoes in the different genera differ in particular characteristics in all stages of their life history. For instance, anopheline larvae, unlike all other mosquito larvae, do not possess a breathing tube or syphon. Being surface feeders, they lie parallel to, and just below the surface of the water. Most culicine larvae rest with their bodies at an angle to the surface of the water, hanging suspended by the syphon. As far as is known, malaria and the other diseases mentioned are caused in no other way than being bitten by infected mosquitoes.

Methods of Eradication.—The only logical method of combating malaria, yellow fever, dengue, filariasis, etc., is to practice methods of control for the eradication of the mosquito. One must be familiar with the life histories and habits, habitats, breeding places and binomics of the different species of mosquitoes. Also detailed information is required concerning the diseases they transmit, the characteristics of the etiological agents, how they develop in the mosquitoes, and how the latter transmit these offending agents. Among the general methods of control are to be found the following useful procedures.

1. *Destroying the Breeding Places of These Insects.*—This is the most valuable method as it deals with the direct eradication of them at their source. All collections of stagnant or standing water should be eliminated as far as is possible. The usual steps are to see that there are no buckets, barrels, pans, vases or other receptacles serving as aquaria for the larvae. If these are necessary or cannot be disposed of, they should be covered or screened. Pools and all swamps containing stagnant water should be drained and filled in with earth. If this is impractical the free use of larvicides should be employed. This consists in using a highly toxic fuel oil (usually one-half ounce per square yard) as frequently as may be necessary or at least once every ten days during the breeding season. If desired, oiled sawdust or a dusting powder can be spread over the surface of the water by aeroplane or by hand dusters. This can consist of (2 to 5 per cent) Paris green (finely powdered) diluted with finely powdered soapstone or road dust. At least one-half to one pound of this powder per acre is required. Paris green is effective against surface feeding anophelines but has no effect on culicine larvae. Fink and associates (*U. S. Bur. Ent. and Plant Quarantine Pub.* **E-425,** 1938), in a study of 400 synthetic organic compounds on culicine mosquito larvae found more than half of them effective to kill about 50 per cent of the insects at a concentration of 100 p. p. m. and phenothiazine gave a 100 per cent kill at a concentration of 1 p. p. m. (see Insecticides.)

2 *Temporary Measures around Dwellings and Personal Protection.*—Houses can be rid effectively of most mosquitoes after being screened with fine mesh wire by fumigation with hydrocyanic acid or sulfur dioxide or other fumigants as described under Insecticides or Fumigation. The use of repellents as described here and under Insecticides has a temporary value.

Repellents should never replace the use of mosquito netting. They may be used as an adjunct to the latter. In anopheline-infested areas, where there is no objection to coal-tar creosote oils (technical grade), this is sprayed on the walls and ceiling in the proportion of 1 gallon to 420 square feet. Sprays of pyrethrum extract in kerosene or in mixtures of kerosene and carbon tetrachloride (1:4) or similar insecticidal sprays (containing also rotenone) in the proportion of 10 cc. per 1000 cubic feet of space, act not only as repellents but also are destructive agents to those mosquitoes present in the environment being treated. Oils of citronella, pennyroyal, cedarwood, bergamot, cassia, cloves, anise, peppermint and lavender used freely (not rubbed in) on exposed parts of the body afford protection against these pests. They are frequently diluted (1:4 to 1:12) with liquid petrolatum, olive oil or kerosene to retard evaporation. The addition of 1 per cent phenol or 1 to 2 per cent thymol or camphor is recommended. A trade-marked preparation "sta-way," which contains diethylene glycol monobutyl ether acetate and diethylene glycol monoethyl ether, is used in some foreign countries as a mosquito repellent. Individuals on a hunt for the breeding places or generally infested regions will find it best to protect themselves by the use of high boots, gloves, veils, tightly fitting suits, etc.

The "Mosquito Bar," used in barracks, hospitals, etc., is advocated to be employed over the steel cot. This consists of a canopy made of netting. The bar is provided with tying tapes by which it is fastened securely to "T" bars which are attached to head and foot of the cot. The netting used is made of cotton and has a construction of approximately 200 meshes per square inch. This netting is satisfactory to exclude the mosquito, fly, tick and other pests. The "Mosquito Headnet," designed for use as protection against mosquitos, flies, etc., is supplied with drawstrings at the top and bottom and can be adjusted to fit over the various types of hats, helmets and headgears used by the soldiers and others in the tropics. The netting used in the headnet is a cotton netting (marquisette) with a construction of approximately 624 meshes per square inch. The mosquito glove has more recently been adopted for protection of the hands against mosquitoes, sand flies, and other pests. They are made of cotton Canton flannel and are provided with a knitted rib wrist portion.

Roaches.—These pests are among the commonest and most disliked insects with which man comes in contact. They belong to an Order, known as *orthoptera*, which includes crickets, locusts and grasshoppers, few species of which frequent human habitations. Domestic roaches do not withstand cold very well. It is for this reason that they are abundant in oven rooms of bakeries, pantries, kitchens, behind radiators and hot-water pipes, and in or about fireplaces. Heat, moisture, and the presence of food play a leading role in the production of infestation. Their diet is varied. Though partial to sweets, ordinary foodstuffs and attracted by beer, they will consume paper, hair, etc. They cannot withstand starvation for long periods of time. Roaches are scavengers and will consume dead animal matter. On account of their flat thin bodies, they are capable of finding their way into almost all spaces for concealment, coming forth mainly in the dark (especially during the night). There are really more places infested with these pests than what is actually believed, but inasmuch as their presence can in many instances be detected only at night, it is difficult to know whether or not places are infested. The spread of roaches is not due to their own migratory instincts as much as to their introduction with furniture, clothing, materials, through commerce, etc.

The development from the young to adult stage is very slow and, as reported by some investigators, may even take years, especially if the food supply and temperature are not favorable. Their abundance is not due to their rapidity in multiplication but mainly to the power of preserving themselves from the ordinary means of destruction. There are four species of domestic roaches which are found in almost all countries: the *American roach* or *cockroach* (*Periplaneta americana*), the most widespread and troublesome species; the *Australian cockroach* (*Periplaneta australiasiae*); the *Oriental* or *common cockroach*, or so-called *black beetle* (*Blatta orientalis*), common in Europe; the *German* or *croton roach* (*Blatella germanica*).

The roaches feed on almost all kinds of materials. Though no direct evidence has been established, it is claimed that potentially because of their filthy habits they may become agents in disseminating disease, especially typhoid, dysentery, cholera and other gastro-intestinal as well as some respiratory infections, by coming in contact with contaminated materials in drains, etc.; and in turn as mechanical distributors, they may contaminate food and drink. The actual damage in the products consumed or as carriers of diseases is very little as compared with the spoilage of materials which have been tainted with the "roachy odor." This odor (coming from the fluids of the mouth, secretions from the scent glands, both of which are mixed with the excrement) is very disagreeable. There are several authentic cases on record where these pests as pseudoparasites in the ear caused severe pain. They frequently attack the face, eyelashes, fingers, etc., being mainly attracted by the grease.

Unless measures are taken to eradicate these pests, they will increase rapidly and infest neighboring premises. Strict cleanliness and the removal of all food debris must be practiced. Cracks and crevices should be filled in or sealed. Poisoned baits (see page 400), if frequently renewed, are useful. The use of kerosene or kerosene with pyrethrum extracts followed by a sodium fluoride powder (see page 416) containing 10 to 20 per cent pyrethrum is very effective. The application of heat, 130° F. or higher, preferably in the form of steam vapor, is used wherever possible.

Ruinous Pests.—The following members of this class are grouped here, for they are of interest primarily, as in the case of roaches, because they are annoying or are destructive to our household effects. With but few exceptions, they are non-parasitic and do not spread disease.

Ants.—There are many (approximately 3500) species of ants (family—*Formicoidea*) in existence, but in the western continents about 25 species have been observed, and only a few of these are to be found in the household. None of them have been regarded as disseminators of disease, though ants have been incriminated as mechanical carriers and spreaders of the bacilli of dysentery, typhoid and the vibrio of Asiatic cholera.

Ants may be kept from food on tables by the use of poison bait (see page 400) tied around the legs of the table. If an infestation occurs, keep all food covered and destroy or remove food scraps and rubbish. Poison bait, placed at suitable positions to attract the ants can be used. The adult pests can be killed by the use of boiling water, kerosene, or 10 per cent of naphthalene in the latter. A useful killing powder contains 40 to 60 per cent of sodium fluoride with cornstarch or sugar and some pyrethrum. If the nests are located, the liquid insecticide is sprayed in the latter, followed if necessary by blowing the powder insecticide into the haunts by means of a powder spray or bellows.

Moths.—Moths belong to the order *lepidoptera* which includes skippers, butterflies, etc. Some members have been reported as pseudo-parasites of man. Severe dermatitis and affections of the eyes are produced by several species. Many of them are injurious to clothes, tapestry, etc. It is the latter important species with which we are more apt to come in contact in this country and which are of interest to us because they are so widespread and so destructive.

Millers or moths observed around the household generally possess a buff color. The ones that are the chief offenders among fabric pests are rarely found directly around lights. The latter prefer darkness and, therefore, conceal themselves in clothing, cracks and dark places. The moths that are frequently found about the lights in the home are the ones that feed on vegetation on the outside rather than on household fabrics, and their presence is really accidental, being attracted into the homes by the lights. It may be of interest to note that the adult moth cannot feed on clothing, as it possesses imperfect mouth parts. Their main interest is the fact that the moth lays its eggs upon the object it attacks, generally in or about clothing. From the eggs are hatched the larvae or worms. It is the latter that cause the destruction. If conditions are favorable the larval stage then passes to the pupa, and finally the adult moth is the result. One may, therefore, observe that the destruction of the adult moth will eventually save clothing and other furnishings by the prevention of the laying of more eggs. The three most important and commonly found species of clothes moths are the *webbing clothes moth*, the *case-making cloth moth* and the *tapestry moth*. The webbing clothes moth is the most abundant and injurious of these species, causing damage to clothing, furniture, all types of fabrics, carpets, rugs, stuffings in animals, birds, in furniture, etc. The tapestry moth is not so common in this country as the other two species, and it is claimed that it prefers heavier and coarser materials, as blankets, felt, furs and even wallpaper.

Carpet Beetles.—Buffalo moths, more frequently called carpet beetles, are closely associated with clothes moths in their destruction of household materials. Though the larvae are found most frequently beneath carpets, they have been found to feed upon other articles, such as upholstered furniture, dried animal matter and articles containing wool, fur, hair bristles or feathers. These pests, frequently responsible for damage to the latter, are very distinct from the true clothes moth, being in reality a beetle and not a moth. Of the six species found, four have proved to be serious offenders in the household.

Closely related to the common carpet beetle we have the black carpet beetle and the varied carpet beetle, which possess different color arrangements. They are not unlike the common carpet beetle in so far as their most important characteristics of general interest are considered. The other important species is the furniture carpet beetle, which is well established in certain quarters of this country, and is a serious pest, destroying hairs, leather, linen and other coverings.

Spiders.—Most spiders are greatly feared but with little cause as many of them cannot be induced to bite. There is but one common species known to be poisonous. *Arachnidism*, spider-bite poisoning, is usually due to the bite of the "black widow" or "shoebutton spider" (*Latrodectes mactans*). For a consideration of black widow spider bites, see Halter and Kuzell (*Mil. Surgeon*, 1943, **92,** 427). If individuals will learn to recognize this insect, destroy it, its web and eggs, the deaths which now occur annually will not happen. This spider possesses a shining black globular abdomen, is rather small in size, possessing long legs, no hair and on its underneath side there is a bright red patch shaped like a short thick dumbbell or even roughly like an hour-glass. Its web consists of straggly, uneven, coarse, sticky threads, running in all directions and in all three dimensions. There is not present the geometrical exacti-tude which gives to webs of other spiders a certain aesthetic charm.

Other Annoying and Objectionable Pests.—There are many insects widely dis-tributed other than those mentioned, which are annoying pests to man. They are considered briefly:

The *House Cricket* (*Gryllus domesticus*) is commonly found on refuse dumps, in refuse destructors, around bakeries and in warm dwellings. Though they do no harm, most people object to their presence and especially to the characteristic shrill noise produced by the male when rubbing its wings together. The use of baits made with Paris green or arsenic trioxide and methods as practiced for the eradication of roaches are successfully employed for eliminating crickets.

The *Silver Fish* (*Lepisma saccharina*) acts as a scavenger. It attacks various substances, though its preference is starchy and sweet food. It generally is found near warm places, as hot-water radiators and pipes, fireplaces, etc. Books and papers are frequently attacked. The silver fish is one of the most primitive of insects. The body of the adult is covered with silvery scales, as in a fish; and at the termina-tion of the abdomen, there are three bristle-like appendages. The presence of the latter account for the name "bristle-tail" given to this pest. The *firebrat* (*Thermobia domestica*), closely related to the silver fish and found in the same haunts, can with-stand higher temperatures. Control measures for both of these insects comprise the use of poison baits containing arsenic trioxide or sodium fluoride; and kerosene, pyrethrum-kerosene or other liquid insecticidal sprays in their haunts, followed by dusting about powder insecticides (one containing 50 per cent sodium fluoride, 15 per cent each of borax and pyrethrum, and 20 per cent sugar); or sulfur dioxide gas fumigation when necessary.

Book Lice (*Psocids*) and *Wood Lice* are both nuisance pests and do no or very little damage. They are associated generally with damp places. Drying the infested area will eliminate these pests. If necessary, the use of arsenical poison baits near their haunts and fumigation as the last resort, when carried out properly, will be found to be most effective.

INSECTS GENERALLY INJURIOUS TO GARDEN, CROPS, ETC.

Enormous losses by agriculturists and others are caused annually by insect scourges. Due to modern rapid methods of transportation, insects foreign to different countries and territories soon infest the latter to present new problems in insect control. It is impossible in a volume such as this to consider these pests in detail or even describe them. It seems desirable, however, to at least mention the names of the greatest offenders, so as to have such a list available for those for whom this work is intended.

The European corn borer (*Pyrausta nubilalis*), the larger cornstalk borer (*Diatroea zeacolella*), the lesser cornstalk borer (*Elasmopalpus lignosellus*) and the corn earworm (*Chloridea obsoleta*) infest corn and may cause considerable damage. Other food plants and even fruit and foliage may be affected by these pests. The Hessian fly (*Phytophaga destructor*), the wheat-joint worm (*Harmolita tritici*), the wheat-straw worm (*Harmolita grandis*) and various species of aphids attack several grains and especially wheat. Potatoes and related plants are attacked by the potato-stalk borer (*Trichobaris trinotata*), the potato-tuber worm (*Phthorimoea operculella*), various flea-beetles (of the genus *epitrix*), beetles and aphids. The Mexican bean beetle (*Epilachna corrupta*), the broad-bean weevil (*Mylabris rufimanus*), the bean weevil (*Mylabris obtectus*), the pea weevil (*Mylabris pisorum*) and various aphids attack beans, peas, etc. Melons, squash, beets, celery, onions, spinach, rhubarb, sweet potatoes, carrots, parsnip, etc., and, in fact, all garden crops become involved and are at times seriously affected by insect pests.

The boll weevil (*Anthonomus grandis*), one of the most destructive pests ever known in this country, causes damage amounting to at least $250,000 annually to the cotton-growing industry in this country. Other pests affecting cotton are the cotton boll-worm or corn earworm (*Chloridea obsoleta*), the melon or cotton aphid (*Aphis gossypii*), the cotton worm moth (*Aletia argillacea*), etc. Fruit insect pests are numerous. The Japanese beetle (*Popillia japonica*) feeds on plants, roots of grasses, weeds, fruit and shade trees, etc. The codling moth (*Carpocapsa pomonella*) is one of the important orchard pests, and known for its destructive effects upon apples. Peaches, pears, cherries, grapes, strawberries, blackberries, raspberries, currants and the citrus fruits are injured and at times suffer heavy losses due to insect pests. The red scale, most serious pest of the citrus fruits, is even capable of tolerating cyanide fumes.

The literature supplied by the respective state departments of agriculture as well as that available at the U. S. Department of Agriculture should be consulted, as much valuable information in contained in these publications. The list of publications of the Division of Insecticide Investigations and other sections of the U. S. Department of Agriculture is extensive and at least some of the data are known to many. On the other hand, few people recognize the worth-while efforts of many of the respective state divisions and the various agricultural experiment stations. The latter are more frequently in a position to serve better in specific local problems. Throughout this and other chapters, references are given to the publications of the U. S. Department of Agriculture. As an example of publications and contributions by state agricultural groups, a few of the many published recently are directed to your attention: "Common Insects of the Flower Garden" (N. Y. State College of Agr., *Bull.* **371,** 1942); "Current Contributions on Insect Control" (N. Y. State Agr. Expt. Sta., *Bull.* **698,** 1942); and "Insect Control in the Vegetable Garden" (N. Y. State College of Agr., *Bull.* **503,** 1942).

Chapter XXVIII

RODENTS, SNAKES AND HIGHER ANIMALS

RODENTS

THIS NAME is applied to a large class of pests, many of which are injurious as well as beneficial to mankind. There are at least 80 different groups in North America alone with which man comes in contact. Some are of benefit to man, inasmuch as they keep a check upon the increase of pests that are injurious. Others, as the beaver, badger, etc., have an economic value as fur bearers. The rabbits and squirrels are useful as human food, while the mice and rats are the most destructive pests known. There are but few of these rodents that are capable of causing direct injury to man, but many of them may become actively injurious either by acting as intermediate hosts in the transmission of disease, or on account of their rapid reproduction and increasing numbers, even useful rodents (as rabbits, etc.) may depredate property. Under these conditions it may become necessary to resort to measures for relief.

Ground Squirrels.—Many species are found in this country. The most destructive species is the California ground squirrel, which is known to be a carrier of bubonic plague, usually becoming infected from diseased rats through the intermediary agent of a specific species of fleas. Squirrels may serve as intermediate hosts of immature stages of various species of ticks, especially the one causing Rocky Mountain spotted fever. Infected animals, through the agency of biting insects, may transmit tularemia or *Francis' disease* to man. Other species are so destructive to crops as to make it necessary to adopt means of ridding areas infested with large numbers of these pests. Trapping does not seem to be effective. The use of poison baits, consisting of oats or barley soaked with a sweetened strychnine solution, have proved successful.

Prairie Dogs.—Prairie dogs, known also as marmots, are widely distributed in various parts of the country just east of the Rocky Mountains. Inasmuch as they subsist on vegetation, means have been practiced to exterminate them. Poison baits as used for ground squirrels have proved most satisfactory.

Rabbits.—Rabbits are generally looked upon as useful animals. They rarely cause trouble and are not regarded as disseminators of disease. A parasite known as coccidans (*Eimeria stiedae*), and belonging to the group sporozoa, may infest the liver and intestines of rabbits. A few cases have been reported where this parasite has been transmitted to man by eating rabbits' liver which had not been cooked long enough. They may occasionally be the intermediate hosts for specific species of tongue worms. Infected with *rabbit fever*, they may transmit this disease, known as tularemia or *Francis disease*, to man. Biting insects are probably the intermediary agents.

Rats.—The *Rattus norvegicus* (the brown rat) and *Rattus rattus* (the black rat) are

393

the commonly observed species of rats. The previously mentioned synonyms are misleading as the brown rat is frequently gray and the black rat possesses at times a brown color. Rats are very prolific if food is available. They begin to breed at the age of three or four months and produce about five litters a year, each averaging 10 young. Other than the destruction of foodstuffs and material, rats assist in the spread of disease. *Bubonic plague* is spread by several species of fleas (in particular the Indian rat flea), which infest different species of rats that are diseased. Hogs may eat rats infested with particular kinds of roundworms (*Trichinella spiralis* and *Ascaris lumbricoides*), and if pork is not cooked well these parasites may be transmitted to human beings. Rats have been shown by Japanese investigators to serve as a reservoir for the spirochetes (*Leptospira icterohaemorrhagiae*) causing infectious jaundice or *Weil's disease*, an infection occurring in Europe and Asia and reported from various parts of North America. The organisms are found especially in the kidneys, being constantly excreted with the urine.

Rat-bite fever (Sodoku) is contracted when bitten by rats harboring the causative agent, *Spirochaeta morsus muris* (*Spirillum minus*). This disease is characterized by the appearance of a maculopapular eruption. There is a primary edematous lesion, followed by the swelling of regional lymph nodes. Febrile periods with alternate afebrile intervals occur. Infected tissue obtained early in the disease is inoculated into white mice, rats or guinea pigs, and the blood of the experimental animal is examined for the spirochete. The disease is found in many parts of the world, and especially in Asia. Arsphenamine is a specific in treatment.

Dwarf tapeworms and probably other worms commonly found in rats may find their way through the feces into foodstuffs, which when taken into the human system may cause disease. Evidence is accumulating showing that many animal and vegetable parasites commonly observed in man are also able to live in mice and rats, and it may be that in the near future it will be found that the rat is the direct or indirect cause of many of the disease conditions in man, the source of which has not as yet been clearly established. The common house mouse, *Mus musculus*, though not as destructive as the rat, is responsible for the spread of *salmonella* food infections, rat-bite fever and other diseases.

The anti-rat measures commonly practiced consist in:

1. Preventing rats from entering homes, buildings, vessels, by means of guards, screening, filling in holes in walls, etc. If possible, concrete floors and cellars should be installed and ratproof construction in general should be used in buildings, homes and vessels.

2. Keeping foods and all supplies, garbage, etc., under cover and carefully protected. Strict enforcement of sanitary regulations is to be observed.

3. Proper fumigation of infested areas.

4. The use of traps and poison mixtures.

For environments already infested the use of one of the commonly found rat traps should be used in conjunction with any of the numerous poison mixtures consisting usually of flour or any of the grains, in powder, mixed with arsenic, phosphorus, strychnine, thallium sulfate, or cyanide of potassium sweetened with a little saccharin. A biologically tested red squill powder or extract is very effective and is employed for rat and mice control. This drug is not very toxic to humans or animals, but, if fresh or biologically active, it is highly toxic to rodents.   Equal parts of plaster of Paris and flour (sweetened) are used as an efficient mixture, inasmuch as the rats after eating the mixture are forced to leave the building to find water, which hardens the plaster of Paris, causing death.   The author has used this with success.   Fumigation with hydrocyanic acid is to be practiced where possible.   This can be done on vessels and in buildings or compartments which are not inhabited.   In those places where hydrocyanic acid fumigation cannot be employed the fumes of sulfur can be used.   An effective rat warfare can only be accomplished through the co-ordination of all efforts and a consolidation of all available forces.   Frequent inspections and constant sanitary effort will aid considerably in the reduction of rat population.   For further details, see Olesen and Sherrard (*U. S. Pub. Health Service Repts.*, 1942, **57**, 1966).

HIGHER ANIMALS IN THE TRANSMISSION OF DISEASE

Higher animals transmit the following diseases considered briefly below.

Cattle.—Beef tapeworms, other animal parasites and many gastro-intestinal bacteria may be transmitted through the use of infested and infected cattle meat which is not thoroughly cooked.   Anthrax and glanders are transmitted by cattle or by-products from the latter.   *Lumpy jaw* or actinomycosis may be transmitted to human beings by infected discharges from cattle.   Tubercle bacilli (bovine) and other pathogenic bacteria from diseased udders, especially streptococci, may be found in milk (a product from the cow) and the latter will in turn convey this to man. Cattle may be the hosts of several species of ticks (found in spotted fever districts) and stable flies.

Cats.—Rabid cats may transmit biologically, by biting man, the virus producing rabies or hydrophobia.   There is the possibility of cats acting as the hosts for various parasites which may infest man, especially the intestinal parasites.

Dogs.—Rabid dogs more frequently than any other animals are directly the cause of hydrophobia in man.

Infantile kala-azar occurring in the Mediterranean regions is probably disseminated through the dog as an intermediary host.   Dogs are carriers of several species of trypanosomes, tapeworms, trichinia and tongue worms, which may find their way to other animals and occasionally in some cases to man, causing disease.   They are also hosts of several different species of fleas and ticks which attack and annoy man and other animals.

Fish.—Various animal parasites, mainly intestinal and especially species of flukes and tapeworms, have been transmitted to man by eating contaminated fish which has been only partially cooked.

Hogs.—Hogs transmit trichinosis and tapeworms.   They may probably assist in the transmission of balantidial dysentery and other intestinal protozoan infections.   They are the carriers of *Bacillus* (*Salmonella*) *suipestifer*, which may be responsible for food infection in man.   They may be hosts of different species of ticks and fleas.

Horses.—Horses may transmit anthrax, actinomycosis, glanders and probably certain species of ticks.   They are also hosts for different species of trypanosomes (especially the disease surra, caused by a trypanosome) and stable flies.

SNAKES AND SNAKE VENOMS

In this country poisonous snakes are practically in our midst when we consider the facilities of travel. For a detailed description of the distribution and characteristics of poisonous reptiles, the student is referred to the different works on this subject. See an extensive article by the author on snakes and snake protection (*Am. J. Pharm.*, 1929, **101**, 385, 484); Gloyd ("The Rattlesnakes (genera *Sistrurus* and *Crotalus*)," Chicago Acad. Sci. spec. pub. No. **4**, 1940); Allen (*Florida Water Snakes*, Reptile Institute, Silver Springs, Fla., 1941); Clark ("Venomous Snakes. Some Central American Records," *Am. J. Trop. Med.*, 1942, **22**, 37); Davis and Brimley (*N. C. State Museum*, 1944); and Klauber (several publications in the Transactions of the San Diego Soc. Nat. Hist. and Bulletins of Zool. Soc., San Diego, California).

Snakes.—Snakes are vertebrate metazoa, members of the Order *ophidia* in the class of reptiles. They are distinguished primarily by their elongate body and absence of limbs and eyelids. The two families to which the poisonous snakes (thanatophidia) belong are the *colubridae* (colubrine snakes) and the *viperidae* (viperine snakes).

The *colubridae* are subdivided into three sections: The *aglypha*, which are solid-toothed, harmless colubrines; *opisthoglypha* (back-fanged snakes), which are suspicious as possessing poisonous venom; the *proteroglypha* (front-fanged snakes, with grooved teeth), among which are to be found the important poisonous colubrines. The proteroglyph snakes are divided into two subfamilies, the *elapinae*, or poisonous land colubrines, and *hydrophinae*, or poisonous sea snakes. The latter are mainly found in tropical, subtropical and warm countries. The most important elapines are found mainly in Australia, Africa and Asia. The several species of cobras, belonging to the genus *naja*, and the various species of kraits, belonging to the genus *bungarus*, are members of this subfamily. The American elapines are mainly found in South America, though two important members may be found in North America. The latter belong to the genus *elaps* or *micrurus*, and the two important species are the harlequin snake (*Micrurus fulvius*) and the Sonaran Coral snake (*Micrurus euryxanthus*), the former being found in southeastern United States and the latter in the southwestern part of this country.

The *viperidae* are found in Asia, Africa, Europe and America. They are divided into two subfamilies, the *viperinae* and *crotalinae*. There are practically no members of the *viperinae* found in this country. The *crotalinae* or "pit vipers" are solenoglyphs (highest stage of evolution of the poisonous fang, and possessing maxillary teeth which embrace a longitudinal tubular duct), and occur throughout temperate and tropical America and to a minor extent in Asia. The following important genera are included here:

(*a*) *Agkistrodon* (*ancistrodon*), which contains the important copperhead snake (*Agkistrodon mokassen* or *Agkistrodon contortrix*) and the cotton-mouth or water moccasin (*Agkistrodon piscivorus*), found in Central America and central and southern United States.

(*b*) *Lachesis*, containing many species found chiefly in South America and none found in North America.

(*c*) *Sistrurus*, found east of the Rocky Mountains. This genus contains the ground or pigmy rattler (*Sistrurus miliarius*), found through the southern part of United

States; the massasauga (*Sistrurus catenatus*), found in areas from Canada to Mexico; the *Sistrurus ravus*, found in the lowlands of eastern Mexico.

(*d*) *Crotalus*, or rattlesnakes, the several species of which are distributed from Argentina to Canada.

Of the true rattlesnakes, five species are of importance as a menace to man. They are the Florida Diamondback Rattlesnake (*C. adamanteus*), the Texas Diamondback Rattlesnake (*C. cinereous*), the Timber Rattlesnake (*C. horridus*), the Prairie Rattlesnake (*C. confluentus*) and the Pacific Rattlesnake (*C. oerganus*).

The most important poisonous snakes in North America belong to the subfamily *crotalinae* (*idae*). The rattlesnakes (*crotalus*), the copperhead (*Agkistrodon mokassen*) and the cotton-mouth or water moccasin (*Agkistrodon piscivorous*) are widely distributed in this country. The diamondback rattler is perhaps the most dangerous. Of the poisonous snakes in this country, bites from the water moccasin are not frequent, due probably to the semiaquatic habits of this species. Though the copperhead is present in large numbers in certain areas, it is not of considerable annoyance, because of the fact that it is not aggressive, will only strike if approached within 10 inches and but a small amount of venom is secreted. From the practical standpoint, the most widely distributed and most dangerous snakes in North America are the several species of rattlesnakes.

For details in the treatment of poisonous snake bites, see Staley (*Weekly Bull. St. Louis Med. Soc.*, 1939, **33**, 548), Young (*Am. J. Nursing*, 1940, **40**, 657) and Fish (*Nat. Safety News*, 1941, **43**, 18).

Venom.—From the practical standpoint, only certain varieties of snakes secrete an amount of venom which is harmful. The venom itself is a viscous, yellowish fluid, capable of exerting a toxic effect or destructive action when coming in contact with the inner tissues of a host.

Venoms are grouped with the proteins. *In vitro* they can be detoxified by heat or upon the addition of alkali, silver nitrate or potassium permanganate. Snake venom differs from microbial exotoxin in being relatively heat-resistant, in some cases withstanding fairly high temperatures. · Cobra venom is destroyed by heating to 100° C. only after long exposures. The snake venoms contain toxic elements against red cells (classified as hemotoxins and hemagglutinins), against nerve cells (neurotoxins), ngainst white blood cells (leukotoxins) and endothelium (endotheliotoxin, endotheliolysin or hemorrhagin). The hemorrhagin is especially marked in the rattlesnake. The venoms that are neurotoxic usually cause death by paralysis of cardiac and respiratory centers.

For further details, see Grasset (*Quart. Bull. Health Org. Eng., Nat.*, July, 1936) on snake venoms; Kellaway on snake venoms (*Bull. Johns Hopkins Hosp.* 1937, **60**, 1, 159); Peck and Marx on moccasin venoms (*J. Pharmacol. & Exper. Therap.*, 1937, **60**, 358) (*J. Mt. Sinai Hosp.*, 1940, **6**, 271); Macht and associates on cobra venom (*Proc. Soc. Exptl. Biol. Med.*, 1940, **43**, 458); Grasset and associate on "Boom slang" venom (*South African M. J.*, 1940, **14**, 236); Slotta and associates (*Nature*, 1939, **144**, 290) on crotoxin, the active principle in rattlesnake venom; and Weuse (*Biochem. Ztschr.*, 1939, **302**, 426) on the chemical nature of snake venoms.

Cobra and other snake venoms are being used with some success as an analgesic in the treatment of intractable pain due to cancer and other affections. See Hodes and

Thorner (*Am. J. Roentgenol.*, 1941, **45,** 866) and a preliminary report of the Council on Pharmacy and Chemistry on cobra venom (*J. A. M. A.*, 1940, **114,** 2218; **115,** 1196).

Bee venom supplied in lyophilized form is marketed in vacuoles, each containing the whole venom of ten bee stings.   It is employed in the treatment of acute and chronic arthritis and neuritis and appears to be most valuable in the extra-articular manifestations.   Bee venom *in solution* is extremely labile and loses its potency rapidly at room temperature.   Ainlay (*Nebraska M. J.*, 1939, **24,** 298) reports on its therapeutic efficiency.

PART V

INSECT CONTROL, INSECTICIDES AND FUMIGATION

Chapter XXIX

INSECT EXTERMINATION AND INSECTICIDES

INSECTS ARE directly or indirectly concerned in the spread of disease. They may transmit the causative agent directly to our system or indirectly to foodstuffs, etc., whence it is taken into the body, causing infection. In addition to the harm that may directly affect human beings, these pests may also interfere with the productiveness of crops and assist in the destruction of all kinds of foodstuffs and material. For success in the eradication of insect pests, the operator must be familiar with the environment being treated and the life history and habits of the insects or pests which are being attacked. The best procedure to be adopted so as to prevent invasion by insects is personal, environmental and general cleanliness, as the breeding places of most insects are in dirt and filth. The best means of getting rid of insects is *by preventing the formation of breeding places*, as personal cleanliness, general personal hygiene and avoidance of association with unclean companions, pets or unclean environments.

METHODS OF ERADICATION

Uniform cleaning-up methods in the home will materially lessen the number of breeding places and, in turn, the number of insects. Closets, as well as cellars, basements and other storage places should be regularly ventilated. Floors in cellars, garages, etc., should be of cement or other impervious material. All food, garbage and refuse should be placed in covered containers. Decaying vegetable or animal matter in or near the house, especially dense undergrowth, should be removed or treated with proper destructive agents. Buckets, barrels, or other receptacles in or around the home should be covered, screened or turned upside down, and no stagnant water should be allowed to stand in or collect around the house.

It is advisable that carpets should not be tacked to the floor. The latter as well as clothing and other apparel in closets, chests, trunks, etc., should be removed at least once or twice a year, shaken well and allowed to receive the benefit of the air and sunshine for a short period of time. Pets, such as cats, dogs, etc., should be provided with sleeping places that can be kept clean. If at any time a home is infested with insects it will be found best to burn the dust and refuse that is collected when cleaning rather than throwing it in a container to be taken away. Cracks and holes in floors, walls, around pipes, brickwork, etc., should be filled in with suitable filling materials. Careful inspections will reveal many possible hiding and breeding places which should be sealed. Ventilators should receive special attention. The hanging of pictures, mirrors, etc., should be discouraged. Windows and outside doors should be properly screened, especially during the warm months. Exposed foodstuffs, not only in homes, but also in shops selling food supplies, should be screened or otherwise covered, so that flies cannot gain access to them. In public places the free use of electric fans will help to keep flies away. People in infested regions will find it necessary to use various precautions. The wearing of boots, gloves, headnets and the use of bars and various nettings are frequently essential prophylactic measures. It may even be advisable to take various drugs, as quinine or atebrin for malaria, as a preventive measure. Finally it is necessary to stress repeatedly the importance of creating and maintaining a very high standard of cleanliness both in our environments and in our personal hygiene. This will do more to eliminate insect pests than any careful method of disinfestation in which primary cleanliness is absent.

In spite of all the precautionary measures, these insects may gain access and find their way into the household. Once these pests have become entrenched, determined effort is required to eradicate them. An endless variety of control methods has been introduced, and a countless number of destructive agents have been exploited and advocated as part of the proper campaign to be assured of the riddance of these pests. The use of baits, adhesive papers, swatters, traps, repellents, poisons, insecticides and fumigation is advocated. Unfortunately some of the most efficient of these are agents and procedures that can be used only occasionally.

Baits.—Baits containing various poisons are most effective for the destruction of many of the pests, but can only be used where children and domestic animals are not about and only by responsible individuals. A very effective poisonous bait for ants is to moisten a sponge or piece of bread with a syrup or molasses made by dissolving 1 ounce of sugar and 10 grains of arsenite of soda or 3 grains of thallium sulfate in 2 ounces of hot water. These compounds are poisonous and care must be exercised in their use. In some areas, it is illegal to sell and use these chemicals except by certain officials.

Poison baits and poison preparations for flies are also common. Some of them are made with compounds of arsenic (formula as above). The use of the latter, as mentioned, is attended with danger. A 2 to 5 per cent solution of sodium fluoride in a sugar solution is employed as an indoor poison for flies. In place of these it will be found that a weak solution of formaldehyde is very effective. One fluidounce of the latter added to 1 quart of milk or sweetened water can be conveniently placed in glasses, saucers or small, shallow pans in the doorway, in the pantry or wherever the flies are found. Some have at times advocated the placing of phosphorus paste on the inside of small tubes of folded cardboard, paper, etc., as a bait for roaches and even other pests. Small dishes filled with mixtures of equal parts of flour and plaster of Paris, where roaches and other insects appear, have been found as another effective bait. It is claimed that the insect is soon compelled to drink water, which results in the hardening of the plaster of Paris and death of the insect.

Baits are employed in traps of many patterns to attract Japanese beetles. A most effective formula is bran moistened with one-half of its weight of molasses and this mixture containing at least 10 per cent geraniol and 1 per cent eugenol

The normal method of stopping outbreaks of grasshoppers which have been such a nuisance within recent years is to distribute baits of arsenic-poisoned bran where the young insects crawl the thickets, before they get their wings and move over a wide territory. Pests in the field and garden and especially the fruit moth, Japanese beetle, cutworms, army worms, grasshoppers and crickets are controlled in part at least by poisoned baits. The one most frequently used (5 to 10 pounds per acre) is a bran containing 4 per cent white arsenic or Paris green moistened with a sufficient quantity of water containing one-quarter of its volume of molasses and flavoring (usually oranges or lemons ground with peel) to make a mash which is damp but from which water cannot be squeezed.

It is important to remember that if baits are to be employed they should be placed in environments, either frequented by the insect pests or where they are apt to be present, care being taken to place them in inaccessible compartments, so that children and pets may not reach them. It is also desirable that the baits should be distributed freshly and freely at frequent intervals.

Trapping.—The trapping of certain house insects is perhaps a very effective procedure, and is highly recommended where the use of poisons seem to be inadvisable. This method is to be desired and should be more commonly used. The traps are generally so constructed that the particular insect may easily get into them but cannot escape. Traps for roaches and especially for flies have been found very effective. There are many types on the market, but homemade devices are easily made. As a bait both for flies and roaches a mixture of 3 or 4 parts of water and 1 part of molasses which has been allowed to ferment has been proved to be very attractive. The trap is baited daily, and the catch destroyed by treatment with boiling water. It is important that traps employed for flies should be constructed so as to permit plenty of light to appear from the top, as otherwise the bait may not be seen by them. Various devices for catching fleas and mosquitoes are available, but are not as yet employed extensively.

Trapping by means of sticky flypaper or "Tanglefoot" is helpful. The latter is a mixture prepared by adding 8 parts of powdered resin (technical grade) to 5 parts (by weight) of hot castor oil (technical grade), and after simmering for ten to twenty minutes it is spread on glazed paper or other suitable material.

Swatting is effective for flies when they are annoying. Leather flaps or wire mesh attached securely to handles are conveniently used.

Temperature Control.—The possibility of temperature control in the eradication of insect pests from the household is of considerable interest, perhaps most effective, one of the simplest of methods and one which is infrequently employed. In real cold climates or in those localities where the winter is cold and homes untenanted, having been used for summer residence only, if a temperature slightly below freezing is maintained constantly in infested houses for a few weeks, the eggs, newly hatched young and most of the adults of most insect pests would be exterminated. Cold as employed in cold-storage warehouses (40° F. or lower) serves in keeping foodstuffs and all material free from attack by insect pests as the latter cannot develop in the temperatures maintained.

More efficient than cold temperatures, and a technique which can be more readily applied, is the maintaining of high temperatures in households for destructive purposes. Temperatures varying from 120° F. and over are found sufficient to quickly destroy fleas, flies, roaches, bedbugs, lice, moths and other insects and their eggs. The temperature must be maintained for a sufficient length of time so as to be assured that penetration into the lairs of the insect pests is attained at the degree of heat indicated. A minimum of eight to twelve hours may be necessary in inhabited quarters. The presence or absence of humidity apparently is not of much importance if this degree of heat is maintained. The superheating of houses in summer or during other favorable climatic conditions, from 120° to 140° F., is practical, will not affect household materials and equipment and is most effective for the destruction of insects. Clothing and other materials that may be infested with either insects or their eggs, by being exposed in rooms for at least one hour at a constant temperature as indicated or being boiled in water, if practical and convenient, or if exposed to the heat of hot irons, as in the process of laundering, will be quickly rid of these pests. Where hot-air chambers or hot-air rooms are used, the introduction of agents or methods to produce moving hot air is to be preferred. The exposure of cereals and other foodstuffs to a temperature of 140° to 160° F. has been employed as a satisfactory means for insect control. The temperature and period of exposure vary depending upon the destructive effects of the heat to the grain or foodstuffs and the insect pests and the stages of the latter to be destroyed.

In this connection mention may be made that the liberal use of hot water or live steam is an effective method for the destruction of both the active insects and their eggs. This may be used providing there is no danger of affecting furniture, fabrics and other materials with which it may come in contact. It is especially convenient for the destruction of bedbugs in beds made of material other than wood; ants in the home and garden; moths, lice and eggs from other insects on fabrics and clothing that will not be injured by water, roaches, etc. The use of the autoclave at 15 pounds' pressure (121.5° C.) for twenty to thirty minutes for disinfestation is a safe and very effective method. Treatment by steam under pressure, when available and applicable, is highly recommended. The rays of the sun during the warm season can also be used to obtain the required degree of dry heat. The old-time custom of sunning clothing to kill moths in fabrics is very effective and can be readily employed.

Grain pests are being eliminated also by passing the grain over a conveyor which is constantly subjected during its passage to an *electric field* between two poles. The insects are killed by electric shock.

Storage.—The use of cold storage as a method of protection against injury by fabric pests of all kinds is practiced extensively today. It is employed by dealers in upholstered furniture, blankets, curtains, robes, carpets, furs, woolens and other merchandise. Cold-storage rooms or warehouses are today a part of the equipment of all well-conducted business enterprises. The temperature that is maintained is rarely below 40° F. It will be found that this temperature, if maintained constantly, will protect articles only during the period of storage.

Moth bags.—So-called *mothproof* bags are employed for the storage of all kinds of wearing apparel, etc. Mothproof paper bags or tight wrappings do not kill moths. It is, therefore, of great importance to be assured that all articles laid away are first freed of moths and their larvae. Frequent brushing, cleaning, beating and aeration in the sun or even dry cleaning, if necessary, should be practiced. Special care should be given to the brushing of all seams, pockets, crevices, etc., during the cleaning of such material. These then should be protected by being wrapped in paper or placed in tight chests or sealed boxes and exposed in any place without danger of infestation from without.

Mothproofing of wool, feathers, hair, furs, rugs, upholstered furniture and similar materials is practiced extensively today.   Properly carried out, it is somewhat effective and saves the cost of storage or the use of special bags, chests, closets and insecticides. Various silicofluoride solutions, cinchona alkaloids, rotenone (*J. Econ. Entomol.*, 1930, **23**, 1014) and other compounds have been used as mothproofing agents.   The literature of mothproofing is to be found largely in patents, and information concerning these compounds has been compiled by Roark and Busbey ("The Indexes of Patented Mothproofing Materials," 1931, 1933, 1936, *U. S. Bur. Ent. and Plant Quarantine Pub.*).   The applying of mothproofing agents is best served during the manufacture of the fabrics, for if applied later, they are subsequently removed by washing or dry cleaning.   A recently introduced compound, pentachloro-dioxy-triphenolmethane sulfonic acid, is said to be able to withstand washing and dry cleaning.

USE OF INSECTICIDES

Insecticides may be classified under two heads:
  1.   For the destruction of household vermin.
  2.   For the destruction of pests infesting farms, plants, crops, etc.

The term *insecticide* is defined in the Insecticide Act of 1910, Sect. 6: "That the term 'insecticide' as used in this Act shall include any substance or mixture of substances intended to be used for preventing, destroying, repelling or mitigating any insects which may infest vegetation, man or other animals, or households, or be present in any environment whatsoever."   Regulation 14 of "Rules and Regulations of Carrying Out of the Provisions of the Insecticide Act of 1910" (United States Department of Agriculture, Office of Secretary, Circular No. 34, second revision, August 24, 1917, pp. 5 and 6) defines an insect as follows: "The term 'insect' as used in the Act and these Regulations is understood to mean any of the numerous small invertebrate animals which generally have the body more or less obviously segmented, for the most part belonging to the class insecta, comprising six-legged, usually winged forms, as beetles, bugs, bees, flies, etc., and to other allied classes of arthropods whose members are wingless and usually have more than six legs, as spiders, mites, ticks, centipedes, wood lice, etc."

A *fungicide* in its general meaning is anything which will kill or prevent the growth of fungi in any environment.   In its restricted definition it refers to the killing of fungi or preventing their development when applied to living and actively growing plants without destroying or seriously affecting the latter.   Chemicals or chemical solutions employed to kill animal parasites as itch mites, ticks, lice, fleas, bedbugs and the like are known at times as *parasiticides*.   Chemicals used to kill rodents as rats, ground squirrels, woodchucks and other burrowing animals are known as *rodenticides*.   Insecticides, fungicides, etc., may be effective against one type of insect or one species of fungi but not necessarily against all members in these respective groups.   Insecticides, rodenticides, etc., usually act as *stomach poisons* or *contact* (respiratory) *poisons*.   In using insecticides, rodenticides, parasiticides and similar agents, the various rules and regulations noted on page 291 are to be observed.   It is also important to note that many of these products and especially some insecticides may destroy only certain insect pests. Where infestation is due to several different insects or where bacteria and fungi are also envolved, it is a common practice to employ mixtures which will be useful at the same applications for all affections. Where this is practiced, it is necessary to see that the various chemicals used in the mixture are compatible with each other, so that an inert or ineffective preparation will not be produced.

Some States and many communities have regulations which require insect powders to be colored, so that such material will not be mistaken for flour or other baking ingredients. The addition of coloring to all powder insecticides is a sound practice and should be made compulsory by legal measures.

Insect Control.—It should be remembered that all control measures are palliative and frequently only of temporary value. The cause of infestation must be determined, if possible, and eradicated. Where poisonous chemicals or drugs are used as insecticides, they must be swallowed to produce death (*stomach poisons*) or as *contact poisons* they are absorbed through the breathing pores or the cuticle and only infrequently by smothering the insect through the clogging of the pores. Stomach poisons are most effective for insects which feed by biting or chewing as is practiced by beetles, cockroaches, crickets, caterpillars and grasshoppers. Contact poisons are most effective for those insects which suck. They puncture their food supply and through their proboscess suck up the juices, as is practiced by animal lice, aphids, fleas, flies, leaf hoppers and scale insects. Insecticidal fumigants are definitely more effective than the use of liquids or powders and, wherever applicable, should be used as they are effective against all types of insects, biting-chewing or piercing-sucking.

Fumigation.—*Premises*, whether small or large rooms or compartments, cellars, foundries, granaries, orchards (closed in with sheeting), greenhouses or any other closed-in structure *can be effectively rid of any kind of insect pest or rodent by hydrocyanic acid gas fumigation.*

The *fumes of carbon disulfide* have been used. This gas is an effective destructive agent against all vermin, but it is inflammable, violently explosive, and poisonous to human beings, though not as deadly as hydrocyanic acid gas.

The *fumes of burning sulfur* are frequently used in the destruction of all insects in different premises. Some observers have found success in burning pyrethrum and rotenone-bearing drugs (see page 427) in infested environments, the smoke and vapors of the latter having been found effective in destroying but more frequently in repelling or stupefying some pests. There is no danger of fire, explosion or injury from the latter vapors. *Chloropicrin* has been used in fumigating mills, elevators, ships, boxcars and food factories. *Orthodichlorobenzene* ($C_6H_4Cl_2$), a liquid, has been employed in greenhouse fumigation and for the control of certain wood-infesting larvae and beetles. Heating preparations containing free *nicotine* is widely used as a method of insecticidal fumigation in greenhouses, etc. One of the coal-tar products containing *cresyl* is volatilized by means of an alcohol lamp (see page 431). The vapor does not, however, possess the penetrating power of hydrocyanic acid and sulfur dioxide, and accordingly it is of value only for the destruction or *repelling* of exposed insects, as mosquitoes. Recently many other fumigants have come into favor and their use is rapidly increasing. (See Fumigation.) Fumigation with gases that have insecticidal properties should be practiced wherever possible as the best procedure for the destruction of insect pests. But such technique is not always practical (as in ridding human beings, ditches, ponds, etc., free from these pests or in such environments which are constantly inhabited, gases cannot be used). It is, therefore, apparent that means other than the use of gases alone are employed. This consists mainly in the proper application of powders, liquids or both, and the method of application varies depending upon the insecticide used and the insects against which it is applied.

Insecticides for Foliage.—Kerosene in the form of a diluted "kerosene emulsion" is used as a spring and summer spray on foliage for the destruction of plant pests and on lawns to control sod insects. The general formula for the "kerosene emulsion" is: soap, $^1/_2$ pound; water, 1 gallon; kerosene, 2 gallons. This emulsion is used in aqueous dilutions of 1:15 and 1:20 and weaker, and directed in a very fine spray to the foliage of the plant to be treated. *Lubricating-oil emulsions* and emulsions made of *tar-oil distillates* are extensively used as insecticidal agents to replace kerosene and lime sulfur sprays.

A liquid which as a valuable repellent has a wide use as an insecticidal and especially as a fungicidal spray on foliage, etc., is *Bordeaux mixture* prepared with lime or with lead arsenate, as follows:

Crystallized copper sulfate	3 pounds
Dry lead arsenate	1 pound
Water	50 gallons

If lime is to be used instead of lead arsenate 6 pounds of hydrated or 4 pounds of unslaked lime (90 per cent CaO) are added. The latter strength is expressed: "Bordeaux 3–4–50." In severe fungous diseases it may be necessary to increase the content of the fungicide, $CuSO_4$, to 4 pounds per 50 gallons (4–4–50). *Burgundy mixture* (sodium carbonate and copper sulfate) and *ammoniacal copper carbonate* (copper carbonate and ammonia) are less effective than *Bordeaux mixture* and may even burn foliage, but are used, at times, as a substitute.

LIME-SULFUR SPRAY

Lime (fresh)	3	pounds
Salt	1	pound
Sulfur	$1^1/_2$	pounds
Water	5	gallons

Boil the sulfur and lime with the water for a few hours, then add the other ingredients. This is a contact insecticide used after dilution as an orchard spray, except in hot weather. Lime-sulfur dilutions are also used as a dip in the control of mange and scab of hogs and other livestock pests.

The Arsenicals.—Arsenic and its compounds have been employed for years as the almost perfect insecticide and only recently due to the residue of this poison on sprayed plants there have been introduced other substitutes for orchard work. *Arsenate of lead* ($PbHAsO_4$ more frequently used than the basic lead arsenate) (1 to $1^1/_2$ pounds per 50 gallons of water) with lime or a fungicide or in strengths of 5 to 15 per cent as a dusting powder and calcium arsenate in the same strengths are widely used as stomach or internal poisons. The lead arsenate is used mainly on fruit and shade trees and the calcium arsenate is applied to cotton and vegetable crops. Distributing 5 pounds of lead arsenate to each 1000 square feet of surface on lawns or 1500 pounds per acre (disking, harrowing and then reseeding) is an effective method in rendering soil immune for a period of years to the attacks of grubs of the Japanese beetle. As a spray for foliage, etc., a 6 per cent lead arsenate spray is used for the control of the beetles.

Paris green, aceto-arsenite of copper, is used as a poison bait for grasshopper and caterpillar control, for the control of the potato beetle and where lead arsenate is employed except that it is not as satisfactory as the latter. The other arsenical products, if used as insecticides, are generally employed solely in poisoned baits. As a dust, Paris green is used in 10 to 20 per cent concentrations. As a spray, a widely used formula consists of 1 ounce of Paris green, 2 ounces of hydrated lime in 6 gallons of water. Dearborn (*J. Econ. Entomol.*, 1937, **30,** 804) presented an interesting survey on Paris greens and he introduced a number of homologues prepared by substituting other organic acids for acetic acid. Some of these possess an insecticidal power superior to that of Paris green and are less injurious to plants (*J. Econ. Entomol.*, 1935, **28,** 710; 1936, **29,** 445; 1937, **30,** 140, 958). Zinc arsenite is similar to Paris green in use and effectiveness. Roark (U. S. Bur. Ent. and Plant Quarantine, *Pub.* **E-564,** 1942) discusses many of these new but little-used copper-arsenic compounds which he regards worthy of trial and study. *Magnesium arsenate* (U. S. Bur. Ent. and Plant Quarantine, *Pub.* **E-451,** 1938) was at one time the only efficient agent used in the control of the Mexican bean beetle.

Copper Compounds are primarily fungicides, but do possess some insecticidal properties. The important copper compound used in addition to those mentioned above are combinations of copper sulfate or copper chloride with aniline, the basic sulfate and basic carbonate. For further details, see Nelson (*J. Phys. Chem.*, 1928, **32,** 1185; U. S. Dept. Agr., *Circ.* **452,** 1937). Cuprous oxide, available on the market as *cuprocide* (which contains 93 per cent cuprous oxide) is used in concentrations of $1^{1}/_{2}$ to 2 pounds per 100 gallons of spray or 100 pounds of dust. It is compatible with most materials except lime-sulfur.

Other suitable substitutes for copper fungicides are being investigated due to the wartime shortage of the latter. Organic compounds such as phenothiazine, tetramethyl thiouram disulfide and ferric dimethyl dithio carbonate are being investigated. Recently, Clayton (*Science*, 1942, **96,** 366) reported on the fungicidal value of the salicylates. The following yielded promising results: bismuth subsalicylate, benzyl salicylate, salicylic acid, zinc salicylate, butoxyethyl salicylate, dinitrosalicylic acid and salicyl salicylic acid.

Mercuric bichloride has been and is being used as a dip for many vegetable and flower seeds for controlling various diseases. It is usually used in 1:3000 to 1:1000 aqueous solutions, preferably containing 1 per cent hydrochloric acid. Mercuric oxide has been used by some in place of bichloride.

Ethyl mercury phosphate (1 to 5 per cent) and *chlorophenol mercury* with or without *nitrophenol mercury* are used in the control and treatment of various plant diseases. Mercurous and mercuric chlorides and other mercurial compounds are used, at times, as soil fungicides and in preventing various soil-borne lawn diseases.

Sprays and Washes.—The use of sprays and washes for the destruction of plant pests seems to be the most practical procedure as by contact with the insects the destructive agent is in a better position to exert its effect. The best method of applying these washes is to use some form of force pump with adequate pressure and to which is attached a nozzle which will produce a fine mist. A thorough moistening of all portions of the plant is generally necessary.

The wetting and spreading properties of solutions must be taken into consideration. Cupples (*J. Ind. Eng. Chem.*, 1935, **27,** 1219; 1936, **28,** 60, 434; 1937, **29,** 924; 1939, **31,** 1307) developed a quick and easy method of determining the spreading power and studied the spreading ability of the salts of many fatty acids. The wetting and spreading powers can frequently be increased by the addition of different chemicals as adjuvants. Various emulsifying agents are used for the preparation of oil emulsions. Cressman and Dawsey (*J. Agr. Research*, 1934, **49,** 1) determined the influence of many emulsifiers as to the quantity of oil deposited from various emulsions. In some instances, adhesive agents or stickers are required in emulsions, so that the active ingredients will stick to the foliage or material being treated. It is essential that the operator have a clear understanding of the role played by the supplementary or accessory materials, which are added to insecticides, so as to improve their application and usefulness. The addition of flour, soft soap, ammonium caseinate and other substances to any liquid mixture will give adhesive properties to the latter. Lime-sulfur or copper and lead arsenate are effective and cheap sprays.

Particle size in sprays of all insecticides plays an important role in the value of the latter. Smith and Goodhue (*Ind. Eng. Chem., Ind. Ed.*, 1942, **34,** 490) discuss in detail particle size in relation to insecticide efficiency. The kind of emulsion used and the method and frequency of spraying occupy prominent places not only as to the final result obtained, but residues on fruit and other substances treated must be readily and effectively removed by washing procedures, so as to meet the arsenic and lead tolerances established by the Department of Agriculture for marketed products. The dangers from poisonous residues must be recognized. For the relative efficiency of different lead arsenate sprays, see Steiner and associates (*Tr. Indiana Hortic. Soc.*, 1935) and for data concerning calcium arsenate, see Goodhue (*J. Econ. Entmol.*, 1937, **30,** 466), Nelson and Cassil (*ibid.*, 1937, **30,** 474; 1938, **31,** 278).

Nicotine, the volatile liquid alkaloid of tobacco (*Nicotiana tabacum*), is a valuable insecticidal fumigant. Sold mainly as an aqueous solution of the sulfate, containing 40 per cent of nicotine, it enters into the composition of many contact insecticides. It kills a wide range of both chewing and sucking insects. Nicotine is unrivaled as a destructive agent for plant lice. It can also be prepared to serve as an efficient stomach poison for some pests. Nicotine can be used as a spray for almost all types of plants as it will not injure the most delicate foliage. It is, however, more expensive and toxic to vertebrates. It is water-soluble, but should be kept in tightly stoppered containers as it decomposes very quickly. Nicotine combines well with other spray materials in general use and when employed by itself, soap is added as a spreader to make it more effective. Painting perches with a 40 per cent nicotine sulfate solution just before roosting time is a most effective method for the control of poultry lice and probably chicken mites. A satisfactory formula is:

Nicotine (commercial—usually 95 to 98 per cent)	8 ounces
Soft soap (or saponin—2 ounces).	10 pounds
Water	100 gallons

The nicotine content may be increased to from 10 to 16 ounces when caterpillars or similar pests are to be destroyed. It is best to use the spray when the sun is not shining.

Nicotine bentonite (U. S. Bur. Ent. and Plant Quarantine, *Pub.* **E-428,** 1938) is now being used extensively as a poison for chewing insect pests and especially for the control of the codling moth.   See Steine, *et al.* (*Trans. Illinois Hortic. Soc.*; 1938, **72**, 439). The formula is:

Nicotine sulfate solution (40 per cent nicotine) . . . .   1 pint
Wyoming bentonite . . . .   5 pounds
Soybean oil . . . .   1 quart
Water, to make . . . .   100 gallons

The nicotine is fixed and is not so volatile.   New compounds of nicotine have been prepared and are under investigation.   Other species of the genus *Nicotiana* and hybrids of these with tobacco have been studied for constituents of insecticidal value. *Anabasine* (*J. Am. Chem. Soc.*, 1935, **57**, 959) from *Nicotiana galuca* and *laevo-nornicotine* (*J. Econ. Entomol.*, 1937, **30**, 724) from *Nicotiana sulvestris* are two such constituents under investigation.   New nicotine compounds, as nicotine peat (*J. Ind. Eng. Chem.*, 1936, **28**, 648; 1938, **30**, 1199), nicotine humate (*ibid.*, 1936, **28**, 648) and salts with the alpha-bromo derivatives of palmitic and stearic acids, have been developed. For a consideration of homemade nicotine spray solutions and their preparation from tobacco, see U. S. Bur. Ent. and Plant Quarantine, *Pub.* **E-361**, 1935, and for a complete bibliography of nicotine and its insecticidal uses, see U. S. Bur. Ent. and Plant Quarantine, *Pub.* **E-384**, 1936; **E-392**, 1937.

Morkwood (U. S. Bur. Ent. and Plant Quarantine, *Pub.* **E-561**, 1942) recently presented a review of information on *Nornicotine*.   It is a colorless liquid alkaloid, present in many species of *Nicotiana*.   It is closely related to nicotine chemically, is less volatile, more stable, equally or possibly more toxic toward insect pests, but less active toward human beings and warm-blooded animals.   Provisionally, its prospects are excellent as an effective insecticide.

Dipridyl oil and related compounds have been recommended as an effective remedy for the eradication of some of the injurious plant pests (see *J. Am. Chem. Soc.*, 1928, **50**, 1936, 2471–2487; 1930, **52**, 397; 1931, **53**, 277).

Derris powders and derris extracts (containing *rotenone* as the active ingredient) have about the same range of application as nicotine and are employed for spraying in gardens and greenhouses.   Sprays of *sodium silicofluoride* (0.5 per cent aqueous solution) have been found to have a decided effect in checking the bacterial spot of peach on the leaves.   Sodium fluoride and sodium fluosilicate sprays (0.5 to 1 per cent) have been recently recommended to replace the arsenicals in the destruction of many pests on plants, fruits, vegetables, etc.   Carter (*Science*, 1943, **97**, 383) presented preliminary results on *D-D Mixture* (equal parts of 1,3-dichloropropylene and 1,2-dichloropropane) in which it appears that this may be a useful soil disinfectant.   In pineapple fields, 150 pounds of the mixture per acre give favorable results.

Dusts.—Dusts are preferred by some individuals who claim that they possess better penetrative properties, are easier to apply and they can be made to adhere to the foliage.   The operation is, however, more costly, the insecticidal action is slower and if the wind is blowing it may be impossible to apply properly.   Paris green and other arsenicals, slaked lime and flowers of sulfur are frequently used, diluted with flour, kaolin, gypsum or any other inert carrier.   The finer the grade of dust, the greater efficiency will result, due to the adhesiveness, penetration and killing power.   Various liquids may be used as dusts by incorporating them with an inert carrier as kaolin, flour, etc. A 2 per cent *nicotine* dust is used by some individuals in treating plants, etc., to rid them of pests. Sodium, calcium and barium *fluosilicates* have been used in bean beetle control and are being proposed instead of arsenicals. Sodium fluoride and sodium fluosilicate dusts are being used in the control of poultry lice. They are also used as baits for crickets and other insects. Barium fluosilicate and sodium fluoaluminate are employed occasionally as dusts. Pyrethrum, as a dusting powder, has been used to control vegetable insect pests. Dusts containing rotenone-bearing drugs, having a minimum content of 0.75 per cent rotenone, are replacing the arsenicals or vegetables. Spraying or dusting of crops, etc., requires special adaptations especially as to the arrangement of the discharge. A fine, uniform spray under good pressure is most effective and economical.

Insecticides for the Home.—Wherever possible and practical, a liquid insecticide should be used first, and then followed by a powder. The former can be sprayed or dropped into cracks, crevices, etc., and because of a free flow or a vapor that may be produced, a greater surface can be reached. Due to the rapid evaporation of liquid insecticides, they should be applied freely and frequently. In applying them care should be taken that a large surface is reached. Spraying or squirting on a small scale and especially by the inexperienced is only to be employed when mopping or the application of the insecticide with a paint brush cannot be used. It is advisable that the operation which is employed should be repeated at intervals of four or five days for at least three successive applications, so that any eggs that may have hatched during the intervening period may be destroyed. It is important to insist upon thoroughness in directions employed when exterminating insects.

The use of pressure sprays is of value, as they aid in introducing quickly a large quantity of a fine mist of insecticidal agents over a large surface area, and this is done with comparative ease. The military of our country in this present World War is equipped with so-called *aerosol bombs* for overseas use in combating ants, flies, mosquitoes and other insect pests (*Soap and Sanit. Chemicals*, 1942, **18**, 91). The term *aerosol* here refers to a fine spray and is not to be confused with *Aerosol*, a trademarked name for a group of wetting agents. The aerosol bombs contain a refined concentrated pyrethrum extract, which is propelled as a fine mist or spray by a gas (dichlorodifluoromethone) under pressure. The aerosol method (*Science*, 1944, **99**, 85) will undoubtedly come into extensive use as a more effective method for dispersing insecticides and other applications.

Kerosene or *coal oil, benzine, gasoline* and *carbon disulfide*, in their order named, are the most effective and most frequently used of the liquid insecticides. Care must be taken that these are employed in such places that they will not be a fire hazard. Carbolic acid or, better still, cresol, a liquid obtained in the destructive distillation of coal tar, can be added to the extent of from 1 to 5 per cent, so as to make a more effective and useful solution. Some have advised adding about 10 or 15 per cent of turpentine to the coal oil or kerosene before adding the cresol. Turpentine is not only in itself an effective insecticide, but will disguise somewhat the coal-oil odor.

Kerosene or closely related *hydrocarbons* may be employed to destroy mosquito larvae in stagnant pools by covering the surface of the latter with a thin film of the oil or, to be exact, using 1 fluidounce of kerosene for each 15 square feet of water surface. The film is to be replaced after the coal oil evaporates. *Gambusia*, employed especially in European countries, has been found effective in standing water as an eradicator of the aquatic stages of the mosquitoes. The treatment of breeding places with 5 per cent Paris green in a fine dust carrier, using at least 1 pound per each 2 acres treated is effective mostly for malarial mosquitoes which feed on the surface. Minnows and fish eat mosquito larvae and are at times employed for this purpose. See also under respective insect pests.

Many of the liquid insecticides on the market, which are sold under various trademarks and fancy names, are essentially nothing more than kerosene, to which may be added pyrethrum concentrates or rotenone or cresol or a closely related chemical, and the coal-oil odor is disguised by the addition of any one or a mixture of the following oils, which in most instances possess some insecticidal properties themselves—oil of mirbane, oil of sassafras or safrol, oil of eucalyptus, oil of camphor, oil of cassia, oil of wintergreen and oil of pine. There is this, however, to be said on behalf of these marketed products: that the coal oil used is generally of a grade which is known as water-white and also one which possesses a high flash point. The water-white grade generally is stainless, an effect especially to be desired if clothing, rugs, etc., are to be sprayed with a liquid insecticide.

Strong solutions of bichloride of mercury have been advocated and recommended. A saturated solution of bichloride of mercury in denatured alcohol and a mixture of denatured alcohol and turpentine have been proclaimed as efficient preparations, especially for bedbugs.

Instead of kerosene, water has been used to make a solution of bichloride of mercury and carbolic acid and a mixture of soap and water has been used to dissolve cresol. These aqueous solutions have been used as efficient insecticides.

Various powders, especially Dalmatian or Japanese insect powder (16 ounces of powder to 1 gallon of hydrocarbon oil), and rotenone-bearing drugs have been macerated or percolated with coal oil, and to the resulting mixture after filtration there has been added one or more of the volatile oils to destroy the coal-oil odor. Pyrethrum extracts assayed as to total pyrethrums are used today. These preparations are widely used, especially for flies and mosquitoes, and are of value for all commonly found insect pests.

Wherever fumigation cannot be practiced kerosene emulsions or kerosene containing coal-tar derivatives or, better, kerosene containing pyrethrum concentrates or rotenone or lethane or mixtures of these will be found efficient as an insecticidal agent for the destruction of many pests. It is important that the preparation should be used freely, frequently and the directions that are employed should be thorough and practical.

Lice (Body, Head, etc.).—Perfect personal cleanliness should be practiced. The head should be thoroughly washed with kerosene containing 2 to 3 per cent phenol or cresol or apply for twenty-four hours equal parts of kerosene and olive oil or vinegar. Some have been using a 15 to 30 per cent solution of xylol in liquid petrolatum. The head is covered with a cloth, and after several hours washed well with hot water and soap. In the case of body lice the clothes are fumigated or sterilized. This being impractical in the household, the next best thing is to soak them in kerosene containing 2 to 3 per cent of a coal-tar disinfectant for one hour and then washing in soap and warm water. Patients should be cautioned of the danger of inflammability when kerosene is employed. It is advisable to remove all hair on the body and even on the head, especially in males, as one of the best means of eradicating these pests when successive treatments have failed.   Sponging the entire body with a solution of mercuric chloride (1:1000 either in water or vinegar) and washing the body after several minutes is effective for all species except head lice.   All insecticidal applications should be followed by a hot bath.   Derris powder, or powders of rotenone-bearing drugs, or *N. C. I.* powder (naphthalene, 96 per cent; creosote, 2 per cent; iodoform, 2 per cent), dusted on and rubbed into the seams of underwear and clothing, are effective lice repellents.   A brilliantine, consisting of 25 per cent laurylthiocyanate or 25 per cent Lethane 384 or a cream containing 1 per cent rotenone and 7 per cent derris extract applied to the roots of the hair will remain effective against lice for from seven to ten days.   The head should not be washed for ten days after applying to the scalp these preparations in doses of from 2 to 8 Gm.   For infestation of the eyebrows and eyelashes, a 2 per cent yellow oxide of mercury ointment in petrolatum or petrolatum and lanolin are recommended.

DDT, *dichloro-diphenyl-trichloro-ethane,* known also as *gesarol* and *neocid,* has proved of great value in military areas where the removal of body lice and the eradication of mosquitoes are factors in the control of typhus fever and malaria. It is reasonably nontoxic to humans, does not possess an objectionable odor and has a pronounced staying power.   It is insoluble in water, but will dissolve in the latter if a wetting agent is present.   It is generally employed in suspensions, in sprays, as a dusting powder or in the so-called aerosol "bombs."   A 1:20 dilution in kerosene will kill all mosquitoes if the suspension is sprayed in a room and 1^1/$_2$ ounces are enough to control an acre of swamp.   It is a contact as well as an internal poison.   Dusted into the clothing in the form of a powder, a single application provides anti-louse protection for a month.   Laundering of clothes does not appreciably diminish its insecticidal effects.   A 1:100 and still better a 1:25 spray is very effective against flies, roaches and other insects which are a menace to humans, animals and plants.   It is effective against the coddling moth worm, the spruce bud worm, the wood tick and the potato psyllid.

Phenyl cellosolve, MYL, Powders No. 153 and No. 452 are other anti-louse preparations which have been used by the military.

Infestation with the crab louse should be treated as the other lice infestations.   The entire area should be shaved (if practical) to remove all nits.   This may be followed by the use of 25 per cent xylol in liquid petrolatum, vinegar containing bichloride of mercury (1:1000), one of the other insecticidal preparations, or an application of diluted mercurial ointment, to be followed by a hot bath.   *Cuprex* (manufactured by Merck and Co., Rahway, N. J.), a colorless and almost odorless solution of an organic copper salt containing tetralin, acetone and liquid petrolatum, is also recommended for the destruction of all three varieties of lice.   It is generally not necessary to sacrifice the hair.   This liquid is inflammable and is irritating to the eyes and open wounds and sores.   The mosquito repellent "sta-way" (see page 388) has been recommended by Spencer (*Rev. Applied Entomol.*, 1941, **20,** 143) for the control of the crab louse.   It is applied with a shaving brush or cotton.   No ill effects have been observed on the skin.

Derris powder and other rotenone-bearing powders and soaps containing the latter have proved of great value as remedies for some of the external parasites of domestic animals and plants (lice, fleas and certain mites).   Tar and nicotine soaps are also used for the control of pests on animals.

Other than the kerosene type preparations, there is really no other liquid which can be regarded as a general insecticide. There are, however, liquid preparations which are effective when used for the specific purposes as follows: Turpentine or wood alcohol or a mixture of the two containing bichloride of mercury have been found effective for bedbugs; cedar-leaf oil for moths; carbon disulfide for ants and their larvae; extracts of hellebore and coal-tar emulsions as preventives against the breeding of flies and mosquitoes; extracts of larkspur, sabadilla seed or fishberries for lice; 2 or 3 per cent solutions of coal-tar disinfectants for fleas on cats, dogs and domestic animals.

Itch Mites.—Sulfur in the form of sulfur ointment or *Kathiolan* (containing sulfides which liberate H_2S), employed in the Danish method of treatment, is a very effective agent for the destruction of the itch mites, which are the cause of itch, scabies or mange in various human beings or other animals. It is advisable to precede the application of the sulfur by a warm bath with a vigorous soapy massage, so as to open the pores. The ointment is allowed to stay on overnight, applied again the next morning and evening within which time the hydrogen sulfide which is formed in contact with the skin will act as the destructive agent. This should be followed by another bath. Such treatment may not kill the eggs. It is, therefore repeated within two weeks to destroy any other mites that may have developed. With *Kathiolan*, a single application is usually sufficient. Individuals who cannot stand this treatment or who quickly develop sulfur skin rashes will find that application of an ointment of betanaphthol alone or in combination with balsam of Peru, every four hours, on the affected area will be effective. An ointment containing 27 per cent of an extract of pyrethrum flowers (representing 0.75 per cent of pyrethrin I and II), as well as a jelly base containing 2 per cent rotenone, has been used effectively in the treatment of scabies. *Scabicide* (an ointment) where only one application is used in the treatment, preceded and followed by a hot bath, has been advocated.

Repellents.—Of temporary value in infected places is the use of a number of substances that are known as repellents. The latter act by driving the insects away rather than destroying them. There are many liquids which act as repellents. The volatile oils are especially suited for such purpose. Oils of eucalyptus, pennyroyal, wintergreen, etc., and powders such as iodoform and naphthalene are of temporary value in flea-infested places by applying the oil or powder to the clothing, between bed sheets, on windows, screens, etc. Oils of citronella, anise, peppermint, pennyroyal, cedarwood, bergamot, cassia, cloves, lavender and other volatile oils are used in like manner for mosquitoes. Dr. Howard, of the United States Department of Agriculture, has recommended an effective application in the following formula: oil of citronella, 2 parts; spirits of camphor, 2 parts; oil of cedar, 1 part. The chemicals used in mothproofing are repellents as are those phenolic compounds used on wood for repelling termites. Sprays of various odorless hydrocarbon distillates containing pyrethrum concentrates, or rotenone, or lethane are used not only for their killing effect but also for their repellent action. They are employed especially on livestock. "Sta-way" used as a repellent for mosquitoes is also used for crab lice and other insect pests. A preparation similar to this has been found effective against flies, chiggers, mosquitoes, etc., and it is noninjurious to humans. It consists of 65 per cent diethylene glycol monobutyl ether acetate and diethylene glycol monoethyl ether, 28 per cent alcohol and 7 per cent corn oil.

Repellents have come to the forefront especially during the present war. Troops on many fronts in tropical and semitropical regions find repellents of great value as one of the important measures in the preventive campaign to keep away mosquitoes and other annoying and disease-carrying insect pests. The problem here is complicated in that many factors must be considered, such as: the effective staying powers of the repellent, the nonirritating properties of the compounds used when coming in contact with the skin of man and animals, their availability (for instance, rotenone, pyrethrum and other suitable agents are scarce during war times) and their effectiveness against all species of the insect pest being repelled (some repellents will be found to be efficient for anopheline mosquitoes but will have little effect against species of other genera). The penetrating odor of a repellent may be objectionable during the actual skirmishes and when in combat. It may aid the enemy by quickly supplying information as to hide-outs, etc. Among the newer mosquito repellents, *dimethyl-phthalate* and a preparation designated as *612* have found wide use. Pine-tar oil was found useful as a repellent for the screw-worm fly and other flies on cattle, sheep and other animals (see Leake and associates, U. S. Dept. Agr., *Tech. Bull.* **270,** 1931). Mothproofing (see page 403) is in reality the application of the practical use of repellents. Many repellents (liquids and powders) are considered in other parts of this chapter and under the respective insect pests.

The term *chemotropism* has come into use and refers to the study of agents used for attracting insects to traps or poison baits or employed to repel insects from man and domestic animals or crops. Freeman and Haller (*J. Am. Chem. Soc.*, 1938, **60**, 2274) describe various amyl esters of salicylic acid which are useful as *attractants* for the tobacco-hornworm. Attractants or, as some call them, *attractors* are useful in other programs for eliminating various insect pests, as is commonly practiced for reducing the numbers of Japanese beetle. Different volatile oils are used as baits to attract the pests into containers or environments where they cannot escape, and they are then killed or burned.

Powders.—It has been the author's observation that by opening a program in the eradication of insects by first using a heavy spray or application of a cresol-kerosene mixture more effective results are obtained. Then follow with a powdered insecticide, which will act as an internal poison, or probably clog up their breathing passages, eventually killing those that remain. This powder should be sprinkled in places where it can be left undisturbed for a long time.

So-called *insect powder* has a wide range of application. There are many powders available which are used as insecticides, as powdered tobacco, hellebore, stramonium, various species of chrysanthemum and many other plants belonging to the plant family *compositae*. It may thus be seen that the term insect powder may be used both in a general and a specific sense. Inasmuch as various species of *chrysanthemum* have been supplied for years as "insect powder," the Department of Agriculture ruled (see Insecticide Decision No. 1, issued August 26, 1911) that:

"Insect powder when used without qualification means an insecticide made from the powdered *flower heads* of species of *chrysanthemum:* (1) *Chrysanthemum* (*Pyrethrum*) *cinerariaefolium;* (2) *Chrysanthemum* (*Pyrethrum*) *roseum;* (3) *Chrysanthemum* (*Pyrethrum carneum*) *marshalli.* The stems are not to be preferred, but if used statements to that effect should be made. The stems are practically worthless as insecticidal agents. Species No. 1, *Chrysanthemum cinerariaefolium*, is *Dalmatian insect powder*. Species No. 2 and No. 3 are the Persian variety, so-called *Persian Insect powder*.

Persian insect powder, known also as *insect or pyrethrum powder*, is a common remedy which has been employed to assist in insect eradication. It is nontoxic to man and domestic animals. Its use as a fumigant and as an effective remedy against mosquitoes has been mentioned. As sold or as stored around the home, pyrethrum powder may become stale and then possess little or no value. Relief with its use can only be obtained if the fresh powder is liberally and frequently applied.

McDonnell, et al. (U. S. Dept. Agr., Tech. Bull. **1938,** 1930), report on the relative insecticidal value of different commercial grades of pyrethrum and call attention to the fact that open flowers are more efficient insecticidal agents than closed flowers. The two principal insecticidal constituents of pyrethrum, pyrethrin I and pyrethrin II, look like glycerin, but are complex in their chemical composition and structure, and even possess differences in their action and toxicity. Sullivan, et al. (Soap, 1938, **14,** 101) revealed that pyrethrin II was responsible for the "knockdown" on flies and pyrethrin I for the "kill." Various solvents are used, especially ethylene dichloride, for extracting the pyrethrins (Ind. Eng. Chem., 1929, **21,** 1251) and concentrated pyrethrum extracts are widely used as ingredients in liquid sprays. For a consideration of the chemistry of pyrethrum flowers, see Haller and La Forge (Pests, 1939, **7,** 9). It is of interest to note that the common field daisy which closely resembles and has been used to adulterate pyrethrum does not contain the pyrethrins or other active insecticidal substances (Soap, 1936, **12,** 109). West (Nature, 1943, **152,** 660) reported that concentrates rich in pyrethrins I and II, stored in the dark for some months, showed an "apparent" high pyrethrin content, but nevertheless a marked reduction in toxicity and a corresponding reduction in effectiveness against house flies.

The National Association of Insecticide and Disinfectant Manufacturers has adopted standards for pyrethrum and rotenone insecticidal preparations, for the liquid hydrocarbon bases employed and for an Official Control Insecticide (O. C. I.), the latter to be used as a standard for evaluating unknown insecticides, especially liquid fly sprays. The Peet-Grady Entomological Kill Test or modifications of the latter are used to determine the efficiency of fly sprays. For details of insecticide tests, see Badertscher (Soap, Sept., 1936, and Sept., 1937). Recently, on account of the scarcity of pyrethrum and rotenone, the standards have been lowered. Formerly the total pyrethrin content was to be not less than 0.3 per cent per 100 cc. of preparation. This was lowered recently to 0.2 per cent. Some observers have advocated the sprinkling of pyrethrin on floors after coal oil or cresol and coal oil have been used, so as to assist in the eradication of fleas, or use a kerosene-pyrethrum solution or spray. Symes (War Med., 1942, **2,** 340) uses and advocates light dustings of pyrethrum powder, twice weekly, for insect control as a repellent for mosquitoes, flies, fleas, bedbugs, cockroaches and lice. He recommends one ounce for each 500 square feet area on inside surfaces and in latrines, three ounces per seat, twice weekly.

This powder, when fresh, will destroy the larvae of moths in clothes, if the latter are thoroughly dusted with the powder and then placed in a tightly constructed chest or trunk or wrapped well in unbroken paper. Effective against roaches and other insect pests, one may find that pyrethrum is frequently used by itself or as an ingredient of powder insecticides. The minimum standard for a satisfactory insecticidal and especially fly spray is a kerosene solution containing 100 mg. of total pyrethrins in each 100 cc. Pyrethrum powders or extracts are purchased on their content of total pyrethrins, so that it is convenient to estimate the amount of these substances required per gallon of kerosene or other suitable liquid or powder to obtain a minimum standard fly spray or an effective insecticidal liquid or powder. For a consideration of home-made pyrethrum-kerosene sprays, see Gertler and Haller (*Soap*, 1939, **15**, 1). Beetles, many larger soft-bodied insects found in the garden and pests infesting orchards are killed by pyrethrum and its preparations.

Derris.—The history of the use of *derris* as an insecticide was compiled by Roark (U. S. Bur. Ent. and Plant Quarantine, *Bull*. **E-468,** 1938). Various species of derris (*D. elliptica* and *D. chinensis*) found in Asia were found to contain as the most active insecticidal constituent, *rotenone*. LaFarge and associates (*Chem. Rev.*, 1933, **12,** 181) determined the chemical structure of the latter. Subsequently other insecticidal constituents were found in species of derris, namely, *deguelin, tephrosin* and *toxicarol* (*J. Am. Chem. Soc.*, 1932, **54,** 3000, 4454; 1933, **55,** 422, 759; 1934, **56,** 987). Later it was observed that other plants contained rotenone and even some of the latter constituents. *Lonchocarpus*, a genus of tropical shrubs and trees, represented by more than 40 species found in South America, contains rotenone (even in larger amounts than derris) and at present is the principal source of the latter used in the United States. Several of these species are toxic to fish and these fish-poisoning species are known in the respective South American countries by such names as *cube, barbasco, timbo, haiari* and *nekoe*. These names are used also in commerce for species of *Lonchocarpus*. However, it is well to remember that in Spanish-speaking countries, such synonyms may apply to any fish-poisoning plant. *Tephrosia* (*Cracca*) *virginiana*, or devil's shoestring (a plant native to the United States), and other species of *tephrosia* were found to contain rotenone and related compounds.

Rotenone possesses a low toxicity to human beings and warm-blooded animals, being only one-thirtieth as toxic as lead arsenate when fed to rabbits. It is, however, highly toxic to most insects. For instance, as a stomach poison to silkworms, rotenone is 15 times as toxic as lead arsenate and 30 times as toxic as nicotine to bean aphids. It is used in many insecticidal sprays found efficient for flies, and for combating insect pests in the home and greenhouse, on cattle and other animals, and for horticultural use. As a rotenone dust, it is widely used for combating insect pests attacking gardens and truck crops, and as a constituent of many insect powders used in the home. Insecticidal preparations should contain more than 0.1 per cent and preferably at least 0.5 to 0.7 per cent rotenone. For other uses, see under respective insect pests. For details on rotenone and rotenone-bearing drugs, see Roark (*J. Econ. Entomol.*, 1941, **34,** 684, and U. S. Bur. Ent. and Plant Quarantine, *Pub*. **E-446, 452, 468, 514, 516, 563** and **605**).

Thiocyanates.—The insecticidal value of the vapors of volatile organic thio-cyanates was first shown by Neifert (U. S. Dept. Agr., *Bull*. **1313,** 1925). Many different synthetic aliphatic thiocyanates and aromatic isothiocyanates are avail-.able as efficient insecticides. Naphthyl isothiocyanate (*Kessocide*) (see *Soap*, February, 1938) and lauryl thiocyanate (*Loro*) are marketed.

Lethane is the trade-marked name of a synthetic aliphatic thiocyanate insecticidal concentrate. Two preparations are available—*Lethane 384* and *Lethane 384 Special*. Both are equal in killing power but the former adds the important property of repellency, which frequently is desired, as in a cattle spray. Lethane 384 is a 50 per cent solution in kerosene (deodorized hydrocarbon distillate) of *n*-butyl carbitol thiocyanate (beta butoxy), (beta' thiocyanodiethyl ether). A spray containing 5 per cent *Lethane 384 Special* (or an equal quantity of lethane and pyrethrum 20:1) in kerosene is an efficient insecticide especially for crawling pests (in all stages, as bedbugs, flies, fleas, cockroaches, ants, moths, carpet beetles, lice, etc.). It is stable, possesses only a slight odor, is noncorrosive, does not stain and is without health hazard to warm-blooded animals in the recommended concentrations. This product or, better, *Lethane 60* combined with reduced amounts of pyrethrum and rotenone is being employed in the manufacture of dusts to be used in agriculture wherever the ordinary botanical dusts are usually applied and especially in the control of aphis, asparagus and Mexican bean beetles, spotted cucumber and striped cucumber beetles, leaf hoppers, thrips, cabbage loopers, diamondback moth, Colorado potato beetle, potato flea beetle, rose slugs, imported cabbage worm and tomato horn worms. The use of lethane in a body belt for the destruction of lice has proved effective (*War Medicine*, 1943, **4**, 223).

Lethane and other thiocyanates have not, as yet, been found as effective for flies as preparations containing pyrethrum. The knockdown or stunning properties of both types of preparations are equally satisfactory, but the subsequent killing effect is more effectively displayed by pyrethrum preparations. However, the cost of the latter can be reduced by replacing some of the pyrethrum extract with lethane or other suitable thiocyanates.

Thanite, the thiocyanate of a secondary terpene alcohol (discovered by chemists of the Hercules Powder Company, Wilmington, Del.), is recommended as a substitute for pyrethrum and rotenone in fly-killing sprays. It is said to be effective against mosquitoes, roaches, ants, mites, bedbugs, centipedes, spiders and moths. Thanite, unlike pyrethrum sprays, is as effective against female flies as it is against the male. It is used as a spray in a 5 per cent solution in heavy mineral oil.

Piperonylamides when used alone in concentrations of 10 mg. per cc. produce a mortality in house flies at least as high as a standard solution of 1 mg. per cc. pyrethrin and possess a definite synergistic effect when added to pyrethrin-containing solutions. They do not possess, however, a rapid paralytic or knockdown action. For other data, See Gertler, *et al.* (*Soap and Sanit. Chemicals*, 1943, **19**, 105).

Other Powders.—*Sodium Fluoride.*—One of the most simple and effective powder insecticides is commercial sodium fluoride. This chemical forms the basis of most roach powders on the market. It may be used undiluted, but most frequently there is added from 10 to 50 per cent of some inert substance, as flour, etc. Employed as a dusting powder in or around cracks, crevices, closets, etc., this powder, if used persistently, with frequent and free applications, will eventually rid badly infested environments of roaches. It has been claimed that sodium fluoride scattered frequently and freely on floors or blown about in infested places, will be found to be somewhat effective against fleas and other insects, as it is against roaches and ants. A mixture of sodium fluoride, containing about 10 per cent of borax, some flour and a small percentage of sugar or powdered chocolate, will make an ideal powder to be used for general insecticidal purposes. Sodium fluoride has also been used to kill lice on fowls and other livestock. It is applied dry or fowls are dipped in an aqueous solution containing one ounce of sodium fluoride per gallon. For a review of the use of fluorine compounds as insecticides, see Busbey (U. S. Bur. Ent. and Plant Quarantine, *Pub.* **E-466**, 1939). *Quassia* wood and infusions of the latter were used at one time extensively in the control of flies, but have been replaced by more conveniently used and more effective preparations. As an insecticide, quassia is used today mainly for the control of the hop aphid. For a complete bibliography, see Busbey (U. S. Bur. Ent. and Plant

Quarantine, *Pub.* **E-483,** 1939). *Powder sabadilla seed (Veratrum sabadilla)* is effective for roaches and lice. Extracts of the latter drug and also of *hellebore (Veratrum album and Veratrum viride)* and, still better, the alkaloids of these rather than extracts or the powdered drug are used as stomach poisons for many insect pests. *Borax* is partially effective for roaches and of greater value for the destruction of ants. It is also said to be of value for the destruction of flies and their larvae in manure without affecting the fertilizing value of the latter. Borax in concentrations of 0.2 per cent or greater is fatal to the larvae or "wigglers" of mosquitoes that breed in rain and other water present in barrels, cisterns and other exposed reservoirs. A mixture of borax and red lead or barium carbonate, if spread around the hiding places of beetles, will be found effective. This chemical may be found entering the compositions of many insect powders. Solutions of *sodium fluosilicate* have recently been recommended for stable refuse, etc. (instead of borax solutions), for the destruction of house flies, their maggots or larvae. In the concentration employed they are effective against the insects and not harmful to plants.

Phenothiazine (thiodiphenylamine), a heterocyclic compound containing both sulfur and nitrogen, is a canary-yellow crystalline powder, insoluble in water, slightly soluble in alcohol and ether and soluble in many other of the volatile solvents. For detailed information concerning this compound, see U. S. Bur. of Ent. and Plant Quarantine, *Pubs.* **E-1344, E-399,** and *J. Econ. Entomol.,* 1934, **27,** 1176; 1935, **28,** 727; 1936, **29,** 532. It has proved more effective than nicotine, lead arsenate and many other powder insecticides, does not injure foliage and does not appear to be toxic to higher forms of life including man and animals. In a concentration of 1:1,000,000, it is toxic to mosquito larvae and is very effective against codling moth larvae. See also *Trop. Dis. Bull.,* 1944, **41,** 102.

As an anthelmintic, phenothiazine is widely used in veterinary medicine. It has proved effective against strongyloids in horses, ascarids in swine, nodular stomach worms in sheep and cecal worms in poultry. It is being used extensively for livestock and it holds out promise as a single-treatment anthelmintic.

Recently, phenothiazine was reported as effective in killing roaches. For such use, it must come in contact with the outside of the bodies. As the phenothiazine passes through the shells, it is apparently converted to another compound, which appears to be responsible for the killing, as feeding phenothiazine to roaches is ineffective. Telford and associates (*Science,* 1943, **97,** 354) report a 100 per cent mortality against cattle-sucking lice by using phenothiazine as a dust. A mixture of sodium fluosilicate (2 parts), phenothiazine (1 part) and white flour (1 part) gave excellent control of both sucking and chewing types of lice and this dusting mixture may replace the use of pyrethrin and rotenone. Zukel (*Science,* 1942, **96,** 388) recently reported on the use of *Phenothiazine.*

Picrotoxin, a convulsive powder is a constituent of fish berries, *Anamirta coccalus,* and other species of *Anamirta.* It is used as an ingredient of various trade-marked insecticidal preparations. Little is known of its chemistry and insecticidal properties.

Camphor, Flaked Camphor, Etc.—Moth balls or powdered moth balls, commonly known as flake camphor and scientifically known as naphthalene, is a well-known substance employed for protecting materials against injury by moths and carpet beetles. A chemical similar in appearance to the latter which is just as effective, but somewhat more expensive, is used in some quarters as a remedy in moth control. This is known as paradichlorobenzene, also sold under the trade name of *Dichloricide*. Lump or gum camphor is used in the same manner as the previously mentioned powders but is less effective. To get results from the use of these three powders they must be used in tightly closed containers or environments. The fumes given off by slow evaporation must be confined, for if allowed to escape its value is but limited and generally is then only partially effective. At least one pound of the powders should be used to each 10 cubic feet of space. If there is a possibility of the fumes escaping, as would be the case in loosely constructed drawers, closets, chests or trunks, from two to three times this amount should be used.

If carpet beetles persist beneath carpets or rugs, upholstered furniture, etc., the use of these powders cannot be depended upon. Flake camphor rubbed into the fur of domestic animals will stupefy and destroy fleas that may be present. There seem to be no ill effects caused to the pet, except at times the animal may be made ill for a day or two. One of the best ways in ridding an infested home of fleas is to sprinkle or scatter at least 5 or more pounds of flaked naphthalene over the floor of an infested room. The latter is to be kept tightly closed for at least twenty-four hours. After this period the flaked camphor may be swept into another room which is to be treated. This is very effective for the destruction of all adult and larval fleas. It is best to be sure that all eggs have been destroyed by then washing the floor with one of the following: kerosene, kerosene to which has been added cresol, a weak solution of bichloride of mercury or hot soapsuds. After the floor coverings are thoroughly aired and beaten they should be sprinkled with either kerosene or freely with alum, pyrethrum powder or flaked camphor. The free use of these powders is said to give very satisfactory results Paradichlorobenzene has been used for many years as the standard remedy for borers in peach trees. This chemical and naphthalene are effective for mites and thrips and may be found of value for soil insects whose attacks are confined to the roots of plants grown singly or in hills.

D. D. T.—For a consideration of this insecticidal agent, see page 411.

Dithane (diethylene-sodium-bisdithiocarbamate) has been recently introduced as a new agricultural insecticide. It is fatal to chewing and sucking insects and certain fungi infesting food crops, but harmless to plants and man.

Chapter XXX

FUMIGATION

FUMIGATION IS THE process of ridding environments free of bacteria and insects by means of a smoke, gas or vapor. Rooms, compartments, buildings, enclosures, etc., cannot always be disinfected properly with liquids, powders, etc., for it is difficult to reach all surfaces and then hold such preparations in contact for a sufficient length of time, so as to obtain the desired end result. The choice of fumigant to use will depend upon many factors, which concern the fumigant as well as the material or environment to be treated. The important fumigants (gaseous agents used in fumigation) are formaldehyde, sulfur dioxide, hydrocyanic acid gas, ethylene oxide, ethylene dichloride, pyrethrum fumes, chloropicrin, heavy naphtha, carbon tetrachloride, carbon disulfide, carbon monoxide, orthodichlorobenzene, methyl bromide, chlorine, fumes from stramonium, cresyl and "Mimm's culicide," etc. Any individual, using fumigation, should not attempt this method unless he has familiarized himself with the correct technique to be used, the properties of the gases employed and a knowledge of the agents to be destroyed. Unless practiced by qualified operators, fumigation, which can be effective in many instances, will be found to be ineffective if carried out in a casual manner or by those unskilled. If fumigation is used for foodstuffs, the action of the fumigant on the food treated must be known or studied.

The following general principles are to be considered in using fumigants. Regardless of the fumigant or method used, these regulations are to be carried out before the actual process of fumigation is started.

1. Quantities of material to be used are usually recorded in amounts required per 1000 cubic feet. The quantities of material generally recommended make available the minimum concentration of gas required for effective fumigation, and it therefore is important that these minimal amounts be used. If the gas is not confined in a sealed space, several times the amounts given must be used.

2. All fireplaces, registers, ventilators, cracks of doors and windows and other openings in the enclosure to be treated should be sealed by closing with paper, or using paper and paste or adhesive tape or other nonporous and nonabsorbent material. The door of exit is sealed from the outside to prevent the escape of gas. Arrange, if possible, for the opening of doors or windows from the outside, unless the operator is supplied with a suitable mask. Proper sealing is very important, so as to be assured that an adequate concentration of the gas is maintained for a sufficient length of time.

3. Cupboards, bookcases, suitcases, drawers, etc., should be opened and all articles thrown about loosely or hung on a line, so that they will be exposed to the action of the fumigant. This is especially important when fumigants are to be used as bactericidal agents, as formaldehyde and other bactericidal fumigants possess but limited penetrating powers.

4. Select the proper vessels in which the gas is to be generated. It is advisable to

419

place these vessels on bricks, the latter in turn extending out of water placed in a wide shallow basin or tube.

5.   Allow a clear passageway to the door and to the windows which are to be opened when fumigation is completed, if arrangements were not made to open them from the outside.

6.   All domestic animals and foodstuffs should be removed from the premises. All cisterns and vessels containing liquids should be emptied or removed. It may be advisable to turn off the water supply at its main inlet, and the gas and electricity supplies at their respective meters. Smoking should be prohibited and no naked light should be permitted in rooms where inflammable vapors of fumigants are present. Efficient gas masks and emergency first-aid kits should be at hand.

7.   Fumigants should be allowed to act for at least six, preferably twelve and, if convenient, twenty-four hours.

8.   All rooms should be thoroughly ventilated before being occupied.

The applications of fumigants under specialized or uniform conditions are frequently practiced. Commercial fumigating vaults and fumigation chambers in various quarters lend themselves to more effective treatment in a shorter period of time. Here the exact lethal concentrations under varying conditions are determined. In some instances, the time element is very important. The use of a vacuum of 25 inches or more in steel fumigating chambers will hasten the penetration of the gas through many layers of goods and materials, so that the time of exposure is less than at atmospheric pressure. Salle and Korzenovsky (*Proc. Soc. Exptl. Biol. Med.*, 1942, **50,** 12) report on experiments which show that formaldehyde gas is bactericidal in one-twelfth to one-twentieth the time in a chamber evacuated to 28 (mercury) inches as compared to the absence of this vacuum. The effect of the vacuum is considered as due to an increased penetration.

In fumigating several rooms all communicating doors should be opened and the fumigant should be generated separately in each room. Large rooms, cellars, garages, etc., should be prepared in the usual way, and two or more pails or vessels in which the fumigant is to be generated should be distributed throughout the room. If fumigation is to be conducted over a large building, and the fumigants are lighter than air (most of them are), the process should be started on the uppermost floors and, should then proceed to the lower floors. In like manner, when ventilating the premises to get rid of the gas, the upstairs quarters should be opened first, followed by the lower-floor rooms. Wherever possible, arrangements should be made for the opening of a window or outlet from the outside, so that the gas may be allowed to escape after the process of fumigation is completed. A clear passageway should always be made for the operator to leave the room after the fumigation has been started, and for entrance after fumigation is completed, if it is necessary to open a window from the inside.

FORMALDEHYDE

Formaldehyde gas is always employed in preference to any other fumigant when a gas is required to rid environment free of bacteria.

Formaldehyde gas is not an insecticide. No attempt should be made to use formaldehyde and an insecticidal fumigant (as sulfur, etc.) *at the same time. Instead of acting as synergists, they seem to oppose each other.* The gas is usually liberated by some means from *Liquor Formaldehydi*. The temperature must be higher than 65° F., and the humidity above 65 per cent of saturation. The gas is nontoxic to man, but produces an irritation of the mucous membranes of the eyes, nose and throat after a prolonged exposure. This quickly passes away. Many methods are commonly practiced for the production of this gas:

1. Mechanical methods.
2. By the aid of chemicals.

See page 419 for general regulations.

Mechanical Methods.—(*a*) One of the older methods consists in heating formaldehyde solution in an autoclave. The gas that is liberated is passed into the room to be treated. Inasmuch as the evolution of the gas is rather slow, a larger amount of the solution will be required.

(*b*) *Sheet-sprinkling Method.*—Formaldehyde solution is evenly distributed over sheets by immersing in the solution or by spraying the solution quickly upon the sheets, using not over 10 ounces of solution for every 30 square feet of sheet surface. The sheets are then hung over lines. There is usually not more than 12 or 14 ounces of solution required for each 1000 cubic feet of air space. The time of exposure should be a minimum of four hours, preferably from six to twelve hours.

(*c*) By the use of so-called *formaldehyde candles:* paraformaldehyde, a polymeric condensation of formaldehyde (known also as paraform and trioxymethylene), is a white crystalline powder which when heated to a temperature of over 135° C. will liberate formaldehyde gas. Many special devices and so-called fumigators are available for the generation of formaldehyde from paraform, but a tin cup heated by a small alcohol flame will suffice. The conditions of heat and moisture are required here as well. Two ounces of paraformaldehyde are to be heated for each 1000 cubic feet of air space for an exposure of a minimum of four hours and preferably from six to twelve hours.

Generating Formaldehyde by the Aid of Chemicals.—(*a*) *Permanganate Method.*—The following technique is practiced: After the general rules have been observed the chemicals are placed in a galvanized iron pail (with a flared top), as a 10-quart milk pail. The latter is placed on a number of bricks contained in a large tin pan in which a small quantity of water is found. For each 1000 cubic feet of space, 10 to 12 ounces of formaldehyde solution and 4 to 6 ounces of permanganate are sufficient, providing the room is warm and humid. If cold and dry the quantities are increased and from 1 to 2 pints of formaldehyde solution and $1/_2$ to 1 pound of permanganate are necessary. Some workers constantly use 16 ounces of permanganate and 20 ounces of formaldehyde solution to each 1000 cubic feet of space. The formaldehyde solution should always be poured into the definite amount of permanganate placed in the pail. Always see that the solution is poured from a wide-mouth container or vessel. *Never throw the permanganate into the formaldehyde solution*, as an explosion may result. The time of exposure is a minimum of four hours and preferably from six to twelve hours.

(*b*) *Dichromate Method.*—Due to the greater cost of permanganate, sodium dichromate and sulfuric acid have been used to replace the former. Glycerin is added to minimize polymerization. The quantities employed for each 1000 cubic feet of space are: Sodium dichromate, 10 ounces; Formaldehyde solution, 1 pint; Sulfuric acid (technical) 1.5 ounces; Glycerin 1.5 ounces.

(*c*) *Chlorinated Lime.*—In Great Britain, 2 pints of solution of formaldehyde and 2 pounds of chlorinated lime for each 1000 cubic feet of space are used. The formalin is placed in a galvanized iron pot and the chlorinated lime wrapped in a thin paper is pierced and added quickly. Exposure is for twenty-four hours.

Terminal and Concurrent Disinfection.—Concurrent (or concomitant) disinfection is the application of disinfection to discharges immediately after leaving the body of an infected person and similar treatment of infectious material or articles soiled with infectious discharges as found in the sick room and before their removal from the room. The environment is kept as free as possible from infection and attendants are to observe care in disinfecting their hands after handling the patient or discharges from them.

Terminal disinfection is the disinfection of all infectious material and the rendering of the environment, clothing, etc., of the patient who is no longer a source of spreading the infection (or who died), free from the possibility of conveying the infectious agent to others. Even though concurrent disinfection may have been practiced terminal disinfection is necessary and is employed. When fumigants are used at the termination of the disease, it is spoken of as terminal fumigation.

Bactericidal Fumigants and Liquid Disinfectants

Fumigation for the destruction of bacteria and insect pests carried out by those qualified by training to properly employ this procedure is most effective. However, as an efficient method for the destruction of various insects, fumigants that are efficient insecticides are being used more frequently, but as a bactericidal agent, gases are being used to a limited extent only. Fumigation as it is commonly practiced cannot take the place of disinfection. Even at best the action of vapors is merely on the surfaces reached and the penetrative powers are usually slight.

The laity is compelled to depend extensively upon the properties of disinfectants, inasmuch as the technique for their use is simple; they are most economical, and in the hands of laymen they are more effective than the other methods that have been outlined. Where the proper technique of formaldehyde fumigation cannot be carried out the following method of disinfection will be found satisfactory: wash the floors, window sills, bed, etc., and everything which is not injured by water with a 1 to 2 per cent coal-tar disinfectant solution (preferably hot). Aerate the premises as much as possible, and allow the rooms to receive the beneficial effects of the sun. Sheets, bed linens and all material should be treated with the solution of the disinfectant and then laundered. Mattresses and other material which cannot be disinfected conveniently in the home should be aerated and allowed to receive the beneficial effects of the sun for as long a period of time as possible. Terminal fumigation is unnecessary after cases of the commonly observed communicable diseases and is usually employed only in the case of insect-borne diseases.

Soil Disinfestation.—Formaldehyde, as a liquid or dust, in dilutions of 1:50 to to 1:20 applied in the proportion of 2 quarts per square foot of surface, is used in the disinfestation of soil and especially to destroy pathogenic fungi and bacteria. Combinations of formaldehyde and steam are also used.

SULFUR

In burning sulfur, fumes are produced. The gas is noninflammable, nonexplosive, colorless, is irritating and possesses a pungent odor. It is both a surface disinfectant and an insecticide. To act as a disinfectant moisture must be present. Under such conditions the sulfur dioxide will also bleach or otherwise injure fabrics, papers, furnishings, etc., and it will also attack most metals. On this account this gas is rarely employed as a disinfectant in households and environments where materials are present that are likely to be bleached. Its use as a disinfectant is practically limited to empty buildings, environments containing equipment that will not be injured or providing formaldehyde is not available. If the environment is not damp, or supplying steam from pipes or radiators is not possible, boiling a pot or kettle of water will supply the moisture needed when this gas is to be used as a bactericidal fumigant.

Dry sulfur dioxide (burning sulfur without moisture) is practically without germicidal value, but it is efficient for the destruction of mosquitoes, flies, fleas, rats, etc. It is therefore mainly employed as an insecticide and, inasmuch as it is not as poisonous as some of the other more efficient insecticidal fumigants, it is probably one of the most useful products available for the general destruction of all kinds of vermin. Being heavier than air, it diffuses very slowly and possesses poor penetrative powers. It cannot be depended upon to kill insects and especially their eggs which may be present in deep crevices, unless more than one application is employed (two within three weeks). The surfaces of machinery and all metal should be oiled or greased to prevent any action by the gas.

The principal method employed is the following: a number of broad, shallow iron pots (about 1 to 2 feet in diameter with sides from 3 to 6 inches high) are best employed. The sulfur (powdered or coarsely broken stick sulfur) should be placed in these at a depth of not more than 2 inches, and sloped toward the center so as to form a crater. As an insecticide at least 3 to 4 pounds of sulfur should be used for each 1000 cubic feet of space. This should be evenly distributed in the different pots available for this purpose. The pots are placed in different parts of the room to be treated and preferably at different levels to assist diffusion. When everything is ready the sulfur is ignited by pouring alcohol into the crater or placing into the central depression cotton saturated with alcohol, which is lighted. This in turn ignites the sulfur. The latter also can be lighted by means of a hot coal or a red-hot bolt or by mixing the flowers of sulfur with a small quantity (3 to 4 per cent) of sodium or potassium nitrate. Paper wicks are also used. The operator should be assured that all pots of sulfur are ignited before the enclosure or room is closed, as the sulfur dioxide does not begin to come off immediately. The pots should be placed on stones or sand and, better still, on bricks contained in a tub of water. The pot should not touch the water as moisture will be liberated, this being desired only if the bactericidal effect of sulfur dioxide is wanted. The time of exposure should be at least eight hours and preferably from twelve to twenty-four hours.

As a bactericide it will not kill spore-bearing organisms and does not possess deep, penetrative properties. If used as a germicide because of lack of better disinfectants, at least 6 pounds of sulfur are required for each 1000 cubic feet of space, moisture to be provided so as to obtain the necessary humidity, and an exposure of at least twenty-four hours is necessary.

Liquid sulfur dioxide, obtainable commercially, and frequently under various proprietary names, may be used for fumigation in place of generating the gas as previously mentioned. When this process is employed the technique is the same; the liquid is poured from the tight metal containers into earthenware vessels or the gas is allowed to discharge from the cylinders in which it is present under pressure, employing 2 pounds of the liquid for each pound of the dry sulfur as mentioned in the previous paragraphs. Volatilization of the gas is rapid. The method is a costly one, being about eight to ten times as expensive as the other techniques mentioned. Sulfur dioxide is injurious to most plants, so that this method of fumigation to destroy plant pests cannot be used.

HYDROCYANIC ACID

This gas has little or no bactericidal efficiency. It is, however, the best insecticidal fumigant available, and can be used successfully for the fumigation of vessels, mills, greenhouses or any other closed structure or enclosure. It is noninflammable, nonexplosive, does not bleach or affect furnishings and textiles, and is noncorrosive, though it may slightly tarnish nickel. Hydrocyanic acid gas has effective penetrative properties, diffuses rapidly with the air, and is readily removed from a warm, dry atmosphere by ventilation. It is highly poisonous to man, and it should never be employed in environments where humans may be found, nor should it be used except by those thoroughly trained for the technique of hydrocyanic acid fumigation. Care should always be taken that there is no possible avenue of escape for the gas into adjoining rooms, houses or buildings, which may be occupied. It is always a safer procedure to warn everyone, so that the fumigation will be performed when no one is around. Operators should wear suitable respirators. See page 419 for general regulations. A rapid evolution and quick diffusion of hydrocyanic acid gas are obtained best in the presence of moderate and high temperatures; the temperature in the premises being treated should be above 60° F. and preferably at or above 70° F. Unless the latter prevails, the preheating of the environment by stoves or, better, by electric heaters should be carried out. In the so-called *pot method*, the gas is generated by the action of dilute sulfuric acid on sodium or potassium cyanide. The minimum quantity of cyanide to use is $3^3/_4$ ounces of sodium cyanide or 5 ounces of potassium cyanide for each 1000 cubic feet of space. This is satisfactory for exceptionally tight compartments, as found on vessels. For loosely built structures as dwellings, mills, etc., larger quantities, at least twice the amount given above (or more), are necessary. For each ounce of potassium cyanide used, 1 fluidounce of commercial sulfuric acid and 3 fluidounces of water are employed. One and a half fluidounces of commercial sulfuric acid and $1^1/_2$ to 2 fluidounces of water are allowed for each ounce of sodium cyanide used. If an environment is being treated to destroy lice twice the quantities given should be used. A stone crock or generator made of wood is to be employed, as metal is slightly attacked and glass would be broken by the heat produced in the reaction. A 1- or 2-gallon generator is to be preferred, so as to be large enough to prevent the fluids from spattering on the floor.

After the enclosure has been made airtight and liquid foodstuffs, etc., removed (as they may absorb sufficient quantities of acid to later exert an injurious effect) the required amount of water is placed in the crock. Into this is poured the measured quantity of sulfuric acid. After another inspection the cyanide is weighed out or the required amount is preferably represented by 1-ounce balls of cyanide. The operator without undue delay and holding his breath should place the correct weight of cyanide, wrapped in paper, into the acid mixture. The door is then sealed. The time of exposure will depend upon the thickness or depth of the cargo, etc., in the enclosure, inasmuch as the gas will take a longer time to penetrate several feet of cargo in a vessel than would be required for rooms in a building. The fumigation should be extended over a period of at least three hours and from six to twenty-four hours, depending upon environments to be treated and the amount of absorbent material present. Better results are obtained at a temperature of 70° F. or above. The enclosure should be thoroughly aired before any attempt is made to enter. If a building or a house is to be fumigated with this gas the rooms in the upper floors should be treated as directed and the operator should work downward since the gas rises, being lighter than air.

The toxicity of hydrocyanic acid gas is usually recorded in terms of "volume per cent" and a concentration of one volume per cent (1 volume of gas in 100 volumes of air) is the minimum recommended dosage. This is obtained by using $12^{1}/_{2}$ ounces of hydrocyanic acid in each 1000 cubic feet for a period of three hours.

Though it is desirable to have present high concentrations of the gas to be assured of effective results, it must be remembered that the greater the concentration, the more gas will be absorbed in the environment being treated, with a consequent slow clearance of the latter after the treatment. The occupancy of certain quarters is frequently of importance, as in the case of large ocean vessels. If the entire personnel, frequently consisting of thousands of men, are to be given time off because of the fumigation being conducted, a greater expense is entailed if more time elapses before the quarters can be inhabited. Fabrics and other materials may retain the gas. Humidity and temperature also are important factors affecting the retention of the gas. The gas is soluble in water and is thus retained by moist air. The lower the temperature, the less the diffusion; and, conversely, the higher the temperature, the greater the diffusion. The persistency of the gas is therefore less in warm, dry premises. The following minimum dosages and time periods are required for all stages of bedbugs, assuming that all other requirements have been met: one-half volume per cent HCN requires five hours; one volume per cent requires three hours; and two volume per cent requires two hours.

With a view of lessening the dangers associated with cyanide fumigation, a method has been introduced which provides for the presence of a lachrymator. This procedure provides an additional measure of security before and after the actual appearance of the gas. The following material (for minimum quantities of cyanide) is used for each 1000 cubic feet of space:

4 ounces powdered sodium cyanide
3 ounces sodium chlorate
2 ounces talc
17 fluidounces hydrochloric acid (comm.) (specific gravity, 1.2)
34 fluidounces water

or

5 ounces powdered potassium cyanide
4 ounces potassium chlorate
2 ounces talc
20 fluidounces hydrochloric acid (comm.) (specific gravity, 1.2)
40 fluidounces water

The talc and chlorate are mixed in a bag and the cyanide is then added and mixed. The acid is added to the water in an earthenware crock. After having the rooms prepared, the operator wearing a mask (containing pumice impregnated with caustic and iron gel) then places the bag (containing chlorate, cyanide and talc) into the acid mixture and seals the doors behind him.   The talc reduces fire and explosion hazards. In addition to hydrocyanic acid, cyanogen chloride is evolved simultaneously.   This is also an effective insecticide.   It, however, causes an unbearable irritation of the eyes and nose (a powerful lachrymator).   It is generated immediately and persists long after the hydrocyanic acid has escaped.   Its presence, however, affords a satisfactory and efficient procedure to warn one of the possible presence of the highly poisonous and treacherous hydrocyanic acid.   The operator, wearing a suitable mask, opens the windows or outlets at the expiration of the proper time limit, and when the complete disappearance of lachrymation is obtained, the premises may be occupied.   Chloropicrin also has been used as a lachrymatory or warning gas.   The addition of lachrymatory warning gases to hydrocyanic acid gas has a definite value and is highly advocated, but they may provide a false sense of security.   Clearing of the warning gas may occur before the HCN itself has cleared to a safe concentration.   Extreme care, therefore, is necessary in the rehabilitation of premises treated with HCN.   Emergency treatment for accidental poisoning by hydrocyanic acid gas should always be at hand. Operators should be familiar with the physiologic action of HCN.   The use of chemical tests is practiced as a valuable aid.   Scraps of paper impregnated with various test solutions are used.   These test papers produce characteristic color reactions when exposed to the atmosphere or on surfaces contaminated with HCN.   Among the test papers and tests used are to be found: methyl orange test paper; Thiery's test (alkaline solution of copper sulfate and phenolphthalein); Schonbein and Pagenstecher's test (alcoholic solution of copper sulfate and guaiac); Guignard's test (solution of sodium picrate); and Sievert and Hermsdorff's test.   The latter is preferred and is performed as follows: equal quantities of a 0.1 per cent benzidene acetate solution and a 0.3 per cent copper acetate solution are mixed just before testing.   The strips of paper are dipped into this mixture as required.   The presence of HCN is noted on the paper by a change in color from colorless to a pale and finally a deep blue.   It will detect concentrations as low as 0.001 part per 1000.   For further details concerning fumigation, technique, properties and other data on HCN, see O'Donnell, *et al.* (*J. Indust. Hyg. & Toxicol.*, 1940, **22**, 253).

Liquid hydrocyanic acid with either cyanogen chloride or chloropicrin as a warning gas as well as other fumigants are also available commercially, this being the gas in cylinders under pressure.   The latter can be released or vaporized or sprayed under their own pressure or that of compressed air into the environment to be fumigated. Two volumes per cent (in each 1000 cubic feet) of hydrocyanic acid gas is obtained from 25 ounces of the liquid.   Liquid hydrocyanic acid gas absorbed in fibrous material (disks, powders, etc.), to which various stabilizers and lachrymators are added, is marketed so that definite units carry quantities of material suitable for the fumigation of definite amounts of space.   These are known as the *unit method of fumigation*.   A marketed proprietary unit, available in some localities, is known as *Zyklon* or *Zyklon Discoids* (sold by American Cyanamid and Chemical Corp.).

The horticulturist and agriculturist have been using *cyanogas*, also known as *calcyanide* to replace other cyanides as the source of hydrocyanic acid gas.   This, calcium cyanide, usually in the form of flakes, gives off the gas in the presence of atmospheric moisture.   All that is necessary is to apply the material in a thin layer over a rather large area in the enclosure to be fumigated (using 1 ounce per 100 cubic feet of space)

Hydrocyanic acid is about the best insecticidal fumigant used by the fruit grower, florist, farmer, etc. Most foliage is not injured by the gas. It is generated in the usual way as previously mentioned. The vessel containing the chemicals is placed at the bottom of the tree, shrub or bush, which is covered before the gas is generated with a tent, cloth or canvas, oiled or greased so as to keep in the vapor. Fumigation is preferably applied at night. In the morning the cloth is removed by pulling a string kept at a distance and attached to the covering before the fumigation was started. Hydro-cyanic acid gas fumigation is most frequently used only after all other available measures of getting rid of the pests have failed. Sherbard (*U. S. Pub. Health Repts.*, 1942, **57,** 753) presents a comparative study of the insecticidal properties of five fumigants, including HCN. One must remember that there are many variables in field fumigation, some of which are not always amenable to control.

OTHER FUMIGANTS

Pyrethrum.—Fumes of burning pyrethrum are inferior as an insecticidal agent, but are especially effective in ridding rooms of pests that do not hide in places which are not easily reached by vapors, such as mosquitoes and occasionally fleas. It either kills them or stupefies these pests, so that they can be swept up and burned. The fumes are noninjurious to humans. It may, however, stain certain wallpaper, etc. The technique is the same as in the sulfur fumigation. Three to 4 pounds of pyrethrum are used for each 1000 cubic feet of space. The time of exposure is three hours. Good-hue and Sullivan (*J. Econ. Entomol.*, 1940, **33,** 329) discuss the toxicities to the house fly of smokes from pyrethrum and derris and insecticidal smokes in general (*Soap and Sanit. Chemicals*, 1941, **17,** 98).

Carbon Disulfide.—The vapor of carbon disulfide is effective as an insecticidal agent. It is not as poisonous as hydrocyanic acid, but it is inflammable and at times explosive. It is not necessary to ignite this chemical to obtain the vapor. The liquid when left exposed will quickly give off vapors, due to the fact that it is volatile. It is mainly used for the destruction of rodents (which burrow into the ground), by pumping the vapor into the burrows, or stuffing cotton saturated with the liquid into the latter and where grain and grain products are stored. Carbon disulfide fumes also have been advocated as an efficient remedy for the destruction of moths, roaches, ants, etc., especially in trunks, closets and small tightly constructed rooms and compartments. From 8 to 10 pounds of the liquid are required for each 1000 cubic feet of space to be treated. Most all gases or vapors employed as fumigants are lighter than air. It is, therefore, only necessary to see that the gas is generated so that it may rise. Carbon disulfide gas is heavier than air. This gas must be generated by placing the liquid at the top of the compartment or near the ceiling of a room, and then allowing the gas to escape slowly. It then falls to the bottom, thus mixing with the air. Exposure should be for at least six to twelve hours. A temperature of at least 60° F. is required to obtain efficient results. The warmer the environment to be treated, the more effective will be the fumigation.

Carbon disulfide is only valuable and applicable if the vapor can be confined. The gas is explosive, and every precaution should be taken to see that no fire is in or around the environment during the treatment. If a sufficient quantity of the gas is inhaled various ill effects become apparent. The result may not only be merely that of suffocation, but distinctly poisonous in an operator who persists in remaining around the premises when dizziness has developed. The vapor also seems to have an effect upon heart action, and individuals having any heart condition are, therefore, cautioned against using this gas or being present when it is employed.

Carbon disulfide has been and is used as an effective fumigant in the control of insect pests in grain, tobacco, etc. It is highly recommended against insect pests in corn stored in bins, for exterminating wasps, for destroying the Japanese beetle, in ant control, and it is effective against the garden centipede. For further details, see Vivian and Acree (U. S. Dept. Agr., Div. of Insect Invest., *Circ.* **E-359,** 1941).

Carbon Tetrachloride.—Carbon tetrachloride has been advocated as a substitute for the disulfide. Like the latter, the gas is generated by allowing the liquid carbon tetrachloride to volatilize, this being exposed in dishes at the top of the compartment. The gas is heavier than air, is neither inflammable nor explosive and does not possess the irritating and poisonous properties characteristic of the fumes of carbon disulfide. It is, however, only about one-half to one-third as effective as the latter. One would, therefore, have to use from 20 to 30 pounds of carbon tetrachloride for each 1000 cubic feet of space. Though effective, this would make such fumigation very expensive. Carbon tetrachloride and closely related volatile solvents may affect certain colors and paints on floors, walls, linoleum, furnishings, etc. In such cases they cannot be used unless the painted surfaces are protected with suitable coverings, or if painted furnishings, the latter can be removed from the quarters being treated.

Carbon Tetrachloride and Ethylene Dichloride.—A mixture of these two liquids in the proportion of 1 part of the tetrachloride to 2 or 3 parts of the other is used as a very effective remedy against insect pests, especially moths, carpet beetles, roaches, bedbugs, weevils in grain, etc. A temperature of 70° F. or over is preferred during fumigation for maximum efficiency. This mixture is cheap, noninflammable, nonexplosive and noninjurious to humans and stored material. The carbon tetrachloride is added so as to reduce the fire hazard of ethylene dichloride. Overexposure to the concentrated vapors may, however, cause a severe nausea and an accumulative toxic effect. It is five times as toxic as is carbon tetrachloride alone and is used just as the latter, employing 15 pounds of mixture per 1000 cubic feet of space.

The ethylene dichloride has been replaced in some cases by *propylene dichloride* which is equally effective. These mixtures have replaced cold storage treatment in many warehouses storing woolens, furs, clothing and household goods. They leave no odor or residue. For further details, see Gersdoff (U. S. Dept. Agr., *Misc. Pub.* **117,** 1932) and Roark and Cotton (U. S. Dept. Agr., *Tech. Bull.* **162,** 1930).

Ethylene Oxide.—Ethylene oxide is another fumigant employed against insects and is valuable because the vapors exhibit marked penetration. Two to 3 pounds are recommended per 1000 cubic feet for twenty-four hours.

Carboxide made by mixing 2 pounds of liquid ethylene oxide with 14 pounds of liquid carbon dioxide, marketed in cylinders, and using this quantity for each 1000 cubic feet to be fumigated for twenty-four hours has found use as a fumigant. The mixture issues from the cylinder as a liquid which is atomized to a fine mist. *Etox, Carboxide,* and other similar marketed preparations are mixtures of ethylene oxide and carbon dioxide in varying proportions (frequently 1:10). Cotton and Young (*Proc. Entomol. Soc. Wash.,* 1929, **31,** 97) presented the important observation that the addition of carbon dioxide increases the insecticidal efficiency of fumigants. The presence of carbon dioxide increases the toxicity by stimulating the respiratory organs of insects. It reduces fire hazard, as ethylene oxide boils at 53° F. and burns readily. Carbon dioxide increases the absorption of ethylene oxide and aids in the expulsion of the latter from the cylinders in which the mixture is marketed. Mixtures of ethylene oxide and carbon dioxide yield vapors which are heavier than air.

Ethylene oxide is chemically inactive, does not affect foodstuffs, does not bleach, will diffuse at reasonably low temperatures, is highly toxic to insect pests and their ova, possesses marked penetrative powers, and is not too expensive. If inhaled by human beings for long periods of time, cyanosis will be produced, which is counteracted by the inhalation of carbon dioxide gas. Smoking and open flames must be eliminated. The mixtures of ethylene oxide and carbon dioxide are used at temperatures above 70° F. in dosages as given above, but the concentration may be varied depending upon the materials being treated, the insects being destroyed and the time of exposure. The mixture is somewhat deficient in penetrative qualities and may require prolonged exposure to obtain effective results. The gas is emitted from the cylinder through a fine jet inserted through the keyhole or other opening and it is discharged in an upward direction. Operators should wear gas masks.

Ethylene oxide will destroy molds, fungi, other plant life (including bacteria) as well as insect pests; and is widely used for this purpose for packaged spices, cereals, fruits, tobacco, bagged rice, clothing, furs, books, papers, etc. Wherever convenient, it is best employed in vacuum fumigation chambers (see Cotton and associates for vacuum fumigation, *J. Econ. Entomol.*, 1937, **30,** 560). It leaves no residue, odor or flavor. It is highly recommended for the disinfestation of foodstuffs in homes, warehouses, holds of ships or barges, and in all quarters. For the destruction of microorganisms, it is useful where other methods cannot be employed. It may prove very useful to the agriculturist for the sterilization of many products including soil. Roberts and associates (*J. Bact.*, 1943, **45,** 40) in a preliminary study on soil sterilization with ethylene oxide report that the latter has no apparent effects on the physical property of the soil. For further details, see Cotton and Roark (*Ind. Eng. Chem.*, 1928, **20,** 805) and Young and Busbey (U. S. Div. Insect Invest., *Pub.* **247,** 1935).

Heavy Naphtha.—This clear colorless liquid, a product of tar distillation, is a complex mixture of aromatic hydrocarbons and related compounds. It has a specific gravity between 0.835 and 0.910, a distillation range between 160° and 190° C. (at least 90 per cent distills), and a flash point of not less that 105° F. Among the constituents present are: pseudocumene, tetramethylbenzene, mesitylene, cumarone, indene and small quantities of naphthalene and methylpyridines.

It is an efficient insecticide especially for bedbugs, is used in amounts of 2 gallons per each 1000 cubic feet of space and exposure is for twenty-four hours. Its action depends upon the vapor liberated. It is practically harmless to human beings. If the temperature of the environment being treated is below 60° F. preheating by the use of stoves (preferably electric) is necessary. The higher the temperature, the more successful the fumigation. Heavy naphtha is inflammable and all naked flames must be removed and smoking prohibited. Respirators with suitable filters should be used by operators on account of the heavy concentration of the naphtha. After all preliminary regulations have been carried out (see page 419), the liquid is sprayed preferably by means of a pressure-type spray. Some precautions are necessary to observe when using heavy naphtha. Certain paints from the floors, walls, furnishings, linoleum, etc., may be affected and the colors may run. In such cases, naphtha cannot be used unless the painted surfaces are protected with suitable coverings, or if painted furnishings, the latter can be removed from the premises or quarters being treated.

Orthodichlorbenzene.—This chemical is a liquid which liberates vapors that are very effective for the destruction of all insect pests and their eggs. It is especially effective for bedbugs. One gallon is sufficient for each 1000 cubic feet for twenty-four hours. It is applied by spraying, using preferably a pressure spray pump. The premises should be warm, and preheating is employed if necessary. Naked flames are to be removed. To increase the penetrative powers of the vapors, some workers add varying amounts of carbon tetrachloride or even methyl alcohol or methyl chloride. Operators must wear respirators when spraying. The use of orthodichlorbenzene is limited, especially to empty buildings or uninhabited premises, as it may cause among human beings various physiological changes, such as necrosis of the kidneys and fatty degeneration of the liver.

Chloropicrin was used as a tear gas during World War I. It is added to HCN to serve as a lachrymator. This gas is an efficient insecticidal and fungicidal agent, possesses certain bactericidal properties, possesses excellent warning characteristics and is free from fire and explosion hazards. The objection to this gas is the necessity for prolonged aeration following ventilation. It is used commercially for the disinfestation of foodstuffs, grain, warehouses, ship holds and also injurious pests and microorganisms in soil. The operator must wear a suitable mask, rubber gloves and other protection for the exposed parts of his body. The minimal dosage is 1 pound per 1000 cubic feet for twenty-four hours. For further details, see Roark (U. S. Dept. Agr., *Misc. Pub.* **176,** 1934) and Roark and Busbey (*ibid.*, first suppl., **E-351,** 1935). Chloropicrin has possibilities as a fumigant for lice, bedbugs, roaches, etc., as it is one of the safest and most effective of all fumigants. The intense lachrymatory irritation properties must be controlled.

Formates.—The volatile esters of formic acid possess high insecticidal properties. *Ethyl formate* (*aeronal*) and *methyl formate* (*areginal*) are used commercially for the fumigation of dried fruits, raisins, nuts, various foodstuffs, stored tobacco and other commodities. Other esters are also being employed. The minimal dosage for ethyl formate is $1^1/_4$ pounds and for methyl formate is $1^1/_2$ pounds per 1000 cubic feet for twenty-four hours. For further details, see Nelson (*Ind. Eng. Chem.*, 1928, **20,** 1382) and Cotton and Roark (*ibid.*, 1928, **20,** 380; U. S. Dept. Agr., *Tech. Bull.* **162,** 1930).

Methyl Bromide is highly toxic to many insects and has been employed for the destruction of household insect pests. It is free from fire and explosion hazards and has no effect upon fabrics, etc. It is, however, difficult to detect this gas by the sense of smell or taste. Inasmuch as toxic symptoms may develop later, if this gas is inhaled, it is a dangerous fumigant to use in quarters to be inhabited. When employed, it is used in the proportion of 1 pound per 1000 cubic feet of space at a temperature of 75° F. or higher. Dudley and associates (*U. S. Pub. Health Repts.*, 1940, **55,** 2251) present interesting studies on the use of this gas in the fumigation of foodstuffs, especially fruits and vegetables. It appears that varying amounts of methyl bromide may be absorbed with resultant intoxication. Caution should be exercised in its use unless definite information is available under certain conditions.

On the other hand, Fullaway, entomologist of the Hawaii Board of Agriculture and Forestry, reported recently the largest successful fumigation of stored cereal ever undertaken. A six months' supply of wheat, corn, rice, etc., heavily infested was saved only after fumigation with methyl bromide. Special gas masks were used for the operators. A blockade and invasion of the islands would have meant starvation if this stored cereal had not been available. Roehm and associates (*J. Dairy Sci.*, 1943, **26,** 205) recommended highly the use of methyl bromide fumigation for dairy products claiming that this fumigant is highly active at low temperatures, easily applied, possesses exceptional penetrating powers, is relatively insoluble in water, and is rapidly vented. Lotta & Yeomans (*J. Econ. Entomol.*, 1943, **36,** 402) used this gas effectively for delousing lice-infected clothing by a short exposure at relatively low temperatures. Dawson (*Soap Sanitary Chem.*, 1944, **20,** 96) found methyl bromide superior to other agents as an effective fumigant for packaged goods and other materials.

Carbon Monoxide.—This gas is very poisonous, odorless, nonexplosive and inflammable. It is not a disinfectant. In the so-called *Harker's system* it is used mainly on vessels to destroy rats and also to extinguish fires. In this method special devices and apparatus are made which distribute the flue gas (containing about 1 per cent carbon monoxide and 10 per cent carbon dioxide) to the cargo or any part of the ship.

Chlorine.—This gas, though an efficient disinfectant, is not to be recommended on account of its poisonous property. As a bactericidal agent moisture must be present, and at the same time it acts as a powerful bleaching agent. Due to the foregoing facts and also to its destructive property, chlorine is rarely employed as a fumigant. When used in empty buildings containing material not apt to be bleached the gas is produced by the interaction between potassium chlorate and hydrochloric acid. The generators containing the chemicals are to be placed close to the ceiling, as the gas is heavier than air and falls to the floor.

Chlorine is capable of killing smut spores of grains under controlled conditions. It appears to be of value in controlling fungi on garden seeds. For further details, see Leukel and Nelson (*Phytopathology*, 1939, **29,** 913).

Other Fumigants.—Fumes from stramonium or jimson weed, cresyl, equal parts of camphor and phenol (known as Mimm's culicide) and even dried orange peel are sometimes used as fumigants to assist in the eradication, especially of mosquitoes.

Powdered jimson weed, 8 ounces to each 1000 cubic feet of space, to which is added one-fourth of its weight of saltpeter (so as to make it burn more readily), will produce fumes that are nonpoisonous to humans, will not injure furnishings or metals and is said to be effective against mosquitoes.

Fumes produced by burning 4 ounces of camphorated phenol (equal parts of camphor and crystal phenol or carbolic acid known as "Mimm's culicide") to each 1000 cubic feet of space in closed compartments have been found effective in destroying and driving away flies and mosquitoes.

All the fumigants mentioned thus far are only effective providing the general regulations as given for fumigants are adhered to. The fumes of cresyl (obtained by burning one of the coal-tar products, $1/4$ pound to each 1000 cubic feet) and of dried orange peel are of value as deterrents, rather than as destructive agents, against mosquitoes. By burning these, fumes are produced that are noninjurious to humans, do not affect household goods, their work of driving mosquitoes away is performed without having the rooms vacated and they can be used to burn at night in one's sleeping quarters.

Frear (*Science*, 1943, **98**, 585) is engaged in the preparation of a catalogue of insecticides and fungicides.

PART VI

IMMUNITY, ALLERGY AND BIOLOGICAL PRODUCTS

Chapter XXXI

IMMUNITY, ANTIBODIES AND OTHER DEFENSIVE FACTORS

IT IS NOT TO BE supposed that a host is wholly at the mercy of pathogenic microorganisms. Our systems attempt to protect themselves against invading pathogenic organisms.

MECHANICAL BARRIERS

The body possesses various barriers which defend it against attack by microorganisms. The unbroken skin and to a lesser extent the healthy mucous membranes serve as efficient barriers to infection. Pathogenic organisms lodging on the skin or between the superficial horny cells cannot penetrate deep into the tissues and cause infection, unless a cutaneous injury occurs. Bacteria may occasionally pass through ducts of the sweat glands and the hair follicles and gain entrance into the underlying tissues, but such an actual occurrence is rare. Even if organisms do penetrate the skin, the subcutaneous connective tissues present obstacles, which serve as a barrier against further invasion. The healthy membranes of the nose and throat hold invading organisms and prevent their entrance into the alveoli of the lungs. The natural secretions present here aid mechanically in the removal of microorganisms or their toxic products. The secretions also possess feeble bactericidal properties, and of minor importance is the fact that antibodies may be found in the serous element present. Normal gastric juice due to the presence of 0.4 per cent free hydrochloric acid is decidedly unfavorable to the growth of many bacteria.

Other Barriers.—The invasion of the body by foreign material, living or dead, is followed by a prompt response of cellular activity. This activity, one essentially of protecting the body from infection, is possessed by two types of cells: the free-moving white blood cells (known also as leukocytes or phagocytes) (and in particular only certain types of leukocytes) and the endothelial cells (fixed connective tissue cells). The leukocytes are attracted in great numbers to the point of infection and aid the tissue cells to overcome the invaders by ingesting and digesting (actually capturing and devouring) the bacterial cells. This is known as *phagocytosis*. But the body cannot and does not rely upon the leukocytes alone for protection. The tissue cells, if normal and healthy, begin to form certain accessory substances, enzymes and antibodies. These circulate in the blood stream and possess the power of neutralizing the poisonous excretions of bacteria, while others may assist in preparing microorganisms for phagocytosis. By such means, the invaders are destroyed. Should the tissue cells become abnormal or lowered in efficiency by the previously mentioned predisposing causes, then the bacteria gain a foothold, and commence to multiply at the expense of the tissues themselves. For a detailed consideration of phagocytosis, see Mudd and associates (*Physiol. Rev.*, 1934, **14,** 210).

Opsonins (*Tropins*).—An important accessory substance present in the normal and abnormal blood is the opsonin. Opsonins prepare bacteria for phagocytosis so that they are rendered more digestible to the leukocytes. Opsonins are present in normal serum but increase in amounts in the serum of animals as they develop a resistance (immunity) against the disease. Opsonins are distinct from complement and are thermolabile. Without the co-operation of the serum containing these opsonins (food preparers), the power possessed by the leukocytes to take up bacteria is greatly diminished. Study of the opsonins has led to numerous controversies especially as to some of the following: (1) that the opsonins present in the normal and immune animals are not similar substances; (2) the latter known also as *bacteriotropic substance*, are specific for (prepare, change or sensitize) the stimulating microorganism (and no other organism), while the "normal" opsonins, which are less resistant to the action of heat, are nonspecific. Their exact structure, their relation to other antibodies and more facts concerning their action are still in doubt. Final opinions are not available and will be possible only after these controversies are settled.

Opsonic Index.—The degree of development or relative amount of opsonins in the blood and their action on organisms as observed by the consequent power of the white blood cells to ingest and digest these microorganisms are measurable. The method of determining the opsonic index, a technique generally employed to obtain this measurement, is one which establishes a ratio between the opsonic action of a serum to be tested with that from a normal individual or, better still, the pooled (mixed) serum from several normals. The latter constitutes the standard measure and its opsonic index is regarded as normal and recorded as 1. The opsonic index of the serum to be tested is determined by various methods (especially Wright's) and recorded by a decimal figure. The latter indicates the relative phagocytic power of the individual's blood which was tested as compared with the normal (it may be above, below, or the same figure 1). Determination of the opsonic index is not used so extensively as formerly.

Variations in Cell Activity.—It has been found that occasionally the cells of apparently healthy individuals display increased phagocytic power without regard to opsonins or presence of other factors in the serum. Workers are inclined to regard this characteristic as one due to some physical condition of the cell itself, as, perhaps, difference in the age, etc., of the various cells, rather than to any marked acquired cell characteristics.

Leukocytic Extracts.—Leukocytes (certain varieties of) contain bactericidal substances which can be extracted by various methods. The latter, known also as *endolysins* and *endoferments* or *endoenzymes*, are present in the individual types of leukocytes so as to aid in the digestion of the microorganisms. They are more thermolabile than antibodies; a temperature of 75° to 80° C. is necessary to destroy them. Commercial preparations of extracts of leukocytes containing these substances are marketed and used by some for their protective and therapeutic value.

It may be mentioned at this time that the presence of capsules, spores, waxy membranes as in the tubercle bacillus, and general walled-in areas as formed by some of the animal parasites, are primarily aids for protection of the respective parasites, so that phagocytosis is made more difficult, if it is performed at all.

ANTIBODIES

More important than these physical methods by which the body combats disease are the chemical and especially the biological methods. Of considerable interest and import is the ability of the tissues of members in the animal kingdom, and chiefly the blood and lymph of vertebrate animals, to react against invading cells whether bacteria, animal parasites, or cells from plants and other unrelated animals, both poisonous and innocuous, by producing certain antagonistic substances, known as antibodies (protective substances). Antibodies, if present, can be found in the blood and they appear to develop in response to infection or invasion by an agent (antigen) foreign to the blood of the animal injected. As far as workers have been able to determine, certain organs, especially various cells of the reticulo-endothelial system, the endothelial cells of the spleen, liver (Kupffer cells), lymph glands, bone marrow and also the wandering macrophages of the tissues and the blood seem to be more actively concerned than are other cells in the production of antibodies. It may be, as some workers believe, though it has not been proved experimentally, that antibody formation may be a widespread cellular function in which all the body cells participate to a greater or less degree. Recently Besredka has put forth the hypothesis that the defensive mechanism of the body, in regard to the initial entry of pathogenic organisms, is less an affair of general resistance common to all tissues than a local matter concentrated in the tissue which is primarily the seat of disease and through which the organism normally gains entry into the body.

The substance possessing the power of causing the production or formation of antibodies is known as an *antibody-producer* or an *antigen*. Antigens, as far as observed, belong usually to the group of proteins, and are primarily of colloidal character, though some crystalloidal substances have been found as possessing antigenic properties, and are derived from the animal or plant kingdom. The antibodies produced by the body possess an antagonistic action, which is specific for the antigen which has caused their production. They will not attack any other antigen. This specific antagonistic action may be the neutralization of its antigen if the latter is an enzyme or toxin, or it may render harmless, or kill and disintegrate the specific antigen, etc. The antibodies are usually demonstrable in the blood serum and other body fluids.

The substances stimulating the production of antibodies (that is, act as antigens) can be divided into two classes:

(1) The extracellular products which primarily include such substances as microbial exotoxins; zootoxins, soluble toxins secreted by members of the animal kingdom as the venoms of snakes, scorpions, etc.; and phytotoxins, which are soluble toxins secreted by plants.

(2) Endocellular products or cellular proteins, as microorganisms, pollen, etc.

ANTITOXINS

1. The first class of antigens, the exotoxins, stimulate the production of antibodies which neutralize the soluble toxins and are specifically known as antitoxins. An antitoxin, therefore, as a specific antibody, has the power of uniting with and neutralizing only that soluble toxin which stimulates or causes its production. This combination or neutralization of antitoxin with its specific toxin deprives the latter of exerting its effect, which frequently is a destruction of various body cells, due to the fact that the specific body cells and toxin combine and form permanent unions. Antitoxins are prepared commercially and marketed as efficient biological preparations to be used in the treatment of those diseases in which the serious effects of the latter are primarily produced by the soluble toxins given off by the agent causing the specific disease. Antitoxins are prepared for neutralizing the soluble toxins of *Corynebacterium diphtheriae*, *Clostridium tetani*, *Clostridium botulinum*, etc. (See also page 460.)

Antitoxins have not been obtained in a pure state. When serum or plasma is treated to precipitate the antitoxin, the latter is attached to the globulins (or globulin fraction). Antitoxins are relatively stable. The combination of toxin and antitoxin *in vitro* does not necessarily mean a complete destruction of either component. Various physical and chemical processes, such as simple dilution, freezing, heating and treatment with weak acids, will cause a dissociation of this weak combination. A more stable union depends not only upon the individual toxin and antitoxin, but upon such factors as the character of the medium, temperature, concentration, reaction, etc. The amount of toxin neutralized by antitoxin varies according to the manner in which the antitoxin or toxin is added. If the toxin is added in bulk, all at one time, more is neutralized than if this same amount is added in fractions, allowing a lapse of time between additions. By adding the toxin in several portions spaced at proper intervals of time, a considerable amount of toxin will not be neutralized. This reaction is known as *Danysz phenomenon*.

The three most important theories explaining the toxin-antitoxin reactions are those advanced by Ehrlich, Arrhenius and Madsen, and Bordet. Ehrlich conceived the "side-chain" theory and characterized antitoxins as "an antibody of the first order," regarding them as a simple haptophore which unites directly with the toxin molecule. It is essentially similar to the neutralization of *strong* acids and bases. Arrhenius and Madsen, though regarding the toxin-antitoxin combination as a chemical reaction, compared it as being more closely allied to the interaction between *weak* acids and bases, as between boric acid and ammonia. Neither of these theories explains satisfactorily the Danysz phenomenon and other observations and they are not generally accepted at the present time. Bordet regards the combination of toxin and antitoxin as an adsorption phenomenon between two colloids. The smaller toxin molecule is considered to be adsorbed on the surface of the larger antitoxin molecule, in the same manner to a staining effect as noted in the adsorptive reaction of filter paper when added to stains. Add a large piece of filter paper to a staining solution and it will be dyed or stained uniformly. On the other hand, if the same paper is torn into several pieces and added piece by piece, the first ones will be stained deeper than those added later. The evidence of such a phenomenon is very strong. However, it does not explain the marked specificity of toxin and antitoxin. A chemical theory must be added to explain this. It is highly probable that the reaction is a physicochemical procedure.

2. Endocellular products or cellular proteins (microbial or plant) stimulate the production of antibodies (antimicrobial or antiprotein antibodies) which attack the specific antigen. These antibodies may include any or all of the following: agglutinins, precipitins, bacteriolysins, bactericidal or other microbicidal or proteinicidal substances and immune opsonins. All of the different kinds of antibodies, all specific for the same antigen, may be present in the same serum in equal or in varying degree, or as mentioned before one or more of them may be entirely absent. For a more detailed consideration, see Marrack ("The Chemistry of Antibodies and Antigens," Medical Res. Coun., Spec. Rpt., Ser. No. 230, 2nd Ed., 1939), Heidelberger (*Bact. Revs.*, 1939, **3**, 49), Wells (*Chemical Aspects of Immunity*, Chemical Catalogue Co., New York, N. Y.), Landsteiner (*The Specificity of Serological Reactions*, Thomas, Springfield, Ill., 1936), Zinsser, Enders and Fothergill (on *Immunity, etc.*, Macmillan, New York, N. Y., 1939) and Boyd (*Fundamentals of Immunology*), Interscience Publishers, New York, N. Y., 1944.

AGGLUTININS

Agglutination is a phenomenon wherein microorganisms, living or dead (or antigens) are agglutinated or aggregated into clumps or irregular masses when brought in contact with a serum obtained from an animal (human or otherwise) who is diseased by or has been immunized (the creating of resistance) against the same organism (or antigen). The serum from such animal containing antibodies is spoken of as an immune serum. If the organisms are motile, they become immobile first before they are clumped together. This immobility and agglutination can be observed microscopically. If the test is performed in the test tube (macroscopic technique) the clumps settle to the bottom of the tube as a precipitate and the supernatant liquid is clear, as compared with the original turbid or clouded bacterial suspension. The agglutinating power of a serum is due to the presence of specific antibodies, known as *agglutinins*. The (antigenic) substance stimulating the production of agglutinins is called the *agglutinogen*. The latter is found in the antigen, dead or living cell, which is injected, or otherwise gets into the system of the animal. Agglutinogen appears to be liberated only after the disintegration or dissolution of the antigen. The formation of agglutinins is therefore reactions produced in response to the body substances of the microorganisms, dead or living, or antigens themselves and not to any toxic substances produced by the latter. Agglutination depends upon the nature and concentration of the electrolytes present, the electrical charge on the cells, the cohesive force tending to draw them together, and perhaps other factors. The agglutination reaction is highly specific within certain limitations.

The exact composition of agglutinins and, in fact, of all other antibodies is unknown, though that of the agglutinins is regarded as being more complex than the antitoxins. Various facts concerning their resistance to heat, acid, alkali, etc., and their general behavior *in vitro* and *in vivo* are known. Agglutinins resist heating at 60° C. or lower and are completely destroyed at 75° C. or higher. They exert their effects best in a neutral or slightly acid medium and are inhibited in their action in an alkaline medium. They are not dialyzable and are precipitated with the globulin fraction of the serum. Just as normal sera of all animals contain varying amounts of bactericidal substances, so do many of them contain varying amounts (though usually very small quantities) of agglutinins. These so-called *normal agglutinins* are rarely found in the new-born so that their presence in older animals is probably traceable to a slight immunity produced by the latter against the various microorganisms parasitic in or upon the human or animal body. Agglutinins are produced with all the known bacteria and many other substances used as antigens. Artificially their production and the production of other antibodies in the sera of animals are brought about by the introduction of the microorganism (or antigen) intraperitoneally, subcutaneously, intramuscularly or intravenously. The most abundant and quicker results in the production of antibodies are given by the intravenous method.

The *immune agglutinins*, produced naturally during a disease or otherwise in contact with the antigen, and artificially by injecting the antigen into human beings or animals, are generally specific but within certain limitations. The different organisms, dead or alive, and antigens vary in the number or quantity of agglutinins or other antibodies which they can produce. The amount of infection, or contact with given amounts of antigen, or the amount of injected antigen bears a relative proportion to the amount or quantity of agglutinins or antibodies that are produced. The more the antigen present, the greater the agglutinin and antibody contents. However, when the agglutinin and antibody contents reach a certain height or peak, which varies for each animal depending upon individual characteristics, the addition of even a very marked increase of antigen will have no effect upon a corresponding increase in agglutinins or antibodies. Agglutinins and antibodies do not develop immediately as the antigen comes in contact with our systems or those of animals. The agglutinins develop within a week after infection or contact with the antigen, and their numbers gradually increase, unless contact with the antigen is removed or the maximum limit or peak of agglutinin content is reached. The content then gradually diminishes after contact with the specific antigen is removed.

Cross Reactions.—Immune agglutinins act not only on the specific bacterium (or antigen) which was responsible for their production but under certain conditions may agglutinate closely related bacteria. Recent studies have supplied the reason for this. It has been found that the bacterial cell does not constitute a simple antigen, but it possesses a complex antigenic structure, with the various antigenic components distributed in different parts of the cell. The antigenic heterogeneity of a bacterium is responsible for a multiple antibody content in a homologous serum, with certain agglutinins revealing only a specificity and others a so-called *cross reaction*. In the latter instance, the agglutinin reacts with an antigenic component which happens to be present not only in the bacterium used to produce it, but which is also found in closely related species of the same group. They are known as *group agglutinins*, the reaction as *group agglutination;* and the phenomenon is especially observed among the Gram-negative intestinal pathogenic and nonpathogenic rods.

Agglutinin Adsorption or Absorption.—If a suspension of bacteria is mixed with a proper dilution of its homologous serum, incubated at the proper temperature for a sufficient length of time and then centrifuged, the supernatant diluted clear serum mixture will be found to have lost its ability to agglutinate the bacterium present in the original suspension. Agglutinins specific for the bacterium as well as for closely related bacteria were adsorbed. If, instead of the original suspension, there was added a suspension of a closely related species of bacteria, the supernatant fluid after centrifugalization would agglutinate the specific bacterium but not the related species.

In other words, the specific and common or group agglutinins are completely adsorbed by the homologous bacterium (or specific antigen). A closely related species will only remove wholly or in part the group agglutinins and leave behind all or most of the specific agglutinins. This agglutinin-adsorption test is used to some extent as a diagnostic aid and especially in the study of antigenic structure and the relation of different bacterial species to each other.

Prozone Phenomenon (*Pre-zone or Proagglutinoid Reaction*).—At times, it will be found that immune sera revealing high agglutinin titers show poor or even no agglutination with their homologous organisms in concentrated or strong (low) dilutions. The dilution range showing this phenomenon is designated as the *prozone, pre-zone* or *proagglutinoid zone*. Ehrlich pointed out that the presence of heat, acid, etc., will affect agglutinins, so that they will lose their ability to clump but not their power to combine with the specific agglutinogen. These altered agglutinins he called *agglutinoids* and compared the reaction with that of the change of a toxin to a toxoid. Prozones although observed at times in fresh sera are more frequently encountered with heated or old sera. Heating or aging causes the production of agglutinoids which form a protective colloid on the bacterial cells preventing clumping with any agglutinins which may be present. Agglutinins will and agglutinoids will not pass through bacteria-excluding (Berkefeld) filters.

"O" and "H" Agglutination.—As was pointed out elsewhere in this volume, motile "S" strains of bacteria contain "O" or somatic antigens, which are found at or near the body surface of the cell and the "H" or flagellar antigen, which is superficial. Immunization with the whole bacterial cell containing both antigenic components will usually result in the production of an immune serum with "H" agglutinins, present generally in high titer, and "O" agglutinin, generally active in lower concentrations (1:1000 or less). Macroscopically it will be noted that the nature of the agglutination will differ depending upon the agglutinogen which is being acted upon. The "H" or flagellar antigen produces a "floccular" or "fluffy" type of agglutination with its specific agglutinins. The "O" or somatic antigen produces a finely granular agglutination with its specific agglutinins.

Practical Application of Agglutination Reaction.—The use of the agglutination test, in that specific organisms (antigens) will become agglutinated by appropriate dilutions of their respective and specific agglutinins, has been and is utilized by laboratory workers throughout the world. The test is employed in three ways:

1. The test is employed as an aid in the diagnosis of various specific diseases. The agglutination test for typhoid bacilli is specifically and more frequently known as the Widal test, in some areas as the Gruber-Widal test. The direct agglutination reaction for diagnostic purposes has only a limited application. In the first place, it can only be used in diseases in which agglutinins are produced freely and are present in sufficient quantities in the blood stream. Usually other methods as aids in diagnosis are available earlier in the disease. Then we must be sure that a positive reaction, indicative of the presence of agglutinins may not be due also to the fact that the individual is immune, having had a resistance created either through a previous infection or artificial inoculation. Agglutination tests are used in human and veterinary medicine as aids also in the diagnosis of glanders, brucellosis, bovine and equine infectious abortion, swine erysipelas and for pullorum disease.

2. The agglutination test is employed in identifying and differentiating bacteria

that possess the same microscopic, staining and other similar characteristics; also in identifying specific types as in the typing of pneumococci.

3. The determination of the agglutinin content in the sera of immunized animals is performed in some instances to approximate the potency (or strength) of these therapeutic sera, before they are marketed as efficient biological preparations in the treatment of disease.

There are two methods commonly used in performing the agglutination tests, namely, the microscopic and macroscopic or sedimentation methods. The latter should be the method of choice wherever it can be performed conveniently. For further details, see pages 506–508.

Role of Agglutinins.—Agglutinins do not possess a true protective and curative power as do the antitoxins. Pathogenic organisms are not killed by the process of agglutination, so that agglutinated organisms may display as much virulency as they did before the act of agglutination, or when nonagglutinated. Agglutination is probably a sort of preliminary step or aid to phagocytosis and probably to bacteriolysis (disintegration). Agglutination, like other immunity reactions or immune phenomena, is not limited to bacteria. It is a manifestation of broad biological laws. Agglutinins specific for other cells can be produced and especially for erythrocytes (red blood cells) and known as hemagglutinins; certain protozoa; leukocytes (white blood cells); epithelium; and spermatozoa.

Agglutinins are produced in the serum of rats recovered from an infection with *Trypanosoma lewisi* or if immunized with the latter. In like manner birds and monkeys produce agglutinins specific for certain species of *Plasmodium*. The serum of an animal recovered from strongyloidiasis will contain agglutinins specific for the filariform larvae of *Strongyloides*. Inasmuch as it is difficult to prepare parasites in the form of a suitable agglutinable suspension, agglutination tests are not generally used as aids in the diagnosis of parasitic infections.

Hemagglutinins.—The hemagglutinins in human serum specific for human corpuscles are of considerable interest and of practical importance. Hemagglutinins present in human beings and which agglutinate the corpuscles in the blood of other animals are specifically known as *heterologous hemagglutinins*. Hemagglutinins present in the humans and which agglutinate the corpuscles in the blood of other humans are known specifically as *isohemagglutinins*. The latter have assumed considerable practical importance in relation to blood transfusion. Research revealed the fact that human sera contain four different and specific groups of isohemagglutinins. The significance of this fact is utilized in the selection of blood in blood transfusion and in medico-legal cases. Various methods are employed in the preliminary testing of the blood of the patient (recipient) and the blood of the otherwise suitable donor (one giving or supplying blood) so as to be assured that compatible blood is being employed in the transfusion. A donor belonging to the same group as the patient is employed. The corpuscles of adults will always remain in the same group throughout life.

PRECIPITINS

When the clear filtrates of various broth cultures, from which the bacteria have been removed, or certain clear protein (antigenic) solutions are mixed with their respective immune or antisera (produced by animal inoculation and therefore containing specific antibodies), there will be produced a powdery precipitate which is visible macroscopically. This phenomenon is known as *precipitation*, and the antibodies producing the precipitate are known as *precipitins*. The substance present in the antigen which stimulates the production of precipitins is termed the *precipitinogen*. The precipitins are closely allied to the agglutinins in their properties and general characteristics, mechanism of reaction, specificity (and occasional group precipitation for bacterial precipitins), pre-zone phenomenon, precipitin adsorption, etc. Precipitins may be divided into two broad groups, the zooprecipitins, precipitins specific for the albumins of animals, and the phytoprecipitins, precipitins specific for the albumins of plants. In the group of plant precipitins are to be found the following:

Bacterioprecipitins.—Precipitins uncommon in the normal individual or animal (normal precipitins), but which are found in the sera of human beings or animals, who are infected with certain bacterial diseases (few in number) and in animals only after prolonged and intensive artificial immunization. These precipitins are specific for the respective bacteria or a solution of the albuminous constituents from the latter.

Mycoprecipitins.—Mycoprecipitins include those precipitins specific for the albumins of yeasts and fungi.

Hematoprecipitins.—Hematoprecipitins include those precipitins specific for the albumin present in blood serum or solutions of extracts of blood (dried or otherwise). They are usually obtained from immune sera.

Lactoprecipitins.—Lactoprecipitins are those which precipitate milk casein. They are usually obtained from immune sera.

Precipitins derive their names from their respective precipitinogens (substances which stimulated their production). If human serum were injected into rabbits for the preparation of precipitins, the latter would be known specifically as human seroprecipitins. Precipitins have been produced for the albumins of higher plants, especially the different kinds of flour, meats, egg white, spermatozoa, etc.

The presence of precipitins has been reported in the serum of humans and animals with protozoan infections, such as amoebiasis, malaria and coccidiosis and in various helminth infections. The precipitin test as a diagnostic aid for parasitic infections has not been generally used.

Development and Practical Application of Precipitins.—The precipitinogen or stimulant used to produce bacterioprecipitins may be living or dead bacteria or solutions of their albuminous substance obtained by autolysis or extraction. The mechanism of attacking and affecting their specific antigen, and their role in resistance to infection and recovery, appear to be similar to those of the agglutinins. The precipitate, however, which is carried down when the precipitin and precipitinogen react contains all of the antibodies and protective substances present in the serum. Bacterioprecipitins are not commonly demonstrated in the serum of individuals infected by many of the bacteria frequently causing disease. Because of the absence of appreciable amounts of precipitin, the precipitin reaction with the serum of the infected host, as in the case of the agglutination test, has been employed practically very little as an aid in the diagnosis of disease. Application of the precipitin test in bacterial infections is employed in the diagnosis of glanders in animals.

Bacterial Precipitinogens in Inflammatory Exudates.—The earliest application of the precipitin test for the diagnosis of disease was when attempts were made to detect specific precipitinogens in inflammatory exudates. Spinal fluid was tested for meningococcus precipitinogen by treatment with antimeningococcus serum. A similar precipitin test for pneumococcus precipitinogen is used by mixing antipneumo-coccus serum with the clear urine, the pus or a clear soluble saline extract of the heated and coagulated saliva, obtained from the suspected case of pneumonia.   Precipitin reactions for the detection of other precipitinogens, and thus the bacteria, are employed to a less extent.   The use of bacterioprecipitins for the identification and differentia-tion of unknown bacteria is not practiced to any great extent.   Specific agglutination and other tests are more decisive in their results.

Zooprecipitins.—Albumins from animals will, when injected especially in rabbits, produce precipitins, which display a marked species specificity, so that the immune sera can be used for diagnostic purposes.   The precipitin test is one of several im-portant tests used in medico-legal work for the identification of blood stains.   After the latter have been found, by chemical (benzidine, guaiac and hemin crystal) tests, microscopic observation of blood cells, and if possible spectroscopic examinations, to be hemoglobin, then the precipitin test is applied to a clear, soluble extract of the dried stain to see whether the precipitinogen is a human or nonhuman species.   In the test proper, potent antisera (containing precipitins specific for the albumin of human blood) must be used.   Many controls are to be employed and great care is to be observed in the technique used.   It must be remembered that it is not possible to distinguish be-tween different individuals or different races of human beings by the precipitin test.

The precipitin test is employed in the examination and identification of spermatozoa in seminal stains, especially in medico-legal cases.   Attempts have been made to use this test in the differentiation of the different kinds of milk (human, cow, goat, etc.), but most workers prefer other biological reactions, which they regard as being more clear-cut and decisive.   The precipitin test is used by some workers for the detection of meat adulteration, as the presence of horse, cat and flesh of animals other than the flesh from cows in sausages, smoked meats, etc.   See also page 505.

Precipitation or Flocculation Reactions in the Diagnosis of Syphilis.—Numerous precipitation or flocculation reactions or tests on the blood serum and spinal fluid of suspected cases have been devised as aids in the diagnosis of syphilis for the purpose of replacing the Wassermann and other complicated complement-fixation tests now more frequently employed for the detection of this disease.   These tests are easier to perform, require less material, and they are time-saving.   Among the colloidal pre-cipitation reactions for syphilis which are used and give satisfactory results are the methods of Sachs and Georgi, Meincke's third modification of the latter method, the Kahn test, Kline test, Eagle test, Hinton test, Boerner-Lukens test, Laughlen test and Mazzine test.   The precipitation test for syphilis is not a reaction by precipitino-gen and specific precipitin.   It may be best to speak of them as flocculation tests. The reaction is apparently a physicochemical phenomenon, resulting in the interaction of substances in colloidal suspension.   See also page 503.

THE CYTOLYSINS

Nuttall (*Ztschr. f. Hyg.*, 1888, **4,** 353) demonstrated that normal and immune blood, serous exudates, etc., possessed substances which disintegrate (thus killing) cells, bacteria as well as other cells, without regard to the presence of the phagocytic cells. These antibodies were called *lysins* or more frequently named *cytolysins*.   Those cytolysins which disintegrate or dissolve bacteria are specifically known as *bacterio-*

lysins; those which dissolve red blood cells are known as *hemolysins.* Similar cytolysins may be formed for practically all cells including leukocytes, kidney and liver tissues, etc. To the latter, the general name *cytotoxin* has been applied and specifically the correct and more expressive terms are *leukotoxin, nephrotoxin, hepatotoxin,* etc.

The bacteriolysins and cytolysins in general are complex antibodies produced by the interaction of two substances, one a ferment-like substance (present in the sera of all warm-blooded animals, whether normal or diseased) and designated as *alexin* by Bordet, or *complement* or *addiment* by Ehrlich, and the other substance, which is the antibody and is specific for the particular antigen and designated as the *amboceptor* or *sensitizer.*

Complement or Alexin.—Complement or alexin is a ferment-like substance present in the blood serum of normal, diseased or immune warm-blooded animals, which is destroyed by heating to 55° C. for one-half hour (thermolabile). Such heated sera are said to be *inactivated.* Complement unites, fixes or acts with amboceptor or sensitizer to form a complex antibody, the latter, in turn, disintegrating the antigen that causes the production of the amboceptors with which the complement reacted. It is probable that the leukocytes are the source of the complement. It is also possible that one may find slight differences between complements, but these differences are of very little practical importance. Complement is not increased during disease and in the process of artificial immunization. Complement is nonspecific. Bordet and Gengou were the first to show that the complement concerned in bacteriolysis (fixation or reaction with specific bacterial amboceptors producing bacteriolysins) is the same as that concerned in hemolysis, where hemolysins are produced by the fixation or reaction of complement with specific hemolytic (blood-cell) amboceptors. This experiment, known as the *Bordet-Gengou phenomenon,* is the basis of the underlying principle in the so-called *complement-fixation tests.* The latter are employed extensively in determining whether or not a particular serum contains certain specific amboceptors, which are capable of reacting with or fixing complement. Although inactivation destroys complement and it deteriorates rapidly at room or higher temperatures, it may be conserved in the serum in a lyophilized state for several months and at times even years. It is very sensitive to acids and alkalies.

Amboceptors or Sensitizers.—The general structure, formation and action of the different sensitizers or amboceptors, including the bacteriolysins, hemolysins and all other cytolysins, are practically alike. Amboceptors are fairly resistant immune bodies, the exact composition of which is not known. They can tolerate the effects of exposure, drying, various chemicals and can be heated at 65° C. for an hour without showing any marked depreciation in activity (thermostabile antibody). Amboceptors are highly specific bodies, though in some few instances group amboceptors are produced, but this is less common as compared to group agglutination, etc. Just as small or varying amounts of normal (natural or native) agglutinins and antitoxins are found in sera, so, in like manner, varying amounts of amboceptors (bacteriolytic, hemolytic, etc.) may be found in normal serum. The amounts of natural bacteriolytic and hemolytic amboceptor, specific for different bacteria and for different kinds of blood cells, which may be present, vary. Immune bacteriolysins are produced during disease and by artificial immunization. The different bacteria, and all other antigens, vary greatly in the amount of bacteriolysins and even other antibodies (agglutinins, precipitins), which they are capable of inducing the body cells to produce. It has been observed that the latter induce the production of all the different kinds of anti-bodies, but that with each specific antigen there is always an excess and measurable amount of one or two of the antibodies and variable, indefinite amounts of the others. The reason for the production of antibodies in this manner is not definitely known.

The difference between a normal and an infected or an immune serum is that the normal serum contains a number of different kinds of (normal) antibodies in small amounts, while the immune serum contains in addition a greatly increased amount of at least one (immune) antibody specific for a particular cell (or antigen).

Bacteriolysins.—Amboceptor itself cannot destroy the antigen which was the cause of its production, though it may become attached directly to its specific antigen. Complement itself cannot unite with or affect any amboceptor alone. It cannot affect, destroy, or ever become attached to any antigen directly. But after the amboceptor becomes attached to or combines with its specific antigen (sensitizing the latter or preparing it to be acted upon and thus the other name for amboceptor, *sensitizer*), the complement can then become attached to the sensitized antigen. This results in the production of a specific bacteriolysin which destroys the antigen.

Besides the one mentioned in the last paragraph, there are several theories which concern themselves with the mechanism of the reactions regarding amboceptors and complement in the phenomenon of cytolysis. Baumgartner's, Buchner's, Ehrlich's, Bordet's and Metchnikoff's theories are mentioned, so that one interested in a further study of this subject may refer to them. There is a quantitative relationship between the immune amboceptor and the complement required to destroy the antigen which produced the former body.

Practical Application.—The specific immune bacteriolysins are of considerable value and are frequently employed as aids in making a differentiation of organisms, usually obtained from feces, water supplies, etc., and found possessing almost identical staining and microscopic characteristics, especially when the presence of cholera vibrio is suspected. The bacteriolytic power of serum may be tested either in the animal body *in vivo* or in the test tube *in vitro*. The test when performed *in vivo* is known as *Pfeiffer's phenomenon* (*Ztschr. f. Hyg.*, 1894, **17**, 355). The Pfeiffer's test *in vivo* may be employed to determine the bacteriolytic power of a given serum or immune serum (for standardization and to be used for treatment or diagnosis) against a known microorganism.

Complement-fixing antibodies have been found in protozoan infections, such as amoebiasis, trypanosomiasis, leishmaniasis, coccidiosis and malaria. Among the helminth infections, they have been detected in ascariasis, filariasis, trichiniasis, echinococcus disease, schistosomiasis and others. The complement-fixation test has been applied and found useful as a diagnostic aid in several of these parasitic infections.

COMPLEMENT-FIXATION TESTS

In the brief explanation of the Bordet-Gengou phenomenon, we have seen that cytolysis, produced by the action of a serum, depends upon the presence of two components, each being an entirely different substance and radically different in their properties. For all practical purposes, amboceptor is to be regarded as an antibody found only in the serum of animal as a result of an infection or of artificial immunization. Complement, on the other hand, is a component of all sera in humans and in warm-blooded animals, whether normal, immune or diseased. It disappears rapidly from the serum after the latter is withdrawn from the living body. Its potency may be maintained for about a week, but rarely longer, if the serum is frozen, but if lyophilized will remain preserved for long periods of time.

A serum which has lost its complement, by heating at 55°C. for one-half hour, or by aging, is no longer "fresh" and spoken of as an "inactive" serum. An inactive serum may be reactivated by adding to it a little fresh serum, for the latter contains complement. Complement is nonspecific, has no effect upon any antigen, and is not increased in activity during any kind of artificial immunization.

The amboceptor produced during disease or artificial immunization is highly specific for the antigen which caused its production. If a fresh serum containing amboceptor is heated at 55° C. for one-half hour, the complement is destroyed (thermolabile), but the amboceptor shows little or no loss in potency (thermostable). This procedure is employed to obtain amboceptor free from complement when both are present in a serum. Amboceptor can become attached to its specific antigen, producing a fairly stable combination, but such antigen is not killed or in any other way affected. The amboceptor, sometimes known as the sensitizer, is said to sensitize its antigen. If complement is present or added to this sensitized antigen, the complement is bound or fixed, a cytolysin is formed, and the antigen is destroyed. The complement so fixed is not available any longer for further formation of cytolysin. This is the principle of complement-fixation tests, as utilized in the practical diagnosis for the determination in serum of the presence of specific antibodies, capable of binding or fixing complement. In the latter, we start out with a known antigen to find an unknown antibody. The test can be reversed so that by starting with a known amboceptor, or complement-fixing antibody, we can proceed to find a known antigen. In this manner we are also able to diagnose the nature of blood stains, differentiate between the different milk proteins, etc. The actual determination of complement-fixing antibodies in sera by a technique as employed in the complement-fixation reaction is a complicated test requiring great care and skill. In complement-fixation tests, the presence of large amounts of serum, known to contain agents possessing lytic action, may not necessarily show this latter activity. This is said to be due to the presence of *complimentoids*, producing a *pre-zone reaction*, as may occur, at times, in agglutination and precipitation reactions. (See page 439.)

Application of Complement-fixation Tests.—Complement-fixing antibodies possess an extremely high degree of biological specificity for the antigen causing their production. Some antigens produce very little while others produce large amounts of antibodies of this type. Under proper conditions and with satisfactory professional skill, the complement-fixation reaction is a more accurate procedure for identifying organisms and studying biological relationship than are the agglutination and precipitin reactions.

The "Wassermann reaction or test" is a complement-fixation test performed upon the blood serum or spinal fluid of suspected cases as an aid in the diagnosis and as a guide in the treatment of syphilis. For further details, see page 502. See also page 193.

As a practical procedure, the complement-fixation technique is probably of more value as a diagnostic aid in syphilis (or lues) than perhaps in any other infection found in man or animals. In veterinary medicine, this technique is most commonly used as a reliable aid in the diagnosis of glanders. The complement-fixation test is used as a possible aid in diagnosis and in research investigations of the following infections: gonococcus infections, tuberculosis, bovine and equine infectious abortions and brucellosis. Complement-fixation tests are occasionally used for the following diseases with but varied success: pertussis or whooping cough, echinococcus disease of the liver, anthrax in animals, and dourine or horse syphilis.

With a known amboceptor or complement-fixing antibody obtained by immunizing a rabbit against a specific (known) antigen, the complement-fixation technique can be employed to detect and identify an unknown antigen (organism or substance). This procedure has less practical application, though it is used in special bacteriological investigations when an organism may be identified by specific complement-fixation with its specific antibody, present in a known serum. Identification of *Cl. botulinum* and its toxin in cultures, contaminated canned foodstuffs, etc., has been used successfully. Complement-fixation technique to detect unknown antigens, however, is used principally in the differentiation and diagnosis of blood stains whether human or animal and in the differentiation of all kinds of proteins, especially those present in meat, milk, etc.

Other Antibodies

The existence of other antibodies has been reported and different names have been used at times, for the same antibody.

Ablastin is the name given to a reproduction-inhibiting antibody. Though reported for the anthrax bacillus and for the pneumococcus, the existence of an ablastin for bacteria has not been conclusively demonstrated. Rats infected with *Trypanosoma lewisi* produce an ablastin which not only inhibits the reproduction of the trypanosomes but is regarded also as having the capacity of destroying by lysis immature trypanosomes. Other species of trypanosomes probably also produce an ablastin.

The ability of an antibody to prevent infection in animals injected with infectious material is responsible for its being designated as a *neutralizing antibody* or a *protective antibody*. The "protective titers" in antipneumococcus serum and in other antibacterial sera, and in noting the efficacy of immunization with typhoid vaccine and other antigens, appear to supply more useful information as to the efficacy of these and other products than the titration or measurement of the antibody titer whether it be the agglutinin, precipitin or other antibody content. In the case of filterable viruses, it is frequently difficult to prepare a suitable antigenic preparation. Accordingly the neutralization or protective test is used extensively to evaluate the antibody content of antiviral sera or the immunizing capacities (production of antibodies) of specific virus antigens. This neutralizing or protective action of an immune serum is regarded as due to an antibody not identical with agglutinins, precipitins or other antibodies.

An *adhesin* antibody has been found in a few parasitic infections, such as trypanosomiasis, leishmaniasis and filariasis. The *adhesion reaction* has been used as an aid in the diagnosis of these parasitic infections. In the first two protozoan infections named, the red cells will be found to adhere firmly to the parasite if the adhesin antibody is present. In the test, a suspension of the parasite, appropriate red blood cells, complement and the serum to be tested are mixed and incubated. The reaction is specific. In filariasis, the leukocytes adhere to the body of the parasite.

The addition of red blood cells to beef serum or horse serum alone (fresh or inactivated) will produce no reaction, and no hemolysis will result. If, however, the cells are added to a mixture of inactivated beef serum and fresh active horse serum, the cells will become agglutinated and hemolysis will occur later. Bordet and Gay call the principle *conglutinin* and explain the phenomenon on the presence of a thermostable substance conglutinin in the beef serum which is capable of increasing the ability of fresh horse serum to agglutinate and hemolyze red blood cells. A "conglutination test" has been introduced, but it has only a limited practical use.

THEORIES OF IMMUNITY

The development of the science of immunity, both theoretical and practical, forms one of the most interesting chapters in the history of medicine. Many of the older hypotheses and theories are obsolete and are only of historic interest. Pasteur's "exhaustion theory," Chauveau's "retention theory" and others have failed to produce satisfactory explanations for all conditions. It was not until 1883 that we really began to understand some of the several problems concerned in infection and immunity, when Metchnikoff presented his theory of phagocytic immunity. Of the many theories which have been advanced from time to time as the correct one explaining the phenomenon of immunity, only two have remained to receive the attention of the present-day worker. The hypotheses on immunity which have been outlined in the preceding sections cover both of these theories, one known as the *cellular theory* and the other known as the *humoral theory*. The inspiration for the introduction of the former was Metchnikoff with his "theory of phagocytosis." He and his many pupils at the Pasteur Institute at Paris are responsible for the greater part of the theoretical considerations upon which the "cellular theory" as accepted today is based. Parallel with Metchnikoff's phagocytic theory, the "humoral or antibody theory" was developed. The latter ascribes the power to resist infection mainly to the body fluids containing antagonistic elements. Fodor, Buchner, Flügge, Nuttall and others were the early workers who introduced and favored this theory. Ehrlich is probably thought of as the chief exponent of this theory for he with the introduction of his marvelous, fascinating and well-known "side-chain theory" aided to explain the old as well as the new discoveries as they were made. He places the entire theory on a chemical basis. As it is, we find the German school propounding the "humoral theory" as against the French school, who advocate the "cellular theory." Probably the truth of the matter is that the various phenomena of immunity can only be satisfactorily explained by considering the role played by the body fluids and the activity of the body cells. Both theories are directly concerned in the many phases of immunity. The theory of immunity mentioned in the sections on this subject in this volume was considered with this intimate relationship in mind.

More recently, immunology has been characterized by a tentative acceptance of a new dynamic concept of the infectious unit and there is also increasing skepticism in the belief that the protein molecule functions as a single antigenic unit. The bacterial cell is regarded as an organized aggregate of vital colloids or potentials (Landsteiner phenomenon). Two distinct "vital colloids" are thus far tentatively pictured in the bacterial cell and these play an important part in explaining most of the alleged facts of the present-day dynamic microbiology. Interest has reawakened in biochemical identities or cross reactions between pathogenic bacteria, environmental saprophytes and various higher plant and animal tissues. This may be of epidemiological and even immunological importance. In the "Landsteiner phenomenon," it has been revealed that conjugation of a relative simple nonantigenic crystalloid with a specific protein may confer upon the latter a new immunological specificity. This so-called "crystalloid immunology" may be of extreme practical and clinical importance.

Evidence has been presented experimentally of the possible existence of a specific "immunity or integrating center" in the brain, without co-operation of which specific somatic antibodies are alleged not to be formed or liberated. It has also been claimed that properties simulating specific serum "antibodies" appear apparently spontaneously in the circulating blood at the approach of sexual maturity. Considerable interest is being displayed at present in the basic enzymic, genetic, hormonal and neurological factors operative in specific immunity and an exact evaluation of these will have to await more experimental and clinical findings.

It is becoming more obvious that additional conceptions are needed to explain other phenomena as will be mentioned in the chapter on Hypersensitiveness. It must be understood also that a discussion of immunity from all angles is not the purpose of this book. A subject as broad as this would require an entire volume. It may be said that the theory as presented here, will suffice to explain in a fairly tenable way many problems of immunity which are ordinarily encountered.

Immunity.—It has been noted that the antibodies (or protective substances) are formed or produced in quantities greater and in excess of the needs at the time of infection. These antibodies are stored away in the body ready to exert their influence when the system is again attacked. By this means, as well as due to the influence of other factors which have been mentioned, individuals are capable of successfully combating disease. The faculty or power which enables the system to accomplish this is spoken of as *resistance*. When such resistance, which in some degree is common to all, is especially marked, it is spoken of as *immunity*. Resistance and immunity, like pathogenic and similar terms are but relative and not absolute terms. The absence or loss of the power of immunity leads to what is known as *susceptibility*.

The internal defenses in one's system by the presence of which an immunity exists, may be (*a*) a *natural* creation or may have been (*b*) *acquired*. Natural immunity is therefore defined as a natural inborn faculty wherein a race, species or an individual shows marked resistance to infection. Dogs are practically immune to anthrax; human beings are immune to hog cholera and other diseases of the lower animals. These are examples of "species" immunity.

Just as differences in immunity as well as in susceptibility are to be found among various animal species, so the separate races may display immunity to the same infecting agent. This so-called "racial" immunity is to be found among members of the same species of human beings and animals. Ordinary sheep are susceptible to anthrax, while Algerian sheep are immune. White mice are immune to glanders while field mice are highly susceptible. In man the differences are not quite so marked, though it is believed that many races enjoy immunity against certain diseases, as the Mongolians against scarlet fever, and civilized races are less susceptible to tuberculosis than are the aboriginal races.

"Individual" immunity may be found frequently in the observation of many exposed at the same time to the same possible source of infection, and yet variations in the susceptibilities of those individuals are apparent. Certain persons though freely exposed to specific infections rarely become diseased. The factors influencing individual immunity are not absolute and not even always constant. What has been said concerning "individual" immunity applies equally well to "familial" immunity, where members of the same family display immunity against certain diseases. Resistance which does not occur in an individual as a naturally inborn faculty, but which is conferred or given to him, is spoken of as *acquired immunity*.

Acquired immunity may be either *active* or *passive*. *Active immunity* is a resistance which has been acquired due to direct and increased tissue-cell activity. Such active immunity may have been acquired either after an attack or a successful exposure to some particular disease as, for instance, in smallpox and usually diphtheria, scarlet fever, yellow fever, etc., or by a deliberate artificial inoculation with a living or active, a modified, or an attenuated form of the causative agent or products from the latter, as is practiced in the use of modified smallpox virus and the bacterial vaccines. According to Vaughn, immunity established by the inoculation or injection of bacterial vaccines (dead or attenuated bacteria) and their products (bacterial products) is similar to that induced by an attack of a disease, even though the symptoms of the disease itself are not pronounced. Active immunity is acquired slowly, but the resistance so obtained is generally lasting.

In each and every case of active immunity, the body cells and tissues of the individuals and animals so affected, exposed or treated, react themselves to produce the specific immunity.

Passive immunity, on the other hand, is an acquired immunity, in which the body cells and tissues of the patient take no part in the production of those agents which confer an immunity upon the individual. The antibodies or immunity agent is formed in the body of another animal and then passed or transferred to the individual to be protected. The individual plays but a passive part, receiving something possessing prophylactic properties, which has been made outside of his body. Passive immunity is quickly brought about by the mere introduction of the protecting substances, usually a serum containing antibodies. Passive immunity lasts but for a short period as the antibodies are quickly used up. Such immunity is artificially introduced *only* under those conditions, when in acute diseases, the sick individual or animal and those exposed to such infections and presumably nonimmune, are treated with a large quantity of antibodies which are quickly required to combat the invading microorganisms or their toxins. This is commonly practiced when the antitoxins and antimicrobic sera are used, *i. e.*, diphtheria antitoxin in the treatment of diphtheria, tetanus antitoxin in the treatment of tetanus and antipneumococcic serum in the treatment of pneumonia.

In each and every case of passive immunity, the body cells of the individuals treated take no part in producing the immunity.

A combination of passive and active immunity is found advantageous in certain cases. A potent protective serum containing specific antibodies, to supply the passive immunity, is injected and then followed with the active or modified infective agent, which will create the active immunity. The former confers an immediate passive immunity and results in the production of a less marked effect when the active agent which creates the more lasting active immunity is used. Such method of artificial immunization, referred to by some workers as the *simultaneous method* is commonly used in animals to create an immunity against certain diseases, especially in swine ery-sipelas, anthrax, hog cholera, and rinderpest or "cattle plague."

NONSPECIFIC PROTEIN THERAPY

The use of various proteins, and even nonproteins, has been tried in the treatment of diseases in which the agent employed bears no specific relationship to the nature of the infective process. In other words, this unrelated agent can be termed a nonspecific antigen. The first observations were more or less accidental.

The nonspecific antigens and agents that were and are still used are protein and protein-split products of bacterial and nonbacterial origin, sera from normal human beings and animals, antitoxic and antibacterial sera, milk and preparations of milk products, tissue extracts, hypertonic and hypotonic saline solutions, triple distilled water, colloidal metals, etc. The most commonly employed nonspecific agents worth mentioning are: colon, typhoid and triple vaccines, cows' milk or milk products, primary and secondary proteoses, peptone, deutero-albumose and horse serum. Intramuscular injection of milk and its products is being used with good results in many skin, genito-urinary and other affections. Intravenous injections of many of the other products mentioned have been advocated in pneumonia, other systemic infections, and different diseases.

The mechanism underlying the beneficial results of nonspecific antigens are not clearly understood. Several theories have been advanced to explain this. No one particular theory is satisfactory, but a combination of some of them affords a satisfactory explanation of the workings of agents in nonspecific protein therapy. The response is probably due to the following factors: The blood-making or so-called "hemopoietic" organs, which are also probably the producers of many of the antibodies, are markedly stimulated. This results in the throwing forth into the circulation of antibodies already formed, also a marked increase in the production of leukocytes or at least throwing these out into the blood stream in greater numbers, and, generally speaking, an increase in our defensive agents are produced. These appear in larger quantities in the circulating blood than was present before the injection of the nonspecific agent. It may also be that some of the nonspecific ferments, etc., aid in the autolysis of the specific causative agent, or in rendering nontoxic any of the toxic products produced by the latter. So far as known, nonspecific agents never produce a specific immunity.

Chapter XXXII

HYPERSENSITIVENESS AND ALLERGY

THE TERM hypersensitiveness, as used here in a general way, designates that group of conditions in which certain individuals display a marked or an exaggerated susceptibility to various agents, which are ordinarily harmless for normal individuals. This subject is considered under such headings as "allergy," "anaphylaxis," "atopy," "drug and food idiosyncrasies," "hypersusceptibility," "serum sickness," "pollen and food hypersensitiveness," etc. There is at the present time considerable disagreement with regard to the nature of some of these manifestations and as to the terms to be used to indicate the various phenomena of hypersensitiveness. This undoubtedly is due to the fact that we are still ignorant of considerable fundamental information relative to this subject, which is as perplexing as it is important. There are so many different views as to classification, insistence upon the use of new and specific terms, that the entire subject of classifying these phenomena is indeed confusing. Coca and Cook, Doerr, Kolmer, Wells and others have advocated certain criteria, which they insist must be complied with before a hypersensitive reaction can be called by a specific name or classified under any groupings The definitions, as follow, are accepted by most workers, as being the most satisfactory:

"Allergy" (altered energy) is a condition wherein an animal displays an unusual or exaggerated susceptibility to a substance which is harmless in similar amounts for the majority of members of the same species. The exciting substance may or may not be protein in character or composition, and may or may not produce antibodies, demonstrable in the serum of the animal. In other words, all phenomena of hypersensitiveness, hypersusceptibility, or any altered degree of reactivity are best placed under the general heading of *allergy*. "Anaphylaxis" is a state of allergy which can be shown to result from the activity of truly antigenic substances (that is, produce antibodies) of protein composition. The word is derived from the Greek and means "without protection" just as prophylaxis means "for or favoring protection." Hypersensitiveness as a specific term may be defined as a state of allergy resulting from the activity of nonprotein, and probably nonantigenic substances, such as many chemicals and drugs.

There is a marked variation in susceptibility of different animals and humans to allergic reactions, resulting in a variety of symptoms and pathological changes. Acute fatal anaphylaxis in man is not common. The usual forms of anaphylaxis in man are: the so-called *serum sickness*, when horse serum is injected intramuscularly or subcutaneously, wherein any or all of the following symptoms gradually appear: urticarial rashes, fever, pains, especially in the joints, etc. In intravenous injections, there may be an immediate fainting attack and prostration. Allergy to bacterial proteins, present in bacterial infections of the upper respiratory tract, to hair, feathers and effluvia of many lower animals and to pollens are usually manifested by coryza, sneezing and in the first two cases by various forms of *asthma*. Allergy to foods as observed by the idiosyncrasy of certain individuals to or their inability to tolerate various foods may be apparent by the immediate symptoms of abdominal pain, vomiting, diarrhea, etc., or the later development of various skin lesions, urticaria and even serious chronic conditions as found in one or more forms of asthma. The old adage that "one man's meat is another man's poison" is well demonstrated by this type of allergy. Hypersensitiveness or idiosyncrasy to drugs in which an amount of a given drug, nontoxic for most individuals, displays allergic reactions in some humans is usually specific and characterized most frequently by skin reactions, as itching, rash, eruptions, and in some cases by body pain, edema, etc. The following drugs are especially concerned in various allergic reactions: aspirin, belladonna and mydriatic drugs, bromides, antipyrine, arsenic and arsphenamine, chloral hydrate, cinchona and its alkaloids, coal tar, copaïba, digitalis (occasionally), iodides, mercury, morphine and opium, salicylates, etc. Extreme hypersensitiveness to poison ivy, poison oak, poison sumac, etc., is more or less apparent in many human beings.

In all of the allergic reactions in man and animals, while the reaction may vary as far as the general symptoms which appear, the principal indication in most all instances is vasomotor paralysis characterized by the dilation of blood vessels and more or less serous exudation. The reaction seems also to coincide with the distribution of smooth muscle tissue (nonstriated). The tissues of man or animal possessing unusually well-developed smooth musculature are the ones generally affected and probably the essential factors concerned in anaphylactic reactions.

A "sensitinogen" or "allergen" is a substance capable of exciting or inducing a condition of hypersensitiveness or allergy. They are specific. The "anaphylactogens" are specifically protein sensitinogens. They are proteins of animal or plant origin and are responsible for inducing anaphylaxis. Dr. Coca has suggested the term *atopens* for those proteins acting as exciting agents and causing the forms of abnormal sensitization designated as *atopy*. Hay fever and certain forms of asthma are included in this grouping.

The anaphylactogens include practically all proteins which act as antigens and are foreign to the circulating blood (that is, not normally present in the blood) of the injected animal. Soluble proteins are more active than those only partially soluble or insoluble, and therefore in suspension. Temperatures high enough to destroy or disrupt proteins are also destructive to their properties as anaphylactogens. It is, therefore, probable that the whole protein molecule is necessary to induce anaphylaxis. Though all anaphylactogens are soluble proteins, not all soluble proteins have proved to be anaphylactogens. It must be borne in mind that many of our present available data are based upon experiments conducted with the lower animals. Although these are accepted as being applicable to man, time alone will prove this actual parallelism. We know that all substances found to produce anaphylaxis in lower animals usually react the same way in man, but we also know that some substances which do not act as anaphylactogens for lower animals may act as sensitizers for man.

The actual mechanism in anaphylaxis is not definitely known. Several theories have been advanced: that of Vaughn, the one elaborated by Novy and De Kruif, and others have received considerable attention in attempts to explain the mechanism involved in allergic reactions. Vaughn's theory, which is one of the several "humoral theories of allergy," briefly is that there is a nonspecific poisonous group in each protein molecule, which when liberated causes the anaphylaxis. The liberation of this poison is brought about by a specific ferment produced by the body cells when the foreign protein is introduced.

Novy and De Kruif base their explanation on a theory which they have presented and which is comparable in a general way to the mechanism in blood coagulation. They assume the existence in normal circulating blood of a more or less labile substance termed the *poison matrix*. The latter is changed by a catalyzer into an actively poisonous substance or *anaphylatoxin*, which produces the anaphylaxis. It is the foreign substance which induces or accelerates this change.

The "humoral theory" does not take into consideration any of the facts upon which the "cellular theory of allergy" is based. Many investigators have attempted to explain anaphylaxis on the basis that the reaction is a cellular one. Various tests which lead one to assume that the production of the toxic substance is in the cells have led workers to accept most of this theory in preference to the "humoral theory." The proponents of the cellular theory are of the opinion that precipitins play an important role in the reaction, especially since it appears that the precipitin content of a serum and the passive hypersensitiveness conferred are proportionate. It is probable that the most satisfactory theory of allergy will be a combination of both the "humoral and cellular theories," with major emphasis upon the latter. It is possible that the entire reaction is a cellular one, to be explained by a knowledge of physical chemistry. Perhaps in the near future a theory will be proposed which will withstand all attacks and leave no room for doubt.

Allergy may in some cases appear at times to be inherited, but in most instances the condition is probably acquired. If inherited, it is not the specific sensitization but the general tendency to become sensitive, which is inherited. The important anaphylactogens or sensitinogens most frequently observed are:

Zoosensitinogens—albumin present in:

1. Foreign blood serum and corpuscles.
2. Foods, such as eggs, milk, certain meats and fish.
3. Hair, feathers and effluvia of lower animals.
4. Products of animal parasites.

Phytosensitinogens:

1. Foods of plant origin, as fruits, vegetables, grains, etc.
2. Pollen of certain plants.
3. Powders and dust, such as rice powder used for the face; hay and house dusts, etc.
4. Products from bacteria, fungi, etc.
5. Plant substances, as poison sumac, poison ivy, poison oak and the primrose.

Schwartzman Reaction and Arthus Phenomenon.—Schwartzman (*J. A. M. A.,* 1929, **103,** 1965) noted that a local skin reaction can be produced in rabbits by the intradermal injection with filtrates of *E. typhosa, Escherichia coli,* meningococci and other bacteria, if this intracutaneous injection is followed within twenty-four hours by an intravenous injection of the filtrate. This reaction appears within twenty-four hours after the intravenous injection, is usually a hemorrhagic necrosis at the site of the intradermal inoculation and tends to disappear after two or three days. This differs from Arthus phenomenon (*Comp. rend. Soc. biol.*, 1903, **55,** 817). The latter is a peculiar local effect following repeated subcutaneous injections of horse serum into a rabbit. As the animal becomes immune, succeeding injections will produce severe reactions which may take the form of a firm indurated area with local necrosis. This local response can be elicited at any site and is not necessarily confined to the area of earlier inoculations.

THE RELATION OF ALLERGY TO DISEASE AND IMMUNITY

Mention has been made of disease being caused by the pollens of certain plants, by animal emanations and by the ingestion of certain foods in susceptible individuals. The abnormal response to drug administration also has been mentioned. Anaphylactic shock or shocks (reactions) may occur during the course of disease caused by bacteria or animal parasites. It is even reasonable to assume that these allergic reactions are responsible for many of the symptoms commonly observed in these diseases. In fact, von Pirquet considers and groups the exanthemata (skin eruptions) of some of the acute infectious diseases as anaphylactic reactions. It is possible that many of the diseases, headaches, migraines and even the "common cold" are merely expressions of anaphylactic reactions, the symptoms being found primarily and in the beginning at least at the place of introduction of the exciting agent.

The time required for sensitization to result after the sensitinogen has been introduced into the body is known as the *incubation period of active sensitization*. This period varies and is different for each species of animal. The amount of antigenic material, the method and route of its introduction into the body will also influence the time for sensitization to be effected. The duration of active sensitization will also vary. Some animals and human beings lose their hypersensitiveness within a few weeks, while others, especially those who are hypersensitive to drugs, pollens, foods, etc., may remain sensitized throughout the entire duration of their lives.

The specificity of the anaphylactic reaction had led to attempts in the differentiation of proteins. More widely used and of more practical value are the several anaphylactic skin reactions or tests which are employed as aids in the diagnosis of disease and in the attempt to determine a specific agent which may be the cause of an existing allergy or hypersensitiveness. These will be mentioned in another chapter.

In practice, anaphylaxis must be watched and even tested for in some instances before horse serum and other products containing antibodies and protein substances are injected into the human system. This is done to prevent serum sickness or serum disease and marked anaphylactic shock. In regards to the relation of anaphylaxis to immunity and recovery from disease, it is believed that there exists no intimate relationship. It is, of course, known that, during the recovery of a disease or during artificial immunization, anaphylactic reactions or sensitization is observed in the early stages of the disease or at the beginning of administration of the protein. But this does not mean that an anaphylactic antibody, which is produced to overcome anaphylaxis (see below), necessarily can kill or neutralize any virulent antigen. The anaphylactic antibody is powerless to kill and therefore to get rid of or protect against disease. Its duties are primarily to protect sensitized cells against dead proteins.

PREVENTION OF SENSITIZATION—DESENSITIZATION
AND ANTIANAPHYLAXIS

Efforts have been made to prevent sensitization or allergy in the use of antimicrobic sera when employed in the prophylaxis or treatment of disease. A large variety of substances and different techniques have been employed but none of them have been found of practical value in preventing or reducing the sensitizing or anaphylactic effects of the serum.

Antianaphylaxis, better known as desensitization, is the refractory state wherein sensitization to a specific sensitinogen is decreased or entirely removed for varying periods of time or altogether by certain procedures. It is a specific phenomenon which would seem to indicate the development of a tolerance to the sensitinogen which is used. Desensitization is generally accomplished by giving injections of the specific sensitinogen, starting with very small doses and gradually increasing the size of the dose with each subsequent injection. The subject of desensitization is of great importance in connection with the use of antimicrobic sera in man and animals, also in the treatment of hay fever, asthma, drug and microbial allergies.

ENZYMES, AGGRESSINS, ETC.

Other products of microbial metabolism other than previously mentioned also play a role in the production of specific symptoms. Thus we have the bacterial hemolysins produced by many different bacteria, mostly pathogenic, which exert a destructive action on erythrocytes. Staphylococci, streptococci, many vibrios, typhoid bacilli, *Pasteurella pestis*, etc., contain, respectively, staphylolysin, streptolysin, vibriolysins, typholysin, pestolysin, etc. These bacterial hemolysins are nonspecific, in that they will act on the red blood corpuscles of different animals. They, especially those produced by the first two organisms named, are partly responsible for the production of the secondary anemias commonly observed during many of the bacterial infections. *Leukocidin* is a name given to a bacterial product which exerts a destructive action on leukocytes or at least prevents or inhibits their phagocytic action. Certain staphylococci and streptococci produce specific leukocidin.

Enzymes or Ferments.—Mention was made in previous sections that bacteria produce true ferments or enzymes primarily for the purpose of nutrition and the production of favorable environmental conditions to enable the organism to survive. This alone aids in the production or at least in the prolongation of an existing infection, though not directly influencing the latter. But there are some ferments that are able to digest other bacteria and perhaps devitalized body cells, with the production of toxic substances capable of hindering phagocytosis and even exerting toxic symptoms when absorbed. Active proteolytic ferments are produced by *Bacillus pyocyaneus* and pneumococci.

Bail and others believe that the virulency of a bacterium depends on its ability to secrete *aggressins*, or substances which protect the microorganism by preventing antibody (especially opsonin) action or directly repelling the body cells and preventing phagocytosis. Aggressin then may be regarded as a normal antibody of the bacterium, acting against the defensive forces of the body cells of a host. Some workers claim that aggressins are merely liberated endotoxins. Others regard them as similar to some of the other bacterial products, bacteriophages, toxic protein end products, etc.

The bacteriophage, a filterable virus, ultramicrobe, enzyme, or catalytic agent, parasitic on bacteria, and acting as a bacteriolytic agent, dissolving the latter, was mentioned in a previous section.

Chapter XXXIII

BIOLOGICAL PRODUCTS

So THAT OUR bodies may possess a marked resistance, it is the common practice to artificially immunize individuals, as a means of affording protection against disease, and in some instances for the purpose of combating infection that has already set in. Many products are extensively used for this purpose.

Biologic therapy as now practiced embraces the prophylaxis and treatment of disease by agents marketed under any of the following titles: (1) *Bacterial Vaccines* (known also as Bacterial Antigens, Bacterins or Opsonogens); (2) *Sensitized Bacterial Vaccines* (so-called Serobacterins); (3) *Antimicrobic Sera* (Antibacterial, Therapeutic or Immune Serums, or Antiserums); (4) *Modified or Attenuated Viruses* (as so-called Smallpox Vaccine and Rabies Vaccine); (5) *Antitoxins* (Antitoxic Serums); (6) *T-A Mixture;* (7) *Immunizing Toxins;* (8) *Toxoids or Modified Toxins;* (9) *Tuberculins;* (10) *Phylacogens* and *Bacterial Culture Filtrates;* (11) *Aggressins* (natural tissue fluids from artificially infected animals); (12) *Immunogens* (or Ectoantigens); (13) *Antivenin;* (14) *Bacteriophage;* (15) *Extracts* or *Allergens* (bacterial, animal or vegetable or with specific designations as Pollen Extracts or Leucocyte Extract, etc.); (16) *Normal Serum;* and (17) *Diagnostic and Biological Reagents.*

These agents are of a complex biological nature. It is on this account that the author has designated them as *biological products*, which also serves to distinguish them from the many other classes of medicinal and chemical preparations. Their therapeutic action depends on the numerous phases of immunity, which were previously considered, so that the intimate relationship between the two should be clearly understood. For complete details concerning these products, see Gershenfeld (*Biological Products*, Romaine Pierson Publishers, Inc., New York, 1939).

GENERAL CONSIDERATION OF BIOLOGICAL PRODUCTS

Federal Control.—Vaccines, serums and analogous products have been deemed of such importance by the federal government, that their production for interstate sale within the jurisdiction of the United States has been under the special protection of an act of Congress, approved July 1, 1902, antedating even the Pure Food and Drugs Act. Under this law, all establishments producing such products for interstate sale must be licensed by the Secretary of the Treasury upon the recommendation of the Surgeon General of the U. S. Public Health Service.

Biologicals for veterinary use prepared for interstate sale in the United States must receive a license issued by the Bureau of Animal Industry.

Licensing.—The U. S. Public Health Service (National Institute of Health), to whom application must be made, makes inspections and examinations of all facilities and methods of procedure in manufacture, and after having found all samples ob-

tained in the plant and on the open market of a high standard of purity, recommenda-
tions for a license are made. Biologicals made and sold or used solely within the
States of their origin (no interstate sale) do not come, of course, under federal supervision, but in the main they are under the supervision of the respective state health
departments.

Labeling and Dating.—The label must contain the name, address and license
number of the manufacturer. An expiration date, laboratory lot number given at the
particular time when the product was prepared, and the minimum potency or strength,
if such can be determined, are also to be included. The federal law requires that each
package of any of the biological products should be stamped with an *expiration date*
("the date beyond which the contents cannot be expected beyond reasonable doubt to
yield their specific results"), or date of manufacture or issue.

Storage.—Many of the biological products deteriorate very rapidly if kept at room
or higher temperatures. The temperature at which biological products are stored,
particularly rapidly deteriorating preparations, is very important. Pharmacists and
others should, therefore, keep their biological products in cold storage, at as low
a temperature as possible (4° C.), being sure that the latter never exceeds 15° C.
Freezing, however, should be avoided, except in the case of modified smallpox and
rabies viruses. The latter should be kept as cold as possible, the colder the better.

Potency Tests.—Official potency standards are made or official potency tests have
been established by and are conducted at the National Institute of Health for:

Antitoxins—all forms of Diphtheria Antitoxin, Tetanus Antitoxin, Botulinus
Antitoxin Type A, Botulinus Antitoxin Type B, Perfringens Antitoxin, Vibrion Sep-
tique Antitoxin, Histolyticus Antitoxin, Odematiens Antitoxin, Sordelii Antitoxin,
Staphylococcus and Scarlet Fever Streptococcus Antitoxins.

Serums—Antidysenteric Serum (Shiga), Antimeningococcic Serum and Antipneumococcic Serum (Types I and II). Types V, VII and VIII are also being controlled.

Bacterial Vaccines—Typhoid and Triple Vaccines prepared from the typhoid or
typhoid, paratyphoid A and paratyphoid B bacilli.

Toxins or Modified Toxins—Diphtheria Toxin-Antitoxin Mixture, Diphtheria
Toxin for the Shick Test, Diphtheria Toxoid, Scarlet Fever Streptococcus Toxin for
the Dick Test and for Immunization, and Tetanus Toxoid.

Added Preservative.—The bacterial vaccines are prepared under aseptic conditions and sterilized by heat. The other products are prepared under aseptic conditions and forced through a Berkefeld or similar type filter so as to be assured of sterility.
With all these strict precautions, it has been found advisable to add an antispetic,
so as to have an additional safeguard as a preventive against contamination in the
last stages of handling. The small amount of antiseptic present possesses no deleterious effect. The most commonly used antiseptic is cresol (0.25 to 0.4 per cent).
Phenol (0.5 per cent), glycerin, organic mercury compounds (merthiolate and phenyl
mercuric acetate) and chloretone are also used. None is ideal for all purposes. The
efficiency of a preservative varies with the character of the product.

Tests for Purity and Safety.—All biological products, though they have been
sterilized, as previously mentioned, must be tested for their purity before they are
marketed. This generally consists of:

1. A pathogenicity test—by injecting a portion of the material into guinea pigs and if necessary into other laboratory animals. The latter are to be kept under observation for two weeks, to detect the presence of any foreign toxic substance.

2. A cultural test—culturing in suitable media for the accidental presence of bacteria is to be made at each stage and at the end of the preparation of the various products. This includes an aerobic and an anaerobic culture (fermentation test).

Marketing Biological Products in the Dry State.—Many contributions have been made in an attempt to dry antisera and other biological activity. Simple desiccation, however, has many limitations and the resulting product may not be entirely satisfactory (*J. Immunol.*, 1935, **28,** 433). The use of rapid freezing and rapid dehydration, from the frozen state, under high vacuum employing the so-called *Lyophile Process* of preservation offers a practical method for the preservation of the maximum, biological activity of antisera, antitoxins, antivenin, normal sera and plasma, viruses toxins, venoms, stock bacterial cultures and other preparations. Folsdorf and Mudd (*J. Immunol.*, 1935, **29,** 389; 1938, **34,** 469) describe the *cryochem process* and other procedures and apparatus for obtaining such desiccated products. Biologically active products, when lyophilized, appear as porous solids occupying practically the same space (volume) as the liquid (serum, if antisera) from which they were prepared and possessing the property of dissolving completely and readily upon the addition of water. This process is employed commercially for the storage of antisera, antitoxins and other biological products in bulk. As *Lyovac Biologicals* (trade-mark for lyophilized biologicals) there is marketed a *complete line* of lyophilized antisera, antitoxins, antivenin, bee venom solution, complement (pooled guinea-pig serum) (*J. Path. & Bact.*, 1938, **46,** 382) and other preparations. In the marketed package, the lyophilized product is found in one container and in another sterile vial, sterile distilled water (pyrogen-free) is present, to be used to bring the dry product into solution. The lyophile process maintains unaltered the potency of the biologicals for very long periods of time. The *desivac process* (*J. A. M. A.*, 1940, **115,** 1095) and the *atevac process* (*Ann. Int. Med.*, 1940, **14,** 201) are other methods of drying which have been advocated.

Biological Preparations Official in the U. S. P.—In the U. S. P. XII, the following biological preparations are official: *Antitoxinum Diphthericum* (diphtheria antitoxin); *Antitoxinum Scarlatinae Streptococcicum* (scarlet fever streptococcus antitoxin); *Antitoxinum Tetanicum* (tetanus antitoxin); *Globulinum Immune Humanum* (human immune globulin); *Plasma Humanum Normale Citratum* (citrated normal human plasma); *Serum Antimeningococcicum* (antimeningococcic serum); *Serum Antipneumococcicum* (antipneumococcic serum—type specific); *Serum Humanum Normale* (normal human serum); *Serum Immune Morbillosi Humanum* (human measles immune serum); *Serum Immune Scarlatinae Humanum* (human scarlet fever immune serum); *Toxinum Diphthericum Diagnosticum* (diphtheria toxin for the Schick test); *Toxinum Scarlatinae Streptococcicum* (scarlet fever streptococcus toxin); *Toxoidum Diphthericum* (diphtheria toxoid); *Toxoidum Tetanicum* (tetanus toxoid); *Tuberculinum Pristinum* (old tuberculin); *Vaccinum Rabies* (rabies vaccine); *Vaccinum typhosum* (bacterial vaccine made from the typhoid bacillus); *Vaccinum Typho-Paratyphosum* (bacterial vaccine made from the typhoid bacillus and the paratyphoid "A" and "B" bacilli); *Vaccinum Variolae* (smallpox vaccine).

ANTITOXINS

These are the most important of all the biological products. They are generally *specific* and, as their name implies, they counteract the toxins.

Antitoxins (briefly defined) are the sera (or generally the globulins from sera dissolved in isotonic salt solution), obtained from the blood of animals, which have been immunized against specific extracellular toxins and, therefore, containing antibodies known as antitoxins which will neutralize these toxins. The antitoxins, so prepared, are specific, i. e., they will only neutralize the particular extracellular toxins which had produced them.

The methods of preparing the various antitoxins do not differ materially in their general principles, with the exception that the toxin from aerobes is prepared under aerobic conditions and the toxin from anaerobes is obtained under anaerobic conditions. A description of the method of the preparation of diphtheria antitoxins will, therefore, suffice for all.

Preparation of Diphtheria Antitoxin.—The methods for producing diphtheria antitoxin commercially vary only in minor technical details. The first requisite for successful antitoxin manufacture is a potent toxin (see page 485). For antitoxin production on a large scale horses have been found to be the most useful animals. The horses should be young, vigorous and of fair size. They must be absolutely free from disease. Horses possessing some natural diphtheria antitoxin are preferred, as in practice they have been found to produce larger yields of antitoxin after immunization.

The selected horses are given a preliminary intravenous injection of 3000 units of diphtheria antitoxin on the day preceding the first injection of toxin. They are then injected, subcutaneously, every second day with diphtheria toxin, the dosage of the latter being increased.

The horses gradually become immune so that it becomes possible to inject large doses of toxin which if given in like amount at the beginning would have proved fatal. By using diphtheria toxoid instead of diphtheria toxin or mixtures of toxin and antitoxin, it is possible to omit the preliminary injection of antitoxin and also to begin with much larger doses.

Horses, whose serum contains less than 100 units of a ntitoxin per cc. after a period of two months, are discarded as unsuitable for diphtheria antitoxin production. Generally, today, only horses whose minimum yield is over 300 units per cc. of blood serum are used for commercial production. The majority of horses approach a yield of 500 or more units per cc. of serum within three months. High yields are not uncommon.

Bleeding the Horse.—The bleedings are done under aseptic conditions in specially constructed stalls separated from the stables and other buildings. The blood from the jugular vein is allowed to flow through the rubber tube into tall glass cylinders, called "bleeding jars." Where the serum is to be purified and the antitoxic substances concentrated, and this is the common practice, a 17 per cent sodium citrate solution in amounts equal to one-tenth of the volume of blood which is to be added, is placed in the jars. The cylinders of blood and citrate (to which 0.3 per cent cresol is added to prevent contamination) are kept below 10° C.

Concentrated Diphtheria Antitoxin.—In 1906, Gibson (*J. Biol. Chem.*, 1906, **1**, 161; 1907, **3**, 233, 254) announced a method for the concentration of diphtheria antitoxin. Later Banzhaf (Dept. of Health, New York City, 1912–1913, **7**, 114) made important modifications of this technique. Additional researches have led to further improvement in concentration and refinement. This concentration is based on the fact that the antitoxin is found associated with the pseudoglobulins.

Purification by Enzyme Digestion.—Purification by enzyme digestion using such enzymes as pepsin, papain and trypsin has been advocated for the refinement of diphtheria and other antitoxins. The process is based on a controlled method of selective digestion of the proteins of the immune horse serum with one or more of the previously mentioned enzymes, usually pepsin.

Storage.—At low temperatures the annual rate of deterioration of diphtheria and other antitoxins does not exceed 10 per cent, but at temperatures between 15° and 20° C., it may approach 20 per cent per annum.

Standardization.—The unit of diphtheria antitoxin represents that amount of antitoxin which will just neutralize 100 minimal lethal doses (M.L.D.'s) of standard diphtheria toxin. (For definition of M.L.D. see under Diphtheria Toxin.) As a matter of practical advantage, because of the greater stability of diphtheria antitoxin, the toxin is brought into conformity to a standard antitoxin distributed by the National Institute of Health. The antitoxic unit, according to the National Institute of Health, is the amount of antitoxin which will exactly neutralize the L dose of diphtheria toxin when both are injected simultaneously, or if allowed to stand in contact, protected from light, for about thirty minutes and then injected. The expression L+, or "limes death," indicates the smallest quantity of toxin which when mixed with one unit of antitoxin is capable of killing—when injected subcutaneously—a 250-Gm. guinea pig at the end of the fourth day; L0, or "limes zero or threshold," is the largest amount of toxin which is completely neutralized by one unit of antitoxin. Theoretically the L0 dose of diphtheria toxin should contain 100 M.L.D.'s, the L+ dose should contain 101 M.L.-D.'s, and the difference between the two doses should be one M.L.D. Practically, however, the difference is found to be much more. Theoretically the unit of diphtheria antitoxin should be that amount of antitoxin which, when mixed with an L+ dose of toxin and injected subcutaneously into a guinea pig weighing 250 Gm., would preserve the life of the guinea pig for only four days, *i. e.*, the animal would die on the fourth day. In commercial practice where a margin of safety is advantageous the unit of diphtheria antitoxin is regarded as the smallest amount of antitoxin which will permanently save the life of a guinea pig if injected together with an L+ dose of toxin.

In the commercial assay of antitoxin the first step is to standardize the toxin against the standard antitoxin distributed by the government; then varying proportions of the antitoxin to be tested are mixed with the L+ dose of this standardized toxin, the mixtures allowed to stand between thirty and sixty minutes at room temperature protected from light, and these mixtures are then injected into guinea pigs of approximately 250 Gm. By mathematical calculations from the relative proportions of antitoxin and toxin which kill and those which do not kill the guinea pigs, the strength of the unknown may be computed in terms of the standard units of antitoxin. For complete details for official methods of testing the potency, see *Tests of Standard and Commercial Diphtheria and Tetanus Antitoxins* (National Institute of Health, U. S. Public Health Service, 1931).

Use.—Diphtheria antitoxin neutralizes the free toxin in the system and will not overcome the injurious effects caused by the toxin which has combined firmly with the tissues. For this reason it is highly important that the antitoxin in adequate dosage should be used as soon as possible, and all of the antitoxin needed should be administered in the first one or two doses. Antitoxin should be given intramuscularly or, in the more severe cases and those in which an insufficient first dose was given or administration was delayed, an additional injection of antitoxin should be given intravenously.

Diphtheria antitoxin is also employed as a temporary preventive remedy against this scourge by the administration subcutaneously of 1000 units of antitoxin. This immunity and protection do not last longer than from two to four weeks, so that if it is necessary to prolong the period of protection, injections are to be repeated at least once a month or, better still, employ active immunization (see under Diphtheria Toxoid) after the first injections.

The dose of diphtheria antitoxin for treatment may vary from as low as 5000 to 10,000 units in mild cases to from 20,000 to 60,000 in severe cases.

Serum Sickness

Although the use of concentrated and refined diphtheria antitoxic products has to a large degree eliminated the severe serum reactions, the latter may be encountered (in about 1 in each 10,000 persons injected). These reactions usually develop within a few minutes after injection and may be merely an immediate chill of a mild character or, in more severe anaphylactic reactions, the face becomes flushed, respiration is accelerated, and other symptoms may appear such as cyanosis, dyspnoea and urticaria. Upon the appearance of the latter symptoms, 1 cc. of 1:1000 solution of epi-nephrine hydrochloride should be given immediately.   In few instances, death within a few minutes has been reported (Lamson, *J. A. M. A.*, 1929, **93,** 1775).   Individuals who have not reacted badly to a first injection do not need to fear a second injection administered shortly after the latter and given during the duration of the disease; so far as known all fatal results have followed the first injection.   If the injections of serum preparations are months and years apart, the onset of symptoms of serum sick-ness is apt to occur more rapidly than when the antigen was given the first time. Mild degrees of serum sickness may occur from four to twenty days after the adminis-tration of antitoxin.   These late reactions are rarely serious, and their severity will depend on the amount of serum which has been given.   There may be redness, pain or itching at the site of injection, pain in the joints, swelling of the lymph nodes, fever and a general urticaria lasting from a few hours to a week.   If sensitization to horse serum is suspected, or in countries where a horse meat diet is common, or if the patient has a history of asthma, hay fever or a marked susceptibility to hives, the sensitivity of the patient should be tested by the intradermal injection of 0.02 cc. of a 1:10 dilution of the antitoxin or of normal horse serum in physiological salt solution. Some workers advise a test for hypersensitiveness prior to all injections of serum products, especially if administered intravenously.   In a positive reaction an urti-carial wheal appears in fifteen to thirty minutes at the site of the intradermal injection. The ophthalmic test for sensitivity to horse serum by instilling a drop of a 1:10 dilu-tion of horse serum into the conjunctival sac is preferred by many workers over the intradermal test.   A positive reaction is indicated by the occurrence, in fifteen min-utes, of conjunctival redness, swelling and increased lachrymation.

Where the reaction is negative or if it is not possible to perform the latter and the history to sensitivity is negative, it is safe to proceed with the administration of the serum or serum product.   If the patient is hypersensitive to horse serum and serum therapy must be employed, the patient should be desensitized.   A suitable technique consists of administering subcutaneously the antitoxin in fractional doses beginning with 0.025 cc.   If no reaction develops, double the dose every half hour until a total of 1 cc. has been administered.   Doses of 0.3 cc. of epinephrine (1:1000) are injected at hourly intervals until all serum has been administered.   This can be given in the same syringe with the serum.   Then inject intravenously 0.1 cc. diluted with saline solution.   Double this dose every half hour until the full amount has been given. During the desensitization, a syringe containing epinephrine should always be at hand to use immediately if a dangerous reaction occurs.

Histaminase (*J. A. M. A.*, 1939, **112,** 1102, 2398) has been used with encouraging results in the treatment of and as a prophylactic against serum sickness.

In patients especially sensitive to horse serum and where desensitization is not possible or too time consuming, either diphtheria antitoxin or other product prepared in another animal may be used.   *Diphtheria Antitoxin, Bovine* and other bovine anti-toxins and serums are marketed for use in individuals sensitive to horse serum.   In fact, other animals are used for the preparation of marketable biological products to be employed for individuals sensitive to horse serum.   Though fewer persons may be found sensitive to bovine serum, rabbit serum or the serum of other animals as compared to horse serum, the same care must be observed with the former as when using the latter.

Tetanus Antitoxin

The official unit of tetanus antitoxin in this country is ten times the least amount which will save a 350-Gm. guinea pig for ninety-six hours after the subcutaneous injection of the official test dose of standard toxin which consists of one hundred M.L.D.'s of toxin.   In this country an M.L.D. of the latter is the smallest amount which, when injected subcutaneously, will kill a guinea pig, weighing 350 Gm., within ninety-six hours.   It is important to note that the unit of tetanus antitoxin of the American Government is twice as strong as the "International Standard Unit" which has been adopted by some, but as yet not by all, European countries.   It is desirable that the label shall contain a statement of quantity in both international and American units. In this country guinea pigs are used as the test animal but in some European countries mice are employed for this purpose.

In preparing the tetanus antitoxin the general method is the same as that described under *Diphtheria Antitoxin*.   There are, however, certain difficulties in preparing the toxin owing to the fact that species of the genus *Clostridium* are anaerobes and that the toxin is extremely unstable.

Because of the susceptibility of certain individuals toward horse serum proteins, and also because of its veterinary importance, there is manufactured also a *bovine tetanus antitoxin*.   The methods of production are exactly the same as for the equine product except that cattle are used.   The outside label of Tetanus Antitoxin must indicate "the genus of animal employed when other than the horse."   Glaser (*J. Pediat.*, 1941, **19,** 403) recommends the bovine preparation in all instances.

The methods of purification of tetanus antitoxin are the same as for diphtheria antitoxin.

Use.—In man, the most important use of tetanus antitoxin is as a prophylactic agent.   It should be borne in mind that the antitoxic effect passes off in about ten days, and that a single immunizing injection of tetanus antitoxin may not always be sufficient.   As a curative in the treatment of developed tetanus, tetanus antitoxin is of relatively slight value.

The prophylactic dose is 1500 units, given subcutaneously as soon as possible after the occurrence of the wound.   When extensive injury occurs, larger doses are given for the first two injections and 1500 units are administered at weekly intervals until the wound is practically healed.

Chapter XXXIV

OTHER ANTITOXINS

SCARLET FEVER STREPTOCOCCUS ANTITOXIN

AN ANTITOXIN SPECIFIC for this disease was first produced, on a commercial scale, by G. H. and G. F. Dick (*J. A. M. A.*, 1921, **77**, 782; 1923, **81**, 1166; 1924, **82**, 265, 655, 1246).

Scarlet fever antitoxin is standardized by comparing its power of neutralizing scarlet fever toxin with that of a standard antitoxin supplied by the National Institute of Health. The unit for this antitoxin is the smallest amount of antitoxin which will neutralize 50 skin-test doses of scarlet fever streptococcus toxin when they are mixed together, allowed to stand for several minutes, and then injected intradermally (U. S. Pub. Health Service, *Rept.* **1234**, 1928). The standardization of this antitoxin has to be done on children as the toxin is not toxic for laboratory animals. A practical laboratory animal method of measuring the potency of scarlet fever streptococcus toxin and antitoxin has been presented by Veldee (U. S. Pub. Health Service *Rept.* **1533**, 1932). See also the rabbit intradermal methods (*J. Immunol.*, 1935, **28**, 33), and the flocculation method (*ibid.*, 1937, **32**, 321).

Use.—Numerous favorable reports have appeared regarding the use and value of scarlet fever streptococcus antitoxin as a specific curative agent (*J. A. M. A.*, 1934, **103**, 1049). Rhoads and associates (*J. A. M. A.*, 1934, **102**, 2005) in reporting on the protective value of convalescent human serum and commercial antitoxin state that the *latter is more effective*. See also Dick and Dick, *Scarlet Fever*, Chicago, Ill., 1938.

Scarlet fever antitoxin is also suggested as an emergency measure for temporary (passive) immunization of contacts who are Dick-positive (*Lancet*, 1929, **1**, 177). The resulting immunity like that following the use of other serums (passive immunity) will endure for a period of not more than two or three weeks.

Dosage.—As a prophylactic the usual dose is about 2000 to 3000 units. In moderate cases of scarlet fever 5000 to 10,000 units of toxin are given preferably intramuscularly in the anterior muscles of thigh as a therapeutic agent. In severe cases 10,000 to 20,000 units are given intramuscularly or intravenously, the dose generally diluted with saline to 100 cc. Administration as early as possible in the disease is advocated. Additional doses are given if the temperature does not fall within twelve hours to nearly normal.

Schultz-Charlton Phenomenon.—The Schultz-Charlton reaction, regarded as a specific toxin-antitoxin reaction (*Ztschr. f. Kinderh.*, 1918, **17**, 328), has a practical application in the differentiation of the rash in suspected cases of the scarlet fever from that of other eruptive fevers or rashes manifested by drug or food idiosyncrasies. In this test, 0.1 or 0.2 cc. of the antitoxin or of convalescent serum is injected intradermally into the reddened skin of the suspected scarlatiniform rash preferably on the abdomen or chest; if the rash is scarlet fever of less than three days, there will be apparent within less than twenty-four and usually within six hours a permanent blanching several centimeters in diameter around the site of the injection. The reading is made while standing several feet from the patient. The specificity of the test is, however, not universally accepted (see *J. Infect. Dis.*, 1929, **45,** 1; also *Lancet*, 1929, **2,** 296).

STAPHYLOCOCCUS ANTITOXIN

Staphylococcus Antitoxin, available as a marketable preparation, is prepared from the refined and concentrated globulins obtained from the serum of horses injected with certain strains of staphylococcus toxin or toxoid. Ramon and Richou (*Rev. Immunol.*, 1939, **5,** 427) recommend combining the latter with tapioca when injecting horses so as to obtain a serum high in its antitoxin content.

The proposed *International unit of staphylococcus antitoxin* is that amount which will neutralize 200 M.H.D. of toxin. *The Minimum Hemolytic Dose* (M.H.D.) is that amount of toxin which will hemolyze 1 cc. of a 2 per cent suspension of rabbit red cells in one-hour incubation at 37° C. Leirne (*J. Path. & Bact.*, 1939, **48,** 291) discusses the antihemolytic, antidermonecrotic and antilethal values of this antitoxin.

Staphylococcus antitoxin is used in the treatment of generalized infections by staphylococci whenever the infection is accompanied by general signs of toxemia with little or no apparent resistance to the infection or its spread, and in obstinate or spreading localized infections. There is at present some doubt as to its precise value.

GAS GANGRENE (*C. Welchii*) ANTITOXIN (*Perfringens Antitoxin*)

This is an antitoxic serum or a preparation of the latter (refined and concentrated serum consisting of the globulins to which are attached the antitoxic substances) which has the specific power of neutralizing the soluble toxin produced by *C. welchii*. The horses or suitable animals are immunized with gradual increasing doses of a sterile filtrate from a liquid culture of *C. welchii* (containing the toxin) or with an anaculture or with a toxoid (*Comp. rend. Soc. biol.*, 1925, **92,** 1484). The process of preparation, concentration and refinement is similar to that employed for preparing diphtheria and other antitoxins. The finished preparation is tested and standardized according to the method established and described by the National Institute of Health.

Gas Gangrene Antitoxin (**Combined or Mixed**).—The Combined or Mixed Gas Gangrene Antitoxin or Polyanaerobic Antitoxin or Anaerobic Antitoxin is the preparation most frequently marketed and used in the prophylaxis and treatment of gas gangrene. This antitoxic serum is prepared from the toxins of *C. tetani, C. welchii* (*C. perfringens*), and *C. oedematis maligni* (*C. sporogenes*). At times the soluble toxins of only two of the organisms mentioned may be used in the preparation of the marketable product or immunization may be against some of the other anaerobes concerned in gas gangrene (*C. oedematiens; C. sordelli* (*C. oedematoides*); *C. histolyticum*, etc.). The different toxins are prepared individually. Horses or suitable animals are immunized with injections of but one toxin and the different antitoxins after preparation are mixed together. In some instances the same animal is immunized against several toxins simultaneously.

Use.—A mixed gas gangrene antitoxin commonly used as a therapeutic agent consists of perfringens antitoxin, 10,000 units; vibrionseptique antitoxin, 10,000 units; histolyticum antitoxin, 2500 units; oedematiens antitoxin, 1000 units; and oedematoides antitoxin, 200 units. One to four such doses at twelve to twenty-four-hour intervals are administered intravenously depending upon the degree of intoxication, the extent and length of time of the injury, the amount of contamination with dirt, the surgical management, and the response of the patient. Supplementary intramuscular injections in the vicinity of the involved area are advisable. As improvement is apparent, minimum therapeutic doses are given subcutaneously at twenty-four to forty-eight-hour intervals until the patient is out of danger. Combined therapy of a mixed gas gangrene antitoxin and large doses of the sulfonamide drugs are recommended as prophylactic agents and in treatment.

BOTULINUS ANTITOXIN (*Botulism Antitoxin*)

In North America, Type A is the most frequent cause of human botulism, whereas in Europe Type B is found most frequently. Botulinus toxin is extraordinarily potent and remarkable in its ability to withstand the action of heat and body juices.

Preparation.—Antitoxin has been prepared for each of the specific types and it is important to note that antitoxin produced against one series of strains (Type A) has no appreciable effect upon the toxins of the strains of the other types (Type B). The two types of antitoxin which are most commonly employed are prepared by immunizing animals (horses or cattle) against the toxin of each type (*C. botulinum Types A and B*) separately. The procedures for the production of the toxin and antitoxin correspond closely to those given in the technique for producing tetanus antitoxin, except that the whole serum (and not concentrated globulins) is the marketed product.

The two antitoxins (Types A and B) can be mixed (pooled) to yield a polyvalent antitoxin for use in botulism. Some workers prepare a polyvalent antitoxin by immunizing a single horse with toxin prepared from all types of *C. botulinum*. The former technique is advocated, however, as being more satisfactory.

Use.—As a therapeutic agent for human cases Dickson advises intravenous injection after the sensitivity to horse serum has been eliminated (*J. Exp. Med.*, 1923, **38**, 327). Comparatively large doses (50 cc. (10,000 units) daily) of botulinus antitoxin (bivalent serum or of the monotypical serum) Types A and B are given (at the rate of not more than 1 cc. per minute) until recovery. The results of the use of botulinus antitoxin in man have been disappointing. However, since no other effective treatment for botulism is known, the antitoxin should be given a trial. Success can only be expected from serum therapy if the antitoxic serum is administered in the early stages of the disease or preferably as soon as suspicious symptoms appear. Individuals who have consumed food suspected of being infected are given prophylactic doses of 10 cc. subcutaneously (or at least 2000 units) intramuscularly.

Chapter XXXV

ANTIVENIN
(ANTI-VENOM SERUM; SNAKE POISON ANTITOXIN)

NORTH AMERICAN ANTI-SNAKE-BITE SERUM

Antivenin (*Nearctic Crotalidae*) or North American Anti-Snake-Bite Serum is prepared as follows:

The several species of snakes are collected and these snakes are made to imitate the natural "strike." The venoms are thus extracted by these special techniques. This is then centrifugalized and desiccated. The latter is dissolved in equal parts of saline solution and glycerin. It should be neutral (and is neutralized if necessary) and then placed in the refrigerator for one month to become sterile.

Animals are then immunized in the same manner as is done when making diphtheria antitoxin. Horses are used. Mules, cows and goats can be used when horses are not available. North American Anti-Snake-Bite Serum is a purified and concentrated serum globulin to which is attached the antivenin obtained from horses which have been immunized against the venoms of poisonous North American snakes, belonging to the *crotalidae*. Specifically it will antidote the poisons of the copperhead, the cotton-mouth mocassin and the rattlesnakes, but it is not effective against coral-snake venom.

The usual precautionary measures as observed in preparing and marketing all biological products are also observed here. A potency test is always performed to be assured of the value of antivenin. The methods of standardization that are conducted consist in the use of any or all of the following tests: precipitin test, neutralization test (neutralizing activity of venom) and the protection test. The last-named test is usually performed to determine the potency. This consists in injecting a 2-Kg. rabbit with 2 cc. of antivenin. No ill effects should be observed after 1 mg. of desiccated venom is injected two hours later. Pigeons have been used more recently as the test animal.

The preparation is marketed in 10 cc. syringes and more recently in lyophilized form. This is an amount which will protect against the average quantity of venom secreted at one time by small North American serpents, such as the ground rattlers and the copperhead or other snakes of moderate size. Bites by large snakes especially the Florida and Texas diamondbacks and large specimens of other rattlesnakes and mocassins are likely to require two or more syringes of antivenin. Some workers use 50 cc. (5 syringes) of antivenin in all bites by diamondbacks. The injection is given subcutaneously and, better still, intramuscularly as soon as possible. If too much time has elapsed between the bite and the arrival of antivenin, the latter should be given intravenously.

For further details on antivenin, see Githens and Wolff (*J. Immunol.*, 1939, **37,** 33) on the polyvalency of crotalidic antivenins; Grasset and Zoutendyk (*Tr. Roy. Soc. Trop. Med. & Hyg.*, 1938, **31,** 445) on antivenene for treatment of bites by the Gaboon

467

viper (*Bitis gabonica*); and Githens (*Snake Bite Treatment with Antivenin*, Sharp and Dohme Laboratories, 1940).

Bothrops Antitoxin or Antivenin (Bothropic) or Tropical American Anti-Snake-Bite Serum is prepared from and effective against the venoms of the principal poisonous serpents of the genus *Bothrops,* especially *B. atrox* (the Fer-de-Lance).

Antivenin Cascabel (Crotalus terrificus) or Tropical Rattler Anti-Snake-Bite Serum is prepared from and effective against the venom of the tropical rattler, *C. terrificus,* commonly known as the Cascavel or Cascabela, a poisonous snake which is widely distributed throughout the American tropics and northern South America, Central America and Mexico (except the north central highlands). The method of manufacturing, marketing and employing these antivenins (Kolle and associates, *Hand. der Path. Mikroorg.*, III, 1) is with few modifications as given for North American anti-snake-bite serum (see page 467). The Bacteriological Institute at Buenos Aires issues a bivalent serum for *C. terrificus* and *B. alternata.*

Antivenin Ophidic (Bothropic and Cascabel) is a polyvalent equine serum consisting of a mixture of *Bothropic Atrox Antivenin* (Barba-Amarilla) and of *Crotalus Durissus Antivenin* (each prepared separately) and is used in the specific treatment of bites of any of the snakes belonging to the genus *Bothrops,* including the mano-de-piedra (*B. nummifera*); the bocaraca (*B. Schlegelii*); the tamaga (*B. brachystoma*); the jararaca (*B. jararaca*), etc., as well as those of the cascabel and barba-amarilla.

SCORPION ANTIVENIN

A specific serum against scorpion sting or venom is available (*J. Hyg.*, **9,** 69). Such a preparation prepared by the Lister Institute at Elstree, England, has been issued for use in Egypt. *Buthus quinquestriatus* is the common variety of scorpion in the latter country. In Brazil many deaths have been recorded due to scorpion stings and in particular from that of *Tityus bahiensis.* An antivenin effective for the venom of the latter and three other South American species is available (*Mem. Inst. Oswaldo Cruz,* **21,** 5). Scorpion antivenin in common with those derived from snakes and spiders are highly specific.

Black Widow Spider (*Latrodectus mactans*) Antivenin is an equine antiserum useful against the venom of the black widow spider (*Latrodectus mactans*) and, as marketed, contains in each cc. the equivalent in neutralizing power of the venom of at least 50 spiders. Black widow spiders were once found only in rural districts, in grain bins, barns, chicken coops, grape arbors, in clusters of grapes, on tomatoes when removing them from the vine, etc., but within the past few years they have become extremely urban. An injection of 5 cc. of black widow spider antivenin, administered intramuscularly, is the suggested dose and if symptoms are not relieved in an hour or two, the dose may be repeated. Bogen (*J. A. M. A.*, 1926, **86,** 1894) first used the human serum of recovered victims. D'Amour (*Proc. Soc. Exptl. Biol. Med.*, 1936, **35,** 262) prepared sheep serum for several different spider venoms. The use of rabbit serum is advocated as being of greater value (*Proc. Soc. Exptl. Biol. Med.*, 1939, **40,** 686). Voss treated successfully 5 cases of black widow spider bite with *Lyovac Black Widow Spider Antivenin* (*Clin. Med.*, 1941, **48,** 123). A bivalent antivenin for the venoms of *Lycosa raptoria* and *Ctenus nigriventer* (the species of poisonous spiders most frequently responsible for human cases in São Paulo) is available in Brazil (*Trop. Dis. Bull.,* 1927, **24,** 402).

Chapter XXXVI

ANTIBACTERIAL SERUMS

THERAPEUTIC SERA

Antimicrobic Serums

THESE PRODUCTS are serums obtained from the blood of animals (usually horses) which have been immunized (actively) against particular bacteria and they contain antibodies that are specific against the bacteria used in the immunization of the animals. The serums thus prepared depend for their efficiency upon one or more of the following antibodies: agglutinins, precipitins, bacteriolysins or bactericidins, and opsonins or bacteriotropins. It may be that in some instances liberated endotoxin causes the production of some antiendotoxin which may in turn be found in some of the marketable serums. In addition to these immune serums of the lower animals (horses, cattle, goats, rabbits or oxen), immune human serum obtained from individuals convalescent from certain diseases is used at times in the prophylaxis and treatment of various affections.

Animals used in the production of biologic products are kept under competent daily inspection and a preliminary quarantine for the period of at least one week before use. Only healthy animals free from disease are used. Animals of the *Equine* genus are tested for the absence of glanders (mallein test), and those of the *Bovine* genus must be shown to be free from tuberculosis (tuberculin test). All horses, except those which are naturally immune to tetanus, are given not less than 500 units of tetanus antitoxin semimonthly or 2000 units monthly.

Preparation of Antibacterial Serums.—*Most all marketable antibacterial serums are polyvalent* (*i. e.*, prepared from mixed strains of the particular bacterium) unless otherwise labeled.

The horses are usually injected with attenuated cultures for a period of from two to four months with increasing doses after each injection. At the end of this period, injections of small doses of a culture of living virulent mixed strains of the same bacterium are given. These injections with the live bacteria are continued, giving increasing doses at stated intervals until at about the end of from five to eight or even ten months after immunization was started the animal is ready to be bled. The time when to bleed, as in the case of the antitoxins, is solely dependent upon each individual animal. If after preliminary tests it has been found that the specific antibody content is at its maximum, and additional injections do not increase this antibody content, then the animal is ready for bleeding.

With many bacteria, except *streptococci*, *pneumococci* and *Pasteurella* (*Bacillus*) *pestis*, it has been found possible to use living organisms from the start or shortly thereafter. Intravenous injections are most frequently given. But the actual mode of administration, dosage and frequency of the latter depend on the virulency or toxicity of the organism employed and the health and reaction of the horse. In the case of antiplague serum, nonvirulent strains of *Pasteurella (Bacillus) pestis* (the causative agent) are employed throughout the immunization, due to the dangers connected in handling the living organism.

The bleeding here is conducted in the same manner as is the bleeding of the horses in the manufacture of diphtheria antitoxin (which was considered previously). After the clotting of blood, which is collected in sterile containers, to which there is added some preservative, usually 0.25 to 0.4 per cent cresol, the serum is obtained. The serum is usually allowed to stand a few weeks in a refrigerator until further separation of fibrin ceases. It is then filtered, if possible, through a Berkefeld or a similar filter, tested for sterility and toxicity, a preservative is added and the preparation is placed on the market for use. These finished products are the antibacterial serums.

Potency Tests.—The exact composition of the complex bodies which are present as the valuable antibodies, acting as specific therapeutic agents against the bacteria which produced them, is not known. No satisfactory method has as yet been found by which the effectiveness or potency of these sera can be *accurately* determined, as is found possible in the case of the antitoxins. In the case of antipneumococcic serum, there has been established what may be called a protective and not a potency test. In addition to this, other biological tests are applied as agglutination and complement-fixation tests, to determine the content of agglutinins, complement-fixing antibodies, as well as others for different therapeutic sera, but none of them can be said to specifically inform one as to the exact potency of the particular product.

Administration.—The antibacterial serums are usually administered subcutaneously under the skin of the abdomen or between the scapulae. Intramuscular administration is gradually replacing the subcutaneous injections. Intravenous injections are employed in desperate or grave cases and in the late stages. Antimeningococcic serum is administered frequently into the spinal canal (intraspinally).

In most all instances the minimum initial curative dose for adults is 30 cc. unless the serum is of a high potency. Injections are repeated with sufficient persistence until all symptoms disappear. This may be one or even two doses daily. Antimicrobic serums given intravenously or intraspinally are first warmed to body temperature and then administered very slowly. The safest procedure before using antimicrobic serums is to perform the skin test for sensitivity (see page 461).

Antimeningococcic Serum

In the preparation of antimeningococcic serum, polyvalent preparations are usually marketed. Horses which meet the usual rigid physical requirements are selected. Standard meningococcus strains, one or more from the main fixed groups are used. Particular attention is given to the antigenicity of the cultures selected. Various methods of refining and concentrating the prepared antisera are used (*J. Lab. & Clin. Med.*, 1934, **19**, 1324). See Murdick and Cohen (*J. Immunol.*, 1935, **28**, 205) who describe the concentration technique as employed in the N. Y. State Dept. of Health Laboratories and for the technique as used in the N. Y. City Dept. of Health Laboratories, which applies equally to the refining of pneumococcus and meningococcus antisera, see *J. Lab. & Clin. Med.*, 1939, **24**, 417.

Recently, Branham (U. S. Pub. Health Repts., 1943, **58**, 478) in a comparison of rabbit and horse antimeningococcic serums reported that the rabbit serum, refined and concentrated, is far superior to horse serum preparations in potency and in ease and rapidity of preparation.

Methods of Standardization.—An accurate method of standardizing this and other antibacterial sera as is possible with the antitoxins has not as yet been devised and it is, therefore, only possible to approximate the efficiency of therapeutic sera by indirect measures. Among the methods advocated are (a) bacteriotropic titration, determining the opsonin or tropin content; (b) determining the complement-fixation titer (*J. Exp. Med.*, 1908, **10**, 141; *J. Immunol.*, 1938, **35**, 427); (c) determining the protective value or power of the serum against mice treated with virulent cultures of meningococci (*Canad. Pub. Health J.*, 1937, **28**, 265); and (d) by determining the agglutinin content (*J. Exp. Med.*, 1916, **23**, 403). Tests for specific precipitins carried out in test tubes or by plate precipitation are also used. The plate precipitation method was first described by Petri (*Brit. J. Exp. Path.*, 1932, **13**, 380) and recommended by Kirkbride and Cohen (*Am. J. Hyg.*, 1934, **20**, 444) and other workers (*J. Bact.*, 1938, **35**, 24). On May 4, 1942, The National Institute of Health issued "Minimum Requirements for Antimeningococcic Serum," in which the *plate precipitation test* and the *mouse protection test* are employed for evaluating the potency of antimeningococcic serum.

Uses.—The best results in the serum treatment of meningococcus meningitis, as with the use of other antibacterial serums, are secured in the early recognition of the case, avoidance of delay in injecting the specific serum, and the use of a potent preparation in sufficiently large doses as is compatible with safety. Intraspinal injection is frequently employed when using antibacterial serums in the treatment of meningeal affections. Cormack's observations (*African M. J.*, 1936, **12**, 311) reveal that a properly selected serum produces a marked reduction in mortality. It may be important to point out that an effort should be made to culture the meningococci in the infected spinal fluid and ascertain if the organisms are agglutinated by the antiserum used. If not, obtain and use an antiserum which will cause agglutination of the meningococci isolated.

The therapy of meningococcus meningitis as well as that caused by other organisms is being made more effective by the introduction of sulfanilamide, sulfapyridine and related compounds. The latter are replacing serum therapy or they also are being used in combination with antisera.

Meningococcus Antitoxin.—Many workers are of the opinion that the so-called meningococcus exotoxin is in reality an endotoxin as the meningococcus is susceptible to spontaneous autolysis. They believe that Ferry's serum is not a true antitoxin but that it does possess therapeutic activity due to antibacterial and antiendotoxic antibodies (*J. Immunol.*, 1932, **23**, 291; 1937, **33**, 375; *J. A. M. A.*, 1936, **107**, 478). For further considerations see *J. Lab. & Clin. Med.*, 1937, **23**, 252. It appears from the evidence presented that a polyvalent antimeningococcus serum is to be preferred.

Antipneumococcus Serum

Antipneumococcic serum on the market is available as different type-specific serums and only those are marketed which have been released by the National Institute of Health. Any animal may be used in the preparation of the product. The label must, however, indicate the specific type of pneumococcus represented and the genus of animal employed.

The production of Antipneumococcus Serum and concentrates with specific pneumococcus types as a starting point corresponds closely with those procedures described under the manufacture of antibacterial sera.

Antipneumococcus Serums consisting of a combination of two specific types also are marketed. Such dual type serum is generally horse serum, and made available so as to reduce the cost of production. It is prepared by immunizing horses with injections of cultures containing the two specific types designated and as a basis of comparison the finished product is standardized against a control serum of each of the two individual types used.

The introduction of immune rabbit sera (*Science*, 1936, **84,** 579) has resulted in great benefits in the serotherapy of pneumonia. For method of production, processing and standardization of antipneumococcic rabbit sera, see Goodner and associates (*J. Immunol.*, 1937, **33,** 279) and Cooper and Walter (*Am. J. Pub. Health*, April, 1935).

Methods of Standardization.—Standardization by mouse protection experiments (Park and Williams, *Pathogenic Microorganisms*, 1939, p. 341), though not entirely satisfactory as a test of the curative value of the preparation, has been, however, generally accepted as the most reliable method for determining pneumococcus serum potency. Precipitation (*J. Path. & Bact.*, 1932, **35,** 509) and agglutination titers of the serum and other techniques, though of value as partial indicators of the protective and therapeutic value of the preparation, have not received as yet general recognition as acceptable methods for standardizing antipneumococcus serum. For a comprehensive study of standardization techniques see Felton and Stohl (*Nat. Inst. Health Bull.*, **169** (Feb., 1937)).

Felton in his technique of standardization employs varying quantities of plain or refined and concentrated antipneumococcus serum and a constant number of virulent pneumococci. A unit of antipneumococcus serum (plain or concentrated) as the term introduced by Felton and accepted today as a fundamental unit of potency for the latter, is ten times the smallest amount of antiserum which will protect the majority of (20-Gm.) mice inoculated intraperitoneally with 100,000 fatal doses of fully virulent culture of *Diplococcus pneumoniae*. In other words, this provisional unit standard in general use is the amount of antiserum which will protect a (20-Gm.) mouse against (at least) one million M.L.D.'s or fatal doses of a pneumococcus culture. An M.L.D. here is regarded as the smallest amount of a pneumococcus culture which will kill a 20-Gm. mouse (when injected intraperitoneally) in forty-eight hours.

Uses of Antipneumococcus Serum.—Antipneumococcus Serum or the concentrated products prepared from the latter are mainly antibacterial and only slightly antitoxic. Adequate and proper antipneumococcus serum therapy will reduce the average mortality rate in pneumonia of about 30 per cent to an average mortality rate of about 12 per cent (Coll, R., *Ann. Int. Med.*, 1936, **10,** 1). In Type II cases (*J. A. M. A.*, 1933, **100,** 560) and in Type V and Type VII infections (*ibid.*, 1937, **11,** 437), proper and prompt type specific serum treatment will reduce the mortality to about half the average rate. Small series of Types VI, VIII and XIV cases reported have been benefited by specific serums. In the higher types pneumococcal pneumonia, a specific antipneumococcus rabbit serum is to be used.

Administration.—Intravenous injections of 10,000 or 20,000 units are given every two hours until 100,000 or more units have been administered within the first twenty-four hours or until a beneficial effect has been obtained. Subsequent doses are given on the second day and the intervals between injections can be extended to twelve hours if treatment was started during the first three days (*J. A. M. A.*, 1930, **95,** 1547; 1932, **98,** 779). For further details see White and associates (*The Biology of Pneumococcus*, Commonwealth Fund, 1938) and R. Heffron (*Pneumonia*, Commonwealth Fund, 1939).

The *Francis cutaneous test* (*J. Exptl. Med.*, 1933, **57,** 617) is used in conjunction with clinical observation to determine adequacy of dosage. This test consists of an intradermal injection of 0.1 cc. of a saline dilution containing 0.01 mg. specific pneumococcus capsular polysaccharide. A positive test indicating immunity is revealed by the development of an area of erythema at the site of injection within twenty to thirty minutes.

Combined Treatment.—A large number of reports reveals the value in pneumococcus pneumonia of the newer chemotherapeutic agents, sulfapyridine, sulfadiazine and sulfamerazine in all types and sulfanilamide in Type III cases. Sulfonamide compounds are replacing serotherapy in the treatment of pneumococcus infections. A review of the literature, however, reveals that the combined therapy of specific antisera with these drugs is more valuable and is to be advocated as the treatment of choice. Hydroxyethylapocupreine has also been described as equal in effectiveness in the treatment of pneumonia but without the toxic effects of sulfapyridine and sulfanilamide.

Antidysentery Serum

Antidysentery serum consists of the native blood serum of animals (usually horses) which have been immunized against the *Shigella dysenteriae* (Shiga bacillus) and its soluble products of growth (producing a monovalent serum) or against this and other types of the dysentery bacillus producing a polyvalent serum. Usually the strains selected are those representative of the principal types present in the country where the preparation is to be used. In the United States, in the preparation of a polyvalent antidysenteric serum, immunization of the animals is carried out against several strains of Shiga and Flexner or these with Hiss-Y types of dysentery bacilli. The antidysentery serums prepared with the Shiga strains are not only antibacterial but also antitoxic as this type yields a true extracellular toxin which the other strains of dysentery bacilli do not produce. The technique employed in preparing Antidysentery Serum is the same as that given under Antimeningococcus Serum.

The *Shiga Antidysentery Serum* (all forms) is standardized by mouse protection tests, by comparing the quantity of marketable serum required to protect mice against the lethal effect of dysentery (*Shigella dysenteriae*) toxin with the dose of a standard antidysentery serum (Shiga) necessary to give the same protection. The polyvalent antidysentery serum most frequently used in the United States is standardized by determining its agglutinative titer against standard strains of the types of dysentery bacilli used for immunization and especially determining its antitoxic potency when combined with a previously standardized toxic filtrate of the Shiga dysentery bacillus.

Value and Dosage.—Antidysentery Serum prepared for the Shiga type of dysentery bacillus has yielded fairly satisfactory results as a valuable therapeutic agent against this type of bacillary dysentery (*Lancet*, 1924, **2**, 232). Antiserums for the paradysentery strains have not been found to be as efficient in the treatment of dysentery caused by these varieties (*J. A. M. A.*, 1921, **77**, 1863). As a prophylactic dose, 10 cc. may be given subcutaneously. The therapeutic dose given as early as possible is from 50 to 100 cc., administered intramuscularly or preferably intravenously, to be followed at eight hour intervals by doses of 50 cc. each until normal symptoms prevail (*Lancet*, 1924, **2**, 232). Sulfaguanidine and other sulfonamide compounds are being used widely at present in the treatment and prophylaxis of bacillary dysentery.

Antianthrax Serum

Antianthrax serum (*Serum Antianthracicum*) is prepared by immunizing horses against virulent anthrax bacilli. Cattle have been, and are, injected intravenously with living organisms to prepare a marketable bovine antianthrax serum. For effective results, these sera are to be administered at the earliest possible moment in large doses. In slight cases, intramuscular injections are given. In severe cases, initial doses of from 100 to 200 cc. are administered intravenously. Injections of 20 cc. to 50 cc. each are repeated every six to twelve hours, or at suitable intervals if indicated, or until blood cultures are negative. Reports indicating that arsphenamine or neoarsphenamine is useful as a chemotherapeutic agent have resulted in the simultaneous administration of antianthrax serum to which is added 0.9 Gm. or less of neoarsphenamine dissolved in 100 cc. of sterile saline solution (*Ztschr. f. Hyg. u. Infektionskr.*, 1926, **105**, 509). For further details, see *Industrial Anthrax Report* (*Suppl.* to *Am. J. Pub. Health*, 1935, **25,** No. 2).

Antistreptococcic Serums

Streptococcus infections are of relatively frequent occurrence. Their acute and serious character has drawn the interest of many workers who have attempted to develop an efficient serum therapy. Many different immune streptococcus serums have been developed and marketed, these being prepared according to different methods by using various cultures or toxins or both. *Streptococcus Scarlet Fever Antitoxin* was considered previously.

Reports on the value of commercial streptococcus serums in streptococcus infections reveal that their value is not significant. In many instances, there appears no justification for the use of these preparations. The use of the newer chemotherapeutic agents, sulfanilamide, sulfapyridine and related sulfonamide compounds, is more valuable in the treatment of streptococcus infections.

Antiplague Serum

Prompt intravenous administration of very large doses (up to 100 cc.) of antiplague serum is claimed by some workers to be of great value in the treatment of bubonic and even the pneumonic type of plague. The dosage is repeated daily, until an improvement is noted. Intramuscular injections of 20 cc. are advocated as the prophylatic dose. The English Plague Commission has, however, reported that, up to the present, serum therapy has not proved efficacious in the treatment of plague. Naidu and Mackie (*Lancet*, 1931, **2**, 893) have reported encouraging results with a serum prepared by immunizing cattle by a special technique.

Other Marketed Immune Serums

Antibacterial serums other than mentioned are being presented to be used for the prevention and treatment of many diseases. The results of these products have been unsatisfactory, discouraging or indeterminate. In other instances, sufficient evidence has not been made available to warrant their wider use.

Chapter XXXVII

IMMUNE HUMAN SERUMS

WHILE ONE OF the lower animals (horses, mules, cattle, goats, rabbits, etc.) may be utilized to obtain a serum containing antitoxic, agglutinating, bacteriotropic (immune opsonins) or bacteriolytic antibodies for the specific microorganism, immune human sera are sometimes employed as prophylatic agents or in the treatment of specific diseases. Such serums are obtained from convalescent cases of those recovered from the specific diseases. The etiological agents of the latter are usually not known or not available, and it is, therefore, impossible to prepare artificially immune serum by using the lower animals. Complete protection by the use of convalescent sera is of short duration, lasting only a few weeks, but being sufficient usually for protection against one exposure.

Human Measles Immune Serum obtained from one to several weeks after recovery appears to be more effective than normal adult serum or human immune globulin. It is best preserved in a dry state (see lyophile process). If injected intramuscularly in doses of 5 to 8 cc. within three days after exposure, about 95 per cent of all cases are protected. Larger doses are to be given to older children (over three years of age). If given after the fourth day following exposure the dose should be doubled. Administration between the fourth and eighth day will result in prolonging the period of incubation, modifying the disease, and rendering it less severe with less danger of the occurrence of complications. Small doses will not modify the disease if given after the appearence of the rash. In measles which already developed, an intravenous injection of from 40 to 60 cc. given the day before the appearence of the eruption may result in a reduction of the severity of the disease.

Human Immune Measles Serum and *Human Immune Globulin* are to be used to prevent or modify measles and are not recommended for treatment in the late stages of the disease. Reactions are much less frequent with Human Measles Immune Serum or normal adult serum than when using immune human globulin. For further information, see *Brit. M. J.*, 1931, **2**, 977; 1932, **2**, 260; 1937, **2**, 612; 1938, **1**, 1003.

Human Immune Globulin is a preparation made from human placental blood and the human placenta and contains measle-immune bodies or protective substances against measles of the type transmitted from the mother to the fetus. Various methods of preparing this product are used. McKhann and associates (*J. Infect. Dis.*, 1933, **52**, 268; *J. A. M. A.*, 1937, **109**, 2034) detail their method of preparation and discuss the significance of this product. In a review of the literature, the conclusion reached is that *Human Immune Globulin*, also marketed under the name *Placimmunin*, is of value in the prevention and modification of measles. Human immune globulin is equal or almost equal to convalescent or human measles immune serum in its usefulness, but it possesses the greater advantage of easy and universal availability.

Human Immune Scarlet Fever Serum, known also as convalescent scarlet fever serum, is a sterile serum prepared from the blood of humans convalescent from known cases of scarlet fever. *Convalescent scarlet fever serum* is limited in usefulness because of the difficulties in procurement and is being replaced by *scarlet fever streptococcus antitoxin*. It, however, has the advantages over the antitoxin of producing a much lower incidence of reaction, of being homologous without producing sensitization, and it is particularly useful for those who are sensitive to horse serum. This serum may be used in place of Scarlet Fever Streptococcus Antitoxin in the intracutaneous injection when performing the Schultz-Charlton Blanching Test (which see).

Normal Human Serum

Newhouser and Kendrick (*U. S. Naval M. Bull.*, 1941, **39,** 506) review the historical background and describe the development and clinical indications of both normal human plasma and normal human serum. Inasmuch as Citrated Normal Human Plasma is less difficult to prepare and market especially on a large scale and it can be used in most all cases where Normal Human Serum is indicated, the former product is used more frequently in practice. Furthermore reactions are more frequent when intravenous injections of normal blood serum are given.

Citrated Normal Human Plasma.—In August, 1942, the National Institute of Health issued the 3rd Revision of Minimum Requirements for Unfiltered Normal Human Plasma (Liquid, Frozen, Dried). Regulations for Normal Serum Albumin (Human) have also been issued as of January, 1942.

Citrated Normal Human Plasma is available in three forms, the liquid, plasma in the frozen state, and desiccated plasma. Frozen and desiccated or dried plasmas are not to contain added substances other than a preservative. Liquid plasma is brought quickly to the frozen state preferably in suitable containers while the latter are tilted and rotating producing a frozen mass appearing as a shell, the process being spoken of as quick shell freezing. Frozen plasma or, still better, the liquid plasma may be used to produce the desiccated product. The expiration date of the dried plasma is usually about five years. For value of and differences between dried and frozen plasma, see Doane (*Mod. Hosp.*, 1943, **60,** 98).

Human plasma and serum may be stored for months and then administered safely. The most important feature which is of greatest value is that both human plasma and human serum may be employed without the necessity of typing either the donor or recipient. Another important difference is that in cases of shock, these products do not increase the concentration of blood corpuscles which already is increased. The availability of an unlimited supply of plasma and serum will be most helpful in reducing war casualties and deaths occurring in other catastrophies. Shockproof containers are now available for use in wartime and in transportation.

An exact dosage schedule is influenced by such factors as age, weight, sex, condition and response of the patient.

Chapter XXXVIII

ANTIGENS USED AS THERAPEUTIC AND IMMUNIZING AGENTS (BACTERIAL VACCINES)

ANTIGENS (meaning antibody producers) are substances possessing the power or capable of inducing the formation of specific antibodies. Antigens, whatever their composition may be, are used for the production of active immunity, which gives a protection for a considerable length of time (in some cases for years) as compared with the action of therapeutic sera which are of avail only for a few weeks. The antibodies produced though not immediately available last, however, for longer periods of time. The most important antigens used as medicinal agents are modified smallpox virus and antirabic virus, the bacterial vaccines, immunizing toxins, toxoids and tuberculins.

You will note that the antigens are of various types. Smallpox and rabies antigens (or virus vaccines) are attenuated by passage through some animal (bovine species). Bacterial antigens (or bacterial vaccines) are generally attenuated or killed by heat or chemicals. Occasionally, attenuation of bacterial vaccines may be effected by growing the organism under unfavorable conditions (as B. C. G. used in immunization against tuberculosis), or by autolysis (autolyzed pneumococcus antigen and bacteriophage filtrates), or by admixture with an immune serum (activated or sensitized vaccines). In other instances the metabolic products of bacterial growth or preparations of such products serve as the antigens, as in the case of immunizing toxins, toxoids and some of the tuberculins.

VACCINES

The term *vaccine* employed in a broad or general sense, as it is used most frequently today, may be defined as an infective agent so treated or modified as to prevent it from growing and causing disease in the body. It is not, however, changed so as to affect or prevent the production of specific antibodies or protective substances when injected into the body. The term is most frequently used in a specific sense when referring to bacterial vaccines.

Bacterial Vaccines

The term *bacterial vaccines*, *bacterial antigens* or *bacterins* is, however, to include only those products which are suspensions of attenuated or killed bacteria in physiological normal salt solution, usually preserved with 0.5 per cent phenol, 0.2 to 0.4 per cent cresol, 50 per cent glycerin, organic mercury compounds, or a similar effective preservative.

Bacterial vaccines are divided into two main classes: (*a*) *stock* and (*b*) *autogenous bacterial vaccines*. Autogenous bacterial vaccines are those prepared from the patient's own infection. The offending organism or organisms obtained from the lesion or

477

infected part of individuals are used for the preparation of the bacterial vaccine, which is to be later reinjected into them.   Stock bacterial vaccines are those prepared from stock cultures kept in the laboratory and consisting of strains capable of stimulating the body to immunity production.

A *simple bacterial vaccine* is one made from only a single species of microorganism, as plague vaccine, made from *Pasteurella (Bacillus) pestis*.   *Mixed bacterial vaccines* are those containing two or more different species of bacteria, as triple vaccine, made from typhoid bacillus, paratyphoid A bacillus and paratyphoid B bacillus.   A *monovalent bacterial vaccine* is one containing but a single strain of the particular organism or organisms.   *Polyvalent bacterial vaccines* are those prepared from numerous strains of the particular organism or organisms.   These are obtained from many different sources.

Preparation of Bacterial Vaccines.—The first step in preparing bacterial vaccines is to obtain a culture medium most suitable for the growth of the organism or organisms from which the vaccine is to be prepared.   A solid medium is generally used, plain agar being satisfactory in many cases, while in other instances a solid culture medium containing natural fluid as blood agar may be necessary. In preparing autogenous vaccines the preliminary examination of a stained smear of the material will aid in choosing the proper medium.

For stock bacterial vaccines in the main polyvalent strains of the organism or organisms are isolated in pure culture and used.   In mixed bacterial vaccines the individual organisms are obtained or isolated and secured in pure culture and then cultured separately to obtain sufficient organisms for the preparation of the vaccine.   The suspensions of the different species are later mixed together. Freshly isolated organisms are almost invariably of the "S" type (smooth colony variation when cultured) but in continued subculture tend to degenerate into the "R" type (rough variation).   "R" variants have been found to be valueless as protective antigens.   Stock vaccines should therefore be made of recently isolated cultures; where this is impracticable, the cultures should be kept so that they retain their full antigenic value.   Wide-mouth rectangular bottles, so-called Blake Bottles, and Kolle flasks are employed most frequently for mass cultures in the preparation of stock vaccines, bacterial antigens, etc.   On a small scale, slants are made in tubes or flasks or small rectangular bottles may be used.

Generally, the cultures are allowed to incubate for twenty-four hours at body temperature (37° C.). Young cultures are most desirable for preparing bacterial vaccines, but occasionally it may be necessary to extend the incubation period for forty-eight to seventy-two hours or until growth becomes apparent.   This is especially true in preparing autogenous and stock bacterial vaccines from some of the higher forms of bacteria.   At the end of the particular period of incubation the bacteria are procured under aseptic conditions by pouring sterile isotonic salt solution on the solid media, gently shaking or scraping (with a sterile platinum needle) until all the microorganisms have been suspended. If scraping is necessary, avoid removal of any of the culture medium.   If bouillon or other liquid medium was used, the culture is centrifuged at high speed, the supernatant liquid discarded and the sediment containing the bacteria is suspended in sterile saline solution, shaken well, again centrifuged, the supernatant washings discarded and the sediment again resuspended in sterile saline solution. The salt solution suspension of bacteria in either case is examined by stained smear for purity and is then poured into a sterile flask, bottle or tube with or without sterile beads, shaken by some mechanical device or by hand (on a small scale) so as to break up the clumps, and a uniform emulsion is made. Rubbing in a sterile mortar or grinding may occasionally be necessary when making vaccines of fungi. Bacterial vaccines are standardized by estimating the number of bacteria in each cubic centimeter of suspension.

After the number of bacteria per cubic centimeter has been determined the suspension is diluted by adding sterile physiological salt solution, so as to bring the content to 1,000,000,000 per cc. or to any other content desired.   The suspensions are now sterilized by treatment with a bactericide or by heat in a water bath at the minimum temperature and time of exposure that will kill the bacteria, which in most instances is 60° C. for one-half hour to one hour, and then cresol (0.2 to 0.4 per cent) or other suitable preservative is added.

Chemically killed bacterial vaccines are advocated by some workers as being more antigenic than heat-killed preparations. They claim that the heat (56° to 60° C.) used in sterilizing bacterial vaccines destroys part of the antigenic value of the latter and that this is especially applicable to those organisms producing toxins, as the latter are readily inactivated by heat and not by chemicals. Phenol, cresol and, in France, ether, iodine and sodium fluoride have been used. Newer disinfectants have been employed successfully for sterilizing bacterial vaccines, the bacteria possessing a high antigenic effect (Beck and Wolff, *Zentr. Bakt. Parasitenk.*, 1933).

The use of ultraviolet irradiation for attenuating bacterial and virus vaccines has recently been recommended by Levinson and associates (*J. A. M. A.*, 1944, **125**, 531) for the production of more potent antigenic preparations.

In the case of mixed vaccines, separate suspensions of each organism are treated in this manner and then mixed in desired proportions, so as to contain the requisite numbers of individual organism per cc. of finished preparation. The usual tests for sterility (and in the case of stock vaccines fo toxicity) are carried out.

The treatment of bacterial suspensions with formalin (comparable to the preparation of toxoids), producing the so-called *anacultures*, and their successful use as immunizing agents has been reported (*J. Infect. Dis.*, 1925, **37**, 125; 1928, **43**, 189).

Sensitized Bacterial Vaccines or Serobacterins (Antibody Antigens)

To overcome some of the undesirable reactions the sensitized bacterial vaccines or serobacterins were introduced (*Ann. inst. Pasteur*, 1911, **25**, 193, 867; 1913, **27**, 597, 607). These products are prepared in the same manner as the bacterial vaccines, but differ in the following additional steps:

After the bacterial suspension has been thoroughly emulsified, and the number of bacteria per cc. of suspension has been determined, a portion of the serum of an animal (which had been immunized against the same species of bacteria as in the suspension) is added. Though many employ suspensions of the living organism, others have advocated the use of attenuated organisms for sensitization by specific immune serum. The results are apparently just as satisfactory in most cases, and the danger of infection with living organisms is thus avoided. This mixture is allowed to stand for varying periods of time, usually twenty-four hours, in an incubator at body temperature, with occasional agitation. At the end of this time the mixture is centrifugalized and the supernatant liquid (consisting of saline solution with excess of immune serum) is discarded. Normal salt solution is added, the mixture is shaken; and after centrifugalization, the supernatant liquid is again discarded. This treatment, which is repeated a few times, is done so as to remove any adhering serum. Enough cresolated physiological normal salt solution is finally added to give a bacterial content as may be desired. This is then sterilized and marketed after purity and safety tests have been conducted.

The treatment with immune serum is said to sensitize the bacteria so that they are more easily attacked by the forces in the patient's system. Sensitized bacterial vaccines are said to be more rapid in their production of immunity, especially since they give a degree of immediate protection, for the antibodies attached to the antigen are in part set free upon injection. They usually minimize undesirable reactions (*Arch. Int. Med.*, Nov., 1914). Larger doses of sensitized bacteria at more frequent intervals can be given with the production of a higher degree of immunity than it is possible to secure with nonsensitized bacterial vaccines (*Proc. Roy. Soc.*, Ser. B, **98**, 553). Sensitized bacterial vaccines of practically most of the bacteria (simple and mixed, and from which plain bacterial vaccines are prepared) are marketed. They are used in place of the plain bacterial vaccines, yielding results which are convincing as to their value.

Duration of Immunity with Bacterial Vaccines.—The duration of an active immunity produced by injections of bacterial vaccines varies with both the individual and the specific antigen (bacterial vaccine) used. It might be emphasized that immunity following bacterial vaccine immunization is not absolute. A lowered state of general body health and contact with large numbers of the specific infective agent may result in an infection with the particular organism against which an immunity was produced. Prophylactic treatment is not successful if sanitary precautions are to be disregarded by immunized individuals. The use of bacterial vaccines in the treatment of disease does not warrant discontinuance of any of the other forms of treatment. The latter are to be practiced.

The actual duration of immunity by bacterial vaccine immunization is not definitely known. In fact, it is frequently not practical or difficult to determine. It may be as low as one month with some bacterial vaccines to one and even two years with others, rarely more. A good plan to practice is for susceptible individuals or those who are constantly exposed to specific bacterial infections to immunize themselves annually against the specific infective agent (bacterium). In many cases it is practical to keep up the antibody content by giving the initial series of injections first, to be followed every three to four months by a single injection (usually a large or massive dose).

Dosage of Bacterial Vaccines.—In all the above cases vaccine treatment is started with the subcutaneous, or by some intramuscular injection usually of small doses (approximately 50,000,000, depending upon the organism) (less for children). This dose is gradually increased, inoculations being made at three- to eight-day intervals, depending upon the reaction received and clinical results obtained. Dosage and frequency of injections are to be regulated to suit each individual case. Clinical evidence has revealed that children tolerate bacterial vaccines better than do adults. It is therefore a frequent occurrence to observe that the average dose recommended is given to normal individuals regardless of age or weight. More recently it has also been found that intradermal injections, while producing the greater reaction, are nevertheless more productive of antibody response as well as more rapid than other methods of administration (Besredka, *Local Immunization*, London, 1927). Lanolin and other nonspecific substances are being advocated as vector agents when administering bacterial vaccines and other antigens. They act by retarding absorption as the antigens stimulate the defenses of the animal (Pinoy, *Comp. rend. Soc. biol.*, 1935, **118**, 442). Oral administration is also advocated but it is not regarded as effective.

Chapter XXXIX

TYPHOID VACCINE

BACTERIAL VACCINE MADE FROM THE TYPHOID BACILLUS

Preparation.—In the preparation of typhoid vaccine, cultures are made of "strain No. 58" of *E typhosa*. Eighteen to twenty-four hour old beef-infusion agar cultures are washed off with and the growth is suspended in sterile saline (and after agitating well by hand or preferably in a mechanical shaker), the number of bacilli per cc. are determined.

The suspension is then heated at 53° C. for one hour, tricresol, phenol or other equally effective antiseptic is added to a 0.3 per cent or suitable concentration, and tricresolated (0.3 per cent) salt solution is added to produce the desired bacterial content (generally one billion bacteria per cc.). Sterility and toxicity tests are conducted by making aerobic and anaerobic cultures and inoculating a laboratory animal (usually a guinea pig but a rabbit or a mouse or any two of these may be used). If contamination is revealed, the material is discarded. Marketable preparations are generally tested for potency by inoculating several (a series of three) rabbits and then determining the agglutination reaction (agglutinin content or titer) of their sera with the living culture of *E. typhosa* as a measure of the immunity response induced.

In July, 1942, the National Institute of Health issued minimum requirements for typhoid vaccine to be effective as of August 1, 1942. Each lot manufactured must be prepared from strain 58 typhoid bacillus which is to pass a virulency test and the marketed vaccine is to pass a potency test.

Uses.—As a prophylactic, the vaccine (after being shaken well immediately before use) is administered in three doses, the first containing one-half billion bacteria and the second and third each containing one billion organisms per cc. of suspension. For women and children under 150 pounds in weight, the dosage is to be diminished proportionately. Children, however, tolerate the injections remarkably well. The injections given at intervals of a week or ten days are administered subcutaneously, employing the area below the insertion of the deltoid or in the back or abdominal walls. Intradermal injections are advocated by some as being more effective and resulting in less after-effects. Deep and intramuscular injections should be avoided as they are more apt to produce reactions. It is the more common practice to employ the so-called *triple* vaccine. For further details of typhoid immunization, see under Triple Vaccine, page 482.

Oral Administration.—Besredka (*Local Immunization*, translated by H. Plotz, 1927) has recommended the oral administration of dead typhoid bacilli preceded by doses of dried oxbile. Three doses (each pill, capsule or cachet containing some 45,000 millions of dried bacilli killed by heat) are given before breakfast on three consecutive days, and these pills are preceded by requisite doses of pills of dried oxbile. This method has been used on a wide scale in some European and African countries and in this country it has been employed by Hoffstadt and her associates (*Am. J. Hyg.*, 1929, **9**, 1–37). Though favorable results have been reported, further observations are needed and a wider application of this method must be exercised before definite conclusions can be forthcoming. Workers in this country prefer the subcutaneous immunization procedure and it does not appear that the oral method will supplant it.

A new hydroalcoholic typhoid vaccine has been recently adopted by the British Army (*Army M. Dept. Bull.* 4 (Jan. 1944)). It contains the full complement of Vi antigen and general and local reactions are comparatively mild.

TYPHOID-PARATYPHOID A AND B VACCINE

Bacterial Vaccine Made from the Typhoid Bacillus and the Paratyphoid A and B Bacilli

Typhoid Combined Vaccine, Typhoid-Paratyphoid Combined Vaccine, Typhoid Mixed Vaccine Prophylactic, Typhoid-Paratyphoid Prophylactic, Mixed Enteric Vaccine, Triple Vaccine

Typhoid Vaccine Combined, known also as the *Triple Vaccine* or *T.A.B.*, was used during World War I and is used almost exclusively today in civil practice as well as among all military forces. Triple vaccine contains in each cc. of suspension, 1,000,-000,000 of *B. typhosus* (*Eberthella typhosa*), 500,000,000 or 750,000,000 of *B. paratyphosus A* (*Salmonella paratyphi*) and 500,000,000 or 750,000,000 of *B. paratyphosus B. (Salmonella schottmulleri*). In preparing this vaccine the paratyphoid A and paratyphoid B bacterial cultures and suspensions are made separately and in the same manner as described under typhoid vaccine. *B. paratyphosus A* ("Kessel" strain) isolated from a case among the New York militia troops on the Mexican border in 1916 and *B. paratyphosus B* ("Rowland" strain), the English army strain isolated from a case in Flanders in 1915, are the strains most frequently employed in preparing this vaccine for marketable purposes. It is important to select strains of paratyphoid bacilli of complete antigenic composition. After dilutions of the three suspensions are made separately in the laboratory, they are then mixed together in such proportions as to provide the desired concentration of each in the finished product, as previously mentioned. As a prophylactic, three injections are given.

Use.—*For Prophylaxis.*—The first dose is 0.5 cc. and the next two doses are 1 cc. each, injections being given at intervals of seven to ten days as described under Typhoid Vaccine. The dosage is to be diminished for children and women according to weight. For its use in oral immunization, see under Typhoid Vaccine. In a recent change in army regulations governing typhoid immunization, all individuals who have received the basic series of 3 injections of triple vaccine are to receive a stimulating dose of 0.5 cc. annually.

Value.—The value of typhoid and paratyphoid prophylactic therapy has been definitely established. For further details in the prevention of typhoid in the United States, see U. S. Army Medical Workers (*Immunization to Typhoid Fever*, Johns Hopkins Press, Baltimore, 1941). For combined therapy with tetanus toxoid, see page 490.

WHOOPING COUGH VACCINE

Sauer (*J. A. M. A.*, Nov. 4, 1933), has prepared a pertussis vaccine which is a modification of that devised by Madsen and associates (*Centenary Meeting*, Brit. Med. Assoc., 1932) at the Danish Statens Serum Institute. This is made from recently isolated hemolytic strains of *H. pertussis* (Bordet-Gengou bacillus) and grown on Bordet medium containing 20 per cent fresh defibrinated human blood. The growth is subjected to agglutination and absorption tests to prove that the strain belongs to Leslie and Gardner's Phase I (*J. Hyg.*, 1930, **31,** 423). The finished preparation contains 10 billion bacilli per cc. of suspension which are killed by the addition of 0.5 per cent phenol and exposure in the refrigerator for one week, during which time the suspension is agitated daily. As a prophylactic it is used in three doses (0.5 cc., 1 cc. and 1.5 cc.), subcutaneous or intramuscular injections being given at intervals of five to seven days. Sauer further reports: "Active immunity is completed in four months and lasts for years. Infants withstand the injection remarkably well. The best age for immunization is the second half year of life."

Sauer Pertussis Vaccine is to be kept refrigerated at 2° to 12° C. at all times Vaccine that has been frozen or allowed to remain outside of the refrigerator for long periods of time should not be used. To avoid the injection of a chilled vaccine, the latter is to be allowed to stand for a few minutes at room temperature before administration. The unused portion of the vaccine is to be returned to the refrigerator promptly.

Most workers are in agreement that substantial protection is afforded by a properly prepared and properly administered whooping cough vaccine (*J. A. M. A.*, 1939, **112;** 1145; *Am. J. Hyg.*, Sec. B, 1939, **29,** 133). On the basis of the present evidence, a vaccine prepared from virulent *H. pertussis* of complete antigenic structure appears to be of value if properly administered as a prophylactic agent (*Am. J. Dis. Child.*, 1940 **60,** 1172).

HAFFKINE'S VACCINE; PLAGUE BACILLUS VACCINE; ANTI-PLAGUE VACCINE

This is employed especially in India as a prophylactic against plague. It consists of strains of *P. pestis* originally isolated by blood culture from a human case of septicemic plague grown in neutral broth in shallow containers to which a few drops of sterile olive oil or butter fat are added. They are incubated for six weeks at room temperature and shaken once daily. At the end of this period, the cultures are agitated well and heated at 55° to 65° C. for from fifteen minutes to several hours (one to three hours). This material to which 0.5 per cent phenol is added and consisting of bacterial products, attenuated bacteria and broth protein has been and is being used more than any of the other attenuated suspensions of plague bacilli and appears to possess protective value (*J. A. M. A.*, 1921, **76,** 243) (Haffkine Inst. Report for 1927), though the immunity is of short duration, not much over six months (*Bombay Bact. Lab. Rep.*, 1913–1916). Researches by Schutze (*Brit. J. Exp. Path.*, 1932, **13,** 284, 289, 293) reveal that a virulent strain of *P. pestis* is necessary for the production of a good vaccine. One or two injections in doses of from 3 to 4 cc. for adults are given subcutaneously (at intervals of ten days). All military personnel in the present war are being immunized against plague if they are sent to areas where the latter is endemic or is apt to occur.

CHOLERA VACCINE

This vaccine (*Tr. 7th Cong. Far East. Assn. Trop. Med.*, 1937, **1,** 523) is prepared from attenuated or (heat or chemically) killed *Vibrio comma* (*Sp. Asiatic Cholera*).

extracts of cholera spirilla have also been used.   Castellani (*Manual of Tropical Medicine*, 1919) has prepared *T. A. B. C.* or *tetravaccine* consisting of mixed agar culture suspensions of typhoid, paratyphoid A, paratyphoid B bacilli and cholera spirilla. Such a preparation was used in the Serbian Army during World War I.   Prophylactic vaccination is said to afford considerable protection and to be of distinct value. Immunization must be repeated at yearly intervals and certainly every two years (H. Violle, *Le Cholera*, Paris, 1919).

Haffkine used living cultures and later killed organisms in the preparation of his vaccine (*Brit. Med. J.*, 1895, **2,** 1541, and *Protective Inoculation against Cholera*, Calcutta, 1913).   The present vaccines are prepared from saline suspensions of twenty-four-hour old cultures which are sterilized at 53° C. for one hour (*J. A. M. A.*, 1921, **76,** 243).   The final preparation contains 8 billion organisms per cc.   It is administered subcutaneously in two doses of 0.5 cc. and 0.1 cc.   Immunization against cholera has been and is practiced extensively in Europe and Asia.   Though it is difficult to appraise its true value, it appears that its use as a prophylactic agent is of value, especially if the vaccine is prepared from organisms obtained early in an epidemic.   In the present war, all military personnel sent to regions where cholera is endemic or apt to occur are being immunized against this disease.

Chapter XL

BACTERIAL CULTURE FILTRATES, IMMUNIZING TOXINS AND TOXOIDS

FILTRATES CONTAINING only the unaltered products of bacterial growth have been and are being employed in the treatment of affections caused by various organisms. Favorable results have been reported with the employment of these filtrates in the treatment of furunculosis, carbunculosis, deep pustular acne, infections caused by suppurative bacteria following cuts, wounds, surgical operations, etc.

TOXINS AND TOXOIDS

Under suitable conditions the filtrate of many organisms has been found to possess true soluble toxins which are antigenic. It is believed that these exotoxins are largely responsible for the pathological changes which occur in certain affections. The filtrates containing these toxins have been employed also as diagnostic aids along lines similar to the use of diphtheria toxin in the Schick test. The toxins themselves or the latter changed to toxoids prepared in a manner similar to those of diphtheria and tetanus toxoids have been and are being employed for active immunization.

Diphtheria Toxin for the Schick Test

Preparation.—The artificial production *in vitro* and the manufacture of toxin for commercial purposes have been found to depend upon a great many different but definite factors and favorable conditions. The requisite conditions for good development of toxin are: a pure culture of *Corynebacterium diphtheriae* but a strain known to yield a potent toxin (as Park and Williams' No. 8); a suitable culture medium (as a 2 per cent peptone nutrient bouillon made from fresh veal, using suitable meat (avoid horse meat) and peptone and possessing an alkalinity which should be about pH 7.3 to 7.4); the manner of inoculation of the culture medium (grown in flat-bottom bottles or containers, yielding a shallow, thin layer of medium, with a large surface, thus producing better aeration which will result in a more rapid formation of the maximum amount of toxin); and incubation is to be carried out at the most favorable temperature, between 32° to 35° C. Under such favorable conditions, the greatest accumulation of toxin is produced by the bacilli between the fourth and eighth days and usually on or about the seventh day. At this time phenol solution is added to give an approximately 0.5 per cent concentration and the liquid cultures are filtered, as the number of viable organisms rapidly diminish and the conditions for those remaining alive are not suitable for the rapid production of toxin. A description of the production of diphtheria toxin together with a consideration of changes and interesting data concerning Park and Williams' No. 8 organism is given in *Ann. inst. Pasteur*, 1938, **61**, 791. The usual sterility and safety, potency and clinical tests are conducted. Bacteriostatic agents as present in most biological products are not added. The exact chemical composition of such commercially prepared toxin is not definitely known. On the other hand, much is known of its stability, behavior toward chemicals and physical agents and its reactions after it is injected into animals.

Standardization.—Methods have been developed of measuring the degree of toxicity or potency of toxin in terms of the fundamental unit of toxicity. This is the M.L.D. or minimum or minimal lethal dose (or M.F.D., minimum fatal dose), which is the smallest amount of diphtheria toxin that when injected subcutaneously will kill a guinea pig weighing 250 Gm. at the end of four days (ninety-six hours), with the production of lesions typical of uncomplicated diphtheria poisoning. Other units of measurement are derived from this and apply to results obtained with toxoids or with antitoxin, or with a mixture of toxins and antitoxin (which see).

Diphtheria Test Toxin is so standardized that the amount of toxin injected intradermally (intracutaneously) in one Schick test dose represents $1/50$ M.L.D. This dose is measured by noting local reactions as in positive Schick tests obtained in guinea pigs when injected intradermally with $1/25$ but not with $1/50$ of one test dose. For further details concerning techniques for determining the suitability of toxin for Schick testing, see the Report of the Permanent Commission on Biological Standardization, League of Nations Health Organization (London), 1931 and *J. Immunol.*, 1937, **33**, 191.

Use.—Diphtheria Test Toxin is employed in the Schick test so as to determine whether one is immune to diphtheria. Injections are given intracutaneously (intradermally), not subcutaneously (*München. med. Wchschr.*, 1908, **55**, 504).

The *Schick test* (*J. Indiana M. A.*, 1930, **23**, 320) is used to find out whether individuals have in their blood sufficient diphtheria antitoxin to render them immune to the disease. The technique consists in injecting intradermally (between the layers of the skin) 0.1 cc. of the diphtheria test toxin (containing $1/50$ M.L.D.). A positive reaction will be apparent in twenty-four to forty-eight hours, and reaches its height in from forty-eight to seventy-two hours, when readings are generally made. The successful application of the Schick test depends first and foremost upon the use of a product of adequate potency, the selection of a properly prepared control and upon good technical performance.

Diphtheria Toxoid

Diphtheria Toxoid or *Anatoxin* is a detoxified (nontoxic) diphtheria toxin. The conversion of toxin to toxoid is effected by treatment with formaldehyde (or other chemicals) and incubation or exposure during varying periods of time at different temperatures. Horse meat should not be used in making the broth from which the original toxin is made. To a filtered toxin free of bacilli possessing an L+ dose of not more than 0.2 cc. and an M.L.D. of not more than 0.0025 cc. and containing no preservative 0.2 to 0.4 per cent formalin is added. This mixture is incubated at 37° to 40° C. for three weeks or longer, until it becomes atoxic. When no toxic reaction follows the injection of 5 cc. (five human doses) subcutaneously into guinea pigs weighing approximately 300 Gm. and which are held under observation for several weeks (at least thirty days), the toxoid preparation is considered atoxic. A preservative is added and toxicity, sterility, safety and potency tests are made on all marketable products. The amount of formaldehyde used is important. This depends upon the amino-nitrogen content of the toxin. Too much formaldehyde may produce undesirable local reactions.

Toxoids are free of any serum protein which Toxin-Antitoxin Mixture contains because of the presence of the antitoxin. Not containing horse serum, toxoids obviously do not sensitize individuals against the latter.

It must be noted that protein from the culture medium (from which the toxin entering the Toxoid originates) is found in toxoids and slight protein reactions especially in older children (over ten years of age) and adults are possible in those sensitive to such proteins. If found convenient, suspicious reactors may be tested to determine if marked reactions will be produced. This is the so-called *Moloney test*.

Injections of 0.1 cc. to 0.2 cc. of diluted Diphtheria Toxoid 1:100 to 1:200 intradermally will reveal if a local area of redness will develop within three days. Diluted toxoid for the Moloney test is available on the market in a separate package. If the reddened area produced in an injection is less than one-half inch in diameter, Toxoid injections may be given. If greater reactions prevail, T-A mixture may be employed instead of Toxoid. Diphtheria Toxoid when used for children and adults is generally administered subcutaneously in two doses of 1 cc. each at intervals of three to four weeks. Infants under one year of age receive two injections of only one-half cc. in each dose. In the use of this as well as when all other prophylactic agents are employed to obtain a more lasting immunity to diphtheria, the Schick test and control are to be made three to four months or later after the last injection, to determine whether protection has been afforded. Toxoid (Formol-Toxoid) or Anatoxin has generally replaced the T-A Mixture for immunization as less injections are needed, the immunity is developed more quickly and a greater number of Schick positive persons become Schick-negative. Diphtheria Toxoid is stable in its antigenic power, completely detoxified, and not easily affected by temperature changes. A perfectly detoxified toxoid cannot be converted into toxins. The plain toxoid is clear and if it has become too clouded or turbid, it should not be used. The expiration date is two years after date of manufacture or date of issue.

Refined Diphtheria Toxoid (Alum Precipitated).—It has been found that the addition of a small amount of a sterile solution of alum to a toxoid under suitable conditions will produce a complete precipitation. The supernatant fluid which is discarded contains as high as 80 per cent of the protein in the original toxoid. The precipitate, after being washed, is resuspended in isotonic solution of sodium chloride (containing a suitable preservative) and is marketed as a turbid suspension. This product, an alum precipitate of diphtheria toxoid in a highly purified state (free of serum albumin and of most of the albumin or protein contained in the original toxoid), is administered in a single or two-dose treatment subcutaneously or intramuscularly (Glenny and associates, *J. Path. & Bact.*, 1926, **29**, 38). A Schick test is made two months after the last injection. The toxoid is liberated but slowly from the precipitate, so that the antigenic stimulus is maintained for a longer period.

All Alum Precipitated Toxoids, being suspensions, must be shaken well before withdrawing the contents in the vial or container.

Standardization.—Various methods have been presented for determining the antigenic value of Toxoids. The *Animal Test* technique is used by some workers (see National Inst. of Health, *Minimum Requirements for Diphtheria Toxoid*). Many workers always use this protection test as the final control. Other methods are the: *Binding of Antitoxin* and *Ramon's Flocculation Test* (G. Ramon, *Ann. inst. Pasteur*, 1931, **45**, 291; 1938, **61**, 787). When fresh diphtheria toxin and antitoxin are mixed *in vitro* in proportionate amounts, a precipitate or floccules are formed. A similar reaction will not occur with an excess or a too small amount of antitoxin. A similar flocculation reaction will result if the toxin is replaced by toxoid. The reaction will be in the same degree as with the original fresh toxin from which the toxoid was prepared. This phenomenon is an expression of neutralization and demonstrates the combining power of toxin or toxoid with antitoxin. Ramon suggested the term *antigenic unit* for the amount of toxin or toxoid equivalent to one unit of antitoxin as determined by the flocculation test. This is frequently spoken of as the Lf (Limit of Flocculation) dose. It has also been referred to as the *immunizing unit* (*U. I.*) (Schmidt, S., *Comp. rend. Soc. biol.*, 1923, **88**, 105).

Other Terms.—Under diphtheria test toxin, toxoid and antitoxin, the definition of the following values of toxin are given: M.L.D.; L+; Lo; and Lf (or U. I.). Another value is the Lr (Limit of Reaction), which refers to the least amount of toxin which when mixed with 1 unit of antitoxin shows only a slight redness when injected intradermally into guinea pigs (A. T. Glenny and K. Allen, *J. Path. & Bact.*, 1921. **24**, 61). The Lo, L+ and Lr of a stabilized toxin remain fairly constant, and any one of them may be used in the standardization of antitoxins, though in this country, the L+ dose of toxin is the unit of measure. The Lf and Lo doses of fresh toxin are alike if but little toxoid is present. When the latter is formed, the Lo dose increases in size but the Lf dose is not changed to any great extent. The Lf dose of a toxin expresses the combining power of a toxin and its corresponding antitoxin and therefore serves the purpose for determining the antigenic value of toxoids. The M.R.D. (Minimum Reacting Dose) is the least amount of toxin which when injected intradermally into a guinea pig will produce within thirty-six hours an area of hyperemia which is at least 5 mm. in diameter.

Other Diphtheria Preparations Employed as Prophylactic Agents

Other than diphtheria toxoid, the following preparations are also available: *diphtheria toxin-antitoxin (T-A) mixture; diphtheria toxoid-antitoxin mixture*, in which the toxoid is sufficiently neutralized by antitoxin; *diphtheria toxin-antitoxin floccules* and *diphtheria toxoid-antitoxin floccules*, in which the floccules formed after flocculation are washed and then suspended in physiological saline solution. They are all administered subcutaneously and after a lapse of several months following the last injection (if two or more are to be given), a Schick test is performed to ascertain if immunity has been established.

Diphtheria Toxin-Antitoxin (T-A) Mixture.—Toxin-Antitoxin Mixture is a sterile, colorless liquid. It is prepared from diphtheria toxin which has been previously aged and standardized, then mixed with diphtheria antitoxin and finally diluted so that the finished preparation contains a fairly large amount of toxin ($^1/_{10}$ L+ dose) combined with a very minute quantity (0.08 unit) of antitoxin.

The usual precautionary measures for testing the toxicity, sterility, potency, etc., of all biological products must be observed in the marketing of this preparation. *T-A Mixture should not be kept at freezing temperatures, as the toxin is liberated by freezing, thus increasing the toxicity of the product.* It should be stored preferably between 40° and 50° F. (5° to 10° C.). The expiration date is six months after date of manufacture or date of issue.

Use.—Active immunization against diphtheria is accomplished by using a dose of 1 cc. of the T-A Mixture. Three injections, all the same strength, are given subcutaneously in the arm (at the insertion of the deltoid) at weekly or bi-weekly intervals. The development of an immunity frequently requires from eight to twelve months before the Schick test becomes negative.

Value of Diphtheria Prophylaxis.—The efficacy of diphtheria prophylaxis is attested by the marked decline in the death rate of diphtheria wherever immunization procedures are in use. Furthermore, it must be remembered that diphtheria immunization is not compulsory and, therefore, is not used universally. However, voluntary co-operation has been satisfactory in many communities. The procedure recommended by the Committee on Evaluation of Administrative Practices of the

American Public Health Association (*Am. J. Pub. Health*, 1940, **30** (Supplement), 47) is preferred.

Toxoid Combined with Other Antigens.—The simultaneous immunization with a combined diphtheria-toxoid whooping-cough vaccine is advocated by Simon and Craster (*J. M. Soc. New Jersey*, 1941, **38**, 461). Schutz (*Lancet*, 1940, **2**, 192) demonstrated experimentally with injections of a combined diphtheria toxoid and pertussis vaccine that the antigenic potency of each does not suffer because of the presence of the other. See under Tetanus Toxoid, for use of combined tetanus-diphtheria toxoids and use of combined tetanus-diphtheria toxoids and triple vaccine. The use of these different combined antigens unquestionably is desirable, but the various combinations have not been employed extensively as yet to attempt to evaluate these simultaneous procedures as practical measures to be advocated universally.

Scarlet Fever Streptococcus Toxin

In the preparation of this toxin, one or more strains of streptococci from scarlet fever cases for toxin production are selected but this must be attended with care. The strain or strains employed must produce a highly potent toxin and should possess broad antigenic activity. The Dochez NY 5, Dick II and Williams Sc. 2 strains have been found most satisfactory. This toxin is marketed in a diluted form (each 0.1 cc. containing one skin test dose) and generally labeled *Scarlet Fever Streptococcus Toxin for the Dick Test* (or for Determining Susceptibility to Scarlet Fever). In the case of the latter the parent toxin is diluted with a properly buffered isotonic diluent. A boric acid borate buffer solution (B. B. S.) is also recommended as a diluent (*Brit. M. J.*, 1938, **2**, 700).

The other marketable form in a series of graduated doses of suitable strength and number is generally labeled *Scarlet Fever Streptococcus Toxin* (for (Prophylactic or Active) Immunization). The requirements for the culture medium used in producing the toxin to be free of meat extractives are different from the previous requirements and are in accordance with the communication issued by the Dicks (*J. A. M. A.*, 1939, **113**, 1150). For more details and other data concerning streptococcus scarlet fever toxin, see Dick and Dick (*Scarlet Fever*, Chicago, Ill., 1938).

Standardization.—The unit of scarlet fever toxin is the skin-test dose (S.T.D.). "The skin-test dose is the smallest amount of toxin which when injected intracutaneously into persons known to be susceptible to the toxin will induce a reaction equal to that induced on the same persons at the same time by the injection of a skin-test dose of the standard scarlet fever toxin supplied by the National Institute of Health." The dose is contained in 0.1 cc. and a positive test is a circumscribed area of redness and slight infiltration which measures at least 1 cm. in diameter. The readings are made on a group of susceptible children (10 or 20 by preference) in a bright light in from twenty to twenty-four hours after injection and compared with the reaction induced by the standard toxin. The average of the smallest dilution of the toxin tested giving a reaction of 1 cm. and equal to that induced by the standard toxin is recorded as the skin-test dose. Toxins possessing a potency of 40,000 skin-test doses per cc. or greater are obtainable and are to be preferred to the low-potency toxins.

Uses.—*As a Diagnostic Agent in Dick Test.*—Scarlet Fever Streptococcus Toxin is used in the *Dick test*, an intracutaneous test performed to determine susceptibility or immunity to scarlet fever. For this purpose, the toxin is properly diluted with suitable diluent so that a skin-test dose is contained in each 0.1 cc. of marketable preparation. The injections are to be measured accurately, are given intradermally generally on the flexor surface of the forearm after the latter is asepticized, and reactions must be read preferably in a bright light in from twenty to not later than twenty-four hours after the injection.

Active Immunization.—Scarlet Fever Streptococcus Toxin is not to be used in the treatment of scarlet fever patients but it is of value in the preventive treatment of this disease. The administration of suitable amounts of the toxin as a prophylactic will cause the Dick test to become negative in most humans. Upon this basis accepting the Dick test as an evidence of immunity, techniques have been developed for the active immunization of individuals against scarlet fever.

Tetanus Toxoid

A *tetanus toxoid* or *anatoxin*, made in the same manner as diphtheria toxoid, and a refined *tetanus toxoid* (*alum precipitated*) have been used successfully to actively immunize domestic animals against tetanus. Similar preparations have been used for the prophylactic immunization of humans (especially those in military service and others frequently exposed to tetanus).

Immunization with tetanus toxoid usually in two 1 cc. doses at intervals of three months either intramuscularly or by deep subcutaneous injection produces an active immunity lasting probably for many years. Its use eliminates the need for repeated antitoxin injections following injury, the possible subsequent serum reactions, and the possibility of sensitization to horse serum.

Use.—The tetanus toxoids, used only for active immunization, possess great prophylactic value in the limited field of their usefulness. They are employed for the commercial production of tetanus antitoxin, for the active immunization of animals, and their use is practical and safe for the active immunization of humans whose occupation and duties continually expose them to injuries favorable for the development of tetanus infection. Probably the largest field for the practical use of tetanus toxoid is in military service at all times and during wartime among certain civilians especially during a mechanized and air-bombing warfare. Hall (*Ann. Int. Med.*, 1940, **14**, 565) reports a detailed study of immunization with tetanus toxoid in the U. S. Navy since 1934. Tetanus immunization with toxoid has been adopted by the French, Italian, British, and American armies.

Though reactions are infrequent when using tetanus toxoid, Cooke and associates (*J. A. M. A.*, 1940, **114**, 1854) advise making a *scratch skin-test for hypersensitiveness* before administering the second and all later injections.

Simultaneous (*Combined*) *Active Immunization* against two or more diseases has been advocated and has found favor among many. Ramon (*Presse méd.*, 1936, **44**, 1625) was the first to recommend active immunization with *diphtheria and tetanus toxoids, combined.* He showed that the antitoxin contents following a course of immunization with the combined toxoids are higher than those induced by the injection of either toxoid by itself. Bigler and Werner (*J. A. M. A.*, 1941, **116**, 2355) discuss active immunization against tetanus and diphtheria in infants and children and they conclude that combined immunization would seem as practical as immunization against diphtheria alone. The use of these two toxoids combined with pertussis vaccine and also with triple vaccine has been recommended

Chapter XLI

TUBERCULINS AND B. C. G.

TUBERCULINS

Old Tuberculin.—Large shallow flasks containing 5 per cent glycerin alkaline broth are inoculated with a culture of a standard human strain of the tubercle bacillus (*Mycobacterium tuberculosis, hominis*). The flasks or bottles are capped with sterile tin foil and placed in an incubator at 37° C. where they are kept undisturbed for from six to nine weeks depending upon the rate of growth and upon the appearance of a pellicle which first covers the surface of the medium and finally sinks to the bottom. Each container is then agitated well until the pellicle is suspended uniformly throughout the culture medium and the contents are subjected to a current of steam at 100° C. until the mixture is reduced to one-tenth of the original volume. The material is filtered through paper pulp, cresol to 0.3 per cent or other suitable preservative to proper concentration is added and final filtration is conducted through Berkefeld filters. Sterility, toxicity, safety and potency tests are conducted in accordance with the practice for other biological products. This product retains its activity for an indefinite period of time, though the expiration date generally employed is five years after date of manufacture or date of issue. As a matter of precaution, this preparation, known also as *Koch's Old Tuberculin* (*O. T.*), should be kept in a cool, dark place.

Koch's Old Tuberculin is a heated 50 per cent glycerin solution of the soluble products of the tubercle bacilli containing the original elements of the culture fluid. Many attempts have been made to adopt some uniform and simple methods for determining the efficiency of this as well as of the other tuberculins mentioned later. A satisfactory and reliable method has not as yet been made available.

Use.—Koch's Old Tuberculin was introduced originally by Koch as a therapeutic agent. Its use as a curative agent in tuberculosis is not without danger. At present, the use of this and other tuberculins in the treatment of tuberculosis is only advocated to be employed by those practitioners who have a thorough understanding of its limitations and possibilities. O. T. is the tuberculin of choice and the one used most frequently for treatment purposes. B. E. and T. R., because of their slower absorption, are preferred by some workers but they do not appear to be as effective.

Value.—Koch's Old Tuberculin is of greatest value as an agent to be employed as an aid in the diagnosis of tuberculosis in man and animals.

It is to be noted that marketable tuberculins are designated as *Human Type* or *Bovine Type*. The generally accepted opinion is that the bacterial protein responsible for eliciting the allergic reaction is a group antigen and is the same for the bovine as for the human type of the tubercle bacillus. There is no evidence that tuberculins prepared from the two types differ as to their active principle and in practice there is no attempt made to differentiate specifically between infections with the human and

491

bovine types. In most clinics the human type of Old Tuberculin is generally employed for diagnostic testing in humans. For veterinary purposes, the bovine type of the tubercle bacillus is employed in making such tuberculins.

Other Tuberculins and Preparations of Tubercle Bacilli

All extracts and suspensions (1) consisting of the soluble products of the tubercle bacilli in the medium in which they are grown, or (2) containing essentially an emulsion of the insoluble fragments of the bacilli, or (3) possessing a combination of the first two are designated as *Tuberculins*. Only those best known or most widely used will be briefly considered.

New Tuberculin.—The so-called *new tuberculins* of Koch (B. E., T. R., T. O. and T. A.) are used but infrequently today.

T. R. New Tuberculin, Tuberculin Residue, Tuberculin Ruckst or *Tuberkelbacillin Rest* is made from living tubercle bacilli, dried *in vacuo*, and then ground to complete disintegration for many months in a ball mill (*Deutsche med. Wchnschr.*, **23,** 209).

New Tuberculin, B. E.; Tuberculinum Novum, B. E.; Bazillenemulsion; Bacilli Emulsion.—This is practically a bacterial vaccine. The culture is grown as for O. T. The bacilli are filtered out, ground but not washed, and one part of the pulverized tubercle bacilli is suspended in 100 parts of water and an equal portion (100 parts) of glycerin.

Tuberculin Denys; Tuberculinum Denys; Tuberculine Bouillon Filtre; Bouillon Filtrate Tuberculin.—B. F. is simply a glycerin broth culture of the tubercle bacillus passed through a Berkefeld filter. Phenol (0.25 per cent concentration) is added as a preservative. It is prepared like O. T. without the prolonged heating and concentration.

Purified Protein Derivative (P. P. D.).—*Tuberculin P. P. D.* (*Purified Protein Derivative*) (*Am. Rev. of Tuberc.*, 1932, **25,** 724) is obtained from standard B. A. I. synthetic tuberculin by the method of Seibert. In this technique extraneous proteins are eliminated while the substance responsible for the specific reaction is retained. It is diluted with milk sugar and prepared in tablet form so that each tablet contains a definite weight of protein derivative. These tablets being indefinitely stable in this form possess constant activity. They are marketed in two strengths containing, respectively, 0.00002 mg. and 0.005 mg. tuberculin. P. P. D. is used more frequently today than the other tuberculins especially in the intracutaneous tests. Fresh solutions are to be preferred and are made for each testing with a sterile buffered diluent supplied in each marketable package. For further details see *Am. Rev. of Tuberc.*, 1934, **30,** 713; 1937, **35,** 281.

Diagnostic Aids for Tuberculosis.—Tuberculin has been utilized as an aid in diagnosis of obscure forms of tuberculosis, the test being applied in a number of ways. In order of their importance, the following are commonly employed: (1) Intracutaneous test of Mantoux or Mendel; (2) Von Pirquet method (cutaneous test); (3) Moro reaction (percutaneous test); (4) Subcutaneous test; and (5) Calmette's ophthalmic reaction.

Mantoux Test (An Intracutaneous Test). (München. med. Wchnschr., 1908, No. 40).—This test is more delicate and the most satisfactory tuberculin test to be used in humans (*Medical Res. Council,*

1932 spec. Rep. Serv. No. 164, London). It is performed intradermally. The National Tuberculosis Association recommends when using Koch's O. T. that 0.1 cc. volume should contain the desired dose. The first injection should be 0.01 mg. O. T. and if no reaction occurs, 1.0 mg. is ordinarily given. In cases where extra caution seems advisable, 0.1 mg. is used as the second injection, followed by 1.0 mg. if the latter is negative. It is assumed that failure to react to 1.0 mg. O. T. is sufficient evidence that there is no active tuberculosis.

Von Pirquet Test (A Cutaneous Test) (Wien. klin. Wchnschr., 1907, 20, 1123).—One drop of undiluted and 1 drop of 25 per cent Old Tuberculin are placed on the sterilized skin of the front of the forearm, about 3 or 4 inches apart. Midway between the two (a control test) there is placed a small drop of sterile 50 per cent glycerin solution. The chosen areas of the arm are asepticized before any fluid is applied by cleansing with soap and water and then rubbing with alcohol and ether. The skin is then slightly scarified through each of the drops (merely removing the epidermis without drawing blood). In about five or ten minutes the excess of tuberculin is wiped away. No dressing need be applied. The areas are examined after twenty-four and forty-eight hours or, if convenient, every twelve hours, until forty-eight hours have elapsed. The reaction is considered positive if within these periods the tuberculin scarification shows an inflammatory area measuring at least $1/4$ inch, and one which contrasts markedly with the small red spot left by the control scarification.

Moro Reaction (Percutaneous Test) (München. med. Wchnschr., 1908, 55, 216).—This test consists in rubbing gently into the clean skin of the abdomen (some use the chest or other hairless part of the body) over an area of about 3 or 4 inches, a 50 per cent ointment of Old Tuberculin in anhydrous lanolin. A portion about the size of a pea (or about 0.5 Gm.) is employed for about one-half minute and this is allowed to remain so as to be absorbed. A positive reaction will be observed within twenty-four to forty-eight hours by the appearance of red papules.

Subcutaneous Test.—This test (*München. med. Wchnschr.*, 1930, 77, 1662; 1931, 78, 261) is not employed to any extent in human practice today, inasmuch as there is some danger of lighting up a latent process, in addition to the possibility of disseminating the infective material.

Calmette's Ophthalmic Reaction.—One or 2 drops of a 1 per cent purified Old Tuberculin is placed in the eye. A characteristic reddening of the conjunctiva will be produced within twelve to twenty-four hours if tuberculosis exists anywhere in the body. A drop of sterile water or 50 per cent glycerin solution is placed in the other eye as a control test by which to compare and judge the changes in the tested eye. This method should never be employed in the presence of any form of ocular disease. It is rarely used in human cases.

Interpretation of Tuberculin Reaction.—A positive tuberculin reaction is indicative of a tuberculous focus but not necessarily of tuberculous disease. .Other methods are to be employed to find out in which part of the body the focus of infection lies, whether it is active and the extent of such activity. Failure to obtain a positive reaction, however, does not always exclude tuberculosis. Sensitiveness to tuberculin may be absent in acute miliary or generalized tuberculosis and during some acute infectious diseases. It is found occasionally that a child once a reactor may become negative to later tests. Rarely, a calcified pulmonary nodule may be seen in a child that fails to react to tuberculin. In such a case, it is probable that the focus of disease is obsolete and that no living tubercle bacilli are present.

In reviewing the present status of the tuberculins and the performance of the tuberculin test, the best practice to adopt until other data are made available is to use P. P. D. as the diagnostic tuberculin and O. T. if the latter is not available. Wherever possible, the Mantoux test should be performed, using the weak or first strength and if the latter is negative, then use the second strength. If for some reason the Mantoux test is inadvisable or cannot be performed, the patch test is performed, which if negative is followed up with the Mantoux test using the stronger concentration or second strength. The Von Pirquet technique is used when it is not possible to perform either of the above methods.

Patch Test.—The tuberculin ointment patch test has been recommended by many workers. Wolff and Hurwitz (*J. A. M. A.*, 1937, **109**, 2042) conclude that the patch test may be safely substituted for the Mantoux test. Vollmer (*Am. J. Dis. Child.*, 1939, **58**, 527) and Steward (*J. Pediat.*, 1938, **13**, 510) give the same conclusions and further state that severe local and constitutional reactions do not occur and that there is no danger of infection. The reliability of the patch test as compared with the Mantoux test has been reported by many workers (see Taylor, *Am. Rev. of Tuberc.*, 1939, **40**, 236; Savage, *ibid.*, 1941, **43**, 527; Crimm and associates, *ibid.*, 1941, **43**, 799; Pearce, *et al.*, *J. A. M. A.*, 1940, **114**, 227; and Shapiro, *Virginia M. Monthly*, 1941, **68**, 100).

Immunization against Tuberculosis

B. C. G. (*Bacillè Calmette-Guèrin*).—Calmette, Guerin and collaborators of the Pasteur Institute (*Bull. Inst. Pasteur*, 1924, **22**, 593; 1928, **26**, 889) have advocated the immunization of newborn infants, where the parents are tuberculous or where environmental conditions are such that tuberculosis is inevitable, with a culture of tubercle bacilli labeled by them B. C. G. (*Bacille Calmette-Guerin*). *It is not a tuberculin.* This culture (so labeled) is said by them to be an avirulent or an attenuated bovine strain of tubercle bacilli which, though the organisms have lost their virulence by transplanting more than two hundred successive generations upon a medium of 5 per cent glycerin potato saturated with beef bile, still retain their immunizing qualities. They have advocated the administration by mouth of three doses (10 mg. to each dose) of *Bacille Calmette-Guerin* every forty-eight hours before the newborn is ten days old. The mucous membranes of the intestinal tract of the newborn changes after the latter is ten days old and immunization is not so successful.

A large number of reports have accumulated on the use of B. C. G. in man and animals (*Am. Rev. of Tuberc.*, 1933, **27**, 6). Kereszturi, Park and associates in five years' study on more than 400 babies indicate that "B. C. G. vaccination is harmless and gives a very definite resistance against tuberculosis." They also advocate parenteral administration instead of its administration orally or enterally (*New York State J. Med.*, 1933, **33**, 375). Birkhaug (*Nord. med. tidskr.*, Aug. 14, 1937) who prepares B. C. G. for the Norwegian medical profession observed that B. C. G. cannot be accepted as a virus fixe. He concludes that B. C. G. never produces progressive and fatal tuberculosis. He believes, instead of anticipating that the present strains will increase in virulence, that actually B. C. G. will ultimately lose its present ability to confer immunity to virulent tubercle bacilli. He highly recommends the intracutaneous method of administration and further suggests that the usual social preventive measures should be continued. The results of the use of B. C. G. vaccination among medical and nursing students in Chicago is discussed by Rosenthal (*Hospitals*, 1943, **17**, 75). The results have been satisfactory.

Chapter XLII

OTHER BACTERIAL PREPARATIONS USED AS ANTIGENS

Aggressins.—These products are Berkefeld filtered exudates or tissue fluids obtained from affected areas in animals artificially infected or inoculated with virulent organisms, specific causative agents of disease. These preparations, representing the products of growth of the organism in the susceptible animal and also substances evolved by bacterial disintegration, are said to be of value if used properly, for active immunization especially in diseases affecting lower animals. They are sterile (bacteria-free), contain no living organisms, and therefore cannot themselves produce the initial infection. When injected subcutaneously, anti-aggressin is produced, thereby establishing protection against the infection. Aggressins are not employed for curative treatment in infected animals but are used only to actively immunize normal animals. Aggressins have been used successfully in the preventive immunization of all lower animals against hemorrhagic septicemia (see Gochenour, *J. Am. Vet. M. A.*, July, 1924) and as immunizing agents against blackleg in cattle.

Brucellergin is a suspension of nucleoprotein obtained from *Brucella* organisms. In the Brucellergin test, 0.1 cc. is injected intradermally and the reaction read after forty-eight hours and later. Erythema alone is negative, but with edema or induration measuring 0.5 cm. in diameter or more is positive. A positive reaction may be delayed for several days. Brucellergin may be obtained from the Central Brucella Station, Michigan State College, East Lansing, Mich. The commercial Brucella Vaccine diluted 1:10 is used by some workers instead of Brucellergin.

Coley's Fluid (*Coley's Mixture; Coley's Fluid; Erysipelas and Prodigiosus Toxins; Toxicum Erysipelatis et Toxicum Bacilli Frodigiosi*).—This fluid is prepared by growing virulent streptococci (preferably obtained from cases of erysipelas or septicemia) in bouillon for ten days at 37° C. The original formulas called for the inoculation of the latter ten-day growth with *Bacillus prodigiosus* (*Serratia marcescens*). After an additional ten days' incubation the mixture is sterilized in a water bath at 60° C. and the sterile filtered product is used as the vaccine. There is no uniformity of opinion in regard to the value of Coley's fluid but most workers believe that it should be tried in cases of inoperable malignant growths, especially sarcomas.

Johnin.—Johnin is a sterile solution containing the bacterial products of the Johne's bacillus (*Mycobacterium paratuberculosis*) and is prepared from the latter just as is tuberculin. It is employed usually by injecting into or the skin testing of calves and cattle as an aid in the diagnosis of Johne's disease, also known as paratuberculosis or chronic bacterial dysentery of cattle.

Lepromin is prepared by boiling lepromatous tissues in isotonic salt solution for one hour, grinding the residue and extracting this again with isotonic salt solution. The aqueous extracts are strained through gauze (not filtered) and 0.1 cc. is injected into the cutis. For further details, see page 505.

Luetin.—Luetin is an extract of the killed cultures of several strains of the *Treponema pallidum* (*Spirochaeta pallida*) (the organism causing syphilis), which has been found to contain no impurities or foreign toxic substances and to which 0.25 to 0.5 per cent cresol is added as a preservative. Based upon observations by some workers, the *luetin test* has been used as an aid in the diagnosis of syphilis. As prepared originally by Noguchi (*J. Exp. Med.*, 1911, **14,** 99, 557), this worker and others who have employed a preparation made along similar lines have claimed that, when used in the luetin test, it is of value in the examination of tertiary and latent stages of syphilis, where the reaction is most constant, though the Wassermann blood test may be negative. It is said to be usually absent or very mild in the primary and in the untreated secondary cases. In adults with congenital syphilis the reaction is said to be more marked than in infants with congenital syphilis. Alderson (*Arch. Dermat. & Syph.*, 1922, **5,** 610) claims that the available marketable luetin is inert and practically valueless for diagnostic purposes.

The *luetin test* or *reaction* is made as follows: After selecting a suitable area on the arm, the skin is cleansed and sterilized and 0.07 cc. of luetin diluted with an equal quantity of saline solution is injected intradermally (between the layers and not under the skin). A reaction occurs with the formation of papules, which may become pustules. A control is also performed. Barker (*Arch. Dermat. & Syph.*, 1934, **3,** 676) concludes that the luetin test is not reliable; and as a diagnostic and prognostic method for syphilis it is inferior to the Wassermann test.

Lygranum S. T. is a chick embryo antigen used in the *Frei test*. The virus of *lymphogranuloma venereum* is grown in the yolk sac of the developing chick embryo and then separated from practically all of the yolk and other tissue by differential centrifugation (*Proc. Soc. Exptl. Biol. Med.*, 1940, **43,** 332, 410). The virus particles are suspended in isotonic salt solution, inactivated by heat and formaldehyde solution (0.1 per cent), and phenol (0.25 per cent) is added as a preservative. A control (*Lygranum Control*), which is the normal chick embryo antigen, containing the same concentration of formalin and phenol, is used at the same time and in the same manner as Lygranum S. T. See page 504 and also Gelperin (*Am. J. Syph. Gonor. & Ven. Dis.*, 1943, **27,** 697).

Mallein.—Mallein is a preparation similar to tuberculin (which see). It is a glycerin extract containing the toxic principles of *Malleomyces* (Bacillus) *mallei*, the causative agent of glanders. This preparation is used solely as a diagnostic agent in veterinary medicine, especially as an aid in the diagnosis of glanders in horses. The methods commonly employed to perform the *mallein test or reaction* are (1) the intradermal method, (2) the subcutaneous injection, and (3) instillation into the eye (ophthalmic test). The last named is preferred in veterinary work (*Am. Vet. Rev.*, 1913, **44,** 218). This preparation may be used for the diagnosis of glanders in humans, where the dosage is the same as employed when the tuberculins (which see) are used.

Chapter XLIII

VIRUS VACCINES

SMALLPOX VACCINE

JENNER PROVED by a series of interesting and carefully conducted experiments that cowpox or vaccinia (coming from the Latin *vacca*, meaning cow), a very mild disease to which many animals including man are susceptible, is readily transferred and that an attack of this disease and the immunity created protect against smallpox. The causative agent of this condition is spoken of as vaccine virus and is to be found in the material present in the skin eruption of those animals having vaccinia or cowpox. The term *vaccination* then possessing a specific meaning came into use and referred to the method of transferring the virus from the skin eruption of an animal having vaccinia or cowpox into the skin of another animal. Such vaccine virus is obtained today from calves, but may also be obtained from older cattle, goats, horses, mules, rabbits and other mammals. It was in 1860 that vaccination with the "animal lymph" of calves came into more general use, although it was employed more or less since the time of Jenner. Since 1866 when the Beaugency strain was discovered and especially after 1891 when glycerin was employed for purifying and preserving it, the *Bovine Virus* was and is employed mainly for the yield of the present-day smallpox vaccine. This makes possible a constant fresh supply and in amounts as may be required.

Seed Virus.—The initial material used today for preparing the calf virus is designated the *seed virus*. This can be obtained from vaccination and pustules in children, from spontaneous cowpox, or from pustules in calves after several passages of smallpox virus through calves. The virulence of smallpox vaccine virus is usually maintained by intermittent passages through rabbits. The human-rabbit seed is generally used as it is efficient, reliable and easily obtained.

Preparation of Vaccine Virus (Calf Vaccine).—The animals in general use for the preparation of vaccine virus are young carefully selected calves preferably females (though this is immaterial) but they must be at an age of from four months to one year. The younger animals are preferred (two to four months old). They are kept under rigid veterinary observation and supervision for a few weeks previous to and during their actual treatment to insure freedom from disease, the tuberculin test also being carried out, and any reactors are eliminated. The calves are kept under the best sanitary conditions which can meet all known scientific exactness for the latter. These calves are vaccinated. About 20 cc. of seed virus are used for each calf. After the typical vaccinia vesicles develop (usually six or seven days after vaccination), the entire contents of the latter including the serous fluid or lymph and pulpy exudate (but minus the crusts which are removed) are collected under rigid aseptic conditions, employing humane operative procedure. The pulpy mass is ground thoroughly under aseptic precautions in a special mill making an even emulsion with four times its weight of 50 per cent glycerin containing 1 per cent carbolic acid. This finished mixture is stored for three to four weeks at very low temperatures to permit bacteria, which may be present, to die. Every lot of vaccine is then subjected to rigid bacteriological and toxicological examinations to insure a preparation free from all disease-producing organisms (especially anaerobes and hemolytic streptococci) and toxic substances. Autopsies of the calves employed in preparing the marketable virus are made and no virus is used until necropsy reports reveal that the animals were in perfect health. The preparation is then tested on rabbits and susceptible humans to prove that the virus yields a successful *take*, the actual strength or potency being estimated from the speed of the development and the extent of the subsequent reactions and compared with a vaccine of known high potency inoculated on the opposite side of each rabbit. After these operations and tests are conducted exercising every possible care, the preparation is filled mechanically in vacuum jars under rigid aseptic conditions in sterile capillary tubes and then released for the market. The sterile capillary tube sufficient to hold one human dose is the only form of dispensing allowed in this country. A calf usually yields about 10 Gm. of pulp which when made up will produce material to vaccinate about 1500 children.

Preparation of Smallpox Vaccine (other than from Calves).—Various culture vaccines have been presented. Only recently Plotz (*Compt. rend. Soc. biol.*, 1939, **130,** 152) employed an antivariola culture vaccine to vaccinate 11 children and concluded that it confers a lasting immunity. Goodpasture and associates (*Science*, 1931, **74,** 371; 1933, **77,** 119); (*Am. J. Hyg.*, 1935, **21,** 319) introduced the use of the chorio-allantoic membrane of the fourteen-day old chick embryo for the production of a vaccine virus, thus eliminating the hazard of bacterial contamination, but it has not replaced the calf method.

Egg-Embryo-Tissue Vaccine.—Rivers and Ward (*J. Exp. Med.*, 1933, **58,** 635) employed a tissue-culture method of preparation using a medium consisting of 0.1 Gm. of viable chick-embryo tissue suspended in 4 to 5 cc. of Tyrode's solution. Successful vaccinations were made on 100 individuals. Herzberg (*Z. Immunitäts.*, 1935, **86,** 417) made an elaborate study using the Tyrode-egg embryo-tissue and the egg chorio-allantoic membrane cultures and preferred the former preparation. Both of these products have been used intradermally with satisfactory immunological results.

Rivers and associates (*J. Exp. Med.*, 1939, **69,** 875) in a recent study concerning the amount and duration of immunity induced by the intradermal inoculation of cultured vaccine virus conclude that the intradermal inoculation of a vaccine virus attenuated by cultivation on Tyrode's solution and minced chick embryo does not confer a sufficient lasting immunity for practical purposes.

Keeping Smallpox Vaccine.—Smallpox vaccine, so-called vaccine virus or vaccine lymph, cannot be injured by freezing. Tests have shown that a potent vaccine refrigerated constantly at 10° F. will retain its activity for four years. Kept at 50° F. (or 10° C.), the temperature of the ordinary house refrigerator, the potency remains for from three to four months, while at room temperature (70°F. or 21° C.) (as in a drawer, case or bag), the average life of vaccine virus is from one to three weeks and the number of "takes" is reduced to 50 per cent.

Use.—Smallpox vaccine is not used in the treatment of active cases of smallpox. Its primary value is for the prevention of this dreaded disease.

RABIES VACCINE

In preparing Rabies Vaccine or Antirabic Virus, the preliminary step is to obtain virus fixé. The latter is obtainable from established laboratories. The Paris and Kassauli strains are two well-known strains of rabies fixed virus. It is possible to prepare the latter by passing street virus from the medulla (as the virus obtained from natural rabies is known) of a rabid dog through a series of young rabbits (weighing from 700 to 1000 Gm.). The passage in this manner through 25 to 40 rabbits will reduce the incubation period of the virus to seven or eight days, which incubation period then remains fixed (thus the name, virus fixé). The spinal cords of rabbits dead due to intracranial injections of emulsified virus fixé are used as the starting point for preparing *Vaccinum Antirabicum.* Various methods are employed for treating these cords (attenuating the virus), by (drying) suspending them in jars containing caustic potash (Pasteur's method (*Ann. inst. Pasteur*, 1887, 1888)), or dilution (Hogyes method), emulsification with phenol (Fermi (*Suppl. to Ana. d. l'Igiene*, 1916–1926) or Semple (*Brit. M. J.*, 1919, **2,** 333, 371) method), treating with CO_2 snow and drying *in vacuo* at very low temperatures (Harris method (*J. Infect. Dis.*, 1921, **29,** 261)), treatment with glycerin (Philips method (*J. Immunol.*, 1922, **7**, 409)), or formalin, chloroform (Kelser vaccine), or ether (Cunningham's method (*Indian J. M. Research*, 1928, **16**, 245, 253, 259)) or by dialyzing (Cumming's method).   For further consideration, see *Indian M. Research*, Mem. No. 26, 1933.   For marketable preparations, pieces of these treated cords are emulsified with sterile saline solution to which phenol, glycerin or other preservative in suitable concentration is added.   The concentration of brain and cord tissue varies with the different products.   Sterility and safety tests as employed on all other marketable biological products are carried out.

A common method of standardization which is practiced is to place a definite weight of tissue in each dose (125 mg. in each 0.5 cc.).   A noninfectivity test carried out in various laboratories is performed, by intracerebral injection of 0.1 cc. of vaccine into each of 3 rabbits.   These injections must not produce any evidence of rabies in any of the rabbits during an observation period of fourteen days after injection.   A mouse test for noting immunizing potency of antirabies vaccine is being advocated.   See Reed and Muench (*Am. J. Hyg.*, 1939, **27**, 493) and Webster (*Am. J. Pub. Health*, 1941, **31**, 57).   The finished product should be kept at refrigerator temperatures (2° to 10° C.).

Use of (Human) Rabies Vaccine.—Antirabic Vaccine is essentially a prophylactic agent.   The efficiency of its use in the so-called Pasteur Treatment (creating an active immunity) in rabies is no longer problematical.   There are many methods of immunization in use in different countries so that the specific vaccine and the scheme of treatment are subject to variations according to the individual customs of different workers.   It is difficult to say which method is the best (*Am. J. Pub. Health*, 1931, **29**, 59).

There are few data available as to the duration of the immunity after a complete course of rabies vaccine injections but this probably does not last more than one or (the maximum) two years.   An interesting analysis on the results of antirabies treatment from all Pasteur Institutes is presented by McKendrick (*Bull. Health Organ.*, *League of Nations*, 1937, **6**, 17).

IMMUNIZATION AGAINST YELLOW FEVER

The use of convalescent human (and even baboon) serum for passive immunization has been used as a prophylactic for those exposed to the risk of infection.   Findlay (*Bull. Office internat. d'hyg. pub.*, 1933, **25**, 1009) employing the technique of Sawyer and associates (*J. Exp. Med.*, 1932, **55**, 945) actively immunized individuals against yellow fever.

Workers associated with the Rockefeller Foundation are responsible for the present effective program in the use of agents for active immunization against yellow fever and especially jungle yellow fever.   The most efficient product is one designated by them as *Yellow Fever Vaccine Virus (17-D)* (*Am. J. Trop. Med.*, 1938, **18**, 437).

Technique of Vaccination.—The vaccination consists of one subcutaneous inoculation of rehydrated vaccine, diluted according to the virus content and the dosage of virus desired, at the insertion of the deltoid muscle on either arm.   The usual amount inoculated is 0.5 cc., although doses of 1.0 cc. are at times used in the laboratory.   The virus is rehydrated immediately before use and the residue after vaccination is inoculated intracerebrally into mice to establish the viability of the vaccine used.

Test for Immunity.—The intraperitoneal mouse-protection test is used for testing the antibody content of the sera of persons before and after vaccination.   This test serves not only to demonstrate the presence or absence of protective antibodies in a serum, but can be used also to determine the quantity of antibody present by the testing of serial dilutions of a serum in several groups of mice. The antibody titer of a serum is expressed as that dilution of the serum which theoretically, under the conditions of the test, should protect one-half of the mice inoculated.

Fox and Cabral (*Am. J. Hyg.*, 1943, **37**, 93) in a consideration of the duration of immunity following yellow fever vaccination report that adults vaccinated with a virus of established antigenicity will remain immune for a period of four years or longer.

IMMUNIZATION AGAINST POLIOMYELITIS

The methods of specific prophylaxis attempted in poliomyelitis are both active and passive. The clinical impression is that convalescent serum is of some prophylactic value (*J. Pediat.*, 1937, **10**, 111), though attempts to evaluate it have not been sufficiently controlled to give worth-while statistical findings. A high percentage of the adult population is immune to the disease and normal adult blood and blood serum have been advocated as prophylactic agents. Several vaccines have been recommended from time to time for use in active immunization. Most workers, however, do not advocate the use of any of the vaccines so far developed.

Therapy.—The value of convalescent or immune horse serum as an agent in the treatment of poliomyelitis is difficult to analyze. In reviewing all available evidence, clinical and experimental, it appears that convalescent serum possesses very little if any benefit in the treatment of acute poliomyelitis.

IMMUNIZATION AGAINST RICKETTSIAL DISEASES

Spencer and Parker (*U. S. Pub. Health Repts.*, 1925, **40**, 2159) were the first to demonstrate the possibility of achieving immunity in rickettsial diseases when they used potent suspensions of the viscera of infected ticks, ground in a mortar and killed with 0.5 per cent phenol in immunization against Rocky Mountain spotted fever. Weigl (*Die Methoden der Aktiven Fleck-Fieber Immunisierung*, Cracow, 1930) prepared a vaccine for human use as a protective against typhus fever from the intestines of infected lice. The method is not of value for large-scale preparation. Zinsser and Castaneda (*J. Exp. Med.*, 1933, **57**, 381, 391) utilized a formalinized peritoneal exudate from infected rats as their vaccine preparation for immunization against the Mexican variety of typhus fever. Dyer and associates (*U. S. Pub. Health Repts.*, 1932, **47**, 1329) prepared a vaccine from infected fleas and Blanc and Gaud (*J. A. M. A.*, 1935, **105**, 524) report success with the use of the virus of the murine type of typhus isolated from rats.

All military personnel traveling in areas where typhus fever is apt to prevail are being immunized against this disease. At present, in the various fields of military activity and by many nations, different typhus vaccines are being used, such as those prepared by cultivation in insects, in rat and mouse lungs, by tissue culture and in the yolk sac of the chick embryo. Undoubtedly their evaluation will make possible the introduction of preventive methods not only for typhus fever but in other rickettsial diseases. The National Institute of Health issued recently *Minimum Requirements for Typhus Vaccine* and in January, 1942, issued *Minimum Requirements for Rocky Mountain Spotted Fever Vaccine* and *For Anti-Rocky Mountain Spotted Fever Serum*. These pamphlets should be consulted for details.

PROTOZOAN INFECTIONS

Immunization with killed animal parasites or living tissue containing parasites or the use of attenuated organisms has not been sufficiently developed to be regarded of practical value. In many instances, difficulty has been experienced in preparing a suitable product for vaccination against specific parasites. In other instances, failures through vaccination have been reported. In most cases very little experimentation on vaccination against parasites has been carried out. In like manner, the passive transfer of an immunity against some parasites is known, but there has been little practical application of this in human infections. A considerable amount of experimentation is necessary before products from animal parasites will be found useful for vaccination against and treatment of parasitic diseases in humans. For a general review of immunological observations and reactions in protozoan infections, see Talliaferro (*The Immunology of Parasitic Infections*, Century Company, New York, 1929) and Culbertson (*Immunity against Animal Parasites*, Columbia Univ. Press, New York, 1941).

VETERINARY BIOLOGICALS

There are available as marketable products a considerable number of the various types of biological preparations which are employed as preventives or adjuncts to treatment in many diseases in lower animals. Some of these have been mentioned in the previous pages. Aggressins and bacterial vaccines are employed against blackleg and hemorrhagic septicemia. Bacterial vaccines and therapeutic sera are employed in anthrax, brucellosis, equine influenza, etc. Virus vaccines are used successfully against fowl pox, rabies, canine distemper, rinderpest, equine encephalomyelitis, laryngotracheitis of fowls, etc. Vaccines have also been found of value in bovine abortion, equine abortion, fowl cholera, mastitis, mixed infections in cattle, fowls, swine, horses, etc. Tuberculin and mallein are widely used in veterinary practice. Antihog cholera serum and antirinderpest serum (alone) or with virus (simultaneous method) are used as immunizing agents. Tetanus antitoxin (bovine) and Antivenin (veterinary) are also widely employed. Botulism antitoxin has a limited use. More details are considered under individual references throughout this volume. For complete data on veterinary bacteriology and veterinary biologicals, see Kelser and Schoening (*Manual of Vet. Bact.*, Williams and Wilkins, Baltimore, 1943). See also the *Proceedings of the 11th International Veterinary Congress*, London, 1931 and Hagan (*Infectious Diseases of Domestic Animals*, Comstock Pub. Co., Ithaca, N. Y., 1943).

Chapter XLIV

BIOLOGICAL TESTS AS AIDS IN DIAGNOSIS

Complement-fixation Tests (including the Wassermann Test).—Complement-fixation tests are of value as diagnostic aids (see page 445). The so-called Wassermann test is a complement-fixation test performed on the blood serum or the spinal fluid of an individual to detect certain antibodies, the presence of which denotes a syphilitic (luetic) infection. The technique is complicated and it should be performed only by experienced and trained workers. It is, therefore, not intended to describe the technique here, but it is of such importance as to mention briefly the reagents and the different stages of the disease for which the test acts as an aid in diagnosis. It is the consensus of opinion that the Wassermann test or modifications of it are important factors to be used as aids in diagnosis and in the treatment of syphilis.

In primary syphilis, from the appearance of the chancre until the rash is observed, the sera from many patients infected with syphilis may give a negative result. In the later primary and early secondary stages (when the disease is active) the test will be positive in most cases. In the latent stages about 10 to 20 per cent of cases may be negative. In the early active tertiary stages most cases may give a positive test. In the later tertiary, latent tertiary and the parasyphilitic stages most sera from infected patients will give but a faint positive and usually a negative test. In the late secondary, tertiary and even parasyphilitic stages the spinal fluid frequently gives a positive reaction even though the blood serum may give a negative Wassermann reaction. Most cases of congenital syphilis will yield a positive reaction.

Briefly the complement-fixation test for syphilis is based on the fact that fixation of complement occurs when an antigen and its specific antibody (in this case the latter is present in the blood serum and spinal fluids of luetics) are mixed in the presence of free complement. The reagents employed in the test are:

1. Sheep or human red blood cells obtained by defibrinating sheep or human blood or collecting the latter in citrate solution (1 per cent sodium citrate in isotonic salt solution). Before using they are thoroughly washed with saline solution and a 5 per cent or weaker dilution (depending upon the technique) is made of the latter.

2. Hemolysin or serum containing hemolytic amboceptor is prepared by immunizing a rabbit against the same type of blood cells as is used in the test (sheep or human).

3. Complement (here a reagent) is usually freshly collected or lyophilized guinea-pig blood serum.

4. The antigen is liver or heart tissue (normal or syphilitic) extracted with alcohol or a refined product is used. It is impossible to discuss here the theoretical significance of the fact that normal tissue can serve as the antigen but it has been found of practical value for such purpose.

5. The serum to be tested is obtained after allowing the blood to coagulate or by

centrifugalization, the latter being collected in the same manner as when blood is obtained for a blood culture.

The original Wassermann reaction, known also as a complement-fixation test for syphilis, has been replaced by other techniques. These new complement-fixation methods are more sensitive and capable of detecting a greater number of positive luetic cases. So we have the Kolmer method, Noguchi method, Hygienic Laboratory method, Craig modification, modification of Hecht-Weinberg-Gradwohl, Eagle modification, etc. For details of the tests used in the serodiagnosis of syphilis, see "Venereal Disease Information," U. S. Pub. Health Service, Suppl. No. 9 and for the evaluation of serodiagnostic tests for syphilis see *Ven. Dis. Inform.*, 1942, **23,** 161 and consult the same source (many supplements issued since 1935 by the Venereal Information Bureau).

The Colloidal-Gold (Lange's) Test.—This test is applied to the spinal fluid and is probably one of the best diagnostic aids for general paresis, especially where other tests fail as aids to detect central nervous system envolvement.

The Dick Test.—This test is employed to determine whether there exists an immunity to scarlet fever. For details, see page 489.

Flocculation or Precipitation Tests for Syphilis (Colloidal Precipitation Reactions; so-called (erroneously) Precipitin Reactions for Syphilis).—Since Michaelis (*Berl. klin. Wchnschr.*, 1907, **44,** 1477) reported that in mixtures of syphilitic serum and alcoholic extracts of certain tissues colloidal precipitation may occur, a large number of tests for syphilis devised on this principle have been introduced. This reaction and the complement-fixation reaction are the only two types of basic tests for syphilis which have proved of practical value. (See also under Complement-fixation Test.) All of the procedures and techniques in current use as serodiagnostic tests for syphilis are merely modifications of one or the other of these two basic tests. Many of the State Departments of Health in the United States require that laboratories approved to make serologic tests (under the premarital and prenatal laws) shall make two separate determinations on each specimen, one by an approved complement-fixation technique (which see), the other by an approved flocculation (or precipitation) technique. Both types of techniques, if properly performed and interpreted, are accurate and reliable. The *Meinicke Reaction* (*München. med. Wchnschr.*, 1919, **33,** 932), and the *Sachs-Georgi Reaction* (*ibid.*, 1920, **67,** 66) are flocculation tests employed for the serodiagnosis of syphilis. The more recent improved flocculation techniques and especially those which are accepted as standard or approved serological tests for syphilis are the: *Kahn Test* (*J. A. M. A.*, 1922, **79,** 870, 957; *The Kahn Test*, Williams & Wilkins Co., Baltimore, 1928); *Kline Test* (*Am. J. Clin. Path.*, 1931, **1,** 347; 1937, **7,** 490; 1939, **9,** 55 (Tech. Suppl.)); *Eagle Test* (*Am. J. Syphilis*, 1938, **22,** 22); *Hinton Test* (*J. Lab. & Clin. Med.*, 1932, **18,** 198; 1937, **22,** 959); and *Boerner-Lukens Test*. The flocculation tests are said to possess greater sensitiveness than the complement-fixation tests (*Med. Bull. Veterans Admin.*, 1941, **17,** 233) and are not as complicated or as costly to perform. Comparisons of the different flocculation tests (*J. Lab. Clin. & Med.*, 1941, **26,** 637) and their rank in specificity and sensitivity as compared with complement-fixation tests (which see) have been evaluated by many workers (*Am. J. Syph., Gonor., Ten. Dis.*, 1940, **24,** 750). The *Laughlen Test* (*Canad. M. A. J.*, 1935, **33,** 179) and the *Mazzine Test* (*Am. J. Clin. Path.*, 1939, **9,** 163) are other flocculation tests for syphilis recently described but they will require further study before they can be recommended.

Frei Test (*Klin. Wchnschr.*, 1925, **4**, 21; *J. A. M. A.*, 1936, **107**, 1359) is an intradermal test specific for lymphogranuloma inguinale (climatic bubo, lymphopathia venereum), a venereal disease due to a filterable virus and characterized by enlargement of the draining lymph nodes which become adherent, break down and tend to form sinuses. The specific antigen and a control are injected intradermally and the reaction is observed at forty-eight to seventy-two hours. A raised reddened papule from 6 mm. or over in diameter is a positive test. A vesicle or pustule may be present. The reaction slowly subsides leaving a brownish pigmented area. The test which is positive in about 90 per cent of ulcerative cases and in about 95 per cent when buboes have developed becomes positive during the first week and persists indefinitely throughout the disease. The test antigen was formerly prepared from glandular material of proved lymphogranuloma inguinale. Since it has been found that the virus can be transmitted by intracerebral inoculation of mice and especially by growing the virus on chick embryos (chorio-allantoic membrane), the antigen is now prepared from that source. The antigen of chick embryo origin is marketed under the trade name, *Lygranum*, and an editorial review (*Brit. M. J.*, 1943, **1**, 17) regards the latter as the most efficient antigen yet produced for use in skin and complement-fixation tests. Mortara and Greenblatt (*Ven. Dis. Inform.*, 1943, **24**, 14) in a comparative study of various antigens found the chick embryo antigen very reliable.

Heterophile or Heterogenetic or Forssman's Antigen and Heterophile Agglutination.—Forssman (*Biochem. Ztschr.*, 1911, **37**, 78) noted that guinea-pig tissues when injected into the rabbit produced a hemolytic antibody for sheep red blood cells. In his observations with extracts of different animal organs, he definitely established the fact that there existed in the organs of different animals, antigens which did not follow the usual laws of species specificity. Such antigens displaying the lack of biologic relationship between the species containing the antigens and that for which the immune body displayed an affinity are spoken of as "heterophile" or "heterogenetic," or "Forssman's antigens." The criterion of a heterophile antigen is its capability of causing the production of antibodies when injected into animals (especially rabbits), the sera of which will be hemolytic for sheep and goat red blood cells, and the responsible antibodies in turn will be absorbed by these blood cells. The presence of substances in microorganisms which produce in unrelated species identical serological observations as with the Forssman antigen and antibody are of frequent occurrence. A substance similar to the heterophile antigen has been found in some species of bacteria, especially in pneumococci and in some strains of streptococci and *H. influenzae*. Vaccines and other antigens containing the heterophile antigen and sera containing not only the neutralizing antibody, the animal protective antibody, but also a heterophile antibody are available as marketable preparations. For more details, see Gershenfeld (*Biological Products*, Romaine Pierson Publishers, New York, N. Y., 1939, p. 194). Heterophile agglutination (*Am. J. M. Sc.*, 1932, **183**, 90) as a diagnostic aid in infectious mononucleosis or at least as a differential test (*Am. J. Dis. Child.*, 1935, **49**, 1222) for this condition has been advocated and appears to be useful.

Ito-Reenstierna Test.—This test is an intracutaneous specific test employed as an aid in the diagnosis of chancroid. A suspension of inactivated Ducrey bacilli is employed as the test material. See also page 163.

The Mallein Test.—The Mallein reaction is used in veterinary medicine for the detection of glanders in animals (usually horses). For details, see pages 155 and 496.

Mitsuda Reaction or Lepromin Test is of value in the classification of cases of leprosy and in its immunitary and prognostic value. It is a skin test in which 0.1 cc. *lepromin* is employed as the test material. For further details, see Pardo-Costello and Tiant (*J. A. M. A.*, 1943, **121**, 1264).

Neufeld's (Quellung) Method of Typing Pneumococci.—Many techniques have been introduced for typing pneumonia serum, but the Newfeld (Quellen) method (*Prevent. Med.*, 1937, **7**, 39) has been widely acclaimed because of its simplicity, accuracy and ease in obtaining a quick report on a plain micro slide. A loopful of sputum, previously strained and found to contain pneumococci, is mixed separately with an equal quantity of each of the available specific type serums (rabbit) and an equal amount of Loeffler's methylene-blue solution. Examine with oil immersion lens within two to three minutes. A positive reaction reveals the capsules of the pneumococcus greatly swollen and definitely outlined, thereby identifying the type. When the pneumococcus is not the same type as the serum, a change in the appearance of the capsule is not apparent (negative reaction). *Diagnostic Antipneumococcic Rabbit Sera* are marketed to be used for the rapid typing of pneumococci by the Neufeld method. Each of the types is separately available and to facilitate segregation of the types, various combinations of the type-specific sera are also marketed.

Opsonocytophagic Test is employed especially for brucellosis to determine the immunity status of an individual toward species of *Brucella*. The results obtained in this test correlated with findings of skin testing with brucellergin and agglutination tests of the patient's serum may be most helpful in accurately diagnosing brucellosis.

The patient's blood is collected, and to each 5 cc. there is added immediately 0.2 cc of a 20 per cent sodium citrate in isotonic salt solution. A heavy suspension of a suitable strain of *Brucella* is prepared (6 million organisms per cc.). Equal parts of the patient's citrated blood and suspension (0.1 cc. of each) are mixed well and incubated in a water bath at 37° C. for one-half hour. The mixture is then agitated gently, thin smears are made on slides, the latter stained by one of the blood-staining methods and the bacteria present (phagocytized) in each of 25 polymorphonuclear leukocytes are counted and recorded. The presence of 40 or more bacteria per cell indicates a marked reaction; 21 to 40, moderate reaction; 1 to 20, slight; and no phagocytosis is a negative reaction.

The *phagocytic index number* of Foshag and Le Blanc (*J. Lab. & Clin. Med.*, 1937, **22,** 1297) reports the opsonic or phagocytic power in terms of percentage. For its interpretation, see Angle and associates (*J. Lab. & Clin. Med.*, 1942, **27,** 1259).

Precipitin Tests.—Precipitins are antibodies closely allied to agglutinins. They act on clear extracts of albuminous substances in a manner quite similar to the action of agglutinins upon formed cellular elements. Precipitins are specific antibodies produced in the blood of animals inoculated with known bacteria, vegetable or animal albuminous solutions, or other known antigenic substances and possess the power of producing a precipitate in a bacteria-free filtrate or in a clear extract (liquid) of the particular albuminous substance or specific antigen against which the animal was immunized. Precipitin tests may be employed for the identification of a large number of different protein substances. In bacteriological diagnostic work, precipitin tests are used less frequently than agglutination tests. Some of their applications are afforded by tests for determining the types of pneumococci; Ascoli precipitin test for the differential diagnosis of *B. anthracis* (anthrax); in tests for glanders and for swine erysipelas; Rosenow's precipitin test for *Streptococcus scarlatinae* (Scarlet fever); Lancefield's method for classifying streptococci; classifying of pneumococci; and especially for the medicolegal identification of blood and seminal stains and in the examination and identification of milks, meats, eggs and other foodstuffs apt to be adulterated.

Whereas in the agglutination test, the serum is diluted serially and not the antigen, in precipitin tests the antigen is diluted in series and the serum is used undiluted or diluted only slightly. Otherwise the test is performed in a manner similar to the macroscopic tube agglutination test. In another technique, the antiserum and diluted antigen are carefully added so as to form two separate layers. In the tube method, a precipitate forms and settles out leaving a clear supernatant fluid, as in the agglutination test. In the layer formation technique, the so-called "contact" or "ring test," a cloudiness or precipitate forms at the point of contact or juncture between the two liquids. The highest antigen dilution with which the serum forms an observable precipitate or contact cloud is employed to indicate the titer of the serum.

Schick Test.—For details, see page 486.

Skin Tests for detecting the presence of immune bodies or noting sensitivity to different proteins are widely used. For details, see each of the following under their respective headings: *Allergen Skin Test; Brucellergin Test; Dick Test; Frei Test; Ito-Reenstierna Test; Johnin Test; Lepromin Test; Luetin Test; Moloney Test; Mantoux Test; Moro Test; Ophthalmic Reactions; Schick Test; Tuberculin Test;* and *Von Pirquet Test.*

Tuberculosis.—The use of tuberculin has been utilized as an aid in diagnosis of obscure forms of tuberculosis, the test being applied in a number of ways. In order of their importance, the following are commonly employed:

1. *Intracutaneous test of Mantoux;*
2. *Von Pirquet method (cutaneous test);*
3. *Patch test;*
4. *Moro reaction (percutaneous test);*
5. *Subcutaneous test;* and
6. *Calmette's ophthalmic reaction.*

For details, see pages 492.

The Widal and Other Agglutination Tests.—Tests performed to detect agglutinins in one's blood stream are known as "agglutination tests." When a test is performed to detect typhoid agglutinins the test is known as the "typhoid agglutination test" and more frequently as the *"Widal or Widal-Gruber test."* The *Huddleson test* is specifically an agglutination test to detect agglutinins in human blood serum specific for species of *Brucella* and the same test on the blood of cattle is known as *Bang's test.* In addition to these two diseases, agglutination tests are also of value as diagnositic aids in paratyphoid fevers, tularemia, glanders and typhus fever. Agglutination tests are useful for the identification of species of *Eberthella, Salmonella, Shigella, Brucella, Pasteurella* and *Hemophilus,* pneumococci and meningococci.

Agglutination Tests.—When serum (containing agglutinins) is mixed in proper proportions with its specific antigen, and the mixture is incubated, the antigen will become clumped or agglutinated. This is apparent microscopically or macroscopically (to the naked eye). The macroscopic technique is preferred. To be of diagnostic value, this observation must occur with sufficiently high dilutions of serum to rule out the possibility of nonspecific reactions. In some instances, where the antigen suspensions are known bacteria and these are to be prepared, better interpretations are frequently possible and the test is of greater diagnostic significance if both H (flagellar) and O (somatic) suspensions are made from the antigen and the test performed with both suspensions. The flagellar or H antigen is a formalin-treated suspension of an actively motile "smooth" strain of the organism. The somatic or O antigen is an alcohol-treated supension of a "smooth," preferably nonflagellated, strain of the organism.

Macroscopic (*Test-tube*) *Test.*—Serial dilutions of the patient's serum are made from 1:10 to 1:640 using isotonic salt solution. One-half cubic centimeter of these dilutions is mixed in small test tubes with an equal quantity of the known bacterial suspension (or antigen). The final dilutions of serum will be found to be 1:20 to 1:1280 (or higher if desired). The first and last tubes are controls and contain, respectively, serum and saline only and antigen and saline only. All tubes are shaken well and incubated. The incubation period and temperature differ for the particular antigen. The optimum temperature of choice is at 50° to 56° C. in a water bath; 37° C. or even room temperature may be used for large clumping motile bacteria. Twenty-four hours at 50° to 56° C. are required for "O" suspensions; for motile bacteria in general, incubate at least two hours at 50° to 56° C. or eight hours at 37° C. or twenty-four hours at room temperature; for nonmotile bacteria in general, four to twenty-four hours at 50° to 56° C. or twenty-four hours at 37° C. A preliminary reading is made at the end of two hours' incubation; another reading at the conclusion of the incubation period; and a final reading after refrigeration. All tests should be kept in the refrigerator for at least four to six hours and preferably overnight after incubation and for a final reading. In reading the findings, the tubes are observed for clearing of the supernatant liquid and shaken gently to note the amount and character of agglutinated particles or clumps. Complete clumping or agglutination with a completely clear supernatant fluid indicates a four plus reaction. The tube containing the highest dilution of serum showing definite agglutination indicates the *titer*. The H agglutinins produce with their specific antigen large (floccular) flakes, which are easily broken up, while the O agglutinins produce with their specific antigen a small flaky or granular agglutination.

Microscopic Agglutination Test.—Cultures or suspensions of actively motile bacteria free of clumps are preferred as the antigen. Varying dilutions of the serum with isotonic salt solution are made and a loopful of each dilution is placed on separate cover glasses or watch crystals. Add a loopful of the culture or suspension of bacteria to each dilution so as to obtain final dilutions of 1:50 and 1:100 (and others if desired), and mix. Mount each in vaseline on a hanging-drop slide. Prepare a control replacing the serum dilution with plain isotonic salt solution. Examine with a high-dry objective for the loss of motility and clumping of the bacteria as compared with the control. A final reading is made at the end of one hour. Serial dilutions can be used and the highest dilution showing clumping microscopically is recorded as the titer.

Slide Method or Rapid Macroscopic Agglutination Test.—This method is based on the rapid agglutination of certain bacteria or other antigen by their specific serum of high titer. The readings are made within a few minutes. It is of conclusive diagnostic value in few instances especially in *Brucella* infections, and of presumptive value in most all other cases. Serial dilutions of the serum are made and a drop of each is placed separately on a slide or in suitable squares on a glass plate. A drop of the antigen is added to each drop of serum dilution. With a clean toothpick, mix the serum dilution and antigen, using a new toothpick for each mixture. If the same toothpick is used, proceed from the smallest serum dilution to the largest amount of serum mixture. A control is also prepared. Clumping occurs almost immediately, is readily observed and easily read. Tilting the slide or glass plate slightly backward and forward for a few moments will hasten the reaction.

Agglutinin Adsorption (or Absorption).—Agglutinins may be found to be at times both species-specific and group-specific, so that agglutination will occur with the specific bacterium and also with closely related species. The Gram-negative intestinal rods especially display this characteristic. The agglutinin adsorption (or absorption) test is used, in certain instances, to differentiate between these related species or between specific and group agglutination. This test has been most useful in the study of antigen structure and bacterial relationships. If we add to an immune serum a large amount of its specific antigen (organism in this instance), and incubate the mixture, clumping will occur and the clear, supernatant liquid will not be capable of agglutinating either the specific antigen (organism) or closely related organisms. If, on the other hand, the serum is treated similarly with a related antigen (or organism), the species-specific agglutinins will not be reduced appreciably, but the group agglutinins will have disappeared wholly or at least in large part. The fundamental requirements in these tests are suitable reagents and the proper standardization of these reagents.

Chapter XLV

ALLERGIC SKIN TESTS AND ALLERGENS

HAY FEVER—ANIMAL, FOOD, POLLEN EXTRACTS, ETC.

DIFFERENT proteins are fundamentally the agents which produce the symptoms commonly observed in hay fever, asthma and other allergic diseases. It should be remembered that the different kinds of proteins may vary in the different types of amino acids which they contain or the relative proportion and intramolecular placement of the latter. Symptoms of hives, eczema, asthma, hay fever and other allergic diseases may be caused by almost any kind of protein. The symptoms may become manifest after the eating of certain foods, such as eggs, oysters, clams, strawberries, etc. Others develop these symptoms by coming in contact with the epidermal emanations from many of the lower animals, including horses, rabbits, guinea pigs and a host of other animals. In like manner inhalation of the proteins from several sources may be the direct causes of hay fever and asthma. The proteins of the pollen grain from all the important pollenating plants may produce the symptoms, or it may be any of the following: proteins from horse hair or dander; the dust from feathers present in pillows or other feathers and hair which may be a constituent of some object in the house, as the fur of animals; felt usually made from rabbit hair; even the protein from dry glue in furniture. Then we have symptoms in other cases produced by the protein from house and other dusts. Powdered orris root, a constituent of almost all face powders and many cosmetics, may be the exciting cause, or it may be rice powder and other drugs with which an individual comes in contact. See also the recent consideration on allergenic preparations by the Council on Pharmacy and Chemistry (*J. A. M. A.*, 1943, **123**, 1117).

ALLERGIC SKIN REACTION

The skin test for detecting the sensitive protein is very simple. A small amount of the several purified proteins, usually in solution, is applied separately to scarifications made on the skin about one-half inch apart (cutaneous method or scratch test) or an injection is made intracutaneously (intradermally). Controls are made. If the protein is in powder form this is placed on the abrasion, followed by the addition of a drop of water, saline solution or 0.25 per cent NaOH solution. Sensitivity can also be observed by means of the patch test, application being made to the surface of the skin or mucous membranes. If the patient is allergic or sensitive to the particular protein a small urticarial, raised area appears in a few minutes at the point of injection. This lasts for a period varying from several minutes to one and even two hours, or in some instances longer, and then disappears. Reactions are noted one-half hour after the test. No allergy to a particular protein is indicated by the nonappearance of such reaction after the test is made. In the patch test or surface applications, a longer period of time may be required for noting the appearance of inflammation, rash, etc., as compared to the control.

PROTEINS FOR DIAGNOSTIC USE

The problem of detecting the specific protein which may be the cause of the particular symptoms in the individual is frequently a long-drawn-out and tedious affair. At times such detection is impossible. This may be due to the fact that the purified proteins from one or several of the substances to which the individual is sensitive have not been separated out in a relatively pure state to be used for testing allergic persons. In most instances it is necessary to employ a large number of proteins in cutaneous (skin) or intracutaneous (intradermal) tests. The proteins which may be used are frequently selected only after a painstaking search into the history of the patient and his environment. Proteins in dried powder are used only for the cutaneous or skin tests, and several tests can be performed at one time. Proteins in diluted solution are generally used mainly for the intradermal or intracutaneous test, but may be used also for the cutaneous test. Dilutions are always employed when the intracutaneous tests are made and not more than six or eight of the latter should be performed at one time. This is to avoid general systemic reactions. The patch test is used for testing allergens more apt to give reactions when applied to the skin. The scratch and intradermal tests are employed for allergens which ordinarily give rise to reactions when introduced internally. In general, allergenic preparations are from single sources, as the hair or epidermis of one species of animal. Mixtures are employed only occasionally, as in the preparations of the closely related pollens.

Several different methods of preparation are practiced in preparing the proteins in pure form. The technique depends upon the property of the crude material, its general composition, etc. In many instances, some kind of preliminary treatment of the crude material may be necessary. For example, in many cases washing with toluol, alcohol, ether or other solvents is practiced to remove fat, and the defatted material used for preparing the allergen. Extractions are generally conducted with different solvents, either water, solutions of varying strengths of sodium chloride or buffered extracting fluids, 5 per cent dextrose solution, diluted glycerin and alcoholic solutions or any of these containing varying strengths of usually 0.1 to 0.2 per cent alkali. If the extractions are not pure protein, they are further treated with different reagents which precipitate the protein. The latter are redissolved and standardized. The methods of standardization vary. They may be to determine chemically the amount of proteins present, and then the solutions are diluted to any desired protein content. In some few cases complement-fixation and other tests are conducted as a means of determining the activity of the preparation. Those interested in exact techniques of preparation and suitable methods of standardization will find data in reviews and publications on the subject.

It is, of course, understood that solutions of these proteins which are used intracutaneously are to be sterilized and placed in sterile containers. Sterilization is usually conducted by the method of bacteriological filtration, and a preservative is added if one was not present in the liquid used in the extraction. Marketable products are tested for sterility, etc. Inasmuch as allergenic solutions may deteriorate with age, they should be stored at a low temperature and used before the expiration date given on the label.

The various biological houses market or supply on order most of the following proteins (atopens, allergens or antigens) employed for diagnostic purposes and some are used for desensitization:

Animal Extracts (Dried or in Solution).—These are cat hair, cat dander, chamois skin, chicken feathers, cow (cattle) dander, dog dander, dog hair, duck feathers, goose feathers, guinea-pig hair, horse dander, horse hair, horse serum, rabbit dander, rabbit hair and sheep wool.

Bacterial Proteins.—Wherever possible, tests should be conducted with separate autogenous antigens (proteins) prepared from the different bacteria recovered in pure cultures from the nose, sputum or other foci of infection present in the patient to be tested. Stock antigens (proteins) of the different bacteria are available. The latter are killed, dried, disintegrated by grinding and marketed in powdered form.

Food Extracts.—These include foods of animal and vegetable origin. Practically every common food has been implicated. With fruits and vegetables that can be peeled, separate extractions are frequently made from the pulp and ground peelings.

Miscellaneous Protein Extracts.—Many substances which are not included in any of the other groups are listed here.

Mention was made of the sensitivity to the different kinds of dusts. For diagnostic testing the specific dust will have to be collected and the protein extracted. Each case may, therefore, be a specific problem, so that it may not be practical to market protein extracts from any particular dust. In testing allergy to drugs, the latter in powdered form or a solution of this is applied to abrasions on the skin. In the case of the vegetable drugs, fluid extracts may be employed or extracts may be prepared. The following substances occur so frequently as the important factors in the various manifestations of sensitization that they are supplied by several firms either in dried powdered form or as extracts from the latter: cottonseed, flaxseed, glue, hay, kapok, orris root, rice powder (polish), silk and tobacco.

Pollen Extracts.—The biologist is interested in pollens. Hay fever is now commonly regarded as a condition of hypersensitiveness or allergy, especially to pollens. The latter are also the cause of various forms of asthma. The pollens causing hay fever may be those of flowers, grasses, shrubs, weeds or other plants. These are roughly divided into three groups: (a) those causing early spring hay fever, in which the tree pollens in the air are the main causative factors; (b) those causing early summer fever when the grasses are pollinating; (c) those causing hay fever in the late summer or early autumn when the weeds, especially the ragweed, are shedding their pollens. The trees pollinate in March and April. Those producing the lightest and most abundant pollen belong to the oak family. Ash, cottonwood, the walnuts and the poplars also produce pollens which are widely distributed in the atmosphere during the pollinating season. The largest percentage of hay fever cases is caused by the Gramineae (grasses—or Timothy grass, Johnson grass, orchard grass, Bermuda grass, red-top grass) for the spring type, and the Ambrosiaceae (ragweeds as common ragweed, giant ragweed, Western ragweed and rough marsh elder, Burweed marsh elder and cocklebur) for the fall type. Speaking broadly, the brightly colored plants are of less interest in this study than those without colored flowerings. The former possess heavy sticky pollen which is carried by insects from plant to plant. Such pollen is rarely present in the air in high concentrations and surely not at any great distance from the plant; so that if one is sensitive to the pollens of this group of insect-pollinated plants (which includes such plants as daisy, goldenrod, rose, sunflower, etc.), by avoiding the immediate vicinity of these, symptoms of hay fever will not appear. The plants without colorful flowerings and not attracting insects possess lighter pollen grains, which are wind-borne. These may be carried many miles and it is mainly such pollens which one cannot avoid that cause most cases of hay fever. When it is considered that a single plant in some instances may shed millions of pollens within twenty-four hours it can readily be seen how concentrated the air can become with the various pollens.

Individuals who are hypersensitive to one of the grasses usually react to several of the latter. Sensitization is usually multiple and it, therefore, becomes necessary to determine the specific pollens causing the allergy. Cutaneous tests for pollen and other plant allergens are used almost entirely. The different manufacturing firms market a very large variety of pollens and grasses, which are made available in convenient form for immediate use. The manufacture of pollens and pollen extracts requires more care perhaps than is necessary when preparing the other allergens. The pollens must be collected in their respective pollinating season under the supervision of a trained botanist. Only the pollinating portion of the plant is treated, and by means of mechanical shakers or other devices the pollens are removed. The latter are collected, sifted through several sieves, then dried or extracts are made. To determine which pollens to employ for diagnostic tests, the history of the patient will help considerably. Frequently the patient will give a clue by mentioning what he thinks brought on the attack. But a knowledge of the botanical flora in a given locality is frequently an absolute necessity before definite findings are possible. The nature, distribution and abundance of a particular local flora must be known if some patients are to be given relief. The list of pollens (pollen atopens) used in determining the exciting agent in hay fever and pollen asthma is very large. Almost one hundred different pollen atopens are to be found available on the market today and to this there is to be added the several pollen atopens which are obtained in localized areas by those scientists in these respective territories who have found it advisable to prepare them.

In the case of pollen allergens it is advisable to have available the distribution of trees, grasses, etc., and their pollination during the different seasons in the various parts of the country. The New York Botanical Garden has available considerable data on the North American Flora. Other references are Thomen's "Asthma and Hay Fever in Theory and Practice," Publication No. 401 of the Carnegie Institute at Washington, Lobeck's Physiographic Map, and rainfall and humidity maps of the U. S. Weather Bureau.

Group Allergens.—In practice it is not possible at all times to skin test patients with the exceedingly large number of different allergens. Group allergens, five to eight allergens being included in each group, are available and these make possible the shortening and simplifying of the testing procedure. These mixtures are grouped together according to their biologic or genetic relationships or because their association has a basis in clinical experience. A positive group test indicates sensitivity to one or more proteins in that group and tests with the individual members are then performed. Though a negative group test may eliminate all members in that group, this should not interfere with trying an individual allergen in that group should it be suspected.

THEORY OF DESENSITIZATION

The development of tolerance to a specific sensitinogen used in injections is explained differently by several workers. The popular conception is that desensitization depends upon the production of specific antibodies which effectually neutralize small amounts of the sensitinogen (antigen) before the latter reaches the sensitized cells, so that the production of the shock is slowed up or completely eliminated after the introduction of increasing amounts of antigen. The body cells themselves do become increasingly resistant to the action of the sensitinogen. It may be that as one worker expresses it: "Desensitization is a process of restoration of colloidal equilibrium within sensitized cells."

STANDARDIZATION OF PROTEINS

Wherever convenient, especially when preparations of protein extracts are marketed, some method of determining the activity of the preparation and recording its strength should be practiced if possible. The most convenient method is to determine the nitrogen content chemically by the Kjeldahl method. Each 0.00001 mg. of protein nitrogen is spoken of as a unit, so that if a solution has present 0.00025 mg. it is said to contain 25 protein units. Such a method is accurate and lends itself to an easy interpretation of any dosage. The animal, food and pollen extracts for desensitizing treatment are conveniently marketed in bulk and standardized to contain fairly large amounts of protein or protein units per cubic centimeter of solution. These strengths can be employed readily for any scheme of dosage as may be desired. Some manufacturers standardize their pollen allergens and express the dosage merely in terms of nitrogen content, while in other cases manufacturers estimate their protein content from the nitrogen determination by the formula $N \times 6.25$ and label the preparation as containing given amounts of protein in terms of milligrams per cc. In another instance the unit is that quantity of pollen protein per cubic centimeter which can be extracted from 0.003 mg. of pollen or 0.001 mg. by another manufacturer and even other figures are given by those marketing allergenic preparations. It is unfortunate that there does not exist some uniform method of recording the nitrogen content or unitage of the solution or dried allergen represented.

PART VII
APPLIED BACTERIOLOGY

Chapter XLVI

SANITIZATION AND BACTERIOLOGICAL EXAMINATION OF AIR

AEROBIOLOGY has developed very rapidly as a specialized field of study only during the past decade, although investigations in this new branch have been carried on for a long period of time. Wells and Robertson and their associates in the United States, Trillat in France, and Pulvertaft and Twort and their associates in England have been doing yeoman work during the recent development. Improved methods of the sampling of air and Jennison's application of flash or high-speed photography to the study of coughs and sneezes have demonstrated more realistically the dangers of droplet infection. For further details, see the valuable symposium on *Aerobiology*, *Am. A. Advancement Sci.*, Pub. No. **17**, 1942).

Sprays, Mists, Vapors, Smokes and Aerosols.—The problems of purifying air by means of these agents may be more difficult and more troublesome than the use of ultraviolet light. Such agents are more difficult to control and they are apt to be toxic or cause irritation or otherwise be objectionable. On the other hand, they are more readily available, cheaper to install and are easier or may even be the only procedure to improvise in a sudden emergency. Especially is this the case in attempting to purify vitiated air in air-raid shelters, in temporary quarters, or in individual rooms in institutions or private dwellings.

Water Spraying.—Simple spraying, even without the presence of a disinfectant, is employed at times. The purpose here is to supersaturate the air with the liquid, which when falling to the ground or floor will carry along dust nuclei. The latter containing bacteria are placed in contact with a solution of a disinfectant applied to the ground before and after spraying. Water by itself is not satisfactory for spraying, as the water vapor disperses too rapidly. The dust particles dry quickly and are thus carried back or left remaining in the air. The best liquid to employ is one which is nonirritating and nontoxic, possesses a low surface tension, contains a bactericidal agent and, when on the ground or floor, covers the latter as a homogeneous film. An aqueous solution of a detergent or wetting agent is satisfactory. For more details concerning this procedure, see Dodd (*M. Officer*, 1940, **64**, 149).

Bactericidal Sprays, Mists, etc.—Since the days of Lister when, as mentioned elsewhere in this volume, solutions of phenol were sprayed in operating rooms in the practice of aseptic surgery, but little attention was paid to this procedure. In 1938, Trillat

(*Bull. Acad. de Med., Paris*, 1938, **119,** 64) discussed droplet infection and the sterilizing properties of germicidal aerosols. He defined a *liquid aerosol* as consisting of droplets, 1 to 2μ in diameter, dispersed in the air. The compounds which he advocated as being both efficient and practical were sodium hypochlorite and resorcinol, the latter being the germicide of choice. Mastermann (*J. Indust. Hyg. & Toxicol.*, 1938, **20,** 278; *J. Hyg.*, 1941, **41,** 44) advocated fine mists of sodium hypochlorite, reported that 1 Gm. of a solution containing 1 per cent NaOCl displayed a bactericidal effect when atomized in an amount of air as high as 40 million cc., and expressed the opinion that the action was due to the liberation of gaseous hypochlorous acid.

Later, resorcinol and hexylresorcinol aerosols were advocated in a concentration of 1 Gm. in 1000 m.³ of air. Twort and Baker (*J. Hyg.*, 1942, **42,** 266) recommended the latter as the two most suitable phenolic compounds for use as bactericidal aerosols, after conducting researches on a large number of phenolic substances. Hexylresorcinol kills more slowly, acts in a lower concentration and persists longer than resorcinol. It is more suitable when air changes are infrequent and the contacts are not close. Under reverse conditions, resorcinol is the better agent. Phenolic aerosols are more persistent than sodium hypochlorite in aerosol form. While the latter cannot, phenolic aerosols can be volatilized by heat. The choice of solvent is of greater consideration for mechanical than for heating atomization. Chemicals are conveniently vaporized from a hot plate placed in front of an electric fan. Any desired concentration can be attained. The relative humidity, when using aerosols, is a very important factor which must be taken into consideration.

Robertson and associates (*Science*, 1941, **93,** 213, and *Aerobiology Symposium*, 1942, 271) employed the glycols as aerosols and propylene glycol especially was recommended in mist and vapor form owing to its effectiveness, and that it was odorless, tasteless, nonirritating and low in toxicity. These same workers advocated recently the use of triethylene glycol vapors (*Science*, 1943, **97,** 142). In an experimental investigation, using 0.2 cc. (in the form of a vapor) in 800 cubic feet of air, mice were protected completely from air-borne influenza virus and various pathogenic bacteria, while the control animals died. Triethylene glycol is a more efficient bactericidal agent than propylene glycol. Its toxicity is being investigated. Wells and Zapposodi (*Science*, 1942, **96,** 278), in a study of the relationship of humidity, found that high humidity neutralized and low humidity masked the disinfecting action of propylene glycol vapor and that disinfection was most apparent at intermediate humidities. A more detailed study of the effect of humidity in air disinfection is awaited so that these relationships may be better understood and the findings employed in practice so as to obtain more effective results. (See also Editorial, *J.A.M.A.*, 1942, **120,** 625; 1943, **122,** 177.) Stokes and Henle (*J. A. M. A.*, 1942, **120,** 16) reported that a propylene glycol concentration in the air of 1 to 30 or 40 million decreased the incidence of respiratory infection among children in a convalescent home. Vapors of propylene glycol or admixtures possess a fairly high specific gravity. It, therefore, is important to place the vaporizer at least 6 to 8 feet from the floor and have available a sufficient number of fans to insure thorough mixing. Concentrations ranging from 1 Gm. per 5 to 20 million cc. of air, introduced by vaporization, are used. Krueger and associates (*Science*, 1943, **97,** 208) presented a simplified propylene glycol dispenser for field use consisting of an ordinary electric light bulb dipping into a can filled with the chemical. See also Robertson and associates (*J.*

Exp. Med., 1942, **75**, 593). Harris and Stokes (*Am. J. M. Sc.*, 1942, **204,** 403) report on the greatly reduced incidence of respiratory infections with propylene glycol vapor. The latter was produced by allowing the glycol to drip continuously over the end of a 100-watt soldering iron on a shelf 3 feet from the ceiling.

Elford and van den Ende (*J. Hyg.*, 1942, **42**, 240) found that a concentration of 0.04 p. p. m. of ozone was effective against unprotected bacteria but not against bacteria protected by mucus or which had settled on surfaces. Its effectiveness is favored by a high relative humidity (60 to 90 per cent). However, ozone in concentrations which can be breathed safely for prolonged periods of time is not an effective bactericide.

A dense smoke, similar to that produced when burning incense, has been suggested by Twort and Baker (*J. Hyg.*, 1940, **40,** 253). Cardboard is soaked with a solution of the volatile germicidal agent and potassium nitrate and, after drying, is ignited. The smoke of the ignited chemically treated cardboard, even in amounts of 1 Gm. dispersed in 500 million cc. of air has been found to produce effective results.

BACTERIOLOGICAL EXAMINATION OF AIR

Various methods are employed in the examination of air to determine the suitability of atmospheric and environmental conditions. The so-called *working standards* suggested by the industrial hygiene section of the American Public Health Association should be consulted for details (see published reports in Am. Pub. Health Association Year Books for past decade). In air analyses, the following are employed: physical methods to note temperature, humidity, etc.; chemical methods to detect the presence of poisonous and objectionable gases; dust determinations to note whether the particulate matter may constitute a hazard; and bacteriologic procedures to determine the bacterial population.

Bacterial Counts.—The quantitative determination of the bacteria in air will vary markedly depending upon such factors as the method of collection including the sampling time, the culture media used, the period of time the latter is incubated, etc. A simple technique, which, with its known limitations, nevertheless has some value, is practiced by exposing Petri dishes containing suitable culture media for definite periods of time and counting the colonies which develop after incubating the plates at 37° C. or at room temperature for from forty-eight to ninety-six hours. The kind of culture medium used may vary. For a general observation of the bacterial population, blood-agar medium is most suitable. The other methods depend upon filtration, or bubbling air through some liquid medium, or precipitating the bacteria from a given volume of air by gravity or preferably by centrifugation.

In the filtration method, a layer (about 1 cm. in depth) of sterilized sand, which is capable of passing through a 100-mesh sieve, is placed in a small glass tube. The sand is supported by a layer of sterile bolting cloth or small wire screens. Using an aspirator or pump of known volume, a measured amount of air (10 or more liters) is drawn through at a constant rate of suction. The time period is usually one to two minutes per liter. The sand is then placed in 10 cc. of sterile isotonic salt solution, thoroughly shaken and definite volumes of the liquid are plated, using agar or other medium. The plates are incubated, the colonies counted, and the number of bacteria in the air examined is determined.

In another technique, a definite amount of air is allowed to bubble through sterile isotonic salt solution, the latter then plated by the usual technique and the count is determined.

The Wells' centrifuge method (*Am. J. Pub. Health*, 1933, **23,** 58; 1938, **28,** 343) is highly regarded by workers as a more satisfactory procedure. See also page 89. In this centrifugal method, air flow is created by the rapid revolution of a glass cylinder about its vertical axis. The air, which can be measured, escapes along a thin layer of culture medium, the latter being solidified on the walls of the cylinder. Bacteria and particles suspended in the air are deposited on the medium. The cylinders are incubated and the colonies on the collecting medium are counted without the necessity of separate plating. A technique for estimating atmospheric bacterial pollution comparable to the test for coliform bacteria in water has been developed. Streptococci expelled into the air from the respiratory tract and recovered in a selective medium with the air centrifuge are noted for estimating the sanitary quality of air. For further details, see report of subcommittee (*Am. Pub. Health Assoc. Year Book*, 1941–1942, **32,** 137) and for other data, see Wells and Wells ("Aerobiology," *Am. A. Advancement Sci.*, Pub. No. **17,** 1942, p. 99).

Chapter XLVII

EXAMINATION OF WATER

WATER IS an important article of diet, though not regarded as a food. Today we know it as the vehicle for carrying the water-borne diseases, especially cholera, typhoid fever, paratyphoid fever, dysentery and other gastro-intestinal infections. It may be responsible for conveying animal parasites, amœbae, worms, etc. The greatest danger in the use of a water supply is in employing one polluted from human sources. All sewage-polluted water, unless purified, is dangerous and a possible carrier of pathogenic organisms. Besides the specific gastro-intestinal infections which are possible from drinking or bathing in impure water, there are other non-specific diseases that may be attributed to water.

SANITARY ANALYSIS OF WATER

A *complete* evaluation of the sanitary quality of water is only possible after (1) laboratory examinations; (2) a field survey or inspection of the region from where it is derived and of the distributing system; and (3) the clinical observations resulting from the actual use of the water. The field survey is very important as it may reveal the presence of potential dangers. It should be entrusted to a sanitarian who has acquired by training a broad knowledge of all phases of water sanitation.

LABORATORY EXAMINATIONS

These determinations are invaluable aids for estimating the sanitary quality of water. The sanitary analysis consists of (1) physical (macroscopic), (2) chemical, (3) microscopical and (4) bacteriological examinations. Each of these four examinations, dealing with different qualities of water, has its own significance and final interpretations can only be made after the findings in all examinations are assembled and correlated.

Bacteriological Examination of Water.—The sanitary chemical examination of water, though of considerable value, does not give one as much information as is obtainable from a correct bacteriological examination. The detection of offensive odors and the determination of taste, color, turbidity, reaction, total solids, hardness, oxygen, nitrates, nitrites, etc., are of value and useful as supplemental aids, but from a hygienic standpoint the information secured by an examination of the bacterial content of water is of greater value than other determinations.

Collection of Samples.—Water for bacteriological examination should be collected in sterile (preferably wide-mouth, glass-stoppered) bottles holding 100 cc. or more. If water is obtained from a pump or faucet it should be allowed to run for five minutes before the sample is taken. If the water is to be collected from a pond, lake, stream or cistern, the bottle may be lowered by means of a weight (which was preferably attached and sterilized with the empty container) or, if accessible, the bottle may be plunged in with a clean hand, lowered below the surface of the water, and thus filled. Various devices or special apparatus are available or can be improvised to collect samples under varying conditions.   A bottle can be fastened to an end of a pole so as to avoid contamination and this used to obtain water from an inaccessible location. A bottle with a leaded bottom or other weight, even arranged so that a slight jerk will remove the stopper, can be used for wells that have no pumping devices attached. Other arrangements are possible, but whatever the method, care must be exercised at all times, and especially during the collection of the sample, not to permit contamination of the container and especially the stopper from the hands or by other means.   The bacteriological examination should be made preferably within six hours after collection.   If this is not possible, the sample should be kept at a temperature of not over 10° C. until it is examined.   This may even necessitate shipping in an ice-packed case.

Technique of Examination.—"Standard methods" (as advocated by the American Public Health Association) should be adhered to as closely as possible.   The isolation of pathogenic bacteria is difficult, so that the methods that are used are those that give us an approximate estimation of pollution.

The bacteriological examinations which have come to be recognized generally as of most value in the sanitary examination of water are:

1.   The count of total colonies developing from measured portions planted in agar or gelatin plates and incubated for forty-eight hours at 20° C.

2.   A similar count of total colonies developing on agar plates incubated for twenty-four hours at 37° C.

3.   The quantitative estimation of organisms of the coliform group by applying specific tests to multiple portions of measured volume.

Of these three determinations, the test for organisms of the coliform group is almost universally conceded to be the most significant because it affords the most nearly specific test for the presence of fecal contamination.

Total Bacterial Count.—This is estimated by plating different amounts of the well-agitated samples and making two sets of plates.   In one set the culture medium used is gelatin or agar medium (see page 51).   These plates are incubated at room temperature or 20° C. for forty-eight hours.   The other plates are made with standard agar culture medium and incubated at 37° C. for twenty-four hours.   The plates are made as described under Examination of Milk.

Fermentation Test.—Into a series of fermentation tubes, containing standard litmus lactose bouillon there are delivered varying definite amounts of the well-agitated samples of water to be examined.   These are incubated at 37° C. for forty-eight hours, unless gas appears earlier.   The absence of gas formation after forty-eight hours' incubation constitutes a *negative test*.   If tubes show the presence of gas, there is the presumptive evidence of the presence of coliform bacteria.   This constitutes a *positive presumptive test*.   For a positive demonstration that coliform bacteria are present in tubes showing gas formation, a confirmatory test is conducted.

The confirmed test may be carried out using solid media, either Endo's medium or eosin methylene-blue agar medium, or a liquid confirmatory medium such as brilliant green lactose bile broth.   The Endo or E. M. B. plates are streaked from a tube in the positive presumptive test showing gas formation and incubated at 37° C. for twenty-four hours. The presence of gas in the liquid confirmatory medium or the appearance of typical colonies on the solid confirmatory media constitutes a *positive confirmed test*. In the absence of typical colonies on the solid confirmatory media the test is not considered negative and it is necessary to carry out the completed test. In the completed test, transplants are made either from the secondary selective liquid media showing gas or from the solid media showing typical colonies and if not typical, fish two or more colonies appearing most likely as coliform bacteria and transfer to an agar slant and to a lactose broth fermentation tube. Incubate the latter at 37° C. for forty-eight hours unless gas appears earlier and incubate the agar culture for twenty-four hours. The demonstration of Gram-negative nonspore-forming bacilli in the latter and the formation of gas in lactose broth constitute a *positive completed test*. Negative findings are reported if gas formation is absent or Gram-negative nonspore-forming bacilli are not present. McCrady (*Am. J. Pub. Health*, 1937, **27,** 1243) and associates (*Canad. Pub. Health J.*, 1941, **32,** 29) as well as other workers, including Wattie (*U. S. Pub. Health Repts.*, 1943, **58,** 377), report that brilliant green bile lactose broth (B. G. B.) is the most satisfactory confirmatory medium.

The two most widely used methods for detecting the presence of coliform bacteria in water are those of the American Public Health Association (as found in "Standard Methods" and briefly considered above) and of the British Ministry of Health ("The Bacteriological Examination of Water Supplies," H. M. Stationery Office, Bull. No. **71,** 1934). In the former method, some false positive reactions occur and no differentiation is made between the different species of coliform bacteria. In the British method, the technique employed in differentiation is open to objection. Wilson, an experienced British water expert, attempted to overcome these difficulties and devised a method in which two selective media are used, one for the detection of *E. coli;* the other for the demonstration of the intermediate types, *A. aerogenes* and *A. cloacae*. The water is inoculated into tubes of MacConkey's broth and incubated at 37° C., the first step in the British method. The production of acid and gas is presumptive evidence of the presence of coliform bacteria. Transplants are made into (1) tubes of Koser's citrate medium and MacConkey's broth. The latter tubes are incubated at 44° C. in a thermostatically controlled water bath. Under these conditions, usually only fecal *E. coli* strains produce gas. The citrate tubes are incubated at 37° C. In the latter *E. coli* will rarely grow, but the intermediate strains develop. Ferramola (*Am. J. Pub. Health*, 1940, **30,** 1083) reports on the analysis of 10,000 samples of water by Wilson's method with highly satisfactory results as compared with different controls. It is likely that the simple and accurate Wilson method may find a more extended use after other favorable reports are forthcoming.

Bryan (*U. S. Nav. M. Bull.*, 1941, **39,** 632) recommends the use of Dominick Lauter media as a quick and simple method for detecting in water coliform organisms of fecal origin. The formula of this medium is included in Appendix 1 of *Standard Methods of Water Analysis* (8th edition, 1936, 257, 261, Am. Pub. Health Assn.) and it also is marketed as a dehydrated product. A positive test is generally assured within twenty-four hours' incubation and a heavy contamination will yield a positive test within twelve hours. The incubation of tubes for forty-eight hours is recommended when they are not definitely positive after twenty-four hours. The production of gas without the characteristic color change or, conversely, a color change without gas production is regarded as a negative test. In the positive test, there is gas formation accompanied by a typical color reaction (greenish-yellow discoloration).

Interpretation of Findings.—It is generally accepted that if a water shows the presence of coliform bacteria in quantities of 1 cc. or less or one out of five 10-cc. portions reveal organisms of the coliform group, such sample should be regarded as suspicious. If the same findings are observed on re-examination, the water should not be used for human consumption. Coliform bacteria, natural inhabitants of the intestinal tract of man and animals, are taken as an index of pollution. In the absence of coliform bacteria, it is assumed that water-borne pathogens are not likely to be present in the sample. Even if organisms of the coliform group are not present, the total number of bacteria at 37° C. should not exceed 100 per cubic centimeter, the estimate having been made from at least two plates. The 37° C. count should never approximate the number developing at 20° C., as there would be a strong suspicion that sewage bacteria are present.

Recently the Advisory Committee of the United States Public Health Service (*U. S. Pub. Health Repts.*, 1943, **58**, 69) adopted standards for water used for drinking and culinary purposes, supplied by common carriers in interstate commerce. The total bacterial plate counts are not required in their technique as they do not appear to add information of sufficient importance for the type of water considered. This omission should not be construed as minimizing the importance of the 20° and 37° C. counts in routine examinations and especially when made in connection with the control of water purification processes. The techniques recommended are those given in "Standard Methods": "*The standard portion of water* for the application of the bacteriological test may be either ten milliliters (10 ml.) or one hundred milliliters (100 ml.). *The standard sample* for the bacteriological test shall consist of five (5) standard portions of either ten milliliters (10 ml.) or one hundred milliliters (100 ml.) each." The following are the requirements: "Of all the standard ten-milliliter (10-ml.) portions examined per month, not more than ten (10) per cent shall show the presence of organisms of the coliform group. Occasionally three (3) or more of the five (5) equal ten-milliliter (10-ml.) portions constituting a single standard sample may show the presence of organisms of the coliform group, provided that this shall not be allowable if it occurs in consecutive samples or in more than (*a*) five (5) per cent of the standard samples when twenty (20) or more samples have been examined per month; (*b*) one (1) standard sample when less than twenty (20) samples have been examined per month.

"Provided further that when three or more of the five equal ten-milliliter (10-ml.) portions constituting a single standard sample show the presence of organisms of the coliform group, daily samples from the same sampling point shall be collected promptly and examined until the results obtained from at least two consecutive samples show the water to be of satisfactory quality.

"Of all the standard one hundred-milliliter (100-ml.) portions examined per month in accordance with the specified procedure, not more than sixty (60) per cent shall show the presence of organisms of the coliform group.

"Occasionally all of the five (5) equal one hundred-milliliter (100-ml.) portions constituting a single standard sample may show the presence of organisms of the coliform group, provided that this shall not be allowable if it occurs in consecutive samples or in more than (*a*) twenty (20) per cent of the standard samples when five (5) or more samples have been examined per month; (b) one (1) standard sample when less than five (5) samples have been examined per month.

"Provided further that when all five of the standard one hundred-milliliter (100-ml.) portions constituting a single standard sample show the presence of organisms of the coliform group, daily samples from the same sampling point shall be collected promptly and examined until the results obtained from at least two consecutive samples show the water to be of satisfactory quality.

"The procedure given, using a standard sample composed of five standard portions, provides for an estimation of the most probable number of coliform bacteria present in the sample as set forth in the following tabulation:"

Number of portions		Most probable number of coliform bacteria per 100 ml.			
Negative	Positive	When 5–10-ml. portions are examined		When 5–100-ml. portions are examined	
5	0	Less than	2.2	Less than	0.22
4	1		2.2		0.22
3	2		5.1		0.51
2	3		9.2		0.92
1	4		16.0		1.60
0	5	More than	16.0	More than	1.60

SWIMMING POOLS

The bacteriological standards for public swimming pool water should be identical with that for potable drinking water. Since most pools contain residual chlorine, some workers place in the sterile water containers from 30 to 50 mg. of sodium thiosulfate or an amount sufficient to neutralize the chlorine, which would exert its effect in the destruction of bacteria between the time of collecting and testing. The sodium thiosulfate can be added as a dry powder or dissolved in 1 cc. of water and the container and contents are sterilized in the autoclave or a sterile solution of sodium thiosulfate is added to the sterile container.

Routine Examination of Untreated Surface Waters, Sewage, Sewage Effluents and Treated Sewage.—The undiluted and decimal dilutions of the sample are inoculated into lactose broth fermentation tubes, and the latter are incubated at 37° C. (but not over forty-eight hours) until gas is produced. All tubes showing gas at the end of forty-eight hours are regarded as revealing positive presumptive tests for coliform bacteria. The M. P. N. (Most Probable Numbers) or the coliform index can be obtained from these findings after noting the smallest dilution which yields a positive finding and the first dilution which does not cause the formation of gas. For a more conclusive coliform index, transplant a loopful of the growth from the fermentation tubes (revealing gas production) on various differential media and proceed as is done in the examination of water, see page 519.

At the same time as the fermentation tubes are inoculated, dilutions of the sample are planted in agar plates for total counts and incubated at 37° C. for twenty-four hours (see page 520).

Chapter XLVIII

MILK AND DAIRY PRODUCTS

Milk and Infection.—Milk, especially fresh milk, is an ideal medium for the growth of most bacteria. Individual cases and epidemics of many diseases have been clearly traced to contaminated milk supplies. Two sources of infection are recognized: (1) a small number of disease conditions and few epidemics have probably come from the milk of diseased cows. (2) The more common source of contamination is the introduction into the milk of infectious material of human origin. Typhoid fever, dysentery and diarrheal conditions, septic sore throat, foot-and-mouth disease, scarlet fever and diphtheria are the important diseases transmitted by contaminated milk. In continental European countries Malta fever (from contaminated goats' milk), cholera and possibly other diseases may be due at times to milk infections, though milk is usually too acid for the cholera vibrio to survive. Undulant fever or brucellosis is possible from contaminated cow's milk.

So-called *milk sickness*, an acute nonfebrile disease, is attributed to the ingestion of milk and milk products. The actual cause is obscure, though it appears to be due to a poisonous agent rather than bacteria or bacterial toxins. The affection is primarily a disease of cattle and only secondarily of man, being known in the former as *trembles* or *slows*. Toxic principles in various plants, especially the rayless goldenrod, *Aplopappus heterophyllus*, have been implicated. The cattle eat the toxic weed and the active principle, *tremetol* (*J. Agr. Research*, 1930, **40,** 649), is excreted in the milk. *Epidemic arthritic erythema*, a disease resembling dengue clinically, is thought as being milk borne. Place and associates (*Boston M. and S. J.*, 1926, **194,** 285) studied an outbreak of 80 cases in which all but one of the cases consumed raw milk obtained from the same dairy plant. Tuberculosis attributed to milk is due to one of two conditions: (1) it is possible for milk to become infected with tubercle bacilli from tuberculous persons who are employed in the milking or handling of milk. (2) The transmission of tubercle bacilli with the milk of tuberculous cows has been proved.

LABORATORY TESTING OF MILK

There are many tests which are macroscopic, chemical, microscopic and bacteriological that are employed under various conditions, so as to detect the cleanliness and purity of milk. They are: (1) the curd test for flavors, odors and amount of dirt; (2) sediment or dirt test for visible dirt; (3) specific gravity; (4) temperature; (5) specific chemical tests, as amount of total solids, content of butter fat, etc.; (6) reaction; (7) direct microscopic examination for pus cells and bacteria; (8) plating test for approximate bacterial count; (9) alcohol test as an index of the bacterial count and keeping qualities of milk. The reductase or methylene-blue reduction test is at times employed as an aid in milk control, affording a means of determining approximately the quality of milk samples. It is most applicable to raw milk.

Throughout all stages of milk production, the senses of sight, taste and smell are employed to detect undesirable appearances, flavors and odors.

Bacteriological Examination of Milk.—The detection of pathogenic bacteria in milk is extremely difficult. This is due to the fact that the large number of saprophytes constantly present in milk outgrow any pathogenic bacteria on the culture media employed in bacteriological examinations. *Standard Methods for the Examination of Dairy Products* (Am. Pub. Health Assoc., 1941, New York, N. Y.) includes a technique for the detection especially of hemolytic streptococci, species of *Brucella*, and tubercle bacilli. Bacteriological examinations of milk are made primarily to detect the cleanliness of milk. As we know from experience, there is a relationship between the bacterial content of milk, the cleanliness of milk, conditions under which the milk was supplied and milk-borne infections. Even here, no known method can give accurately the bacterial content in a given sample. Estimation of bacterial contents, however, reveal a relationship to the sanitary conditions and care in the handling of the milk on the farm, to the care exercised in proper refrigeration during transportation, to the efficiency of pasteurization, to the handling and proper storage in the milk plant, and as a check on the promptness of delivery or in the proper care which milk dealers observe in the handling of milk.

For the sake of uniformity, bacteriological examinations of milk are made according to the technique as given in *Standard Methods for the Examination of Dairy Products*. Wherever possible, an original unopened bottle or container should be employed in an examination. If this is not practical, samples may be collected as in the case of water, care being taken that the milk is shaken thoroughly, so that a representative sample is obtained. Where there is any question of the thorough shaking of the milk, cream or other liquid dairy product, sampling tubes are to be employed and not dippers or other similar devices. Contamination from the outside should be avoided, and if they cannot be sent to the laboratory immediately or examined at once, the samples should be properly iced. They should be kept at a temperature of below 40° F., but not frozen. When samples reach the laboratory or are ready to be tested bacteriologically they are agitated well (at least twenty-five times) and the samples are diluted with sterile distilled water in the proportion of 1 to 10, 1 to 100, 1 to 1000, 1 to 10,000, the dilution depending upon the grade or possible contamination of the sample of milk. Liquefied standard agar medium, usually 10 cc. (see page 51), cooled to 45° C. is added to each plate and thoroughly mixed with the diluted milk. The mixture is allowed to harden and the plates are incubated for forty-eight hours.

Two temperatures of incubation (37° and 32° C.) are recognized. The enforcement officials in each locality generally advocate or regulate the temperature to use. After incubation for forty-eight hours, the colonies are counted and the number of bacteria in each cubic centimeter of original milk is computed.

In the interpretation of bacteriological findings one must familiarize oneself with the specific requirements promulgated by the State or Local Health agencies as to the permissible total bacterial counts for market milk. Grading systems have been adopted by many communities. "Certified" and Grade "A" raw milks are to contain less than 10,000 bacteria per cc. Pasteurized Grades "A" and "B" are to contain not over 25,000 bacteria per cc. For complete details on milk and milk products, see articles by the author (*Am. J. Pharm.*, 1932, **104**, 176, 540).

For details of the direct microscopic method, see *Standard Methods for the Examination of Dairy Products*. For simplified laboratory control procedures for market milk and for laboratory control of milk under war conditions, see Breed and others (*Am. J. Pub. Health*, 1943, **33**, 386–404).

Bacteriological Examination of Milk Products.—Milk products are examined for the total count and at times for coliform bacteria just as is done in the case of fluid milk, chocolate milk and other flavored milk drinks. The following are examined in an identical manner except that the milk product is weighed instead of using a definite volume. All creams and ice cream mix are preferably weighed aseptically in a sterile butter boat or in a sterile dilution bottle. If a pipette is used, a sufficient quantity is withdrawn to assure the delivery of 1 cc. of cream, well mixed but free from air bubbles. Ice cream and other frozen desserts are collected in wide-mouthed sterile bottles. The container is placed in the incubator or water bath at 37° C. or at a temperature not over 45° C. for a period not to exceed fifteen minutes. The melted and well-agitated sample is weighed as above, and dilutions are made. Condensed, evaporated and dry milks are weighed aseptically. Where there is a suspicion that the milk product may be heavily laden with bacteria, dilutions weaker than 1:100 and 1:1000 are prepared and used.

In interpreting the findings, the presence of coliform bacteria in milk products has the same sanitary significance as they have when found in fluid milk and water. The total bacterial count in flavored milks, all grades of sweet cream and ice cream should not exceed that of market milk, and in many areas lower counts are required. This lower total count requirement is plausible, when we recognize that pasteurization temperatures for chocolate and other flavored milks, cream and ice cream mix are usually higher than 145° F., generally between 160° and 180° F. depending upon the product. Condensed, evaporated and dried milks should be very low in the total bacterial count.

"Standard Methods" details microbiological techniques for the examination of butter in which a yeast and mold count is made. Though not an accurate index of the keeping quality of the butter or of the raw materials used, it is useful as an index of plant sanitation, inefficient pasteurization and carelessness of employees. Microscopic techniques are also given for an estimation of the number of bacteria and mold mycelia in butter and in other milk products.

Chapter XLIX

OTHER FOODS

AN EXCESSIVE amount of fats, proteins or carbohydrates may lead to acidosis favor putrefactive changes and fermentation, respectively. A deficiency of calcium phosphorus and other mineral salts in food for the young may result in poorly developed bones, and other abnormalities. Even absence of iodine may lead to goiter. The presence of fluorides in water causes mottled teeth. Too highly spiced foods may be irritating to the mucous membranes in the gastro-intestinal tract. Lack of fresh vegetables and fruits not only results in a loss of the proper amount of vitamins, but in the absence of the vegetable fiber. The latter gives bulk to the food and mechanically aids in the propulsion and elimination of material. Drinking too little water is another common error. Excessive amounts of food predispose individuals to obesity, gout, high blood pressure, disorders of the gastro-intestinal tract and perhaps others. An insufficient amount of food produces undernourishment in children, which results in a general retardation of growth, anemia, and, due to a lowered vitality, individuals are thus predisposed to all kinds of diseases. Unbalanced diets, due to a lack of variety or the absence or excess of certain essential food substances, may seriously affect our health. The so-called deficiency diseases are caused by such unbalanced diets. Beriberi (polyneuritis) is a disease due to an unbalanced diet, deficient in vitamin, water-soluble B_1 (thiamine hydrochloride). This disease is most common in tropical and semitropical climates. The disease in these areas can be eliminated by using undermilled rice for polished rice. In polishing rice the pericarp is removed and the embryo is discarded. These discarded portions contain the vitamins required to a well-balanced ration. Scurvy is another deficiency disease, due particularly to the lack of fresh food in one's diet, and in which the water-soluble vitamin C is absent. Rickets is due to a combination of bad hygiene, especially lack of sunlight and the absence of vitamin D. Cod-liver oil is usually employed as the preventive cure. Pellagra is included among the diseases in which faulty food is concerned, because of the fact that all diseased individuals have been found to subsist on a restricted or one-sided diet. The so-called pellagra-preventive factor (P-P), regarded now as factors of Vitamin B Complex (nicotinic acid (niacin) and riboflavin (B_2 or G)), are concerned with this deficiency disease. The absence or deficiency of Vitamin A affects epithelial tissues and causes hemeralopia (night blindness) and also xerophthalmia. The absence of Vitamin E causes a failure in placental formation and it is required for nutrition by adults. Dental caries occurs frequently in itself causing various pathological disturbances through interference with masticatory function or through the production of foci of infection. In our present state of knowledge it is designated as an effective disease caused by the overgrowth of specific acidogenic and aciduric types of bacteria and influenced by the controlling factor of diet and nutrition.

527

Foods may also affect health due to the presence of various poisons, which may be present naturally, as in poisoned mushrooms, or as alkaloids in potent drugs or plants. A great variety of substances that may be injurious may find their way into food-stuffs. They may include any of the preservatives or lead, tin, copper, cadmium, infrequently antimony or similar metals coming from containers or eating utensils. Special poisons, as solanin in sprouted potatoes and ergotism produced by the prolonged use of meal made from grain-containing ergot, may at times produce disturbances in the body. Hydrocyanic acid is present in various substances used as food, but the methods of preparation or use eliminate all traces of this poison. However, occasionally serious effects are attributed to the swallowing of cherry stones which contain prussic acid. The Fly Amanita and the Death Cup are the two varieties of poisonous wild mushrooms that are, at times, consumed for edible variety. Children occasionally pull up the plants of water hemlock and poison hemlock and eat the roots in mistake for wild parsnip and sweet cicely. There is also a possibility of various poisonous metals being added to food especially through the use of arsenic or other chemically sprayed fruits and vegetables. Poisonous animal materials used as food, as various species of fish, are apt to cause illness. Certain fish are known, whose flesh contains toxic substances of great potency, as the group of puffers, balloon fish or globe fish, especially Fugu. Food allergy rarely results in death but is responsible for the production of hives and other clinical symptoms among persons who are sensitive.

Poisonous substances may develop in food as a result of bacterial activity. Botulism is the most common example, being caused especially by eating contaminated ham, sausage and canned fish, vegetables or fruits, especially contaminated ripe olives and beans. Botulism is caused by a highly poisonous extracellular toxin produced by the spore-bearing anaerobe *Clostridium botulinum*. The proper heating of canned goods and the use of a brine solution in pickling which will contain at least 6 to 8 per cent of salt, are measures which will prevent the development of this bacillus or its toxin. Mussel poisoning believed to be due to bacterial action upon mussels grown in polluted water is known to occur. Typhoid fever has been traced to oysters and other shell fish, celery and other vegetables. Paratyphoid, dysentery and ordinary diarrheas may also be caused by these. Meats and fish which have not been cooked properly, or uncooked, may be the source of so-called enteriditis. Uncooked or improperly cooked pork which may have been infected may be the cause of trichiniasis. Uncooked ham and sausage are almost as dangerous. Tapeworm is another parasite which is transferred from infected meat to man, especially in beef and pork, and is occasionally present in infected fish. Tubercle bacilli are passed on to man if meat is obtained from infected cattle. Milk and its relation to human disease were considered elsewhere in this volume. Fruits and vegetables may assist in the spread of the commonly known gastro-intestinal diseases, either due to the fact that they were directly contaminated from soil or that contamination may take place by contact with flies, filth and the hands of humans who are infected with pathogenic organisms. It is therefore important to see that vegetables and fruits are either cooked well or, if served raw, are washed with water or the skin peeled whenever possible. Other than botulism, so-called *food poisoning* may follow the consumption of food infected with organisms of the genus *salmonella*, especially *S. typhimurium*, *S. choleraesius* and *S. enteritidis*. Such foods are generally of a character that they are eaten raw, as shellfish, vegetables, fruits, ice cream, etc.; those which cannot be cooked sufficiently, as puddings, cream fillings, meat balls or pies; and finally, foods which should and are not cooked properly. Certain members of the paratyphoid and dysentery groups and toxin-producing staphylococci and streptococci are also encountered. In few instances, other bacteria have been claimed as the causative agents.

BACTERIOLOGICAL EXAMINATION OF FOODS (OTHER THAN DAIRY PRODUCTS)

Eggs and egg products are frequently examined to estimate the total bacterial count and to test for organisms of the coliform group, hemolytic staphylococci and streptococci, putrefactive anaerobes and for fungi. The procedure is essentially that given under Milk and Dairy Products, except with regard to the methods of sampling and the technique used for preparing the samples for analysis. See pages 525 and 526 and also *Standard Methods for the Examination of Dairy Products*, 8th Edition, 1941, p. 191.

Fish and fish products consumed uncooked and especially shellfish are important from the standpoint of disease production. Shellfish refers to such mollusks as oysters, soft-shell clams, quahaugs and mussels. There always is a possibility that the shellfish growing in waters may become contaminated by fecal pathogens, especially *Eberthella typhosa*. The important observation in the examination of both shellfish and the water in which they grow is the estimation of the numbers of coliform bacteria present. The latter are estimated by inoculating several fermentation tubes of a suitable media with varying dilutions of the product being examined. The M. P. N. (Most Probable Numbers) of coliform bacteria are reported. For details concerning the methods of collection and transportation of samples, technique of preparing them for examination and the procedure for estimating the M. P. N. of coliform bacteria (by methods similar to that used for detecting coliform bacteria in water, milk and other products), see the report of the Standard Methods Committee for the Examination of Shellfish (*Am. Pub. Health Assoc. Year Book*, 1941, **32**, 158) and *Am. J. Pub. Health*, 1943, **33**, 582.

FOOD INFECTION, FOOD POISONING AND FOOD INTOXICATION

A preliminary epidemiological investigation will reduce to a minimum the number of suspected food samples to be collected in a given outbreak. Close co-operation between the clinician, epidemiologist and bacteriologist is essential. The noting and recording of pertinent details supplemented by a knowledge of the subject will aid at least in eliminating many substances. Original containers should be collected whenever possible. If these cannot be obtained, aseptic precautions are to be observed in the collection of all samples and the latter are to receive protection from contamination and decomposition during transit.

Where chemical poisons are suspected a toxicological examination for their detection may be necessary. Microscopical examinations of the suspected food may be essential in those instances where poisonous plants, and animal parasites in particular, are suspected as being present.

In the bacteriological examination, a direct microscopic examination is made wherever possible. The morphological characteristics of the bacteria present are observed in Gram-stained films prepared from liquid portions of the suspected foodstuffs or from suspensions of the solid foods. Plates of blood agar, infusion agar, Endo's medium, eosin methylene-blue medium, bismuth sulfite agar and broth are inoculated and incubated at 37° C. It is desirable to make a series of plates, using meat infusion agar, for an approximate quantitative estimate of the predominating bacteria present.

If botulism is suspected, appropriate media are inoculated in duplicate and half of the tubes are heated at 75° C. for thirty minutes; or a portion of the material is heated (as indicated), and unheated as well as heated samples are inoculated and incubated at 25° C., maintaining anaerobiosis. In testing for preformed botulinum toxin, the samples of suspected food, if liquid or salt solution extracts of solid foods, are centrifuged and the supernatant liquid is Berkefeld filtered. A portion of the filtrate is heated in a boiling water bath for ten minutes. Five animals (guinea pigs or white mice) are used. One is injected subcutaneously with 0.5 cc. to 1 cc. of the heated filtrate. The other four animals are injected with the unheated filtrate (0.5 to 1 cc.) and three of these four are injected in addition as follows: one with 1 cc. of Type A antitoxin, another with Type B antitoxin and the third with both A and B botulism antitoxins.

The detection of staphylococci in large numbers, especially *S. aureus*, requires the performance of additional tests before they can be designated as the etiological factors. Hemolysin production, blood-plasma coagulation, mannitol fermentation, gelatin liquefaction by Stone's method (*Proc. Soc. Exptl. Biol. Med.*, 1935, **33**, 185) and growth on bromothymol blue agar are valuable aids. The intraperitoneal injection of kittens (*J. Hyg.*, 1938, **38**, 623; *J. Immunol.*, 1938, **35**, 13) is regarded as a more suitable method for the detection of enterotoxic staphylococci. For further details, see Koser (*Diagnostic Procedure and Reagents*, Am. Pub. Health Assoc., New York, N. Y., 1941, p. 200); Tanner, *Microbiology of Foods*, 1944; and Jensen, *Microbiology of Meat*, Garrard Press, Champaign, Ill., 1944.

It is of sufficient importance and interest to point out that the popularly termed *ptomaine poisoning* is a misnomer. Its retention in literature is unfortunate as the use of the term as commonly applied to food intoxication is incorrect and misleading. Cadaverine, putrescine, methylamine and similar substances designated as *ptomaines* are indicative of the advanced stage of decomposition (of proteins), and they are not toxic when given by mouth.

SANITATION OF DRINKING AND EATING UTENSILS

It is necessary for each individual owner in public establishments to familiarize himself with the regulations relating to the cleansing and sanitization of eating utensils as promulgated by the health authorities in the community wherein he operates. The following are among some of the more important generally accepted practices.

1. *Washing.*—All dishes, glasses or other receptacles or utensils shall be washed after each service until clean to the sight and touch. Clean hot water containing a suitable washing powder is used.

2. *Sanitization.*—All dishes, glasses, etc., shall then be sanitized according to one of the following methods:

(a) Immersion or contact for at least three minutes in water heated to a minimum temperature of 180° F. This section applies only to those places using hand methods and not to those using approved machine washing.

(b) Immersion or contact for at least thirty seconds in a chlorine disinfectant in such quantities as to yield approximately 200 p. p. m. of available chlorine. The time is to be prolonged in weaker chlorine solutions (*i. e.*, three minutes in 100 p. p. m. of available chlorine). The chlorine solutions are to be prepared fresh daily.

(c) Dipping, immersion or contact in a solution of such other germicide as may be found efficient and approved by the local health department. An immersion in Zephiran (1:5000 solution) or other efficient quaternary ammonium compound for at least one minute is satisfactory.

(d) Exposure to ultraviolet radiation applied by equipment of proved efficiency.

(e) Satisfactory cleansing and sanitization in approved motor-driven machines properly equipped with thermo switch for insuring at least 180° F. rinse water during operation of machine, this rinse to adequately spray on dishes, etc., for at least ten seconds.

3. Washing and sanitization are to be two separate and distinct operations. A combination of washing and disinfection at one time is not favored. Towel drying or polishing after sanitization is not desirable and usually is not approved.

4. After cleaning and sanitization, the total count should not be more than 100 bacteria per utensil as determined by a technique approved by the local health authorities. Some (as New York State) require also the absence of coliform bacteria.

Bacteriological Methods for Examining Eating and Drinking Utensils.—Little has been accomplished on the perfection of uniform or standard methods for determining quickly in a practical manner an index of contamination. Various procedures have been proposed for the bacteriological examination of eating and drinking utensils. Some health groups utilize the detection of coliform bacteria as an index of sanitary purity as is done in the case of water and various food products. Dick and Hucker (*J. Milk Tech.*, 1940, **3**, 307) advocate the detection of the presence of *Streptococcus salivarius* as a presumptive index indicating a previous oral contamination of the utensils. Total counts, however, are employed in all instances, even though some special test may also be used. The principle employed by all methods is: (1) swabbing of utensils, (2) agitating of swab in a suitable liquid and (3) bacterial counts by plating and other tests are made from this solution. The total counts are performed as in making a standard plate count for water analysis. The counts are made after incubation at 37° C. for forty-eight hours.

The following procedure for sampling in the field, similar to that in use by other workers but with some variations, is used by the author: A rack or other arrangement is set up containing 24 test tubes (15 cc. capacity); 12 tubes each contain 4 cc. of a sterile buffered distilled water solution or other suitable fluid; the other 12 tubes each contain a sterile cotton swab (steel wire applicators about 14 gauge are preferably used instead of wood). The wire applicator passes through a perforation in the cork or rubber stopper to facilitate sterile manipulation. The swab is removed from the test tube, wetted with the buffer solution or storage liquid and rubbed well over approximately 4 square inches of the dish, glass or silverware or preferably rubbed three times around the inside and outside of the rim of a glass, etc., rotating the swab as it is rubbed over the surface area. It is advisable to ascertain the surface area and technique used by the respective local health or state authorities. Their procedure should also be used even though other techniques are employed. The swab is then dropped immediately into a tube of 4 cc. of buffered solution or other suitable fluid and the tube is stoppered tightly. Sampling is done on ostensibly sanitized equipment. Back in the laboratory, the swab is squeezed out against the walls of the test tube containing the buffered fluid in which it has been transported after the solution is first agitated. The swab also can be prepared and squeezed against the side of the tube immediately after the rubbing on the surface. The swab is replaced into its test tube and returned to the laboratory with the treated storage fluid. This solution is then pipetted, plates are made and incubated at 37° C. for forty-eight hours, and the bacterial content determined. One or two 1-cc. portions of the solution are planted in fermentation tubes of litmus lactose broth and incubated at 37° C. for forty-eight hours. Tubes showing gas formation are subcultured to detect the presence of coliform bacteria. (See page 520.)

Though icing of the samples when in transport is desirable and is to be advocated, this practice is frequently difficult to carry out. Furthermore a suitable fluid storage medium must be employed whether or not icing is employed so that the organisms picked up will not be affected in that there will neither be a reduction or an increase in their numbers during transport to the laboratory. The sterile fluid storage solutions are either isotonic salt solution or distilled water buffered (with acid phosphate and adjusted to pH 7.2). The latter is preferred. (See *Standard Methods for the Examination of Dairy Products*, 8th edition, 1941, p. 126.)

In interpreting the findings, counts in excess of 100 are considered unsatisfactory. In some techniques the moistened swab is rubbed slowly and thoroughly over a 4 square inch surface and 100 bacteria are considered as the maximum limit for this area of sampled surface of utensil. Implements and utensils actually coming in contact with the mouth are of greatest concern, e. g., a fork is more important than a knife; a glass or cup is more important than a plate.

Chapter L

COLLECTION AND BACTERIOLOGICAL EXAMINATION
OF CLINICAL SPECIMENS

Blood.—Collect 10 to 20 cc. of blood by venipuncture, using rigid aseptic conditions. The sample can be expelled into two flasks, each containing different media most suitable for the isolation of the bacteria suspected as being present, and another portion placed in a flask containing a sterile 2.5 per cent sodium citrate solution; or it may be more convenient to expel the 15 cc. of blood in a sterile flask containing 5 cc. of the sterile citrate solution and gently rotating the mixture. Cultures from the latter should be made as soon as possible after collecting the blood. Dextrose infusion broth is a suitable medium for the isolation of most pathogens. Liver-infusion media are used for the cultivation of species of *Brucella*, thioglycollate medium for anaerobes and other special media for certain fastidious bacteria. Tubes of meat-infusion agar are melted and cooled to 45° C. Measured amounts of the citrated blood are added to each tube, the contents shaken well and poured quickly into sterile plates. Plates and cultures are incubated at 37° C. until growth appears. The latter is examined and the identity established by the use of staining methods and, if necessary, employing cultural, biochemical, immunological and other examinations. If the patient is receiving sulfonamide therapy, paraminobenzoic acid is added to the citrate solution or to the culture media. These paraminobenzoic-treated cultures and blood cultures from suspected cases of endocarditis, brucellosis and tularemia are incubated for at least three weeks if growth is not apparent and before reporting them as negative. In most instances, incubation is carried out under aerobic conditions. In some cases, as for the isolation of species of *Brucella*, the containers and plates are placed in a jar containing 10 per cent carbon dioxide, or two sets of cultures can be made, and one set incubated aerobically and the other in an atmosphere of carbon dioxide.

Cerebrospinal Fluid.—The bacteriologist is frequently called upon to perform determinations other than an examination for the bacteria present such as gross appearance, leukocyte count, globulin content, etc. For a bacteriological examination, the fluid is to be prepared immediately after collection. If bacteria are not found in large numbers upon direct smears in clouded samples, or if the latter are not clouded, the specimen is centrifuged at a high speed for ten minutes. The sediment is stained by Gram's method and examined. To detect tubercle bacilli, the centrifugalization is conducted for thirty to sixty minutes and the sediment is stained by one of the methods used for staining acid- and alcohol-fast bacteria (Ziehl-Neelsen, etc.). The finding of Gram-negative cocci is presumptive evidence of a meningococcus infection. Other organisms are also identified tentatively by Gram's staining procedure. Verification by culture and the use of culturing methods, if direct microscopy is inconclusive, are practiced. Both the sediment and the noncentrifuged fluid (in amounts of 0.5 cc. to 1 cc.) are inoculated on media warmed to 37° C., using blood or serum agar, or in tubes of infusion broth. The inoculated media are incubated at 37° C. and the growth when observed is examined. For methods of digestion and the use of special culture media for detecting the presence of tubercle bacilli, see pages 131 and 132.

Feces.—The fecal material is passed directly into a sterile container, such as a fruit jar, basin, bedpan or Petri dish. A small portion can be removed with a sterile implement (spatula or spoon) to a sterile wide-mouth bottle or vial. Specimens may be collected directly on sterile cotton swabs either by a proctologist (especially in ulcerative colitis) or, after cleansing well the perianal skin, the swab (moistened in sterile isotonic salt solution) is introduced into the anus.

Unless the material is fluid or swabs have been made, suspensions of the solid specimen are made with broth or isotonic salt solution. Smears are made and stained by Gram's method and by the Ziehl-Neelsen or other procedures used for staining acid- and alcohol-fast bacteria. Plates of different culture media are streaked with the suspension. Use desoxycholate agar, Endo's medium and other media employed for differentiating the Gram-negative rods. Suspicious colonies are examined and further studied by cultural, biochemical and immunological tests for identification.

The digestion and concentration methods and, if desired, the use of special culture media are employed as more suitable procedures for detecting the presence of tubercle bacilli in feces (see pages 131 and 132).

Fluids from Serous Cavities.—*Pleural, pericardial, peritoneal, ascitic, joint and other fluids from serous cavities* are prepared and examined as is done with cerebrospinal fluid. It is suggested that cultures be made in duplicate and one set incubated aerobically and the other anaerobically.

Sputum.—Collect the sample preferably during the early morning hours or when arising in the morning. Use a sterile wide-mouth container such as a sterile ointment jar or tin or vaseline screw-cap jar. Sterile vials and sterile cardboard cartons are also used. Patients are to be advised to brush their teeth, wash their mouths with boiled saline or water, to cough up, and deposit only expectorated material, avoiding unnecessary introduction of saliva and nasal secretions. Specimens should be kept cold and examined as soon as possible. The procedure used in the examination will depend upon the pathological conditions suspected.

The direct microscopic examination is applicable in routine examinations. Films are prepared using especially the pearly white specks of material. They are stained by Gram's method and by the Ziehl-Neelsen or other acid-alcohol fast technique of staining. For the isolation of streptococci and other bacteria, the sputum is washed with isotonic salt solution by centrifuging, the washed sputum is streaked on blood-agar plates and inoculated in infusion broth, and incubated. The sputum can be used directly for typing of pneumococci by Neufield's *Quellung method*. If the latter is unsatisfactory, the washed sputum is inoculated into white mice.

For a more searching and more accurate examination for tubercle bacilli, after making films, the sputum is digested and concentrated (see page 132). The washed concentrated sediment is stained by the Ziehl-Neelsen technique and cultures are made on special media (see pages 131). If desired, guinea pigs may be inoculated. Cultures for tubercle bacilli should not be reported as negative unless they are incubated for at least three months. Inoculated guinea pigs are kept until death. If alive, they are not killed and autopsied until after a period of at least six weeks and they are preferably held for a period of three months, then autopsied and examined.

Throat Cultures.—The throat should be well illuminated. Sterile cotton swabs, padded tightly with a slightly larger amount of cotton than used routinely, are employed for collecting the exudate. The use of a wire (aluminum) instead of a wooden applicator is advocated for children and infants, who during the collection of the specimen are apt to break the wood. If a membrane is present, the material is taken from underneath the membrane. The other areas of choice follow in order: grayish patches, inflamed surfaces, and in the case of carriers from the crypts of tonsils.

For the method of collection and examination if *C. diphtheriae* is suspected, see page 127. If Vincent's infection is suspected, see page 129, and if whooping cough is suspected, see page 159.

For the detection of hemolytic streptococci blood-agar pour plates are inoculated and incubated. Cultures for other organisms can also be made on Loeffler's blood-serum medium and in infusion broth. Smears are prepared and stained.

Material from ear, nose, mastoid, nasopharynx, sinuses, eye, ulcers, abscesses and vaginal tract are collected on sterile swabs.

It is frequently desirable to use a minimum amount of cotton in preparing swabs. This is especially necessary for swabs to be used in the nose and ear. Cultures and smears are prepared. Blood agar and infusion broth and other desired media are inoculated with the moist swab and incubated at 37° C. aerobically. Another set of the cultures is placed in an atmosphere of 10 per cent carbon dioxide. The growth, when it appears, is examined. *Urethral and prostatic secretions* are examined as above or smears can be prepared by collecting a drop of the respective fluids on clean, dry slides. For culturing, sterile swabs are used for collecting the discharges.

Material from Wounds.—The exudate is collected on a sterile cotton swab or with a sterile platinum loop. The methods of examination depend upon what is suspected and include (a) microscopy from direct smears, (b) culturing and (c) the performing of pathogenicity tests.

The examination of smears stained by Gram's method and for spores will reveal the kind and the number of bacteria present. If it is desirable to estimate the number of bacteria present on different days, before a wound is closed the material for examination should be taken each time from the same sinuses or pockets, with the same size loop, and identical uniform films prepared over the same (standardized) area and stained by Gram's method. The number of bacteria per field are recorded.

Cultures are made in duplicate in Robertson's (or a similar) meat medium. One set is incubated under aerobic conditions. The other set is heated in a water bath at 80° C. for twenty minutes to kill off the vegetative forms and then incubated under anaerobic conditions. Subcultures are made into selective media for further examination.

For pathogenicity tests especially to detect species of *Clostridia*, white mice or guinea pigs are used. Five groups of animals are employed: (1) normal; (2) immunized against *Cl. perfringens* only; (3) *Cl. sporogenes* only; (4) *Cl. Novyi* only; and all three previously mentioned *Clostridia*. All groups are injected with the suspected material. Animals protected against the homologous organisms survive; controls (normal) and the animals from the other groups die. In mixed *clostridia* infections, only those immunized against all species of *Clostridia* (group 5) survive; the others die.

Urine.—Specimens should be collected by catheterization under rigid aseptic conditions in a sterile container. If catheterization cannot be used, the exterior genitalia are cleansed well, treated with a hypochlorite, a mercuric chloride solution or other suitable bactericidal agent and the latter washed off with sterile water. The urine is then collected directly in a sterile container. Specimens are examined as quickly as possible after collection and kept refrigerated until examined. If the patient is receiving sulfonamide therapy, paraminobenzoic acid should be added to the specimen to inactivate the latter. The samples are centrifuged at a high speed for fifteen minutes. Smears of the sediment are stained by Gram's method and by the Ziehl-Neelsen or other alcohol- and acid-fast method. Cultures are also made on blood-infusion agar and desoxycholate agar plates (or other medium used for differentiating intestinal Gram-negative rods) and in infusion broth. The cultures, after incubation at 37° C., are examined and studied further, if necessary, to identify the bacteria present. If species of *Brucella* are suspected as being present, liver-infusion agar plates are streaked with the sediment and these are incubated in an atmosphere of 10 per cent carbon dioxide at 37° C. until growth appears. The specific organisms are identified by agglutination tests, hydrogen sulfide production, by dye and other biochemical tests.

Some workers collect a twelve- or twenty-four-hour specimen when *Mycobacterium tuberculosis* is sought. The entire sample is kept in the ice box overnight. Sedimentation usually occurs. The supernatant clear liquid is siphoned off and discarded. The remaining portion is centrifuged at a high speed for thirty to sixty minutes and washed. Smears are prepared and examined. Cultures and guinea-pig inoculations can be made if desired (see under Sputum).

Examination for Actinomyces, Yeasts and Fungi

Direct smears are useful, especially wet preparations. A mount in water or better, in 30 per cent sodium hydroxide solution (preferably gently warmed) is a most satisfactory routine procedure. The use of a drop of undiluted Giemsa stain (or other blood-staining solution) or India ink or 10 per cent argyrol instead of the noncolored aqueous mounting liquid aids in observing the finer details of structure. Material should not be forcibly rubbed in the mount or when making dry preparations for staining purposes, as structures may be destroyed or altered.

Cultures for yeast and fungi are made on Sabouraud's agar (plates or slants). In the latter, one streak is made near the bottom and the other near the top of the medium. Duplicate cultures are made. One is incubated at 37° C., the other at room temperature. Incubation at room temperature suffices for fungous materials and yeasts. The cultures are incubated for at least two weeks and if no growth is apparent, they are then regarded as negative.

For the cultivation of actinomyces, streaks are made on blood-agar plates and in dextrose ascitic broth. One set is incubated aerobically and the other anaerobically at 37° C. for four to seven days. Duplicates of the aerobic and anaerobic sets are also incubated at room temperature.

Testing Liquids and Solids for Sterility

Methods for the testing of ampul solutions official in the National Formulary are given in N. F. VII, pages 36–38. Sterility testing for liquids and for solids official in the United States Pharmacopoeia are detailed in the U. S. P. XII, pages 609–614. The techniques given in these legalized guides are to be used in their entirety or as final checks for testing the sterility of the respective official products. It is unfortunate that the U. S. P. and N. F. methods for testing the sterility of the liquids are not in agreement, but such uniform technique may and should be established in the near future. Different workers have commented on the techniques given on these official tests and various changes have been suggested. It is possible that the use of a modified Brewer's thioglycollate medium (see page 75) or a similar formula capable of detecting only a few viable bacteria in a product will replace the media in use at present for official sterility testing. A thioglycollate medium or a similar medium which will provide both aerobic and anaerobic conditions in one set of cultures without sacrificing sensitivity to pick up contaminants and at the same time sustain growth, will effect an economy due to the material and time saved.

Chapter LI

TESTING AND EVALUATING THE EFFICIENCY OF DISINFECTANTS

Bactericidal Efficiency of Antiseptics and Disinfectants.—In a consideration of this subject which obviously can be discussed only briefly in a volume such as this, it is well to mention at this point that there is not available, as yet, *one* simple and easily performed *in vitro* test, universally applicable for the evaluation and standardization of *all* antiseptics and germicides. The latter consist of a wide variety of compounds of greatly diverse chemical compositions, are employed for different uses, and react differently depending upon their application. On the other hand, the relative bactericidal efficiency of agents used in disinfection is of considerable practical importance. Neither the chemical structure of such agents nor the composition of antiseptic preparations necessarily supplies information which will evaluate them as germicides. Even the coal-tar disinfectants differ among themselves as far as their relative germicidal efficiency is concerned. This is because of the different kinds of so-called "coal-tar oils" used, and the different methods of preparing these products, so as to obtain a substance soluble in or miscible with water. It is almost impossible to determine the exact nature of phenols present in such an endless variety. And even if such procedure were at all possible, the germicidal value of the particular preparation would still be unknown. Many attempts have therefore been made by bacteriological methods to determine the germicidal value of disinfectants and to develop a possible means of standardization. Numerous procedures, methods and techniques have been introduced, but it is evident that none are given extensive consideration except the "phenol coefficient test."

The bactericidal value of phenol or carbolic acid, recognized as an efficient germicide, is taken as unity. The germicidal value of any other chemical is determined by actual comparison with phenol. Both are tested under identical conditions, using the *typhoid bacillus* and the *Staphylococcus aureus* separately, as the test organisms. By observing the dilutions of the sample which are as efficient as given dilutions of phenol, a ratio of the germicidal power of the disinfectant compared to the germicidal power of phenol can be obtained (especially so, inasmuch as both disinfectants were tested under identical conditions). The ratio is expressed in what is known as the *phenol coefficient*, a numerical figure, which indicates how much greater or in some cases less is the bactericidal efficiency of a particular disinfectant as compared with phenol. Though the principle of performing the phenol coefficient test is the same, there nevertheless exist different procedures and methods or techniques in arriving at the end results. Each method has its advantages and disadvantages. The two important methods of performing this test are:

1. The Rideal-Walker Test (used in Great Britain and by some American manufacturers, said to give a higher coefficient).

2. The United States Food and Drug Administration Method (F. D. A. Test) (adopted by various U. S. Government departments and throughout this country).

At first thought, one can easily see the advantages in a phenol coefficient. A figure is at once available which will show the comparative strengths of the many disinfectants. But the tests are, after all, only relative, and it is a known fact that the conditions imposed upon the laboratory tests are not identical with the action of the disinfectant in practice. The phenol coefficient is almost worthless as a comparative figure to determine the disinfecting value of chemicals of a different nature or which react differently when used in practice. In a modified way, this test is somewhat satisfactory as a figure for comparison of the coal-tar disinfectants. Even here some discrepancies exist. It should be used for coal-tar products only, until such time that better methods of determining relative values of disinfectants will be devised. In practice, the dilution of coal-tar disinfectant used is twenty times the phenol coefficient.

The techniques given in U. S. Dept. Agr. Circ., No. 198 are of value for testing germicides. A detailed description is given in this publication concerning: the F. D. A. Phenol Coefficient Test; the wet and dry filter-paper methods for evaluating the efficiency of disinfectants not completely soluble or miscible in water; and the agar-plate, serum agar-plate and agar cup-plate methods used for noting inhibitory properties of substances to be employed in contact with the body or those which are liquid at the temperature of the test.

Other Methods.—In a volume such as this, it is possible to consider only very briefly those methods for testing disinfectants in common use. References, however, will be made to others which are not employed frequently. It is of interest to note that a test for antiseptic value is given in the monograph of the N. F. Antiseptic Solution. The technique is a modification of the F. D. A. Phenol Coefficient Method, but it is the only bactericidal efficiency test which has a legal status owing to its inclusion in the National Formulary. Kline (*Diagnostic Procedures and Reagents*, Am. Pub. Health Assoc., 1941, p. 51) details a procedure for bacteriostatic titration and the Kolmer bacteriostatic methods for noting inhibitory properties are detailed in *Approved Laboratory Technique* (Kolmer and Boerner, Appleton & Co., New York, N. Y., 1938). Posner and associates (*J. Bact.*, 1936, **31**, 9) present a simple and valuable procedure for determining the antiseptic and bactericidal efficiencies of gases and vapors. Emmons (*Arch. Dermat. & Syph.*, 1933, **28**, 15) and Fernbach and associates (*J. Bact.*, 1940, **39**, 8) outline techniques to determine fungicidal efficiencies and McCrea (*J. Lab. & Clin. Med.*, 1940, **25**, 538) discusses fungicidal testing with a consideration of the methods commonly used. Klarmann and associates (*J. Bact.*, 1941, **42**, 225) describe a method along the lines of the F. D. A. technique for the evaluation of water-soluble or water-miscible preparations, intended particularly for prophylactic purposes and for application to inanimate objects (floors of shower and locker rooms, etc.). *Trichophyton rosaceum* is used as the test organism. Brewer (*J. Bact.*, 1939, **37**, 411) suggests a method for evaluating the antisepticity of dusting powders. Modifications of this technique are found in reports given by the N. F. Committee on Antisepticity (*Bull. N. F. Comm.*, 1940, **8**, No. 6). The author has used a slight modification of Brewer's technique and has found it satisfactory for determining the relative antiseptic value of powders.

In Vivo Tests.—Workers have proposed from time to time tests on living tissue to facilitate the evaluation of antiseptics as used under practical conditions. Where *in vitro* and *in vivo* tests are applicable, both should be employed, but in both instances conditions simulating practical use should be employed.

The following workers have proposed *in vivo* methods: Lambert and Meyer (*Proc. Soc. Exptl. Biol. Med.*, 1926, **23**, 429); German (*Arch. Surg.*, 1929, **18**, 1920); Buchsbaum and Bloom (*Proc. Soc. Exptl. Biol. Med.*, 1931, **28**, 1060); Browning (*Brit. M. J.*, 1934, **2**, 579); Salle and associates (*Proc. Soc. Exptl. Biol. Med.*, 1935, **32**, 665; 1938, **37**, 694; 1938, **38**, 295) (*J. Bact.*, 1937, **34**, 267;

1939, **37**, 639); Nye (*J. A. M. A.*, 1937, **108**, 280); Hunt (*J. Infect. Dis.*, 1937, **60**, 232); Price (*ibid.*, 1938, **63**, 301); Bronfenbrenner and associates (*J. Bact.*, 1939, **37**, 583); Welch and associates (*Am. J. Pub. Health*, 1940, **30**, 129; 1942, **32**, 261) (*J. Lab. & Clin. Med.*, 1942, **27**, 1432); Kempf and Nungester (*J. Bact.*, 1942, **43**, 49); Sarber (*ibid.*, 1942, **43**, 50); Cromwell and Leffler (*ibid.*, 1942, **43**, 51); Witlin (*Proc. Soc. Exptl. Biol. Med.*, 1942, **49**, 27); and Green and Birkeland (*J. Bact.*, 1943, **45**, 42) (*J. Infect. Dis.*, 1944, **74**, 32).

These techniques involve the use of laboratory animals, where skin washings are employed, or lesions are produced and treated *in situ*, or the blood stream of the animal is infected and in another animal the antiseptic is employed simultaneously to note whether the agent prevents infection from setting in. In other tests, skin washings even of human beings following treatment with the antiseptic are examined. Chick embryo heart fragments and other tissue elements, infected chorioallantoic membranes of chick embryos and human and guinea-pig leukocytes are used in other techniques.

These *in vivo* tests certainly need not be applied to disinfectants used on inanimate objects as a means of evaluating the efficacy of such preparations. Here *in vitro* tests are the best guides using, however, as a reliable criterion bactericidal efficiency tests, employing several different organisms and especially those for which the disinfectant is to be used in the practical application of disinfections. For antiseptics used locally on minor cuts and wounds and on the skin and mucous membranes for brief periods of time, information should be obtained from *in vitro* and *in vivo* tests. Findings in the latter, however, should be interpreted in the light of practical use. The evaluation of chemotherapeutic agents which possess antimicrobic properties requires more detailed tests, both *in vitro* and *in vivo*, and in all instances carefully controlled studies and extensive clinical trial are to be carried out.

Salle and his associates (mentioned above) from their combined *in vivo* and *in vitro* technique introduced a number designated by them as the *toxicity-index*. This is defined by them (*Proc. Soc. Exptl. Biol. Med.*, 1938, **38**, 295) as: "the ratio of the highest dilution of disinfectant showing no growth of embryonic tissue in ten minutes to the highest dilution required to kill the test-organism in the same period of time. The tests were run at a temperature of 37° C. in the presence of a standard amount of organic matter. Theoretically the smaller the index the more nearly perfect the germicide." In the author's laboratory, a simple perfusion technique is used. (*Am. J. Pharm.*, 1941, **113**, 203, 353). It may be possible to correlate the bactericidal efficiencies and tissue toxicities of these compounds, but such a correlation would not be satisfactory without considering other conditions experienced in clinical practice, *i. e.*, dilution by blood, serum, mucus, exudate, etc., inhibition of penetration by the formation of metallic albuminates, blood clots, body absorption of the medicament, retention as in argyria and mercury poisoning, rapidity of elimination, incompatability with proteins and body fluids and other interferences. It is factors such as the latter which must always be kept in mind. In the final analysis, actual clinical trial is needed for conclusive evidence as to practical antiseptic efficiencies of any agent.

INDEX

A

Abbé condenser, 30
Ablastin, 446
Abortion, contagious, 149
Acarina, 372
Accessory growth factors for bacteria, 19
Acenthia, 376
Acetic acid as a preservative, 293
    fermentation, 226
Acetarsone, 325, 355, 359
Acetobacter, 226
Acetone, 306
    produced by bacteria, 227
Acetyl-methyl-carbinol, 72
Achorion Schoenleinii, 213
    other species, 213
Achromobacter, 96
Acid alcohol, 35, 45
    production by bacteria, 25, 69
Acid- and alcohol-fast bacteria, 41, 45, 130
Acid-fast bacteria, 41, 44, 130, 134
    definition of, 41
    methods of staining, 44, 45
Acidophilus cultures in intestinal disorders, 166, 224
Acids, disinfecting effects of, 293
Acne, 128
Acquired immunity, 449
Acridine dyes, 334
Acriflavine, 334
Acrivioret, 334
Actinobacillus, 154, 155, 167
    actinoides, 168
    fragilis, 168
    funduliformis, 168
    lignieresi, 167
    serpens, 168
    vulgatus, 168
Actinomyces, 10, 15, 198
    actinoides, 168
    asteroides, 200
    bovis, 198
    candidus, 200
    farcinicus, 200
    foersteri, 200
    gedanensis, 200
    hominis, 198
    madurae, 199
    minutissimus, 217
    necrophorus, 200
Actinomycetin, 340
Actinomycin, 340
Actinomycosis, 198
Active immunity, 448
Activities of bacteria, 23
Acute anterior poliomyelitis, 246, 500
Addiment, 443
Adhesin, 446
Adhesion reaction, 446

Administration of serum, 470
Aedes aegypti, 386
    calopus, 386
Aerobacter, 25, 138
    aerogenes, 138
    cloacae, 138
Aerobes, 19
    cultivation of obligate and facultative, 79
Aerogenes capsulatus. *See* Clostridium perfringens
Aerogenic bacteria, 24
Aerosols, 515
Aestivo-autumnal fever, 360
African relapsing fever, 189, 384
    sleeping sickness, 357, 381
Agar, 51
    medium, 51, 52
        blood, 54
        blood-serum, 54
        blood-smeared, 55
        glycerin, 54
        sugar, 53
Agglutination, 438, 506–508
Agglutinins, 437, 506–508
Agglutinogen, 437
Aggressins, 455, 495
Agkistrodon, 396
Aglypha, 396
Air, 264, 517
Alastrim, 259
Alcaligenes, 148
    abortus, 150
    bronchiseptica, 148
    fecalis, 148
    melitensis, 148
    suis, 150
Alcohol as a disinfectant, 306
    production, 226
Alcohol-fast bacteria, 41
Alcoholic fermentation, 226
Aletia argillacea, 392
Aleuries, 204
Aleurone, 10
Alexin, 443
Algae, 15, 202
Alkali production by bacteria, 25, 69
Alkalies as disinfectants, 294
Alkyl phenolic compounds, 320
Allantoin, 380
Allergens, 511
Allergic skin reaction, 509
Allergy, 451
Allescheria, 200
Amboceptor, 443
Amicrons, 16
Aminoquine, 361
Ammonification, 220
Ammonium chloride bath, 284
Amoeba, 354
Amoebic dysentery, 354

539